# THE ATLAS OF
# THE
# HUMAN
# BODY

# THE ATLAS OF
# THE HUMAN BODY

PROFESSOR PETER ABRAHAMS

**amber**
BOOKS

First paperback published in 2009 by
Amber Books Ltd
Bradley's Close
74–77 White Lion Street
London N1 9PF
United Kingdom
www.amberbooks.co.uk

Copyright © 2002 Bright Star Publishing Plc

ISBN-13: 978-1-906626-40-2

Project Editor: Conor Kilgallon
Additional Designer: Floyd Sayers

Printed in Thailand

# CONTENTS

Introduction                                    6

Head                                            8

Neck                                           66

Thorax                                         84

Upper Limbs                                   124

Abdomen                                       154

Reproductive System                          182

Pelvis                                        196

Lower Limbs                                   202

The Whole Body System                        232

Index                                         248

Picture Credits                              256

# Introduction

Medicine and our understanding of human anatomy has developed enormously over the last few hundred years, often due to the ground-breaking discoveries of a few radical thinkers.

OUR FASCINATION WITH OUR BODIES and how they work, why they go wrong, and what to do to heal them is boundless. Throughout history, countless theories, mostly erroneous, explaining anatomy and physiology have been dreamed up by all manner of physicians, surgeons, quacks, witchdoctors, alchemists, faith-healers, astrologers and charlatans, who in their day, were often well-respected and highly paid professionals.

Despite this catalogue of bad practice, the history of medicine is punctuated by brilliant discoveries and truly visionary thinking that has, against all the odds, hauled us into the modern era of medical science. Hippocrates, 'the father of medicine', practised medicine on the Greek island of Cos in the fifth century BC, and is undoubtedly the most famous and recognizable figure of them all. His achievement was to establish a specialist body of physicians who were governed by a strict code of ethics, and who employed observable scientific methods in their research. This laid the foundation for modern medical practice.

### The four 'humours'

Hippocrates' work had a profound influence on medicine, and his ideas were enthusiastically expanded by doctors in the centuries that followed. Unfortunately, his theories on anatomy and disease were factually inaccurate. He believed that four 'humours', (black bile, yellow bile, phlegm and blood) governed human health and that any illness was a result of imbalances between them.

With the exception of the monks, who grew herbs and plants with some genuine medicinal properties, factual inaccuracy was the trademark of medicine and anatomy during the Middle Ages. The 'humours' theory was still widely held to be true, and Christian and Islamic religious belief was highly influential on medical theory. All sorts of theories, such as blood letting, draining 'noxious fluids' from the body or encouraging 'excess fluids' to move

*In this 17th century diagram by Anastasius Kircher, the human body represents the world in microcosm, which is described as a living organism with metabolic processes.*

about the body freely were commonly put into practice, often accompanied by apothecaries' potions, which contained such bizarre and infamous ingredients as newt's tongues and worm's livers.

With the arrival of the Renaissance in Italy in the late fourteenth century, medical science moved forward. The rediscovery of classical learning encouraged physicians to re-apply scientific methods to medical research, and leave behind the influence of religion and superstition. Great names from the period, such as Leonardo Da Vinci, put forward new ideas. He believed that in order to treat disease it was necessary to first learn about the body and its processes, learning that could ultimately only come through the dissection of human cadavers. Dissection was not, however, a new idea. Claudius Galen, a highly influential second century physician, had dissected animals and had assumed that human anatomy followed the same patterns, an idea that became accepted

**Surgeons can perform today what would have been a miracle only 200 years ago, with a patient survival rate that would have stunned early physicians.**

wisdom for over 1500 years. But by the sixteenth century, the anatomist, Andreas Vasalius, showed Galen was wrong and revealed previously unknown anatomical structures in his book, *de Humani Corporis Fabrica* (the Fabric of the Human Body), in 1543. Procuring bodies for dissection, however, was neither easy or pleasant. The Church forbade human dissection, so anatomists across Europe infamously resorted to robbing graves and cutting down bodies from gallows in order to obtain fresh materials for their research. Other pioneering work recording what had been discovered was conducted by Da Vinci and Vasalius, who sought to accurately represent anatomical structure through detailed diagrams and illustrations.

### Blood circulation

Still, these ideas and methods were controversial and often dismissed. In 1628, the English doctor, William Harvey, stunned the medical world when he published *An Anatomical Disquisition on the Movement of the Heart and Blood*. In this book, he showed that blood circulated around the body and further proposed that the heart pumped blood through arteries. He also realised the significance of the valves of the heart in controlling the flow of blood. Although his ideas were considered outlandish, this scientific method of research was again proved to be the way forward. His findings were confirmed by the invention of the microscope in the late seventeenth century: for the first time in history, scientists could observe more than the naked eye would allow.

By the end of the nineteenth century, many of the practices and procedures we now take for granted were coming to the fore. Crude anaesthetics were developed by James Young Simpson, antiseptics were pioneered by Joseph Lister, and in 1896,

Wilhelm Rontgen amazed the world with a new invention that allowed internal examination of the body without the need for surgery: the x-ray machine was born. Other ground-breaking work by figures such as Louis Pasteur, who established the link between germs and disease, and Karl Landsteiner, who discovered the four main blood groups, paved the way for much more complex surgery such as organ transplants. Surgeons can perform today what would have been a miracle only 200 years ago, with a patient survival rate that would have stunned early physicians.

### Discovering human anatomy

So how much do we actually know about how our own body systems work and how can we better understand what the doctor or surgeon sees and does? *The Atlas of the Human Body* will show you what we are really made of through a thorough examination of human anatomy. The book is structured from the head to the toe, and is broken down into the head, neck, thorax, upper limbs, abdomen, reproductive system, pelvis, lower limbs and general body systems. In turn, each section examines the bones, muscles, nerves, soft tissue and organs and how they work and interact. This book is the beginning of a fascinating journey.

*Conor Kilgallon, Amber Books Ltd*

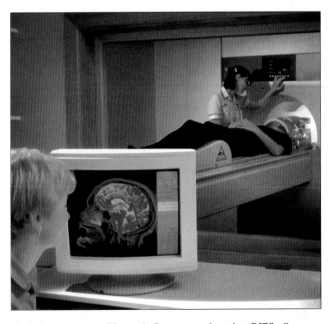

*Techniques such as Magnetic Resonance Imaging (MRI) allow medical staff to gain a 'sliced' image through the body. This can be used to study tumours in soft tissue, such as the brain.*

# Front of the skull

The skull is the head's natural crash helmet, protecting the brain and sense organs from damage. It is made up of 28 separate bones and is the most complex element of the human skeleton.

The skull is the skeleton of the face and head. Its basic role is protecting the brain, the organs of special sense such as the eyes, and the cranial parts of the breathing and digestive system. It also provides attachment for many of the muscles of the neck and head.

Although often thought of as a single bone, the skull is made up of 28 separate bones. For convenience, it is often divided into two main sections: the cranium and the mandible. The basis for this is that, whereas most of the bones of the skull articulate by relatively fixed joints, the mandible (jawbone) is easily detached. The cranium is then subdivided into a number of smaller regions, including:
■ cranial vault (upper dome part of the skull)
■ cranial base
■ facial skeleton
■ upper jaw
■ acoustic cavities (ears)
■ cranial cavities (interior of skull housing the brain).

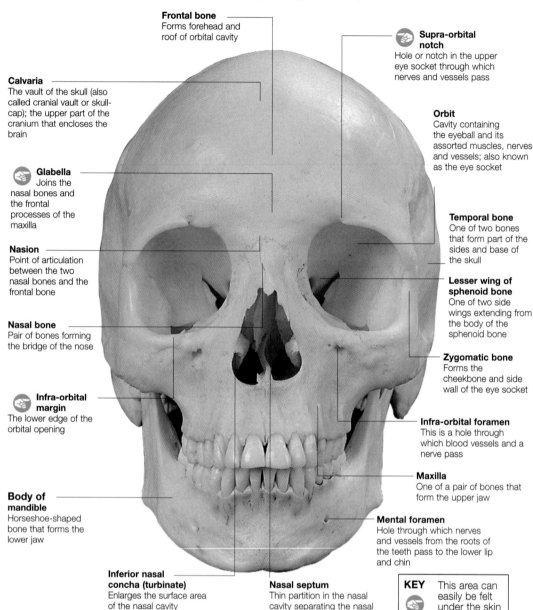

**Frontal bone**
Forms forehead and roof of orbital cavity

**Calvaria**
The vault of the skull (also called cranial vault or skull-cap); the upper part of the cranium that encloses the brain

**Glabella**
Joins the nasal bones and the frontal processes of the maxilla

**Nasion**
Point of articulation between the two nasal bones and the frontal bone

**Nasal bone**
Pair of bones forming the bridge of the nose

**Infra-orbital margin**
The lower edge of the orbital opening

**Body of mandible**
Horseshoe-shaped bone that forms the lower jaw

**Supra-orbital notch**
Hole or notch in the upper eye socket through which nerves and vessels pass

**Orbit**
Cavity containing the eyeball and its assorted muscles, nerves and vessels; also known as the eye socket

**Temporal bone**
One of two bones that form part of the sides and base of the skull

**Lesser wing of sphenoid bone**
One of two side wings extending from the body of the sphenoid bone

**Zygomatic bone**
Forms the cheekbone and side wall of the eye socket

**Infra-orbital foramen**
This is a hole through which blood vessels and a nerve pass

**Maxilla**
One of a pair of bones that form the upper jaw

**Mental foramen**
Hole through which nerves and vessels from the roots of the teeth pass to the lower lip and chin

**Inferior nasal concha (turbinate)**
Enlarges the surface area of the nasal cavity

**Nasal septum**
Thin partition in the nasal cavity separating the nasal passages

**KEY** This area can easily be felt under the skin

## Sinuses of the skull

In the general sense, sinuses are cavities or hollow spaces in the body. In the skull, there are four sinuses, more accurately known as 'paranasal sinuses'. They are named after the bones in which they lie:
■ Frontal
■ Ethmoidal
■ Maxillary
■ Sphenoidal

*This exploded skull shows three of the paranasal sinuses: frontal (1), ethmoidal (2) and maxillary (3). The fourth, sphenoidal, is not clear in this view as it is inside the skull, behind the eyes. All paranasal sinuses are connected to the nasal cavity.*

The paranasal sinuses are air-containing sacs connected to the nasal cavity through narrow – and therefore easily blocked – channels. Their usefulness is limited to adding resonance to the voice, and possibly lightening the skull. The same tissue that lines the nasal cavities lines the sinuses, so they easily become infected (resulting in sinusitis).

The most commonly infected sinus is the maxillary. When this happens, the mucous membrane lining the sinuses becomes inflamed, resulting in a blocked-up nose, a loss of sense of smell and the discharge of pus and mucus from the nose. The main treatment is drainage with or without antibiotics.

# Illuminated skull

Most of the bones of the skull are connected by sutures – immovable fibrous joints. These, and the bones inside the skull, can be seen most clearly using a brightly illuminated skull.

The areas where skull bones meet are called 'sutures'. The coronal suture, for example, occurs between the frontal and parietal bones, and the sagittal suture connects the two parietal bones. It is important to learn the position of these joints, because they can be confused with fractures on X-rays.

In babies, there are relatively large gaps between skull bones, allowing the head to squeeze through the birth canal without fracturing. The gaps are covered in fibrous membranes called 'fontanelles'. In most 'head-first' births, the fontanelles can be palpated (examined using the fingertips) during vaginal examinations to determine the position of the head.

### CHANGE OF FACE

Because children have only rudimentary teeth and sinuses, their faces are smaller proportionally to adults'. (The skull of a newborn, however, is one-quarter of its body size.) As we get older, the relative size of the face diminishes as our gums shrink and we lose our teeth and the bony sockets.

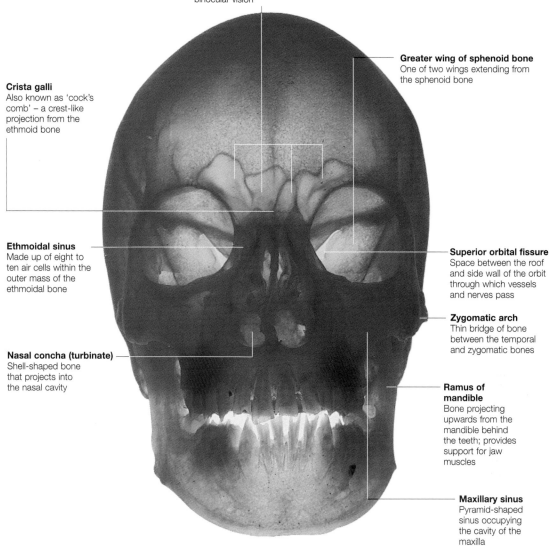

**Frontal sinuses**
Pockets of air connected to the nasal passage; not fully understood, but believed to help shape the orbitals and provide binocular vision

**Greater wing of sphenoid bone**
One of two wings extending from the sphenoid bone

**Crista galli**
Also known as 'cock's comb' – a crest-like projection from the ethmoid bone

**Ethmoidal sinus**
Made up of eight to ten air cells within the outer mass of the ethmoidal bone

**Nasal concha (turbinate)**
Shell-shaped bone that projects into the nasal cavity

**Superior orbital fissure**
Space between the roof and side wall of the orbit through which vessels and nerves pass

**Zygomatic arch**
Thin bridge of bone between the temporal and zygomatic bones

**Ramus of mandible**
Bone projecting upwards from the mandible behind the teeth; provides support for jaw muscles

**Maxillary sinus**
Pyramid-shaped sinus occupying the cavity of the maxilla

## Painted skull

The front view of the skull reveals about nine of the major bones of the head. The painted skull (right) shows these areas clearly:
1 Frontal bone
2 Parietal bone
3 Temporal bone
4 Nasal bone
5 Sphenoid bone
6 Lacrimal bone
7 Zygomatic bone
8 Maxilla
9 Mandible
The other principal features of the skull are the orbits (eye sockets), nasal cavity and teeth.

Some bones in the skull, such as those surrounding the orbital, are relatively thin and prone to fracturing. However, the large number of overlapping bones makes it difficult for doctors to see fractures in X-rays.

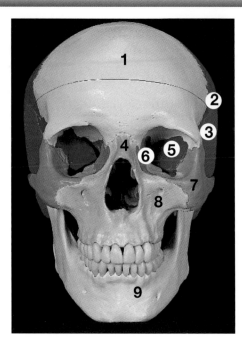

*The colours of this painted skull identify the major bones of the head as seen from the front. In this view – known as an anterior view – some bones, such as the occipital (back of the head) and palatine (plate of the upper mouth) cannot be seen.*

*Skull X-rays clearly show the sutures between the bones. However, the appearance of these sutures makes it difficult for doctors to assess fractures to the skull. In order to identify broken bones, doctors look for five black lines in the white bone. If, however an area of white is seen inside a sinus, this may suggest fluid such as pus or blood inside the cavity.*

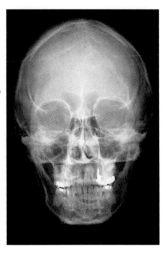

# Side of the skull

A lateral or side view of the skull clearly reveals the complexity of the structure, with many separate bones and the joints between them.

Several of the bones of the skull are paired, with one on either side of the midline of the head. The nasal, zygomatic, parietal and temporal bones all conform to this symmetry. Others, such as the ethmoid and sphenoid bones, occur singly along the midline. Some bones develop in two separate halves and then fuse at the midline, namely the frontal bone and the mandible (lower jaw).

The bones of the skull constantly undergo a process of remodelling: new bone develops on the outer surface of the skull, while the excess on the inside is reabsorbed into the bloodstream. This dynamic process is facilitated by the presence of numerous cells and a good blood supply.

Occasionally, a deficiency in the cells responsible for reabsorption upsets the bone metabolism, which can result in severe thickening of the skull – osteopetrosis, or Paget's disease – and deafness or blindness may follow.

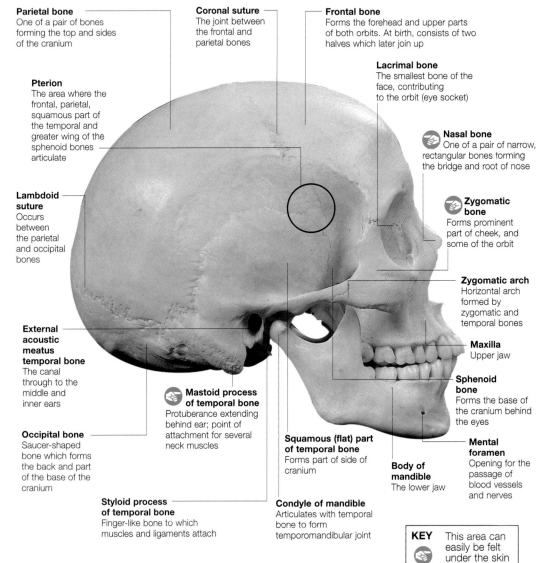

**Parietal bone**
One of a pair of bones forming the top and sides of the cranium

**Pterion**
The area where the frontal, parietal, squamous part of the temporal and greater wing of the sphenoid bones articulate

**Lambdoid suture**
Occurs between the parietal and occipital bones

**External acoustic meatus temporal bone**
The canal through to the middle and inner ears

**Occipital bone**
Saucer-shaped bone which forms the back and part of the base of the cranium

**Styloid process of temporal bone**
Finger-like bone to which muscles and ligaments attach

**Mastoid process of temporal bone**
Protuberance extending behind ear; point of attachment for several neck muscles

**Coronal suture**
The joint between the frontal and parietal bones

**Frontal bone**
Forms the forehead and upper parts of both orbits. At birth, consists of two halves which later join up

**Lacrimal bone**
The smallest bone of the face, contributing to the orbit (eye socket)

**Nasal bone**
One of a pair of narrow, rectangular bones forming the bridge and root of nose

**Zygomatic bone**
Forms prominent part of cheek, and some of the orbit

**Zygomatic arch**
Horizontal arch formed by zygomatic and temporal bones

**Maxilla**
Upper jaw

**Sphenoid bone**
Forms the base of the cranium behind the eyes

**Mental foramen**
Opening for the passage of blood vessels and nerves

**Squamous (flat) part of temporal bone**
Forms part of side of cranium

**Body of mandible**
The lower jaw

**Condyle of mandible**
Articulates with temporal bone to form temporomandibular joint

**KEY** This area can easily be felt under the skin

## Joints of the skull: sutures

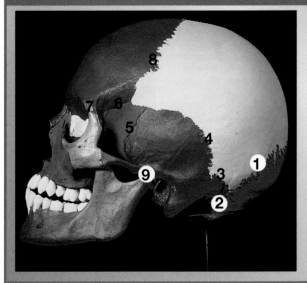

1 **Lambdoid suture**
2 **Occipitomastoid suture**
3 **Parietomastoid suture**
4 **Squamosal suture**
5 **Sphenosquamosal suture**
6 **Sphenofrontal suture**
7 **Frontozygomatic suture**
8 **Coronal suture**
9 **Temporomandibular joint**

The only moveable skull joint is the temporomandibular joint (where the jaw hinges against the cranium) allowing all the actions of chewing and speech.

All the other bones are fixed to each other by joints known as sutures,

*This painted skull shows the location of the 11 major bones and the sutures that join them.*

which are only found in the skull. In the adult, these comprise thin zones of unmineralized fibrous tissue bonding the irregular, interlocking margins of adjacent bones.

The purpose of sutures in the skull of the developing infant is to allow for growth at right angles to their alignment. For example, the coronal suture allows growth in length and the squamosal allows for increase in height of the skull.

During the rapid period of cranial growth, from baby to child, the enlarging brain forces the bones apart at their sutures, and new bone is then deposited at the edge of the sutures, stabilizing the skull at its new size. By the age of seven, the sutural growth has slowed, and the skull enlarges at a slower rate by bone remodelling.

# Inside the skull

The inside of the left half of the skull shows the large cranial vault (calvaria) and facial skeleton in section.

Comparing this photograph with the one of the skull's exterior, many of the same bones can be seen, as well as additional structures. The bony part of the nasal septum (the dividing wall of the nasal cavity) consists of the vomer and the perpendicular plate of the ethmoid bone.

In this skull, the sphenoidal air sinuses are large. The pituitary fossa, containing the pea-sized, hormone-producing pituitary gland, projects down into the sinus. The circle marks the pterion, corresponding to the position marked on the external photograph.

The skull covers the brain, and skull fractures can lead to potentially life-threatening situations. If the side of the skull is fractured in the region of the temporal bone, the blood vessel of the middle meningeal artery may be damaged (extra dural haemorrhage). This vessel supplies the skull bones and the meninges (outer coverings of the brain), and if ruptured, the escaping blood may cause pressure on vital centres in the brain. If not relieved, this can rapidly cause death. The artery is accessible to the surgeon if entry is made near the pterion.

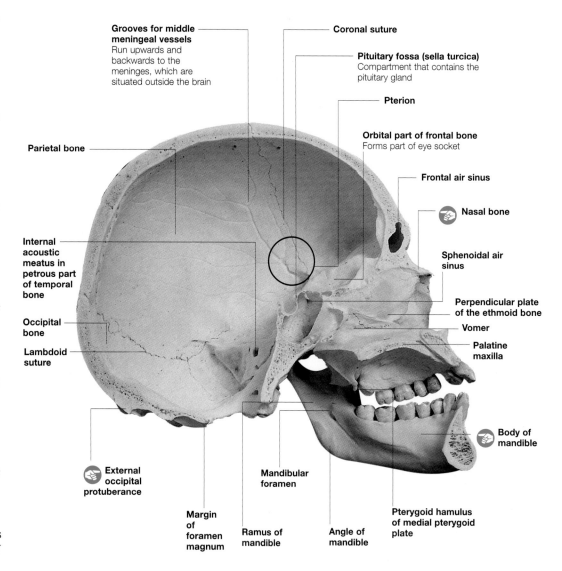

**Grooves for middle meningeal vessels**
Run upwards and backwards to the meninges, which are situated outside the brain

**Coronal suture**

**Pituitary fossa (sella turcica)**
Compartment that contains the pituitary gland

**Pterion**

**Orbital part of frontal bone**
Forms part of eye socket

**Parietal bone**

**Frontal air sinus**

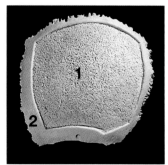 **Nasal bone**

**Internal acoustic meatus in petrous part of temporal bone**

**Sphenoidal air sinus**

**Perpendicular plate of the ethmoid bone**

**Vomer**

**Occipital bone**

**Palatine maxilla**

**Lambdoid suture**

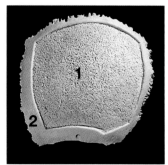 **External occipital protuberance**

**Mandibular foramen**

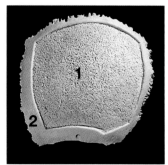 **Body of mandible**

**Margin of foramen magnum**

**Ramus of mandible**

**Angle of mandible**

**Pterygoid hamulus of medial pterygoid plate**

## Types of bone in the skull

Bone is a hard, dense, mineralized connective tissue comprising three components:
■ an organic matrix (about 25 per cent by weight) mostly of the fibrous protein collagen
■ mineralized crystals of calcium phosphate and calcium carbonate (65 per cent by weight), known as hydroxyapatite
■ approximately 10 per cent water.

The combination of mineral and organic material ensures that it has strength and rigidity, as well as the flexibility to absorb loads without being brittle.

The bones of the cranium – that is the frontal, parietals,

occipital and temporals – are 'flat bones', consisting of two thin tables (layers) of compact bone enclosing a looser type called diplöe, or cancellous bone. This is spongy, lattice-like bone containing the marrow.

Blood cells are produced within the marrow, while the bone itself – as elsewhere in the body – is a source of the calcium ions essential for the normal working of nerves and muscles.

The diplöe is unique to the skull, and allows for large, yet light and strong, areas of bone to protect and nourish the brain and vital sense organs.

*This cross-section through the upper jaw reveals the honeycombed nature of the paranasal air sinuses – this makes them lighter in weight, but no less strong.*

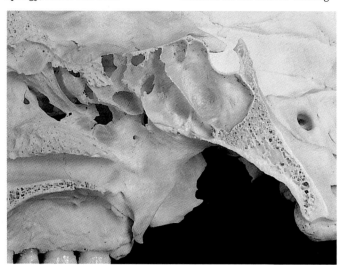

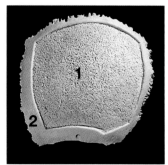

*The right parietal bone, dissected to reveal the diplöe (1), beneath the outer table of compact bone (2). Its honeycomb of cancellous (spongy) bone is visible; under it will be an inner table of compact bone.*

# Top and base of the skull

The calvaria, or vault of the skull, is the upper section of the cranium, surrounding and protecting the brain.

The four bones that make up the calvaria are the frontal bone, the two parietals and a portion of the occipital bone.

These bones are formed by a process in which the original soft connective tissue membrane ossifies (hardens) into bone substance, without going through the intermediate cartilage stage, as happens with some other bones of the skull.

Points of interest in the calvaria include:

■ The sagittal suture running longitudinally from the lambdoid suture at the back of the head to the coronal suture.

■ The vertex (highest point) of the skull; the central uppermost part, along the sagittal suture.

■ The distance between the two parietal tuberosities is the widest part of the cranium.

■ The complex, interlocking nature of the sutures which enable substantial skull growth in the formative years, and provide strength and stability in the adult skull.

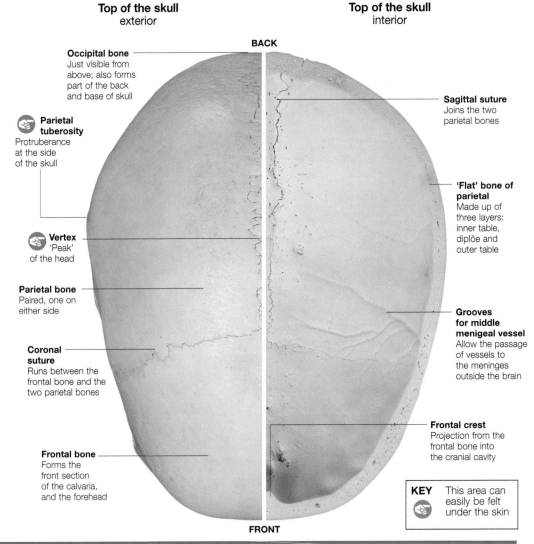

**Top of the skull**
exterior

**Top of the skull**
interior

BACK

**Occipital bone**
Just visible from above; also forms part of the back and base of skull

**Parietal tuberosity**
Protruberance at the side of the skull

**Vertex**
'Peak' of the head

**Parietal bone**
Paired, one on either side

**Coronal suture**
Runs between the frontal bone and the two parietal bones

**Frontal bone**
Forms the front section of the calvaria, and the forehead

FRONT

**Sagittal suture**
Joins the two parietal bones

**'Flat' bone of parietal**
Made up of three layers: inner table, diplöe and outer table

**Grooves for middle menigeal vessel**
Allow the passage of vessels to the meninges outside the brain

**Frontal crest**
Projection from the frontal bone into the cranial cavity

**KEY** This area can easily be felt under the skin

## Skull defects

Because of the unique way in which the skull develops – the growing brain forcing the bones apart at the sutures – any defect either in the component bones themselves or in the sutures may result in drastic changes in the shape and appearance of the baby's or child's head.

Isolated premature fusion of the sutures (where individual joints become fixed and closed before the brain has reached its full size) is called craniostenosis. This greatly reduces the capacity for expansion in the direction normally allowed by the suture.

The brain continues to expand, however, in whatever direction is available, distorting the usual shape, depending upon which suture is affected:

■ scaphocephaly is an elongated, boat-shaped skull resulting from stenosis (premature closure) of the sagittal suture

■ brachycephaly gives a markedly pointed, short skull, caused by bilateral stenosis of the coronal suture

■ plagiocephaly, in which the head takes on the 'twisted' appearance of asymmetrical deformity, is caused by stenosis of one half of the coronal suture

■ oxycephaly produces an abnormally high, sloping skull, usually because of early fusion of the sagittal and coronal sutures.

Disorders in bone production may also result in skull deformation. With achondroplasia (dwarfism of the whole body), the cartilaginous bones are affected. This means that the bones of the base of the skull are foreshortened, while the vault of the skull is normal (the intramembranous bones being unaffected).

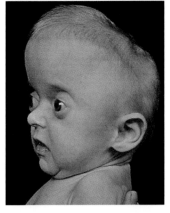

*A baby with oxycephaly displays a peaked crown, and an under-developed vault. The condition may also result in poor eyesight.*

Hydrocephalus ('water on the brain') is a serious condition caused by a build-up of the cerebrospinal fluid surrounding the brain. This enlarges the skull

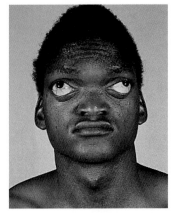

*This man is displaying the classic signs of brachycephaly – a high, pointed head and bulging eyes – due to a fused coronal suture.*

from the inside, putting immense pressure on the brain.

# Base of the skull

This unusual view of the skull is from below. The upper jaw and the hole through which the spinal cord goes can be seen.

The bones found in the midline region of the base of the skull (the ethmoid, sphenoid and part of the occipital bone) develop in a different way from those of the vault of the skull. They are derived from an earlier cartilaginous structure in a process called endochondral ossification.

The maxillae are the two tooth-bearing bones of the upper jaw, one on each side. The palatine processes of the maxillae and the horizontal plates of the palatine bones form the hard palate.

### PALATE DEFECTS

A cleft palate occurs when the structures of the palate do not fuse as normal before birth, creating a gap in the roof of the mouth. This links the oral and nasal cavities. If the gap extends through to the upper jaw, a harelip will become apparent on the upper lip. However, surgery can often improve the defect.

Children with narrow palates and crowded teeth can have an orthodontic appliance fitted which gradually increases tension across the longitudinally running midline palatine.

Over a period of months, the edges of the suture are forced apart, allowing for the growth of new bone, and extra space for the teeth.

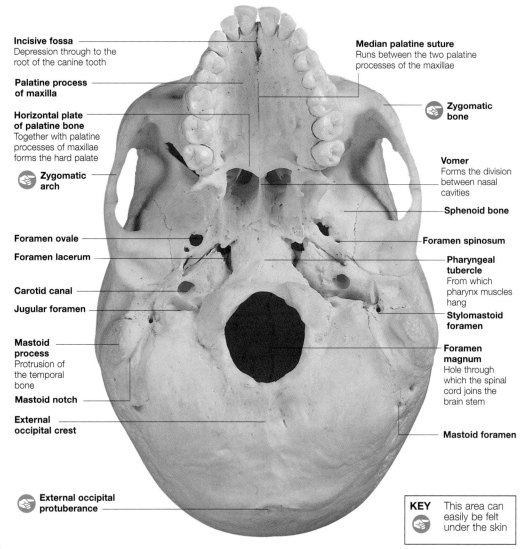

**Incisive fossa**
Depression through to the root of the canine tooth

**Palatine process of maxilla**

**Horizontal plate of palatine bone**
Together with palatine processes of maxillae forms the hard palate

**Zygomatic arch**

**Foramen ovale**

**Foramen lacerum**

**Carotid canal**

**Jugular foramen**

**Mastoid process**
Protrusion of the temporal bone

**Mastoid notch**

**External occipital crest**

**External occipital protuberance**

**Median palatine suture**
Runs between the two palatine processes of the maxillae

**Zygomatic bone**

**Vomer**
Forms the division between nasal cavities

**Sphenoid bone**

**Foramen spinosum**

**Pharyngeal tubercle**
From which pharynx muscles hang

**Stylomastoid foramen**

**Foramen magnum**
Hole through which the spinal cord joins the brain stem

**Mastoid foramen**

**KEY** This area can easily be felt under the skin

---

## Foramina – channels through the skull

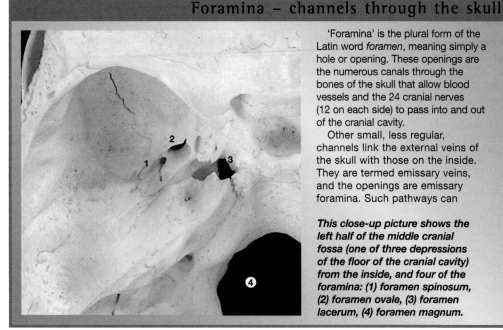

'Foramina' is the plural form of the Latin word *foramen*, meaning simply a hole or opening. These openings are the numerous canals through the bones of the skull that allow blood vessels and the 24 cranial nerves (12 on each side) to pass into and out of the cranial cavity.

Other small, less regular, channels link the external veins of the skull with those on the inside. They are termed emissary veins, and the openings are emissary foramina. Such pathways can allow the spread of an infection from outside the skull to a more serious infection inside. The most important foramina are:

■ **foramen magnum**, where the spinal cord joins the brain stem
■ **foramen lacerum**, between the petrous part of the temporal bone and the sphenoid
■ **foramen ovale** (one on either side), for the mandibular branch of the tregiminal nerve
■ **foramen spinosum**, allows the middle menigeal artery to pass into the interior of the cranial cavity
■ **stylomastoid foramen**, transmits the seventh cranial nerve
■ **jugular foramen**, aperture for the sigmoid and inferior petrosal sinus and three of the cranial nerves
■ **carotid canal**, for the passage of the carotid artery (chief artery of the neck) and associated nerve fibres

*This close-up picture shows the left half of the middle cranial fossa (one of three depressions of the floor of the cranial cavity) from the inside, and four of the foramina: (1) foramen spinosum, (2) foramen ovale, (3) foramen lacerum, (4) foramen magnum.*

# Scalp

The scalp is composed of five layers of tissue that cover the bones of the skull. The skin is firmly attached to the muscles of the scalp by connective tissue which also carries numerous blood vessels.

The scalp is the covering of the top of the head which stretches from the hairline at the back of the skull to the eyebrows at the front. It is a thick, mobile, protective covering for the skull, and it has five distinct layers, the first three of which are bound tightly together.

## PROTECTION

The skin of the scalp is the thickest in the body and the hairiest. As well as its functions of hair-bearing and protection of the skull, the skin of the front of the scalp in particular has an important role in facial expression. This is because many of the fibres of the scalp muscles are attached to the skin, allowing it to move backwards and forwards.

## DENSE CONNECTIVE TISSUE

Under the skin, and attached firmly to it, is a layer of dense tissue which carries numerous arteries and veins. The arteries are branches of the external and internal carotid arteries, which interconnect to give a rich blood supply to all areas of the scalp.

This layer of connective tissue is also attached firmly to the underlying layer of muscle. The connective tissue binds the skin to the muscle in such a way that even if the scalp is torn from the head in an accident, these three layers will remain together.

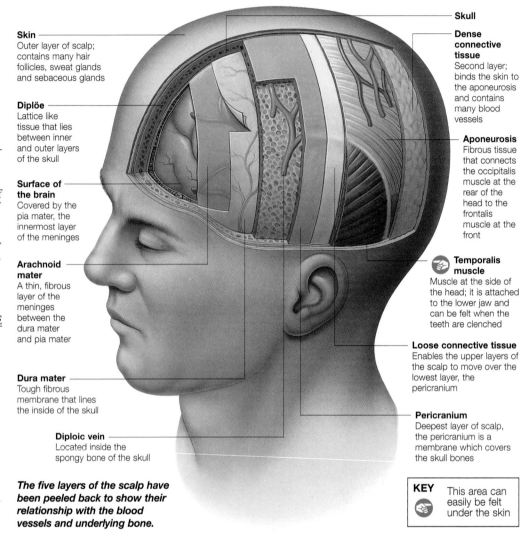

**Skin**
Outer layer of scalp; contains many hair follicles, sweat glands and sebaceous glands

**Diплöe**
Lattice like tissue that lies between inner and outer layers of the skull

**Surface of the brain**
Covered by the pia mater, the innermost layer of the meninges

**Arachnoid mater**
A thin, fibrous layer of the meninges between the dura mater and pia mater

**Dura mater**
Tough fibrous membrane that lines the inside of the skull

**Diploic vein**
Located inside the spongy bone of the skull

**Skull**

**Dense connective tissue**
Second layer; binds the skin to the aponeurosis and contains many blood vessels

**Aponeurosis**
Fibrous tissue that connects the occipitalis muscle at the rear of the head to the frontalis muscle at the front

**Temporalis muscle**
Muscle at the side of the head; it is attached to the lower jaw and can be felt when the teeth are clenched

**Loose connective tissue**
Enables the upper layers of the scalp to move over the lowest layer, the pericranium

**Pericranium**
Deepest layer of scalp, the pericranium is a membrane which covers the skull bones

*The five layers of the scalp have been peeled back to show their relationship with the blood vessels and underlying bone.*

**KEY** This area can easily be felt under the skin

---

## Hair follicles of the scalp

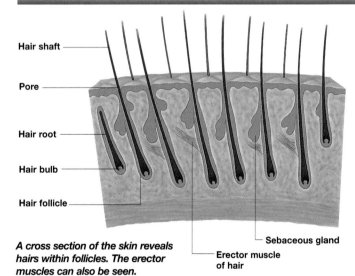

**Hair shaft**

**Pore**

**Hair root**

**Hair bulb**

**Hair follicle**

**Sebaceous gland**

**Erector muscle of hair**

*A cross section of the skin reveals hairs within follicles. The erector muscles can also be seen.*

The hair-bearing part of the scalp is the hairiest region of the body. Scalp hair provides the head with insulation against cold and protection from sunlight and, to some extent, acts to cushion the head from minor injury.

Each hair consists of a root embedded in the skin and the shaft which protrudes from the scalp. Within the scalp, the root is enclosed in a hair follicle. The hair projects from the follicle at an angle of less than 90 degrees and thus covers the skin effectively.

The hair follicles of the scalp go through a cycle of growth and rest phases. After an active growth stage, the follicle and hair bulb rest for a short time.

Hair is shed during the rest phase, but because the growth and rest phases of the individual scalp follicles are staggered, hair loss is not normally noticeable.

Sebaceous glands, which produce an oily secretion called sebum, are also found in the skin connected to the follicles. The sebum lubricates the hair shaft and plays a role in protecting the skin against bacteria and fungi.

Attached to the follicle is a muscle which pulls the hair into an erect position when it contracts, producing 'goose pimples'. The contraction of this muscle also squeezes the sebaceous gland, which in turn releases sebum.

# Muscles of the scalp

The muscles of the scalp lie below the skin and a layer of connective tissue. They act to move the skin of the forehead and the jaw while chewing.

The occipitofrontalis is a large muscle formed by two sections at the front and the back of the scalp, which are connected by a thin, tough, fibrous sheet (aponeurosis). The frontalis is the section of muscle over the forehead, arising from the skin overlying the eyebrow and passing back to become continuous with the aponeurosis. This muscle acts to raise the eyebrows, thus wrinkling the forehead or pulling the scalp forward, as when frowning.

The occipitalis is the section of muscle that arises from the top of the back of the neck and passes forward to the aponeurosis. It acts to pull the scalp backwards.

The temporalis muscle lies at the side of the scalp, above the ears, and runs from the skull down to the lower jaw. It is involved in the action of chewing.

### LOOSE CONNECTIVE TISSUE

The fourth layer, underlying the muscle and aponeurosis, is a layer of loose connective tissue which allows the layers above to move relatively freely over the layer below. It is at this level that the scalp may be torn away during accidents, such as the head going forward through the windscreen of a car.

The pericranium, the fifth layer of the scalp, is the tough membrane covering the bone of the skull itself.

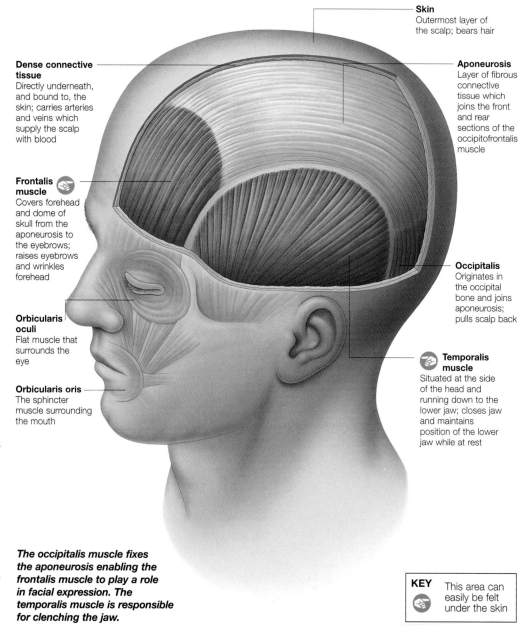

**Skin**
Outermost layer of the scalp; bears hair

**Aponeurosis**
Layer of fibrous connective tissue which joins the front and rear sections of the occipitofrontalis muscle

**Dense connective tissue**
Directly underneath, and bound to, the skin; carries arteries and veins which supply the scalp with blood

**Frontalis muscle**
Covers forehead and dome of skull from the aponeurosis to the eyebrows; raises eyebrows and wrinkles forehead

**Orbicularis oculi**
Flat muscle that surrounds the eye

**Orbicularis oris**
The sphincter muscle surrounding the mouth

**Occipitalis**
Originates in the occipital bone and joins aponeurosis; pulls scalp back

**Temporalis muscle**
Situated at the side of the head and running down to the lower jaw; closes jaw and maintains position of the lower jaw while at rest

*The occipitalis muscle fixes the aponeurosis enabling the frontalis muscle to play a role in facial expression. The temporalis muscle is responsible for clenching the jaw.*

**KEY** This area can easily be felt under the skin

## Trauma to the scalp

Damage to the scalp causes profuse bleeding, even from a relatively minor cut. Two factors together explain why the scalp bleeds so profusely and for so long when it is cut.

To nourish its many hair follicles, the scalp has a much more profuse blood supply compared to the skin of the rest of the body. Blood is supplied to the scalp via several arteries which

anastomose (interconnect) freely within the dense connective tissue layer underlying the skin. These interconnecting vessels provide a good blood supply for the whole of the scalp.

The fibrous tissue within this dense layer acts to hold these blood vessels open, so that they are unable to contract as arteries in other sites would in the event of an injury. If the artery cannot react to damage by narrowing its aperture, then blood clotting is hampered. To stop the bleeding, pressure applied to the area of the wound is needed.

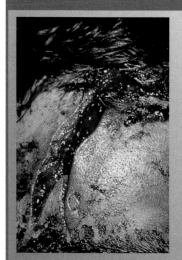

*Major wounds to the scalp bleed excessively as the arteries do not constrict after injury. This hampers the clotting response.*

*Most of the blood that serves the scalp travels through vessels that lie on the surface of the muscles, just below the skull.*

# Brain

The brain is the part of the central nervous system that lies inside the skull. It controls many body functions including our heart rate, the ability to walk and run, and the creation of our thoughts and emotions.

The brain comprises three major parts: forebrain, midbrain and hindbrain. The forebrain is divided into two halves, forming the left and right cerebral hemispheres.

## HEMISPHERES

The cerebral hemispheres form the largest part of the forebrain. Their outer surface is folded into a series of gyri (ridges) and sulci (furrows) that greatly increases its surface area. Most of the surface of each hemisphere is hidden in the depths of the sulci.

Each hemisphere is divided into frontal, parietal, occipital and temporal lobes, named after the closely related bones of the skull. Connecting the two hemispheres is the corpus callosum, a large bundle of fibres deep in the longitudinal fissure.

## GREY AND WHITE MATTER

The hemispheres consist of an outer cortex of grey matter and an inner mass of white matter.
- Grey matter contains nerve cell bodies, and is found in the cortex of the cerebral and cerebellar hemispheres and in groups of sub-cortical nuclei.
- White matter comprises nerve fibres found below the cortex. They form the communication network of the brain, and can project to other areas of the cortex and spinal cord.

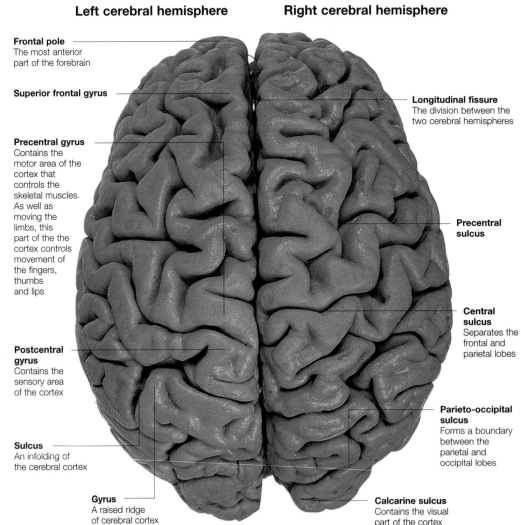

**Left cerebral hemisphere**

**Right cerebral hemisphere**

**Frontal pole**
The most anterior part of the forebrain

**Superior frontal gyrus**

**Precentral gyrus**
Contains the motor area of the cortex that controls the skeletal muscles. As well as moving the limbs, this part of the the cortex controls movement of the fingers, thumbs and lips

**Postcentral gyrus**
Contains the sensory area of the cortex

**Sulcus**
An infolding of the cerebral cortex

**Gyrus**
A raised ridge of cerebral cortex

**Longitudinal fissure**
The division between the two cerebral hemispheres

**Precentral sulcus**

**Central sulcus**
Separates the frontal and parietal lobes

**Parieto-occipital sulcus**
Forms a boundary between the parietal and occipital lobes

**Calcarine sulcus**
Contains the visual part of the cortex

## Ridges and furrows

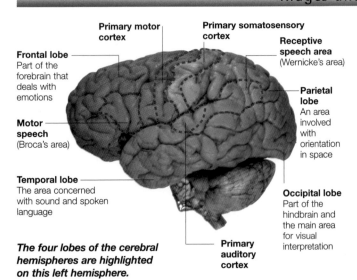

**Primary motor cortex**

**Primary somatosensory cortex**

**Receptive speech area**
(Wernicke's area)

**Frontal lobe**
Part of the forebrain that deals with emotions

**Motor speech**
(Broca's area)

**Temporal lobe**
The area concerned with sound and spoken language

**Parietal lobe**
An area involved with orientation in space

**Occipital lobe**
Part of the hindbrain and the main area for visual interpretation

**Primary auditory cortex**

*The four lobes of the cerebral hemispheres are highlighted on this left hemisphere.*

The central sulcus runs from the longitudinal fissure to the lateral fissure, and marks the boundary between the frontal and parietal lobes. The precentral gyrus runs parallel to and in front of the central sulcus and contains the primary motor cortex, where voluntary movement is initiated. The postcentral gyrus contains the primary somatosensory cortex that perceives bodily sensations. The parieto-occipital sulcus (on the medial surface of both hemispheres) marks the border between the parietal and occipital lobes.

The calcarine sulcus marks the position of the primary visual cortex, where visual images are perceived. The

primary auditory cortex is located towards the posterior (back) end of the lateral fissure.

On the medial surface of the temporal lobe, at the rostral (front) end of the most superior gyrus, lies the primary olfactory cortex, which is involved with smell. Internal to the parahippocampal gyrus lies the hippocampus, which is part of the limbic system and is involved in memory formation. The areas responsible for speech are located in the dominant hemisphere (usually the left) in each individual. The motor speech area (Broca's area) lies in the inferior frontal gyrus and is essential for the production of speech.

# Inside the brain

A midline section between the two cerebral hemispheres reveals the main structures that control a vast number of activities in the body. While particular areas monitor sensory and motor information, others control speech and sleep.

### SPEECH, THOUGHT AND MOVEMENT

The receptive speech area (Wernicke's area) lies behind the primary auditory cortex and is essential for understanding speech. The prefrontal cortex has high-order cognitive functions, including abstract thinking, social behaviour and decision-making ability.

Within the white matter of the cerebral hemispheres are several masses of grey matter, known as the basal ganglia. This group of structures is involved in aspects of motor function, including movement programming, planning and motor programme selection and motor memory retrieval.

### DIENCEPHALON

The medial part of the forebrain comprises the structures surrounding the third ventricle. These form the diencephalon which includes the thalamus, hypothalamus, epithalamus and subthalamus of either side. The thalamus is the last relay station for information from the brainstem and spinal cord before it reaches the cortex.

The hypothalamus lies below the thalamus in the floor of the diencephalon. It is involved in

**Corpus callosum**
A thick band of nerve fibres, found in the depths of the longitudinal fissure that connects the cerebral hemispheres

**Right cerebral hemisphere**
One of two hemispheres that form the largest part of the forebrain

**Ventricle**
Fluid-filled cavity

**Thalamus**
Directs sensory information from the sense organs to the correct part of the cerebral cortex

**Optic nerve**
Carries visual information from the eye to the brain

**Pituitary stalk**
The pituitary gland is not included when the brain is removed from the skull

**Hypothalamus**
Concerned with emotions and drives, such as hunger and thirst; it also helps to control body temperature and the water-salt balance in the blood

**Precentral gyrus**

**Central sulcus**

**Postcentral gyrus**

**Pineal gland**
Part of the epithalamus that synthesizes melatonin

**Parieto-occipital sulcus**
Divides the occipital and parietal lobes

**Calcarine sulcus**
Where most of the primary visual cortex lies

**Cerebellum**
Controls body movement and maintains balance; consists of grey matter on the outside and white matter on the inside

**Medulla oblongata**
Contains vital centres that control breathing, heart-beat and blood supply

**Spinal cord**

**Pons**
Part of the brainstem that contains numerous nerve tracts

**Midbrain**
Important in vision; links the forebrain to the hindbrain

a variety of homeostatic mechanisms, and controls the pituitary gland which descends from its base. The anterior (front) lobe of the pituitary secretes substances that influence the thyroid and adrenal glands, and the gonads and produces growth factors. The posterior lobe produces hormones that increase blood pressure, decrease urine production and cause uterine contraction. The hypothalamus also influences the sympathetic and parasympathetic nervous systems and controls body temperature, appetite and wakefulness. The epithalamus is a relatively small part of the dorso-caudal diencephalon that includes the pineal gland, which synthesizes melatonin and is involved in the control of the sleep/wake cycle.

The subthalamus lies beneath the thalamus and next to the hypothalamus. It contains the subthalamic nucleus which controls movement.

## Brainstem and cerebellum

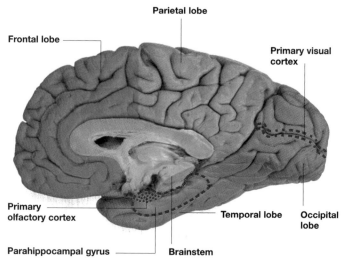

**Parietal lobe**

**Frontal lobe**

**Primary visual cortex**

**Primary olfactory cortex**

**Parahippocampal gyrus**

**Temporal lobe**

**Occipital lobe**

**Brainstem**

The posterior part of the diencephalon is connected to the midbrain, which is followed by the pons and medulla oblongata of the hindbrain. The midbrain and hindbrain contain the nerve fibres connecting the cerebral hemispheres to the cranial nerve nuclei, to lower centres within the brainstem and to the spinal cord. They also contain the cranial nerve nuclei.

Most of the reticular formation, a network of nerve

*A view of the medial surface of the right hemisphere, with the brainstem removed, allowing the lower hemisphere to be seen.*

pathways, lies in the midbrain and hindbrain. This system contains the important respiratory, cardiac and vasomotor centres.

The cerebellum lies posterior to the hindbrain and is attached to it by three pairs of narrow stalk-like structures called peduncles. Connections with the rest of the brain and spinal cord are established via these peduncles. The cerebellum functions at an unconscious level to co-ordinate movements initiated in other parts of the brain. It also controls the maintenance of balance and influences posture and muscle tone.

# Blood vessels of the brain

## The arteries provide the brain with a rich supply of oxygenated blood.

The brain weighs about 1.4 kg and accounts for two per cent of our total body weight. However, it requires 15–20 per cent of the cardiac output to be able to function properly. If the blood supply to the the brain is cut for as little as 10 seconds we lose consciousness and, unless blood flow is quickly restored, it takes only a matter of minutes before the damage is irreversible.

### THE ARTERIAL NETWORK

Blood reaches the brain via two pairs of arteries. The internal carotid arteries originate from the common carotid arteries in the neck, enter the skull via the carotid canal and then branch to supply the cerebral cortex. The two main branches of the internal carotid are the middle and anterior cerebral arteries.

The vertebral arteries arise from the subclavian arteries, enter the skull via the foramen magnum and supply the brainstem and cerebellum. They join, forming the basilar artery which then divides to produce the two posterior cerebral arteries that supply, among other things, the occipital or visual cortex at the back of the brain.

These two sources of blood to the brain are linked by other arteries to form a circuit at the base of the brain called the 'circle of Willis'.

**Inferior (from below) view of the brain**

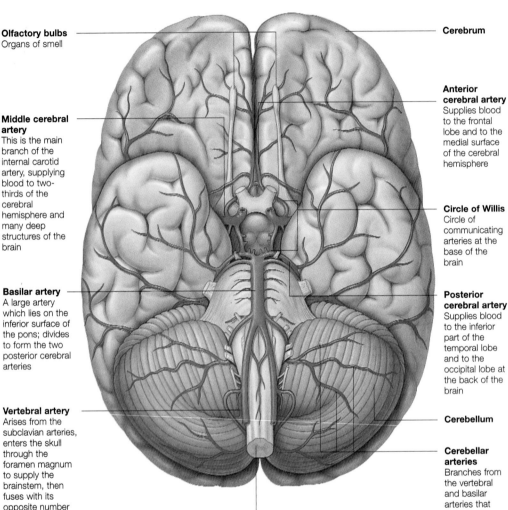

**Right hemisphere**  **Left hemisphere**

**Olfactory bulbs**
Organs of smell

**Middle cerebral artery**
This is the main branch of the internal carotid artery, supplying blood to two-thirds of the cerebral hemisphere and many deep structures of the brain

**Basilar artery**
A large artery which lies on the inferior surface of the pons; divides to form the two posterior cerebral arteries

**Vertebral artery**
Arises from the subclavian arteries, enters the skull through the foramen magnum to supply the brainstem, then fuses with its opposite number to form the basilar artery

**Cerebrum**

**Anterior cerebral artery**
Supplies blood to the frontal lobe and to the medial surface of the cerebral hemisphere

**Circle of Willis**
Circle of communicating arteries at the base of the brain

**Posterior cerebral artery**
Supplies blood to the inferior part of the temporal lobe and to the occipital lobe at the back of the brain

**Cerebellum**

**Cerebellar arteries**
Branches from the vertebral and basilar arteries that provide the blood supply to the cerebellum

**Spinal cord**

## What happens if blood supply stops

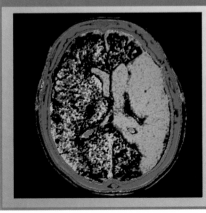

The importance of the blood supply to the brain becomes very clear when that supply is lost, as is seen in a stroke.

Strokes may result from blockage of (ischaemic stroke) or bleeding from (haemorrhagic stroke) an artery. This results in the death

*This false-colour CT scan shows an area of dead tissue (blue) caused by a blockage in a cerebral artery. This may be due to a blood clot.*

of the brain tissue supplied by that particular vessel.

The precise effects on the patient depend on which vessel is affected. In the case of a 'classic stroke' it tends to be the middle cerebral artery that is affected (see scan), resulting in paralysis down the opposite side of the body. This is because the motor cortex, which controls the voluntary movement of muscles on the opposite side of the body, is damaged.

Other symptoms that may be associated with damage to this artery are:
■ Loss of sensation down the opposite side of the body
■ Visual disturbances
■ Language problems (if the damage caused by the stroke is in the dominant left hemisphere)
The extent of damage, and degree of recovery, depends on the extent of the infarct (area of dead tissue). In some cases, the paralysis persists.

# Veins of the brain

Deep and superficial veins drain blood from the brain into a complex system of sinuses. These sinuses rely on gravity to return blood to the heart as, unlike other veins, they do not possess valves.

The veins of the brain can be divided into deep and superficial groups. These veins, none of which have valves, drain into the venous sinuses of the skull.

The sinuses are formed between layers of dura mater, the tough outer membrane covering the brain, and are unlike the veins in the rest of the body in that they have no muscular tissue in their walls.

The superficial veins have a variable arrangement on the surface of the brain and many of them are highly interconnected. Most superficial veins drain into the superior sagittal sinus. By contrast, most of the deep veins, associated with structures within the body of the brain, drain into the straight sinus via the great cerebral vein (vein of Galen).

### FUNCTIONS OF THE SINUSES

The straight sinus and the superior sagittal sinus converge. Blood flows through the transverse and sigmoid sinuses and exits the skull through the internal jugular vein before flowing back towards the heart.

Beneath the brain, on either side of the sphenoid bone, are the cavernous sinuses. These drain blood from the orbit (eye socket) and deep parts of the face. This provides a potential route of infection into the skull.

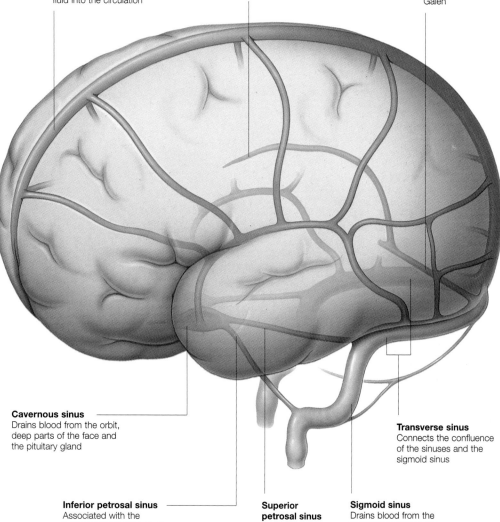

**Superior sagittal sinus**
The largest of the venous sinuses; receives blood from many of the superficial cerebral veins and is also the site for reabsorption of cerebrospinal fluid into the circulation

**Inferior sagittal sinus**
Found at the lower margin of the falx cerebri (a large fold in the dura mater separating the two cerebral hemispheres); receives blood from superficial veins

**Straight sinus**
Drains blood from the inferior sagittal sinus and the deep cerebral veins via the great vein of Galen

**Cavernous sinus**
Drains blood from the orbit, deep parts of the face and the pituitary gland

**Transverse sinus**
Connects the confluence of the sinuses and the sigmoid sinus

**Inferior petrosal sinus**
Associated with the petrous temporal bone of the skull, this sinus drains blood from the cavernous sinus into the internal jugular vein

**Superior petrosal sinus**
Drains blood from the cavernous sinus into the transverse sinus

**Sigmoid sinus**
Drains blood from the transverse sinus to the internal jugular vein; so called because of its 'S' shape

## Visualizing the veins of the brain

The cerebral veins and venous sinuses can be clearly seen using the technique of angiography.

The procedure involves injecting a radio-opaque contrast medium into the internal carotid artery. After about seven seconds the medium has had an opportunity to reach the venous circulation. A rapid series of X-rays is then taken, and the details of abnormalities or problems with

the venous drainage of the brain can be readily visualized.

This technique can be used to detect venous thrombosis (blood clots) and congenital abnormalities in the connections between arteries and veins (arteriovenous malformations, or AVMs).

However, problems with the cerebral venous system are far less common than those associated with the cerebral arteries.

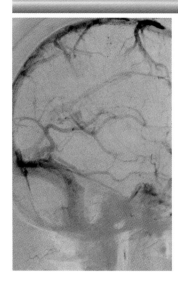

*The veins of the cerebrum are visible on this carotid arteriogram (venous phase). The radio-opaque medium shows up as black.*

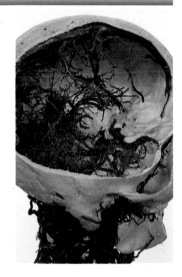

*This cast shows the venous sinuses of the brain, which drain deoxygenated (no longer containing oxygen) blood back to the heart.*

# Ventricles of the brain

**The brain 'floats' in a protective layer of cerebrospinal fluid – the watery liquid produced in a system of cavities within the brain and brainstem.**

The brain contains a system of communicating (connected) cavities known as the ventricles. There are four ventricles within the brain and brainstem, each secreting cerebrospinal fluid (CSF), the fluid that surrounds and permeates the brain and spinal cord, protecting them from injury and infection.

Three of the ventricles – namely the two (paired) lateral ventricles and the third ventricle – lie within the forebrain. The lateral ventricles are the largest, and lie within each cerebral hemisphere. Each consists of a 'body' and three 'horns' – anterior (situated in the frontal lobe), posterior (occipital lobe) and inferior (temporal lobe). The third ventricle is a narrow cavity between the thalamus and hypothalamus.

### HINDBRAIN VENTRICLE

The fourth ventricle is situated in the hindbrain, beneath the cerebellum. When viewed from above, it is diamond-shaped, but in sagittal section (see right) it is triangular. It is continuous with the third ventricle via a narrow channel called the cerebral aqueduct of the midbrain. The roof of the fourth ventricle is incomplete, allowing it to communicate with the subarachnoid space (see over).

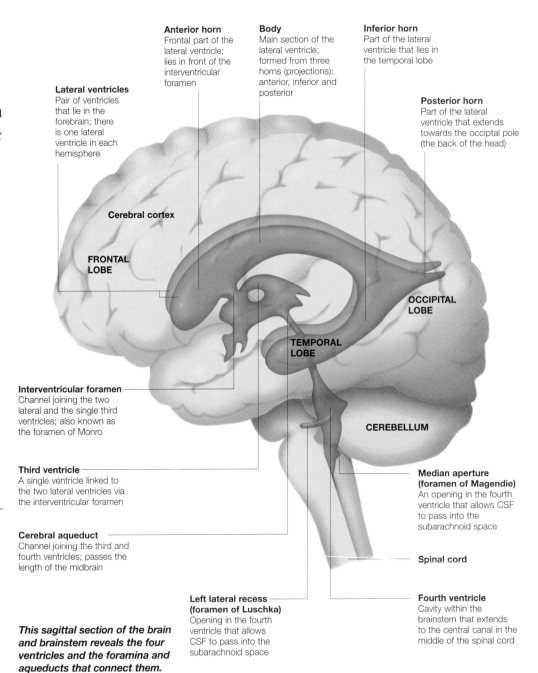

**Anterior horn**
Frontal part of the lateral ventricle; lies in front of the interventricular foramen

**Body**
Main section of the lateral ventricle; formed from three horns (projections): anterior, inferior and posterior

**Inferior horn**
Part of the lateral ventricle that lies in the temporal lobe

**Lateral ventricles**
Pair of ventricles that lie in the forebrain; there is one lateral ventricle in each hemisphere

**Posterior horn**
Part of the lateral ventricle that extends towards the occiptal pole (the back of the head)

**Cerebral cortex**

**FRONTAL LOBE**

**OCCIPITAL LOBE**

**TEMPORAL LOBE**

**CEREBELLUM**

**Interventricular foramen**
Channel joining the two lateral and the single third ventricles; also known as the foramen of Monro

**Third ventricle**
A single ventricle linked to the two lateral ventricles via the interventricular foramen

**Cerebral aqueduct**
Channel joining the third and fourth ventricles; passes the length of the midbrain

**Median aperture (foramen of Magendie)**
An opening in the fourth ventricle that allows CSF to pass into the subarachnoid space

**Spinal cord**

**Left lateral recess (foramen of Luschka)**
Opening in the fourth ventricle that allows CSF to pass into the subarachnoid space

**Fourth ventricle**
Cavity within the brainstem that extends to the central canal in the middle of the spinal cord

*This sagittal section of the brain and brainstem reveals the four ventricles and the foramina and aqueducts that connect them.*

## Cerebrospinal fluid in the ventricles

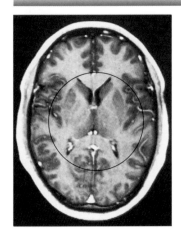

Within each ventricle is a network of blood vessels known as the choroid plexus. This is where the cerebrospinal fluid is produced. CSF fills the ventricles and also the subarachnoid space surrounding the brain and spinal cord, where it acts a protective buffer. CSF is also believed to remove waste products into the venous system. The appearance of CSF can often provide clues to infection.

*The symmetrical arrangement of the ventricles can be seen on this MR scan (circled).*

CSF can be taken from various locations, usually along the spinal cord, in a procedure known as a 'tap'. A small hole is made in the dural sac (the outermost layer of meninges surrounding the brain and spinal cord) and into the lumbar subarachnoid space, where fluid can be aspirated (sucked out).

As CSF is normally a clear, colourless fluid, any change from this can indicate disease. A red appearance, for example, might suggest that the CSF contains blood from a recent haemorrhage.

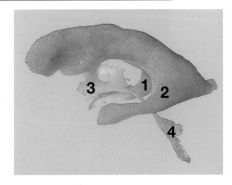

*The ventrical system consists of four communicating cavities, as seen on this resin cast.*

# Circulation of cerebrospinal fluid

Cerebrospinal fluid (CSF) is produced by the choroid plexus within the lateral, third and fourth ventricles.

The choroid plexuses are a rich system of blood vessels originating from the pia mater, the innermost tissue surrounding the brain. The plexuses contain numerous folds (villous processes) projecting into the ventricles, from which cerebrospinal fluid is produced.

From the choroid plexuses in the two lateral ventricles, CSF passes to the third ventricle via the interventricular foramen. Together with additional fluid produced by the choroid plexus in the third ventricle, CSF then passes through the cerebral aqueduct of the midbrain and into the fourth ventricle. Additional fluid is produced by the choroid plexus in the fourth ventricle.

### SUBARACHNOID SPACE
From the fourth ventricle, CSF finally passes out into the subarachnoid space surrounding the brain. It does this through openings in the fourth ventricle – a median opening (foramen of Magendie) and two lateral ones (foramina of Luschka). Once in the subarachnoid space, the CSF circulates to surround the central nervous system.

As CSF is produced constantly, it needs to be drained continuously to prevent any build-up of pressure. This is achieved by passage of the CSF into the venous sinuses of the brain through protrusions known as arachnoid granulations. These are particularly evident in the region of the superior sagittal sinus.

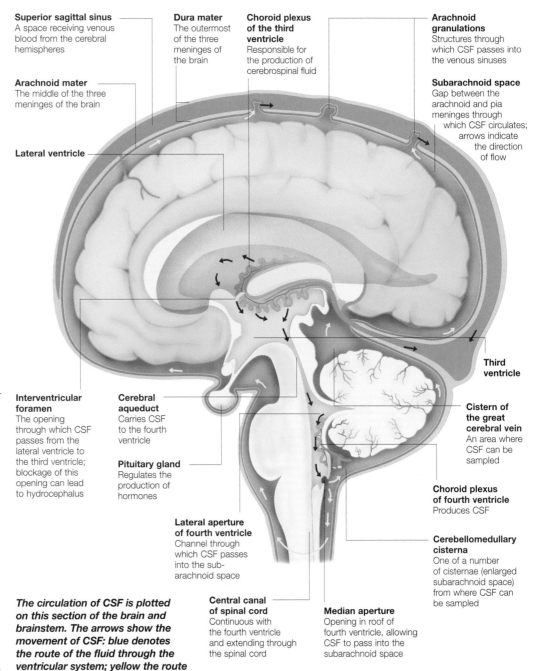

**Superior sagittal sinus**
A space receiving venous blood from the cerebral hemispheres

**Arachnoid mater**
The middle of the three meninges of the brain

**Lateral ventricle**

**Dura mater**
The outermost of the three meninges of the brain

**Choroid plexus of the third ventricle**
Responsible for the production of cerebrospinal fluid

**Arachnoid granulations**
Structures through which CSF passes into the venous sinuses

**Subarachnoid space**
Gap between the arachnoid and pia meninges through which CSF circulates; arrows indicate the direction of flow

**Interventricular foramen**
The opening through which CSF passes from the lateral ventricle to the third ventricle; blockage of this opening can lead to hydrocephalus

**Cerebral aqueduct**
Carries CSF to the fourth ventricle

**Pituitary gland**
Regulates the production of hormones

**Lateral aperture of fourth ventricle**
Channel through which CSF passes into the sub-arachnoid space

**Central canal of spinal cord**
Continuous with the fourth ventricle and extending through the spinal cord

**Median aperture**
Opening in roof of fourth ventricle, allowing CSF to pass into the subarachnoid space

**Third ventricle**

**Cistern of the great cerebral vein**
An area where CSF can be sampled

**Choroid plexus of fourth ventricle**
Produces CSF

**Cerebellomedullary cisterna**
One of a number of cisternae (enlarged subarachnoid space) from where CSF can be sampled

*The circulation of CSF is plotted on this section of the brain and brainstem. The arrows show the movement of CSF: blue denotes the route of the fluid through the ventricular system; yellow the route through the subarachnoid space.*

---

## CSF analysis

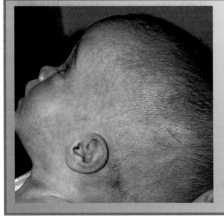

As CSF is continually being secreted, raised intracranial pressure will result if there is interference in the circulation. Such a situation will result from blockage of the interventricular foramen, the cerebral aqueduct or the apertures in the roof of the fourth ventricle, and will

*Hydrocephalus is a condition that results from an obstruction of the flow of CSF within the ventricular system, or in the flow of CSF through the subarachnoid space. A blockage in the ventricular system may occur because of a tumour, and an obstruction in the subarachnoid space may develop after a head injury or be due to infection from meningitis.*

produce the condition known as hydrocephalus (water on the brain). A patient with this condition presents with headaches, unsteadiness and mental impairment.

In the newborn, hydrocephalus may produce a tensed and raised anterior fontanelle and an enlarged skull, and will require immediate treatment to relieve the pressure. If a sample of CSF is required for analysis in an adult, a lumbar puncture may be performed. In this procedure, a needle may be inserted into the subarachnoid space between the bones of the fourth and fifth lumbar vertebrae. This does not damage nervous tissue, as the spinal cord normally terminates at a higher level (between the first and second lumbar vertebrae).

# Cerebral hemispheres

The cerebral hemispheres are the largest part of the brain.
In humans, they have developed out of proportion to the other
regions, distinguishing our brains from those of other animals.

The left and right cerebral hemispheres are separated from each other by the longitudinal fissure which runs between them. Looking at the surface of the hemispheres from the top and side, there is a prominent groove running downwards, beginning about 1 cm behind the midpoint between the front and back of the brain.

This is the central sulcus or rolandic fissure. Further down on the side of the brain there is a second large groove, the lateral sulcus or sylvian fissure.

## LOBES OF THE BRAIN

The cerebral hemispheres are divided into lobes, named after the bones of the skull which lie over them:

■ The frontal lobe lies in front of the rolandic fissure and above the sylvian fissure
■ The parietal lobe lies behind the rolandic fissure and above the back part of the sylvian fissure; it extends back as far as the parieto-occipital sulcus, a groove separating it from the occipital lobe, which is at the back of the brain
■ The temporal lobe is the area below the sylvian fissure and extends backward to meet the occipital lobe.

### Lobes of the cerebral hemispheres

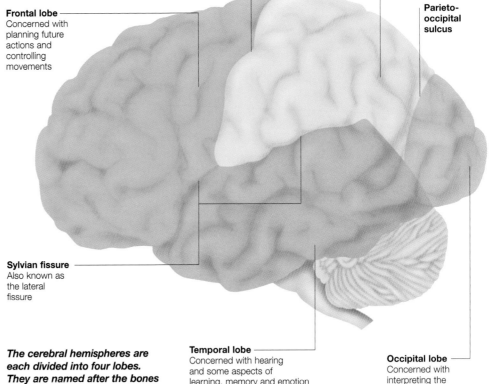

**Rolandic fissure**
The central sulcus

**Parietal lobe**
Concerned with somatic sensation and body image

**Parieto-occipital sulcus**

**Frontal lobe**
Concerned with planning future actions and controlling movements

**Sylvian fissure**
Also known as the lateral fissure

**Temporal lobe**
Concerned with hearing and some aspects of learning, memory and emotion

**Occipital lobe**
Concerned with interpreting the visual scene

*The cerebral hemispheres are each divided into four lobes. They are named after the bones of the skull which lie over them.*

## Gyri and sulci

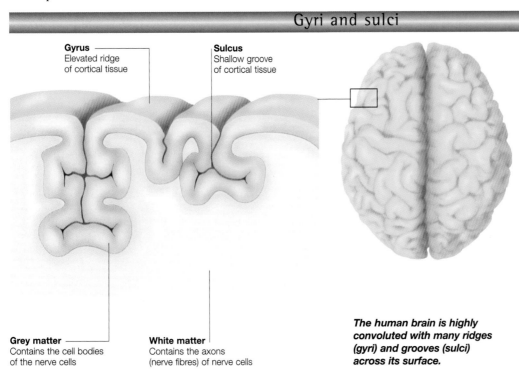

**Gyrus**
Elevated ridge of cortical tissue

**Sulcus**
Shallow groove of cortical tissue

**Grey matter**
Contains the cell bodies of the nerve cells

**White matter**
Contains the axons (nerve fibres) of nerve cells

*The human brain is highly convoluted with many ridges (gyri) and grooves (sulci) across its surface.*

As the brain grows rapidly before birth, the cerebral cortex folds in on itself, producing the characteristic appearance that resembles a walnut. The folds are known as gyri and the shallow grooves between them are the sulci.

Certain sulci are found in the same position in all human brains and as a result are used as landmarks to divide the cortex into the four lobes.

### DEVELOPMENT OF GYRI AND SULCI

Gyri and sulci begin to appear about the third or fourth month after conception. Before this time, the surface of the brain is smooth, like the brains of birds or reptiles. This complicated folding of its surface allows a larger area of cerebral cortex to be contained within the confined space of the skull.

# Functions of the cerebral hemispheres

Different regions of the cortex have distinct and highly specialized functions.

The cerebral cortex is divided into:

■ Motor areas, which initiate and control movement. The primary motor cortex controls voluntary movement of the opposite side of the body. Just in front of the primary motor cortex is the pre-motor cortex and a third area, the supplementary motor area, lies on the inner surface of the frontal lobe. All of these areas work with the basal ganglia and cerebellum to allow us to perform complex sequences of finely controlled movements.

■ Sensory areas, which receive and integrate information from sensory receptors around the body. The primary somatosensory area receives information from sensory receptors on the opposite side of the body about touch, pain, temperature and the position of joints and muscles (proprioception).

■ Association areas, which are involved with the integration of more complex brain functions – the higher mental processes of learning, memory, language, judgment and reasoning, emotion and personality.

**Primary motor cortex**
Controls voluntary movement of the opposite side of the body; electrical stimulation in this area will produce movement of specific muscle groups

**Primary somatosensory cortex**
Receives information from sensory receptors on the opposite side of the body about touch, pain, temperature and the position of joints and muscles

**Auditory association cortex**
Concerned with the interpretation of the meaning and significance of sounds

**Visual association area**
Concerned with recognizing the meaning of visual information and relating it to previous experience

**Broca's area**
Concerned with the production of speech; in about 97 per cent of people this area is located on the left-hand side of the brain

**Primary auditory cortex**
Processes basic features of sound such as pitch and rhythm

**Primary visual cortex**
Receives visual information from the eyes relating to the opposite half of the field of vision

*Some of the major functional areas of the cerebral cortex are mapped onto this side view of the human brain.*

## Motor and sensory body map

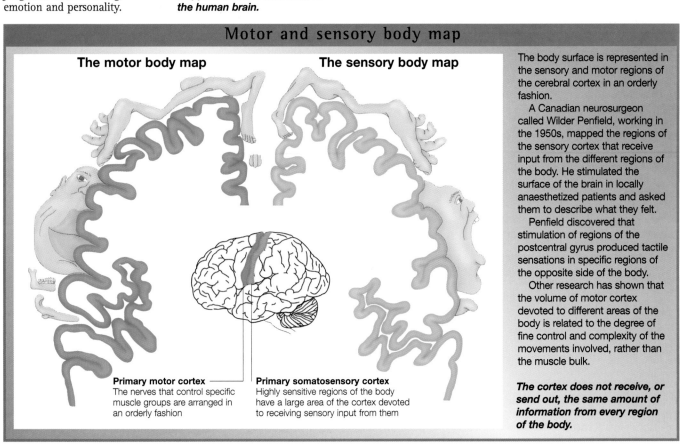

**The motor body map**

**The sensory body map**

**Primary motor cortex**
The nerves that control specific muscle groups are arranged in an orderly fashion

**Primary somatosensory cortex**
Highly sensitive regions of the body have a large area of the cortex devoted to receiving sensory input from them

The body surface is represented in the sensory and motor regions of the cerebral cortex in an orderly fashion.

A Canadian neurosurgeon called Wilder Penfield, working in the 1950s, mapped the regions of the sensory cortex that receive input from the different regions of the body. He stimulated the surface of the brain in locally anaesthetized patients and asked them to describe what they felt.

Penfield discovered that stimulation of regions of the postcentral gyrus produced tactile sensations in specific regions of the opposite side of the body.

Other research has shown that the volume of motor cortex devoted to different areas of the body is related to the degree of fine control and complexity of the movements involved, rather than the muscle bulk.

*The cortex does not receive, or send out, the same amount of information from every region of the body.*

# Thalamus

The thalamus is a major sensory relay and integrating centre
in the brain, lying deep within its central core. It consists of two
halves, and receives sensory inputs of all types, except smell.

The thalamus is made up of
paired egg-shaped masses of
grey matter (cell bodies of nerve
cells) 3–4 cm long and 1.5 cm
wide, located in the deep central
core of the brain known as the
diencephalon, or 'between brain'.

The thalamus makes up about
80 per cent of the diencephalon
and lies on either side of the
fluid-filled third ventricle.
The right and left parts of the
thalamus are connected to each
other by a bridge of grey matter
– the massa intermedia, or
interthalamic adhesion.

### NEUROANATOMY

The front end of the thalamus
is rounded and is narrower than
the back, which is expanded into
the pulvinar. The upper surface
of the thalamus is covered with
a thin layer of white matter –
the stratum zonale. A second
layer of white matter – the
external medullary lamina –
covers the lateral surface.

Its structure is very complex
and it contains more than 25
distinct nuclei (collections of
nerve cells with a common
function).

These thalamic nuclear groups
are separated by a vertical
Y-shaped sheet of white matter –
the internal medullary lamina.
The anterior nucleus lies in the
fork of the Y, and the tail divides
the medial and lateral nuclei
and splits to enclose the
intralaminar nuclei.

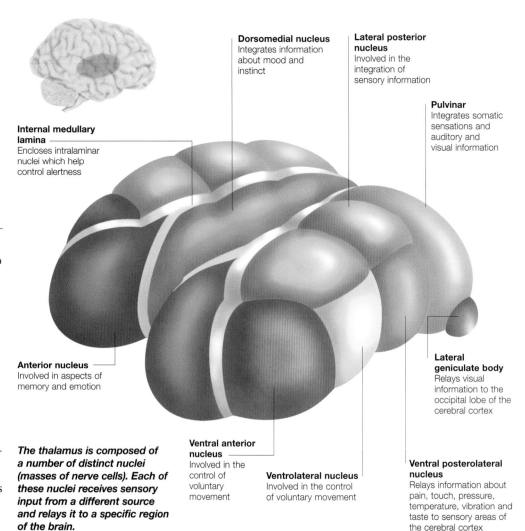

**Dorsomedial nucleus**
Integrates information
about mood and
instinct

**Lateral posterior
nucleus**
Involved in the
integration of
sensory information

**Pulvinar**
Integrates somatic
sensations and
auditory and
visual information

**Internal medullary
lamina**
Encloses intralaminar
nuclei which help
control alertness

**Anterior nucleus**
Involved in aspects of
memory and emotion

**Ventral anterior
nucleus**
Involved in the
control of
voluntary
movement

**Ventrolateral nucleus**
Involved in the control
of voluntary movement

**Lateral
geniculate body**
Relays visual
information to the
occipital lobe of the
cerebral cortex

**Ventral posterolateral
nucleus**
Relays information about
pain, touch, pressure,
temperature, vibration and
taste to sensory areas of
the cerebral cortex

*The thalamus is composed of
a number of distinct nuclei
(masses of nerve cells). Each of
these nuclei receives sensory
input from a different source
and relays it to a specific region
of the brain.*

## Higher brain control

Side view of brain

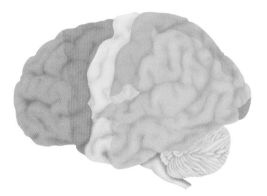

Internal view of brain

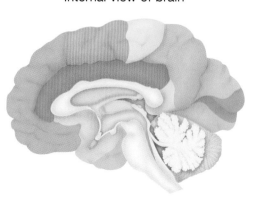

*Each thalamic nucleus is connected to a specific
region of the cerebral cortex (outer tissue of the
brain). The two illustrations above are colour-coded
to the artwork of the thalamus at the top of the page.*

Each thalamic nucleus is linked
to a distinct region of the
cerebral cortex. These
connections are made via a
nerve fibre bundle called the
internal capsule.

Some thalamic nuclei relay
information received from
different sensory modalities,
including somatic (physical)
sensation, vision and hearing, to
the somatosensory cortex.

Others are involved in
transmitting information about
movement from the cerebellum
and basal ganglia to the motor
regions of the frontal cortex.

The thalamus is also involved
in autonomic (unconscious)
functions, including the
maintenance of consciousness.

# Hypothalamus

The hypothalamus is a complex structure located in the deep core of the brain. It regulates fundamental aspects of body function, and is critical for homeostasis – the maintenance of equilibrium in the body's internal environment.

The hypothalamus is a small region of the diencephalon; it is the size of a thumbnail and weighs only about four grams. It lies below the thalamus and is separated from it by a shallow groove, the hypothalamic sulcus. The hypothalamus is just behind the optic chiasm, the point where the two optic nerves cross over as they travel from the eyes towards the visual area at the back of the brain.

Several distinct structures stand out on its undersurface:
■ The mammillary bodies – two small, pea-like projections which are involved in the sense of smell
■ The infundibulum or pituitary stalk – a hollow structure connecting the hypothalamus with the posterior part of the pituitary gland (neurohypophysis) which lies below it
■ The tuber cinereum or median eminence – a greyish-blue, raised region surrounding the base of the infundibulum.

## Hypothalamic nuclei

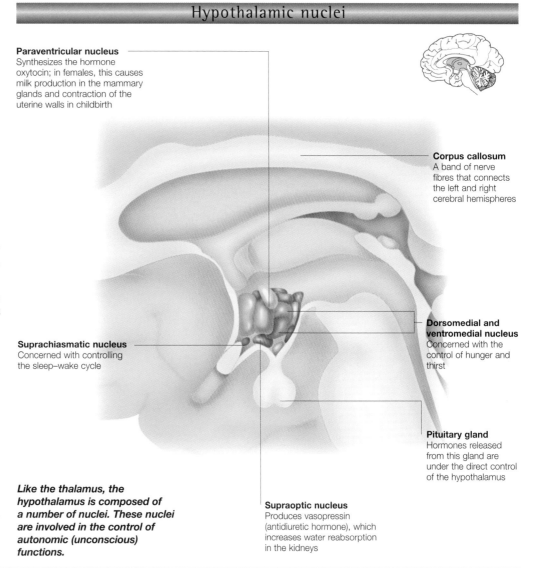

**Paraventricular nucleus**
Synthesizes the hormone oxytocin; in females, this causes milk production in the mammary glands and contraction of the uterine walls in childbirth

**Corpus callosum**
A band of nerve fibres that connects the left and right cerebral hemispheres

**Suprachiasmatic nucleus**
Concerned with controlling the sleep–wake cycle

**Dorsomedial and ventromedial nucleus**
Concerned with the control of hunger and thirst

**Pituitary gland**
Hormones released from this gland are under the direct control of the hypothalamus

*Like the thalamus, the hypothalamus is composed of a number of nuclei. These nuclei are involved in the control of autonomic (unconscious) functions.*

**Supraoptic nucleus**
Produces vasopressin (antidiuretic hormone), which increases water reabsorption in the kidneys

## Hypothalamic control of other functions

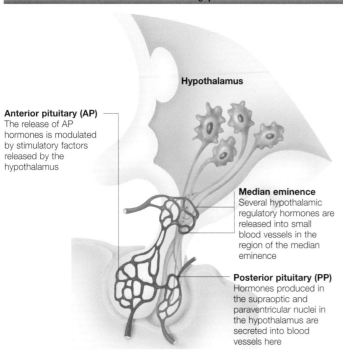

**Hypothalamus**

**Anterior pituitary (AP)**
The release of AP hormones is modulated by stimulatory factors released by the hypothalamus

**Median eminence**
Several hypothalamic regulatory hormones are released into small blood vessels in the region of the median eminence

**Posterior pituitary (PP)**
Hormones produced in the supraoptic and paraventricular nuclei in the hypothalamus are secreted into blood vessels here

The hypothalamus regulates a wide range of basic processes:
■ **The pituitary gland**
The hypothalamus is the main link between the central nervous system and the endocrine system, controlling pituitary gland function
■ **The autonomic nervous system**
Nerve fibres travel from the hypothalamus to the autonomic control centres in the brainstem. By this pathway, the hypothalamus can influence heart rate and blood pressure; contraction of the gut and bladder; sweating; and salivation
■ **Eating and drinking behaviour**
Stimulation of the lateral

*The hypothalamus controls the pituitary gland via nerve fibres innervating the posterior pituitary, and blood capillaries supplying the anterior pituitary.*

hypothalamus increases hunger and thirst. In contrast, activation of the ventromedial hypothalamus reduces hunger and food intake
■ **Body temperature**
Certain areas of the hypothalamus monitor the temperature of the blood and act as a thermostat
■ **Control of emotional behaviour**
The hypothalamus is involved, along with other brain regions, in the expression of fear and aggression, as well as in the control of sexual behaviour
■ **Control of sleep cycles**
The suprachiasmatic nucleus contributes to the daily patterns of sleeping and waking
■ **Memory**
Damage to the mammillary bodies is associated with impairment of the ability to learn and retain new information.

# Limbic system

The limbic system is a ring of interconnected structures that lies deep within the brain. It makes connections with other parts of the brain, and is associated with mood and memory.

The limbic system is a collection of structures deep within the brain that is associated with the perception of emotions and the body's response to them.

The limbic system is not one, discrete part of the brain. Rather it is a ring of interconnected structures surrounding the top of the brainstem. The connections between these structures are complex, often forming loops or circuits and, as with much of the brain, their exact role is not fully understood.

### STRUCTURE

The limbic system is made up from all or parts of the following brain structures:

■ Amygdala – this almond-shaped nucleus appears to be linked to feelings of fear and aggression

■ Hippocampus – this structure seems to play a part in learning and memory

■ Anterior thalamic nuclei – these collections of nerve cells form part of the thalamus. One of their roles seems to lie in the control of instinctive drives

■ Cingulate gyrus – this connects the limbic system to the cerebral cortex, the part of the brain that carries conscious thoughts

■ Hypothalamus – this regulates the body's internal environment, including blood pressure, heart rate and hormone levels. The limbic system generates its effects on the body by sending messages to the hypothalamus.

**Medial view of the limbic system within the brain**

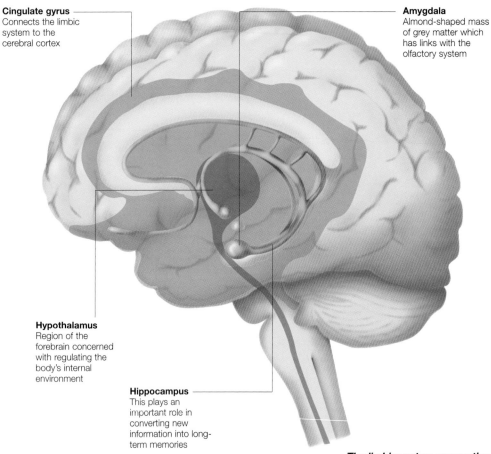

**Cingulate gyrus**
Connects the limbic system to the cerebral cortex

**Amygdala**
Almond-shaped mass of grey matter which has links with the olfactory system

**Hypothalamus**
Region of the forebrain concerned with regulating the body's internal environment

**Hippocampus**
This plays an important role in converting new information into long-term memories

*The limbic system connections encircle the upper part of the brainstem. They link with other parts of the brain and are associated with emotion.*

## The limbic system and the sense of smell

*Our sense of smell is strongly linked to memories of the past or emotions. For example, the smell of a new baby can trigger maternal affection.*

The olfactory system (responsible for the sense of smell) is often included with the limbic system. There is certainly a close connection between the two.

### EMOTIONS

Nerve fibres carrying information to the brain from the sensory receptors in the nose connect with structures in the limbic system, especially the amygdala. These connections mean that different smells are often associated with a variety of emotions and feelings. Examples might be the disgust that accompanies the smell of excreta, or the maternal affection that is associated with the smell of a tiny child.

### MEMORIES

Smell is also linked to memory; it is not uncommon for a passing scent to suddenly evoke memories which are believed to be long forgotten. This may be explained by the role of the limbic system, and especially the hippocampus, in learning and memory.

# Connections of the limbic system

The limbic system has connections with the higher centres of the brain in the cortex, and with the more primitive brainstem. It not only allows the emotions to influence the body, but also enables the emotional response to be regulated.

The human brain can be considered to be made up of three parts. These parts have evolved one after another over the millennia.

### BRAINSTEM
The 'oldest' part of the brain, in evolutionary terms, is the brainstem, which is concerned largely with unconscious control of the internal state of the body. The brainstem can be seen as a sort of 'life support system'.

### LIMBIC SYSTEM
With the evolution of mammals came another 'layer' of brain, the limbic system. The limbic system allowed the development of feelings and emotions in response to sensory information. It is also associated with the development of newer – in evolutionary terms – behaviours, such as closeness to offspring (maternal bonding).

### CEREBRAL CORTEX
The final layer of the human brain is shared to some extent with higher mammals. It is the cerebral cortex, the part of the brain that allows humans to think and reason. With this part of the brain, individuals perceive the outside world and make conscious decisions about their behaviour and actions.

### The developing brain

**The cerebral cortex**
This outer layer of the brain evolved last, and is related to higher intellect

**The brainstem**
This part of the brain evolved first, and is responsible for self-preservation and aggression

**The limbic system**
This system developed secondly and enabled the emotions necessary for mammalian existence, which include caring for offspring

*The three layers of the brain evolved one by one over thousands of years. Each is responsible for different bodily and intellectual functions.*

### ROLE OF THE LIMBIC SYSTEM
The limbic system lies between the cortex and the brainstem and makes connections with both. Through its connections with the brainstem, the limbic system provides a way in which an individual's emotional state can influence the internal state of the body. This may prepare the body perhaps for an act of self-preservation such as running away in fear, or for a sexual encounter.

The extensive connections between the limbic system and the cerebral cortex allow human beings to use their knowledge of the outside world to regulate their response to emotions. The cerebral cortex can thus 'override' the more primitive limbic system when necessary.

## Disorders of the limbic system

*Temporal lobe epilepsy may involve the limbic system. Electroencephalography shows any abnormal electrical activity in particular areas of the brain.*

As the limbic system is associated with emotions, mood and memory, damage to the structures of this system may have effects in these areas.

### WERNICKE'S ENCEPHALOPATHY
Wernicke's encephalopathy is a disorder of the brain in which bleeding from tiny capillaries occurs in the upper brainstem and limbic system.

The condition is caused by long-term alcohol abuse associated with a poor diet; affected individuals experience confusion and may eventually fall into a coma. If a person recovers, there is usually a degree of amnesia and an inability to learn new facts.

### TEMPORAL LOBE EPILEPSY
In temporal lobe epilepsy, seizures arise in the temporal lobe of the brain, close to the limbic system. If the amygdala or hippocampus are involved, the patient may report complex experiences of smell, mood and memory during the seizure. These may even be severe enough to mimic schizophrenia.

# Basal ganglia

The basal ganglia lie deep within the white matter of the
cerebral hemispheres. They are collections of nerve cell bodies that
are involved in the control of movement.

The common term basal ganglia
is, in fact, a misnomer, as the
term ganglion refers to a mass of
nerve cells in the peripheral
nervous system rather than the
central nervous system, as here.
The term basal nuclei is
anatomically more appropriate.

### COMPONENTS

There are a number of
component parts to the basal
nuclei which are all anatomically
and functionally closely related
to each other. The parts of the
basal nuclei include:
■ Putamen. Together with the
caudate nucleus, the putamen
receives input from the cortex
■ Caudate nucleus. Named for
its shape, as it has a long tail,
this nucleus is continuous with
the putamen at the anterior
(front) end
■ Globus pallidus. This nucleus
relays information from the
putamen to the pigmented area
of the midbrain known as the
substantia nigra, with which it
bears many similarities.

### GROUPING

Various names are associated
with different groups of the
basal nuclei. The term corpus
striatum (striped body) refers to
the whole group of basal nuclei,
whereas the striatum includes
only the putamen and caudate
nuclei. Another term, the
lentiform nucleus, refers to the
putamen and the globus pallidus
which, together, form a lens-
shaped mass.

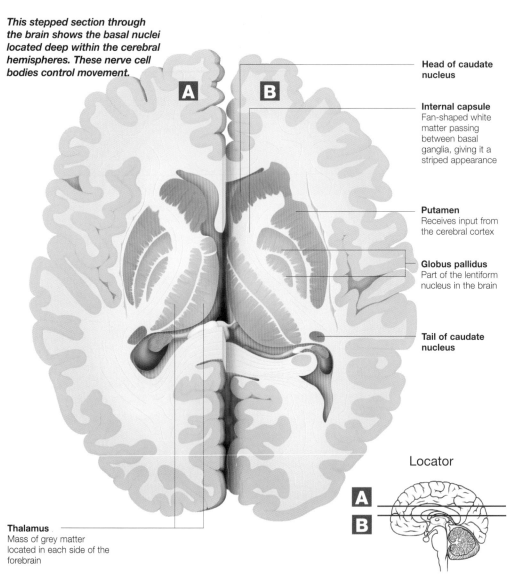

*This stepped section through
the brain shows the basal nuclei
located deep within the cerebral
hemispheres. These nerve cell
bodies control movement.*

**Head of caudate
nucleus**

**Internal capsule**
Fan-shaped white
matter passing
between basal
ganglia, giving it a
striped appearance

**Putamen**
Receives input from
the cerebral cortex

**Globus pallidus**
Part of the lentiform
nucleus in the brain

**Tail of caudate
nucleus**

Locator

**Thalamus**
Mass of grey matter
located in each side of the
forebrain

## Coronal section through brain

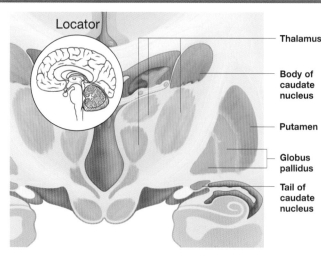

Locator

**Thalamus**

**Body of
caudate
nucleus**

**Putamen**

**Globus
pallidus**

**Tail of
caudate
nucleus**

A coronal section through the
brain reveals two anatomical
factors: the shape of the basal
ganglia and the location of the
ganglia in relation to other
structures in the area.

### SHAPE OF GANGLIA

The coronal section shows that
the lentiform nucleus is the
shape of a brazil nut or an
orange segment.

The putamen lies on the
lateral (outer) side of the paler

*A coronal section through the
brain is shown. It reveals the
relationship of the basal ganglia
to other structures in the brain.*

globus pallidus, which tapers to
a blunt point. Just lateral to the
putamen lies a streak of grey
matter known as the claustrum
(not shown), which is sometimes
included under the heading of
basal nuclei.

### CAPSULE

The basal nuclei lie close to the
thalamus, an important area of
the brain, with which they make
many connections. They are
separated from the thalamus by
the internal capsule, which is an
area of white matter consisting
of nerve fibres that pass from
the cortex down to the spinal
cord.

# Structure and role of the basal ganglia

The overall shape of the basal ganglia (nuclei) is complex, and is hard to imagine by looking at two-dimensional cross-sections.

When seen in a three-dimensional view, the size and shape of the basal nuclei, together with their position within the brain as a whole, can be appreciated more easily.

In particular, the shape of the caudate nucleus can now be understood – it connects at its head with the putamen, then bends back to arch over the thalamus before turning forwards again. The tip of the tail of the caudate nucleus ends as it merges with the amygdala, part of the limbic system (concerned with unconscious, autonomic functions).

## ROLE OF THE BASAL NUCLEI

The functions of the basal nuclei have been difficult to study because they lie deep within the brain and are therefore relatively inaccessible. Much of what is known of their function derives from the study of those patients who have disorders of the basal nuclei that lead to particular disruptions of movement and posture, such as Parkinson's disease.

A summary of what is currently known about the function of the basal nuclei is that: they help to produce movements which are appropriate; and they inhibit unwanted or inappropriate movements.

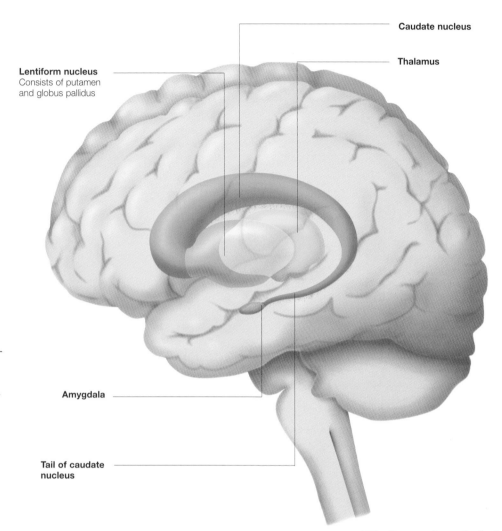

Lentiform nucleus
Consists of putamen and globus pallidus

Caudate nucleus

Thalamus

Amygdala

Tail of caudate nucleus

*This diagram shows the brain in three dimensions. The size and shape of the basal ganglia can be seen in relation to other structures.*

## Disorders of basal ganglia

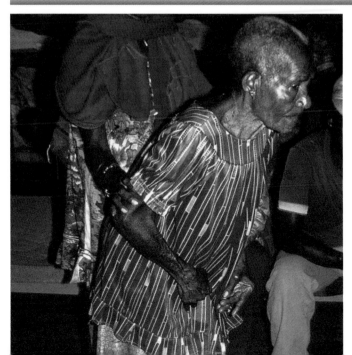

*Parkinson's disease may result from damage to the basal nuclei. Symptoms of the disorder include a stooping posture, tremor and a shuffling walk.*

A range of movement disorders result from damage to the basal nuclei. These disorders include Parkinson's disease, Huntington's chorea and Wilson's disease.

### MOVEMENT DISORDERS

Parkinson's disease is a disease of unknown cause that mainly affects the elderly. It results in various combinations of slowness of movement, increased muscle tone, tremor and a bent posture. Affected individuals have difficulty in starting and finishing a movement and may also have a mask-like facial expression.

Studies of the basal nuclei of those individuals with Parkinson's disease have shown a lack of the chemical dopamine, a substance that allows neurones to communicate with each other.

Huntington's chorea is an inherited disease, which does not become apparent until an individual reaches mid life. It is associated with progressive degeneration of parts of the basal nuclei and cortex, leading to abnormal movements and dementia

Wilson's disease is an inherited disorder associated with damage to the basal nuclei and progressive dementia in the young.

# Cerebellum

The cerebellum, which means 'little brain', lies under the occipital lobes of the cerebral cortex at the back of the brain. It is important to the subconscious control of movement.

The part of the brain known as the cerebellum lies under the occipital lobes of the cerebral cortex at the back of the head. The vital roles of the cerebellum include the co-ordination of movement and the maintenance of balance and posture. The cerebellum works subconsciously and so an individual is not aware of its functioning.

### STRUCTURE

The cerebellum is composed of two hemispheres which are bridged in the midline by the vermis. The hemispheres extend laterally (sideways) and posteriorly (backwards) from the midline to form the bulk of the cerebellum.

The surface of the cerebellum has a very distinctive appearance. In contrast to the large folds of the cerebral hemispheres, the surface of the cerebellum is made up of numerous fine folds (folia).

### LOBES

Between the folia of the cerebellar surface lie deep fissures which divide it into three lobes:
- Anterior lobe
- Posterior lobe
- Flocculonodular lobe.

*The cerebellum has two hemispheres, one on either side of the worm-like vermis. The surface of the cerebellum is made up of thin folds (folia).*

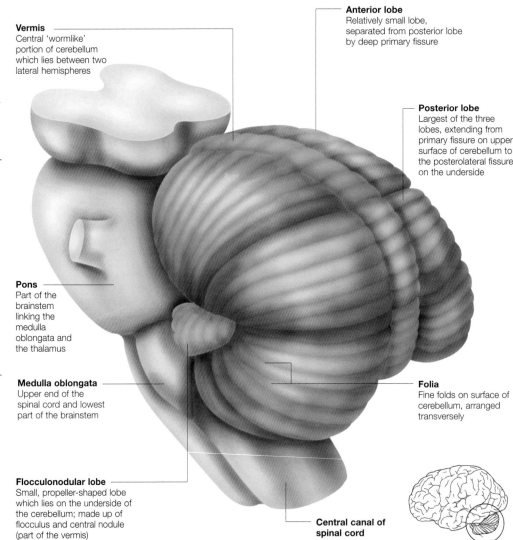

**Vermis**
Central 'wormlike' portion of cerebellum which lies between two lateral hemispheres

**Anterior lobe**
Relatively small lobe, separated from posterior lobe by deep primary fissure

**Posterior lobe**
Largest of the three lobes, extending from primary fissure on upper surface of cerebellum to the posterolateral fissure on the underside

**Pons**
Part of the brainstem linking the medulla oblongata and the thalamus

**Medulla oblongata**
Upper end of the spinal cord and lowest part of the brainstem

**Folia**
Fine folds on surface of cerebellum, arranged transversely

**Flocculonodular lobe**
Small, propeller-shaped lobe which lies on the underside of the cerebellum; made up of flocculus and central nodule (part of the vermis)

**Central canal of spinal cord**

## Cerebellar peduncles

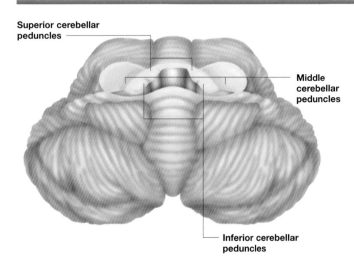

**Superior cerebellar peduncles**

**Middle cerebellar peduncles**

**Inferior cerebellar peduncles**

The cerebellum is connected to the brainstem, and thus to the rest of the brain, by three pairs of nerve fibre tracts which make up the cerebellar peduncles, or stalks. These can be seen on the inferior surface of the cerebellum, where they emerge together. The three tracts are:
- The superior cerebellar peduncles, connecting the cerebellum to the midbrain
- The middle cerebellar peduncles, connecting the

*The three pairs of cerebellar peduncles serve to anchor the cerebellum to the brainstem. The peduncles consist of bundles of nerve fibres.*

cerebellum to the pons
- The inferior cerebellar peduncles, connecting the cerebellum to the medulla.

There are no direct connections between the cerebellum and the cerebral cortex. All information to and from the cerebellum goes through the peduncles.

Unlike the cerebral cortex, where each side controls the opposite (contralateral) side of the body, each half of the cerebellum controls the same (ipsilateral) side of the body. This means that any damage to one side of the cerebellum will cause symptoms in the same side of the body.

# Internal structure of the cerebellum

The cerebellum has an outer grey cortex and a core of nerve fibres, or white matter. Deep within the white matter lie four pairs of cerebellar nuclei: the fastigial, globose, emboliform and dentate nuclei.

The cerebellum is composed of a surface layer of nerve cell bodies, or grey matter, which overlies a core of nerve fibres, or white matter. Deep within the white matter lie the cerebellar nuclei.

### CEREBELLAR CORTEX

Due to the presence of the numerous fine folia (folds) in the surface of the cerebellum, the cortex is very extensive. It is made up of the cell bodies and dendrites (cell processes) of the vast majority of cerebellar neurones.

The cells of the cortex receive information from outside the cerebellum via the cerebellar peduncles and make frequent connections between themselves within the cortex.

### SIGNALS

In most cases, signals from the cerebellar cortex are conveyed in the fibres of the white matter down to the cerebellar nuclei. It is from here that information leaves the cerebellum to be carried to the rest of the central nervous system.

### CEREBELLAR NUCLEI

There are four pairs of cerebellar nuclei which, from the midline outwards, are known as the:
- Fastigial nuclei
- Globose nuclei
- Emboliform nuclei
- Dentate nuclei.

**Cross-section through cerebellum**

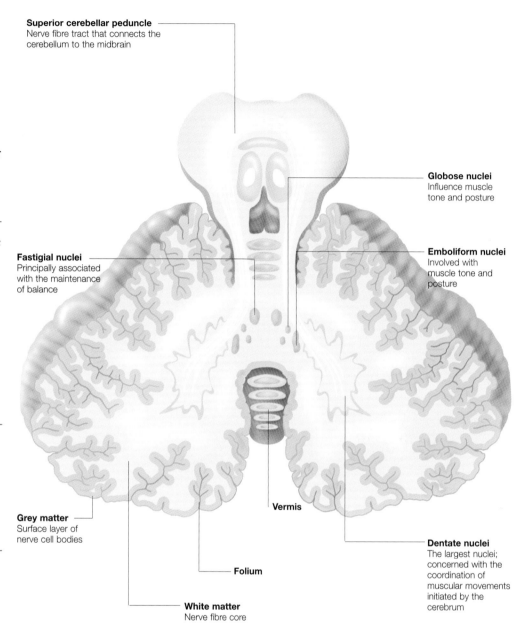

**Superior cerebellar peduncle**
Nerve fibre tract that connects the cerebellum to the midbrain

**Globose nuclei**
Influence muscle tone and posture

**Emboliform nuclei**
Involved with muscle tone and posture

**Fastigial nuclei**
Principally associated with the maintenance of balance

**Vermis**

**Grey matter**
Surface layer of nerve cell bodies

**Dentate nuclei**
The largest nuclei; concerned with the coordination of muscular movements initiated by the cerebrum

**Folium**

**White matter**
Nerve fibre core

## Layers of the cerebellar cortex

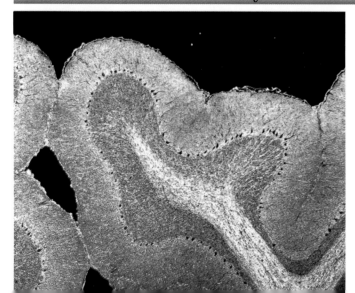

If the cerebellar cortex is stained and studied under the microscope, its structure can be seen to form a quite distinctive pattern of layers:
- Molecular layer (the outermost layer) – contains nerve cell bodies and is rich in nerve fibres from the deeper layers of cells
- Purkinje cell layer (the next layer) – although only one-cell

*A micrograph of a stained section of the cerebellar cortex reveals its complex layered structure. Each layer contains distinctive cell types.*

thick, this is relatively easy to visualize due to the size of the Purkinje cells. These specialized neurones are very important to cerebellar function. They receive signals via their dendrites which lie mainly in the layer above, and send information down to the cerebellar nuclei
- Granular layer (the innermost layer) – this contains the cell bodies of numerous granule cells. These cells receive information via the peduncles and send signals themselves through their axons up into the molecular layer.

# Cranial nerves

There are twelve pairs of cranial nerves which leave the brain to supply structures mainly of the head and neck. The cranial nerves carry information to and from the brain.

Nerves are the routes by which information passes between the central nervous system (CNS) and the rest of the body. From the neck down, these nerves emerge from the spinal cord, passing out through openings in the bony spinal column. However, the cranial nerves emerge directly from the brain.

There are twelve pairs of cranial nerves, which are named and numbered with Roman numerals. The first two pairs attach to the forebrain while the rest come from the brainstem. The cranial nerves serve structures of the head and neck. To reach these they must pass through special openings, or foramina, in the bony skull.

### CRANIAL NERVE FIBRES

Cranial nerves are made up of sensory and motor nerve fibres and so carry information to and from the CNS:

■ Sensory nerve fibres bring information such as pain, touch and temperature sensations from the face as well as the senses of taste, vision and hearing

■ Motor fibres send instructions to head, neck and face muscles, allowing various facial expressions and eye movements

■ Autonomic nerve fibres allow the subconscious control of internal structures such as the salivary glands, the iris and some of the major organs of the chest and abdomen.

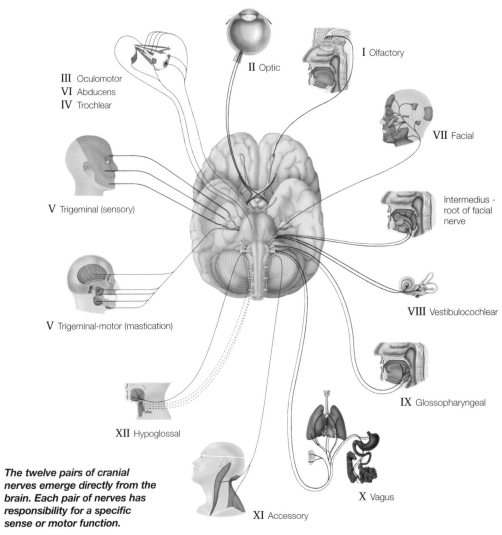

*The twelve pairs of cranial nerves emerge directly from the brain. Each pair of nerves has responsibility for a specific sense or motor function.*

## Functions of the 12 cranial nerves

| Number | Name | Comments |
|--------|------|----------|
| I | Olfactory nerve | The sensory nerve of smell |
| II | Optic nerve | The sensory nerve of vision |
| III | Oculomotor nerve | Supplies four of the six muscles that move the eyeball |
| IV | Trochlear nerve | Supplies a muscle that moves the eyeball |
| V | Trigeminal nerve | Carries sensation from the face and moves the muscles in chewing |
| VI | Abducens nerve | Supplies a muscle that moves the eyeball |
| VII | Facial nerve | Moves the muscles of facial expression |
| VIII | Vestibulocochlear nerve | The sensory nerve for hearing and balance |
| IX | Glossopharyngeal nerve | Helps to innervate the tongue and pharynx (gullet) |
| X | Vagus nerve | Supplies many structures including organs in the thorax and abdomen |
| XI | Accessory nerve | Supplies structures in the throat and some neck muscles |
| XII | Hypoglossal nerve | Supplies the tongue muscles. |

# The olfactory nerves

The olfactory nerves are the tiny sensory nerves of smell. They run from the nasal mucosa to the olfactory bulbs.

**Locator**

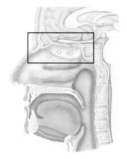

The olfactory nerves carry the special sense of smell from the receptor cells in the nasal cavity to the brain above.

## OLFACTORY EPITHELIUM

The olfactory epithelium is the part of the lining of the nasal cavity that carries special receptor cells for the sense of smell. It is found in the upper part of the nasal cavity and the septum, the partition between the two sides of the cavity.

The olfactory receptors are specialized neurones, or nerve cells, and are able to detect odorous substances which are present in the form of minute droplets in the air.

## OLFACTORY NERVES

Information from the olfactory receptor neurones is passed up to the brain through their long processes, or axons, which group together to form about 20 bundles. These bundles are the true olfactory nerves, which pass up through the thin perforated layer of bone, the cribriform plate of the ethmoid bone, to reach the olfactory bulbs in the cranial cavity.

The fibres of the olfactory nerves make connections (synapse) with the neurones within the olfactory bulb.

**Frontal lobe of cerebral hemisphere**

**Cribriform plate of the ethmoid bone**

**Olfactory bulb**
Two olfactory bulbs receive and process information from the olfactory nerve fibres

**Olfactory nerve fibres**
These fibres arise from the receptor cells in the nasal mucosa

*The olfactory nerve fibres pass from the nasal lining to the brain. Information passes along these fibres and is interpreted in the olfactory centre.*

**Nasal lining**
The olfactory epithelium in the lining of the nose contains receptor cells

**Olfactory tract**
These tracts extend out from the brain to culminate in the olfactory bulbs

### OLFACTORY BULBS

The paired olfactory bulbs are actually part of the brain, extended out on stalks, the olfactory tracts, which contain fibres linking them to the cerebral hemispheres.

Large specialized neurones, known as mitral cells, connect with the olfactory nerves within the olfactory bulb. This connection permits information about smell to be passed on from the olfactory nerves.

The axons of these mitral cells then carry this information to the olfactory centre of the brain via the olfactory tracts.

## Loss of the sense of smell

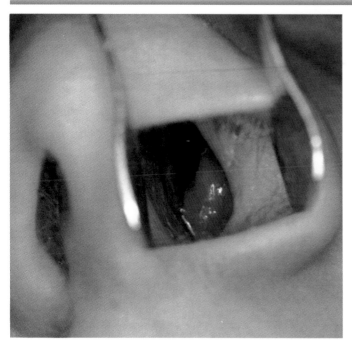

Loss of the sense of smell, known as anosmia, may affect one or both sides of the nose and may be permanent or temporary.

The chief complaint of people with anosmia is of a lack of the sense of taste rather than smell. This is because much of what we think of as the sensation of taste is actually the detection of odours within our food. Without the sense of smell the tongue can only discern four flavours: sweet, bitter, sour and salt.

### EFFECTS OF AGEING

As the body ages there is a progressive loss of olfactory fibres. Elderly people, therefore,

*Rhinitis causes the turbinate bone in the nasal cavity to become swollen. The resulting inflammation affects the smell mechanism.*

often complain that their food has 'lost its flavour' due to a loss of their sense of smell.

### HEAD INJURIES

Injuries to the head can lead to tearing of the olfactory bulbs or breaking of the delicate cribriform plate. This can lead to anosmia, usually affecting one nostril only.

### RHINITIS

Rhinitis, or inflammation of the mucous lining of the nose, may occur as a result of a viral infection such as the common cold or with allergies such as hay fever. This usually causes a blocked or runny nose and sneezing.

In this situation it is common for people to experience a temporary loss of smell due to involvement of the olfactory epithelium.

# Facial muscles

One of the features that distinguishes humans from animals is
our ability to communicate using a wide range of facial expressions.
The power behind this ability is a complex system of facial muscles.

Just under the skin of the scalp and face lies a group of very thin muscles, which are collectively known as the muscles of facial expression. These muscles play a vital role in a number of ways, in addition to their physiological function. They alter facial expression – providing a means of non-verbal communication by transmitting a range of emotional information – and are also one of the means of articulating speech.

Apart from this, the facial muscles also form sphincters that open and close the orifices of the face – the eyes and mouth.

### SKIN AND BONE

The majority of facial muscles are attached to the skull bone at one end and to the deep layer of skin (dermis) at the other. From these attachments, it can be seen see how the numerous muscles alter facial expression, and also how they eventually cause creases and wrinkles in the overlying skin.

A number of small muscles called 'dilators' open the mouth. They radiate out from the corners of the mouth and lips, where they have an attachment to bone. The mouth and lips can be pulled up, pushed down and moved from side to side.

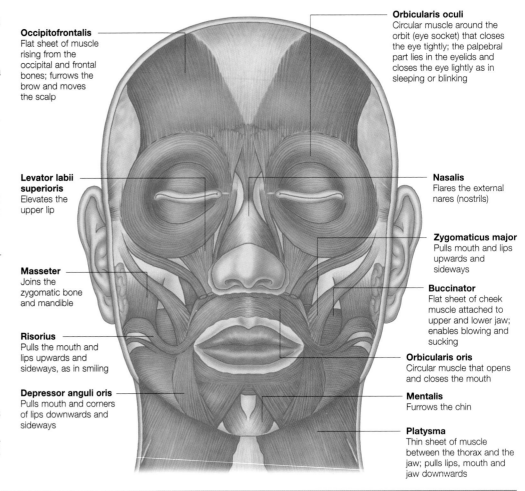

**Occipitofrontalis**
Flat sheet of muscle rising from the occipital and frontal bones; furrows the brow and moves the scalp

**Levator labii superioris**
Elevates the upper lip

**Masseter**
Joins the zygomatic bone and mandible

**Risorius**
Pulls the mouth and lips upwards and sideways, as in smiling

**Depressor anguli oris**
Pulls mouth and corners of lips downwards and sideways

**Orbicularis oculi**
Circular muscle around the orbit (eye socket) that closes the eye tightly; the palpebral part lies in the eyelids and closes the eye lightly as in sleeping or blinking

**Nasalis**
Flares the external nares (nostrils)

**Zygomaticus major**
Pulls mouth and lips upwards and sideways

**Buccinator**
Flat sheet of cheek muscle attached to upper and lower jaw; enables blowing and sucking

**Orbicularis oris**
Circular muscle that opens and closes the mouth

**Mentalis**
Furrows the chin

**Platysma**
Thin sheet of muscle between the thorax and the jaw; pulls lips, mouth and jaw downwards

## Platysma

*The large, flat platysma muscle is a superficial (close to the surface) muscle extending from below the collar bone to the skin and muscle of the mouth and lips. Its main role is lowering the lower lip and jaw, as in a snarl.*

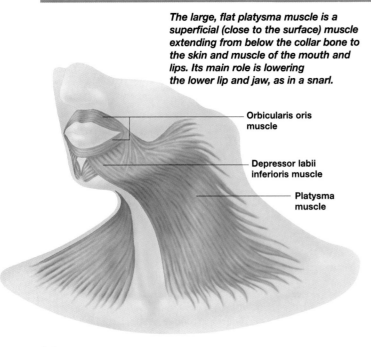

**Orbicularis oris muscle**

**Depressor labii inferioris muscle**

**Platysma muscle**

Although not strictly a muscle of the head, the platysma muscle plays an important role in facial expression. This thin sheet of muscle extends from below the collar bone up to the mandible. It covers the front of the neck, where it tightens the skin, and connects to the muscle and skin at the corners of the mouth.

The platysma's role in altering facial expression is to pull the neck skin out and depress the mandible (lower the jaw). This pulls the mouth down, as in an expression of disgust. It also assists in the movement of the lower lip.

In addition, the platysma is the muscle that is cut and pinned behind the ear during plastic surgery to reduce 'double chins'. This is, arguably, another way in which the platysma can alter the facial expression.

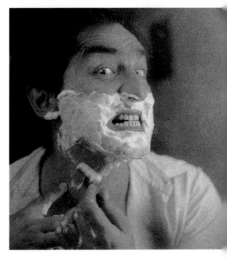

*The platysma muscle is the large sheet of muscle that is tensed while shaving under the chin. This action stretches and tightens the skin of the neck.*

# Opening and closing the eye

Whether fluttered alluringly or squeezed tightly shut for protection, the eyelids communicate a range of non-verbal signals. The eyelids are also vital for cleaning and lubricating the eyes.

The orbicularis oculi is the muscle responsible for the closing of the eye. This flat sphincter muscle lines the rim of the orbit (eye socket), and various sections of it can be manipulated individually.

Part of the orbicularis oculi lies in the eyelid (the palpebral part). This section of the muscle closes the eye lightly, as in sleeping or in routine blinking. This action also aids the flow of lacrimal secretion (tears) across the conjunctiva (the membrane covering the eyes) to keep it clean, free of foreign bodies and lubricated.

### OPENING THE LIDS
A larger part of the orbicularis oculi consists of concentrically arranged fibres that cover the front of the eye socket. The role of this part of the muscle is to close the eye tightly (screw up the eyes) to protect against a blow or bright light.

The second orbital muscle is the levator palpebrae superioris. As its name suggests, this small muscle pulls on the upper lid to open the eye. Unlike the larger orbicularis, this muscle lies within the eye socket.

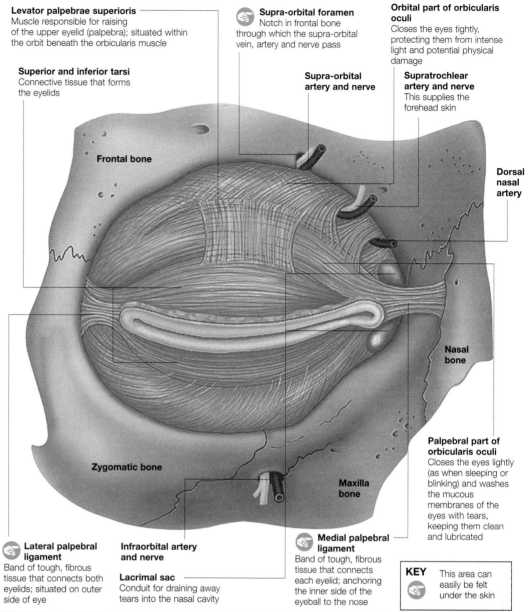

**Levator palpebrae superioris**
Muscle responsible for raising of the upper eyelid (palpebra); situated within the orbit beneath the orbicularis muscle

**Superior and inferior tarsi**
Connective tissue that forms the eyelids

**Frontal bone**

**Supra-orbital foramen**
Notch in frontal bone through which the supra-orbital vein, artery and nerve pass

**Supra-orbital artery and nerve**

**Orbital part of orbicularis oculi**
Closes the eyes tightly, protecting them from intense light and potential physical damage

**Supratrochlear artery and nerve**
This supplies the forehead skin

**Dorsal nasal artery**

**Nasal bone**

**Zygomatic bone**

**Palpebral part of orbicularis oculi**
Closes the eyes lightly (as when sleeping or blinking) and washes the mucous membranes of the eyes with tears, keeping them clean and lubricated

**Maxilla bone**

**Lateral palpebral ligament**
Band of tough, fibrous tissue that connects both eyelids; situated on outer side of eye

**Infraorbital artery and nerve**

**Lacrimal sac**
Conduit for draining away tears into the nasal cavity

**Medial palpebral ligament**
Band of tough, fibrous tissue that connects each eyelid; anchoring the inner side of the eyeball to the nose

**KEY** This area can easily be felt under the skin

## Muscles of the cheek and lips

The buccinator muscle forms the cheek on the side of the face. Its upper margin is attached to the maxilla bone along a line just above the upper tooth sockets, and its lower to the mandible below the lower tooth sockets. Its main action occurs during eating.

The buccinator pushes food that has collected in the cheek during chewing back on to the tongue and between the surfaces of the teeth ready for the next bite. The buccinator is also used in activities such as blowing up a balloon or playing a musical instrument, such as a trumpet (the word 'buccinator' is derived from the Latin for trumpet).

The muscle within the upper and lower lips surrounding the opening of the mouth is the orbicularis oris. It consists of concentrically arranged muscle fibres which curve around the angles of the mouth and are attached to bone beneath the nose at one end and to a region above the point of the chin at the other.

The front margin of buccinator contributes muscle fibres that crisscross at the corners of the mouth, and blend with the orbicularis oris.

The orbicularis oris is the muscle that closes the mouth. It is in continuous use to hold the lips firmly together and prevent saliva, which is being produced all the time, escaping from the mouth and also to retain food in the mouth during eating. It is also used to purse the lips, as in whistling or blowing a kiss.

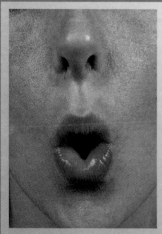

*The orbicularis oris provides sphincteric control of the mouth. When the muscles contract, the orifice closes up.*

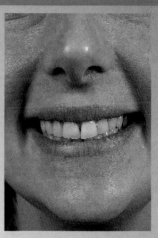

*The versatility of the ring of muscle fibres around the lips helps humans to articulate a wide range of sounds.*

# Arteries of the face and neck

## The pulse you feel in your neck is blood being pumped to the head via the carotid artery.

The head and neck are supplied with blood from the two common carotid arteries that ascend either side of the neck. They are encased, along with the internal jugular vein and the vagus nerve, in a protective covering of connective tissue called the carotid sheath. They have slightly different origins at the base of the neck with the left common carotid arising directly from the arch of the aorta while the right arises from the brachiocephalic trunk.

### BRANCHING ARTERIES

The common carotid arteries divide at the level of the upper border of the thyroid cartilage (Adam's apple) to form the internal and external carotid arteries. The former enters the skull and supplies the brain and the latter provides branches that supply the face and scalp.

Many of the branches of the external carotid artery have a wavy or looped course. This flexibility ensures that when the mouth, larynx or pharynx are moved, during swallowing for example, the vessels are not stretched and damaged.

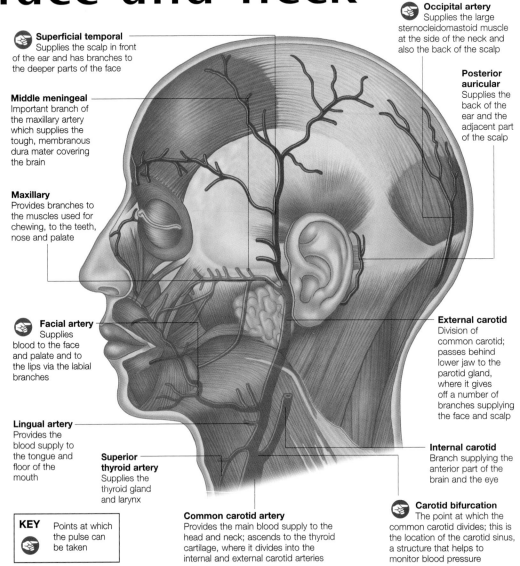

**Superficial temporal**
Supplies the scalp in front of the ear and has branches to the deeper parts of the face

**Middle meningeal**
Important branch of the maxillary artery which supplies the tough, membranous dura mater covering the brain

**Maxillary**
Provides branches to the muscles used for chewing, to the teeth, nose and palate

**Facial artery**
Supplies blood to the face and palate and to the lips via the labial branches

**Lingual artery**
Provides the blood supply to the tongue and floor of the mouth

**Superior thyroid artery**
Supplies the thyroid gland and larynx

**Occipital artery**
Supplies the large sternocleidomastoid muscle at the side of the neck and also the back of the scalp

**Posterior auricular**
Supplies the back of the ear and the adjacent part of the scalp

**External carotid**
Division of common carotid; passes behind lower jaw to the parotid gland, where it gives off a number of branches supplying the face and scalp

**Internal carotid**
Branch supplying the anterior part of the brain and the eye

**Carotid bifurcation**
The point at which the common carotid divides; this is the location of the carotid sinus, a structure that helps to monitor blood pressure

**Common carotid artery**
Provides the main blood supply to the head and neck; ascends to the thyroid cartilage, where it divides into the internal and external carotid arteries

**KEY** Points at which the pulse can be taken

## Carotid angiography

The injection of a contrast medium, and a rapid series of X-ray recordings, can illustrate the branches of the common carotid artery. This process is called angiography.

Angiography is used to study blood vessels and to look for any abnormalities, such as blockages in the carotid arteries. A build-up of fatty deposits in the artery wall, associated with atherosclerosis, can sometimes be found where the common carotid artery divides. It is possible for surgeons to operate and carefully remove the fatty deposit without damaging the vessel walls. This procedure, known as carotid endarterectomy, effectively improves the blood supply to the head and neck, and reduces the risk of a subsequent stroke.

Another abnormality which can be detected using angiography is aneurysm of the artery, where a balloon-like swelling is found in the wall of the vessel.

*A false-colour angiogram of the arteries running from the aorta (the large vessel at the bottom of the image) to the head.*

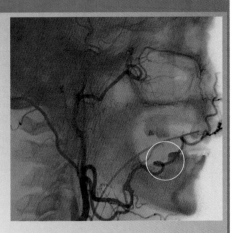

*This digitally subtracted arteriogram reveals branching of the carotid artery. The looped facial artery is circled.*

# Veins of the face and neck

The veins have a similar distribution around the face and neck as the arteries. Many of the veins also share the same names.

Blood drains from the head and neck back to the heart via the internal jugular veins that lie on either side of the neck. As with the common carotid arteries, the veins are protected by the carotid sheath.

Unlike in the rest of the body, the veins of this region generally lack valves, and the return of blood to the heart is by gravity and negative pressure in the thorax (chest).

The superficial (close to the surface) veins are often visible during exertion, and may be seen standing out on the necks of singers, for example.

## JUGULAR VEIN

There is very little variation in the position of the internal jugular vein. Because of this, the vein is used for monitoring central venous pressure (blood pressure within the right atrium of the heart). A cannula (hollow tube) is inserted into the vein and passed to the heart. The other end of the cannula is attached to a transducer, an instrument that records pressure. The blood volume may then be assessed.

As well as the veins draining the face, there is a series of emissary veins communicating between the venous sinuses (which drain blood from the brain) and the veins of the scalp. Along with the diploic veins (found in the bones of the skull), these provide a potential route for infection from the scalp into the brain.

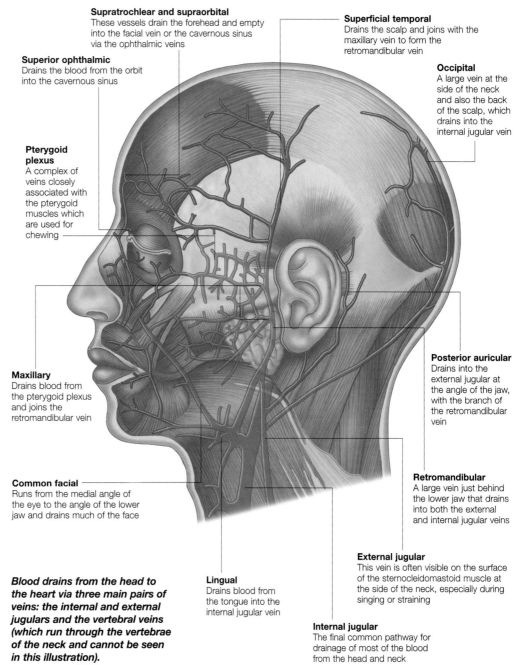

**Supratrochlear and supraorbital**
These vessels drain the forehead and empty into the facial vein or the cavernous sinus via the ophthalmic veins

**Superior ophthalmic**
Drains the blood from the orbit into the cavernous sinus

**Pterygoid plexus**
A complex of veins closely associated with the pterygoid muscles which are used for chewing

**Maxillary**
Drains blood from the pterygoid plexus and joins the retromandibular vein

**Common facial**
Runs from the medial angle of the eye to the angle of the lower jaw and drains much of the face

**Superficial temporal**
Drains the scalp and joins with the maxillary vein to form the retromandibular vein

**Occipital**
A large vein at the side of the neck and also the back of the scalp, which drains into the internal jugular vein

**Posterior auricular**
Drains into the external jugular at the angle of the jaw, with the branch of the retromandibular vein

**Retromandibular**
A large vein just behind the lower jaw that drains into both the external and internal jugular veins

**External jugular**
This vein is often visible on the surface of the sternocleidomastoid muscle at the side of the neck, especially during singing or straining

**Lingual**
Drains blood from the tongue into the internal jugular vein

**Internal jugular**
The final common pathway for drainage of most of the blood from the head and neck

*Blood drains from the head to the heart via three main pairs of veins: the internal and external jugulars and the vertebral veins (which run through the vertebrae of the neck and cannot be seen in this illustration).*

## Interconnections

There are numerous interconnections – called anastomoses – between the arteries on the left and right side of the face and between the branches of the external and internal carotid. This has implications for treating a cut lip, for example, when pressure may need to be applied to both left and right facial arteries in order to stop bleeding.

The extensive array of blood vessels in the scalp also means that injuries in this area may bleed profusely. This is not only because of the plentiful blood supply but

*A resin cast of the veins and arteries serving the face and neck clearly shows the extensive branching networks. Note the particular density of vessels at the front of the neck (the thyroid gland) and the tongue.*

also because the vessels are prevented from contracting rapidly due to the fibrous connective tissue under the skin.

The highly interconnected nature of the veins in the head and neck also means that they are an important potential route for the spread of infection. Boils or spots around the side of the nose may cause thrombosis (clot formation) in the facial vein. This in turn may transmit thrombotic material via the ophthalmic vein to the cavernous sinus (the paired sinus in the sphenoid bone of the skull, into which blood drains from the brain, eyes and nose). The resulting cavernous sinus thrombosis is fatal if not treated with antibiotics. Treatment of this condition was one of the first recorded uses of penicillin in the 1940s.

# Facial nerves

The facial muscles, and the involuntary functions such as tear formation, are served by the facial nerve, which transmits signals to and from the brain.

The muscles of facial expression are supplied by left and right facial nerves, each supplying muscle on their respective side of the face. Each nerve emerges through a hole in the skull (the stylomastoid foramen) next to the lower part of the ear, and reaches the facial muscles by branching through a salivary gland (the parotid) located on the side of the face.

Nerves are bundles of fibres that transmit electrical impulses from the brain or spinal column to the muscles, or from the sense organs to the brain or spinal column. Most nerves – including the facial nerves – are composed of a mixture of the two types, sending and receiving data to and from the brain.

## NERVE DAMAGE

There are 12 pairs of cranial nerves serving various functions from moving the eyeballs to maintaining balance. The facial nerves are the seventh pair, and their principle task is providing motor impulses to the muscles of facial expression. (The muscles of mastication, used for chewing food, are served by the fifth cranial nerve, the trigeminal.)

As well as innervating the muscles (transmitting impulses to them), the facial nerves serve the autonomic functions, such as the production of tears and saliva. They also convey sensory impulses from the taste buds.

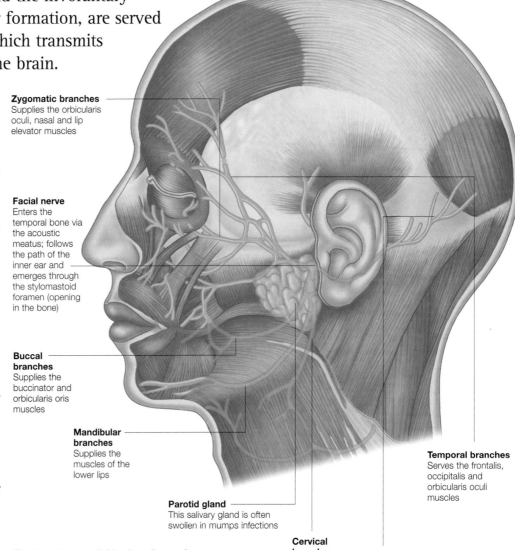

**Zygomatic branches**
Supplies the orbicularis oculi, nasal and lip elevator muscles

**Facial nerve**
Enters the temporal bone via the acoustic meatus; follows the path of the inner ear and emerges through the stylomastoid foramen (opening in the bone)

**Buccal branches**
Supplies the buccinator and orbicularis oris muscles

**Mandibular branches**
Supplies the muscles of the lower lips

**Parotid gland**
This salivary gland is often swollen in mumps infections

**Temporal branches**
Serves the frontalis, occipitalis and orbicularis oculi muscles

**Cervical branches**
Supplies the platysma muscles

**Posterior branches**
Before the facial nerve enters the parotid gland and divides, it serves the occipitalis (scalp) and auricular (ear) muscles

*The facial nerve divides into five main branches: temporal, zygomatic, buccal, mandibular and cervical. These five branches fan out over the face and further divide, serving the muscles of facial expression.*

## Facial nerve disorders

*With a relaxed gaze, a Bell's palsy sufferer displays the characteristic facial droop (in this case the left side).*

*When asked to grin and screw up the eyes, the patient cannot move the left side of the mouth or eye because of paralysis.*

The facial nerve can be damaged by direct trauma to the side of the face or by inflammation, which causes the nerve to swell where it lies in the skull bone (facial canal). This may result in paresis (weakness) or paralysis of the facial muscles, giving that side of the face a droopy expression.

In a person with facial nerve damage, the eye is permanently open, leaving the cornea and conjunctiva in danger of drying. Speech is slurred as the lips cannot articulate clearly and the mouth cannot form an effective seal.

Consequently, saliva and food often spill out of the mouth.

Bell's palsy is a paralysis most commonly associated with the swelling of the facial nerve. The symptoms are numerous, affecting hearing, taste, vision and muscle strength.

The facial nerve can occasionally be damaged if an infant is delivered by forceps. The bony mastoid process (protuberance) at the back of the ear is undeveloped in the new born, leaving the nerve unprotected. Such damage would leave the facial muscles paralysed, preventing suckling.

# Muscles of mastication

The muscles that help us chew our food also play a part in speech, breathing and yawning.

The muscles of mastication are the muscles that move the mandible (jaw bone) up and down, and forwards and backwards, resulting in the opening and closing of the mouth.

This action is used in activities such as speaking, breathing through the mouth and in yawning. The closing action is also used very powerfully in the movements necessary for biting off and chewing up food (mastication), when side-to-side slewing of the jaw is also employed.

### MOVING THE JAW

All jaw movements take place at the pair of temporo-mandibular joints, which lie in front of the ears.

The bones forming the joint are the head of the mandible (the rounded section at the top of the jaw bone) and the mandibular fossa of the temporal bone (the hollow in the skull in which the head of the mandible sits).

The hinge-like action allows up and down movements of the jaw. Additionally, the head of the mandible is covered with a closely fitting disc of cartilage, which allows forward and backward rocking movements. This latter movement enables the lower jaw to be slewed across the upper jaw on opening, and so provides the sideways forces necessary to grind up hard food on closing the mouth and chewing.

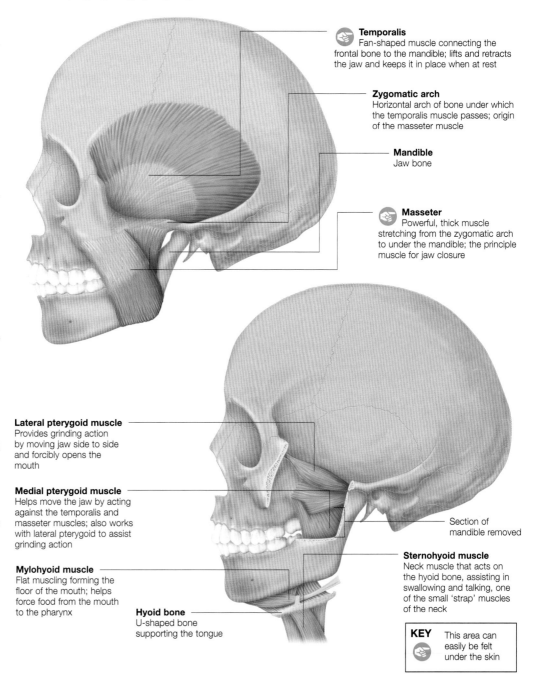

**Temporalis**
Fan-shaped muscle connecting the frontal bone to the mandible; lifts and retracts the jaw and keeps it in place when at rest

**Zygomatic arch**
Horizontal arch of bone under which the temporalis muscle passes; origin of the masseter muscle

**Mandible**
Jaw bone

**Masseter**
Powerful, thick muscle stretching from the zygomatic arch to under the mandible; the principle muscle for jaw closure

**Lateral pterygoid muscle**
Provides grinding action by moving jaw side to side and forcibly opens the mouth

**Medial pterygoid muscle**
Helps move the jaw by acting against the temporalis and masseter muscles; also works with lateral pterygoid to assist grinding action

**Mylohyoid muscle**
Flat muscling forming the floor of the mouth; helps force food from the mouth to the pharynx

**Hyoid bone**
U-shaped bone supporting the tongue

Section of mandible removed

**Sternohyoid muscle**
Neck muscle that acts on the hyoid bone, assisting in swallowing and talking, one of the small 'strap' muscles of the neck

**KEY** This area can easily be felt under the skin

## Dislocated jaw

As the jaw is opened, the head of the mandible and its disc of cartilage moves forward out of the joint socket and on to a tubercle (small protrusion) in front. This forward movement can be easily seen and felt just in front of the ear hole.

If this movement goes too far, as in a wide yawn or enthusiastic laughter, the mandible may slip in front of the tubercle and become lodged under the zygomatic bone. This jams the mouth open, necessitating medical treatment. The same action can result from a blow to the side of the jaw, and is the reason boxers are taught to keep

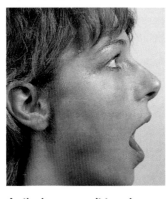

*As the jaw opens, it travels forward on to a tubercle, and can be felt as a swelling in front of the ear.*

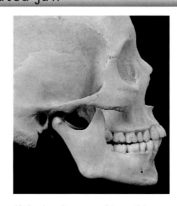

*If the jaw is opened too wide, or is knocked out of place, it can cause a spasm of the temporalis muscle, locking the jaw open.*

the mouth shut and teeth tightly clamped on a gum shield.

Unlocking the jaw and closing the mouth involves pushing the jaw downwards, against the pull of the temporalis, masseter and medial pterygoid muscles. This forces the head of the mandible back over the tubercle, and the joint snaps back into place.

When performing this manoeuvre, it is important not to press down on the teeth using the thumbs. Instead, downwards force should be applied to the mandible, below the tooth line. This prevents the molars biting the doctor's fingers when the jaw snaps back into place.

**39**

# Eyeball

## The eyes are the specialized organs of sight, designed to respond to light.

Our eyes allow us to receive information from our surroundings by detecting patterns of light. This information is sent to our brain, which processes it so that it can be perceived as images.

Each eyeball is embedded in protective fatty tissue within a bony cavity (the orbit). The orbit has a large opening at the front to allow light to enter, and smaller openings at the back, allowing the optic nerve to pass to the brain, and blood vessels and nerves to enter the orbit.

### CHAMBERS

The eyeball is divided into three internal chambers. The two aqueous chambers at the front of the eye are the anterior and posterior chambers, and are separated by the iris. These chambers are filled with clear, watery aqueous humour, which is secreted into the posterior chamber by a layer of cells covering the ciliary body.

This fluid passes into the anterior chamber through the pupil, then into the bloodstream via a number of small channels found where the base of the iris meets the margin of the cornea.

The largest of the chambers is the vitreous body, which lies behind the aqueous chambers, and is separated from them by the lens and the suspensory ligaments (zonular fibres), which connect the lens to the ciliary body. The vitreous body is filled with clear, jelly-like vitreous humour.

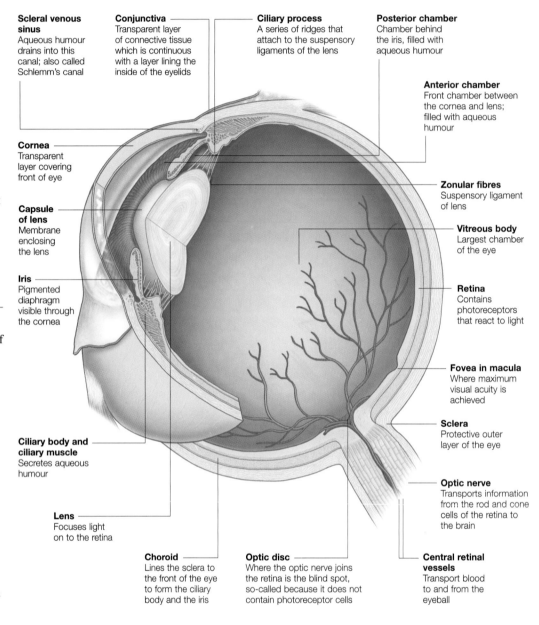

**Scleral venous sinus**
Aqueous humour drains into this canal; also called Schlemm's canal

**Conjunctiva**
Transparent layer of connective tissue which is continuous with a layer lining the inside of the eyelids

**Ciliary process**
A series of ridges that attach to the suspensory ligaments of the lens

**Posterior chamber**
Chamber behind the iris, filled with aqueous humour

**Anterior chamber**
Front chamber between the cornea and lens; filled with aqueous humour

**Cornea**
Transparent layer covering front of eye

**Capsule of lens**
Membrane enclosing the lens

**Iris**
Pigmented diaphragm visible through the cornea

**Ciliary body and ciliary muscle**
Secretes aqueous humour

**Lens**
Focuses light on to the retina

**Choroid**
Lines the sclera to the front of the eye to form the ciliary body and the iris

**Optic disc**
Where the optic nerve joins the retina is the blind spot, so-called because it does not contain photoreceptor cells

**Zonular fibres**
Suspensory ligament of lens

**Vitreous body**
Largest chamber of the eye

**Retina**
Contains photoreceptors that react to light

**Fovea in macula**
Where maximum visual acuity is achieved

**Sclera**
Protective outer layer of the eye

**Optic nerve**
Transports information from the rod and cone cells of the retina to the brain

**Central retinal vessels**
Transport blood to and from the eyeball

## Damage to the eye

Disease or trauma can cause the transparent structures (the cornea or the lens) to become opaque to varying degrees. Increased opacity of the lens (cataract) is a common condition, especially after middle age. It is usually treated by removal of the lens, and insertion of a lens implant.

Disease and trauma can also lead to retinal damage. The retina can become detached and the detached region will degenerate.

A fairly common reason for retinal damage is glaucoma. This occurs when there is a blockage of the drainage of the aqueous fluid in the anterior chamber, which causes pressure inside the eye to rise (raised intra-ocular pressure). This pressure results in damage to the nerve cells of the retina. Intra-ocular pressure is routinely measured in eye tests for early detection of glaucoma.

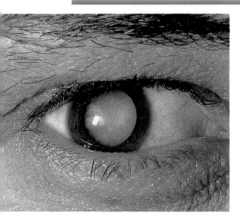

*A mature cataract can be seen on this man's eye. It was caused by gradual denaturation of the proteins that make up the lens.*

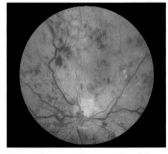

*The retina can be examined for evidence of disease. In this case, the arrangement of blood vessels is indicative of diabetes.*

# Layers of the eye

The eyeball is covered by three different layers, each of which has a special function.

The outer layer of the eyeball is called the sclera, and is a tough, fibrous, protective layer. At the front of the eye, the sclera is visible as the 'white of the eye'. This is covered by the conjunctiva, a transparent layer of connective tissue. The transparent cornea covers the front of the eyeball, allowing light to enter the eye.

### UVEA

The intermediate layer, the uvea, contains many blood vessels, nerves and pigmented cells. The uvea is divided into three main regions: the choroid, the ciliary body and the iris. The choroid extends from where the optic nerve meets the eyeball to the front of the eye, where it forms both the ciliary body and the iris.

### RETINA

The innermost layer of the eye is the retina, a layer of nerve tissue containing photosensitive (light-sensitive) cells called photoreceptors. It lines all but the most anterior (frontal) part of the vitreous body. There are two types of photoreceptor cells: rods cells detect light intensity and are concentrated towards the periphery of the retina. Cone cells detect colour, and are most concentrated at the fovea at the most posterior part of the eyeball.

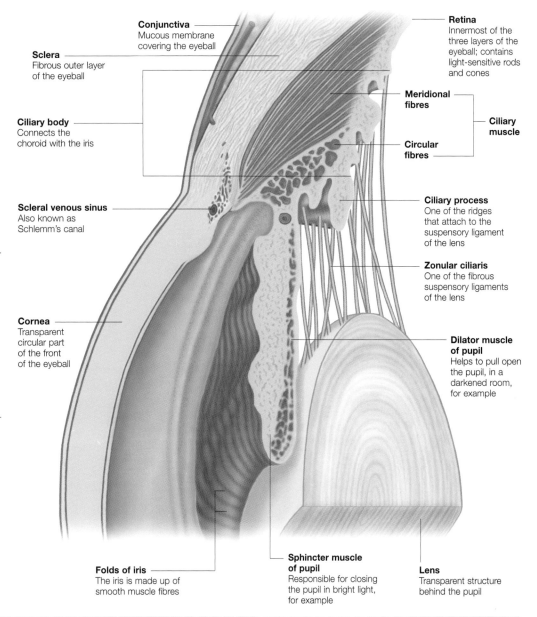

**Conjunctiva**
Mucous membrane covering the eyeball

**Sclera**
Fibrous outer layer of the eyeball

**Ciliary body**
Connects the choroid with the iris

**Scleral venous sinus**
Also known as Schlemm's canal

**Cornea**
Transparent circular part of the front of the eyeball

**Folds of iris**
The iris is made up of smooth muscle fibres

**Sphincter muscle of pupil**
Responsible for closing the pupil in bright light, for example

**Retina**
Innermost of the three layers of the eyeball; contains light-sensitive rods and cones

**Meridional fibres**

**Circular fibres**

**Ciliary muscle**

**Ciliary process**
One of the ridges that attach to the suspensory ligament of the lens

**Zonular ciliaris**
One of the fibrous suspensory ligaments of the lens

**Dilator muscle of pupil**
Helps to pull open the pupil, in a darkened room, for example

**Lens**
Transparent structure behind the pupil

## Impaired eyesight

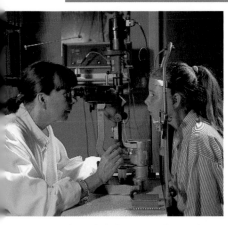

*An ophthalmoscope is used to examine the interior of the eye. Serious conditions, such as glaucoma, can be detected in the early, symptomless stages using this viewing technique.*

Sight can be impaired in a number of ways. The most common are refractive errors. In a normal eye (emmetropia), light rays are refracted by the cornea and the lens to focus on the retina. When looking at a distant object, the lens is relatively flat, stretched by the ciliary body pulling on the suspensory ligaments.

When looking at a near object, the ciliary muscle fibres in the ciliary body contract. This makes the circle of the ciliary body smaller, leading to the relaxation of the suspensory ligaments. This allows the lens to become more globular, therefore more refractive to focus the near image on to the retina, a process called accommodation.

In short-sightedness (myopia), the image is focused in front of the retina because the eye is too long or the curvature of the lens makes it too refractive, while in long-sightedness (hypermetropia) the opposite is true. In astigmatism, the curvature of the eye is not even, resulting in uneven focus which cannot be compensated for by lens accommodation. Refractive errors are corrected by placing appropriate prescription lenses (glasses or contact lenses) in front of the eye.

*In a normal eye (top), light rays converge at the back of the retina. In a myopic eye (bottom), the eye is too long, and light rays fall short of the retina, giving unclear distance vision.*

# Muscles, blood vessels and nerves of the eye

**The rotational movements of the eye are controlled by six rope-like extra-ocular muscles.**

The muscles of the eye can be divided into three groups: the muscles inside the eyeball, the muscles of the eyelids and the extra-ocular muscles, which rotate the eyeball within its orbit.

The six extra-ocular muscles are rope-like, attaching directly to the sclera. Four of the muscles are rectus (straight) muscles – superior, inferior, lateral (the temple side of the eye) and medial (nasal side). Each rectus muscle arises from connective tissue, the common tendinous ring (annulus) at the back of the orbit that passes forward to insert just behind the junction of the sclera and cornea.

### OBLIQUE MUSCLES

The two extra-ocular muscles are the oblique muscles. The superior oblique arises from bone near the back of the orbit, and extends to the front of the orbit. There, its tendon loops through the trochlea, a 'pulley' made of fibres and cartilage, and turns back to insert into the sclera.

The inferior oblique arises from the floor of the orbit, passing backwards and laterally under the eyeball to insert towards the back of the eye.

## LEFT EYE (SIDE VIEW)

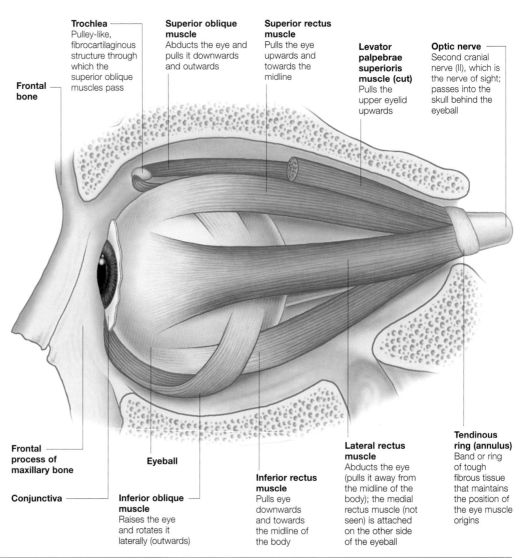

**Trochlea**
Pulley-like, fibrocartilaginous structure through which the superior oblique muscles pass

**Superior oblique muscle**
Abducts the eye and pulls it downwards and outwards

**Superior rectus muscle**
Pulls the eye upwards and towards the midline

**Levator palpebrae superioris muscle (cut)**
Pulls the upper eyelid upwards

**Optic nerve**
Second cranial nerve (II), which is the nerve of sight; passes into the skull behind the eyeball

**Frontal bone**

**Frontal process of maxillary bone**

**Eyeball**

**Conjunctiva**

**Inferior oblique muscle**
Raises the eye and rotates it laterally (outwards)

**Inferior rectus muscle**
Pulls eye downwards and towards the midline of the body

**Lateral rectus muscle**
Abducts the eye (pulls it away from the midline of the body); the medial rectus muscle (not seen) is attached on the other side of the eyeball

**Tendinous ring (annulus)**
Band or ring of tough fibrous tissue that maintains the position of the eye muscle origins

## Eye defects

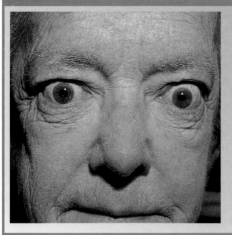

A squint (strabismus) is the consequence of defects in the function of eye muscles. While it will affect the quality of vision, it may also be indicative of serious disease.

The two main types of squint are non-paralytic strabismus and paralytic strabismus. Non-paralytic occurs when muscle functions are intact. It may be the result of incomplete development of eye movement reflexes (correctable by eye patches and/or surgery), or of serious sight defect (such as severe long or

*Exophthalmos (bulging eyeballs) can result from weakness of the extraocular muscles. In this patient, this weakness was triggered by thyrotoxicosis, an overproduction of hormones in the thyroid gland.*

short sightedness, cataract or retinoblastoma).

In paralytic strabismus, one or more of the extraocular muscles is non-functional, usually as the result of a congenital abnormality, or is acquired later in life. It is more common in adults, and is often the result of disease (such as multiple sclerosis, meningitis or brain tumour) or trauma. Determining which eye movements are affected will show which muscles are affected and give clues to potential sites of damage in the eye or brain.

The staring, bulging eyes seen in individuals suffering from hyperthyroidism is the result of effects on eye muscles. With this condition, the levator palpebrae superioris muscle, which opens the upper eyelid, is over-stimulated, resulting in a 'wide-eyed' stare.

# Nerves and blood vessels of the eye

The eye muscles are served by a series of nerves and blood vessels that help to make sight our dominant sense.

Nerves of the eye enter and leave the orbit through its openings posteriorly (at the back). Cranial nerve (CN) II – the optic nerve, which carries the visual signals from the retina to the brain – passes from the orbit to the cranial cavity through the optic canal. The other nerves – including branches of the ophthalmic nerve, the sensory nerve of the eye – enter the orbit through the orbital fissure.

Another nerve important for the eye is the facial nerve (CN VII). This supplies orbicularis oculi (a muscle of facial expression), causes blinking and also controls secretion from the lacrimal gland, which keeps the eye moist. They secrete fluid (tears) continuously, which is spread over the surface of the cornea by blinking. Irritation of the cornea can cause an increase in tear production.

### ARTERIES OF THE EYE

The main artery of the eye is the ophthalmic artery, which is a branch of the internal carotid artery. The ophthalmic artery enters the orbit within the sheath of the optic nerve, and then branches to the extraocular muscles, the eyeball, the lacrimal gland and surrounding tissues.

The retinal artery remains within the optic nerve stalk until it reaches the optic disc, where it sends out branches supplying the retina. Veins drain the orbit to the cavernous sinus in the cranial cavity and to the facial vein, thus forming a connection between the blood vessels of the face and brain.

**LEFT EYE (FROM ABOVE)**

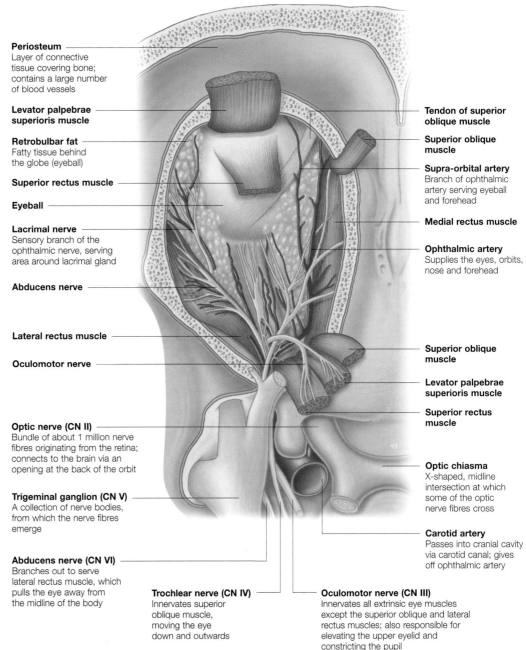

**Periosteum**
Layer of connective tissue covering bone; contains a large number of blood vessels

**Levator palpebrae superioris muscle**

**Retrobulbar fat**
Fatty tissue behind the globe (eyeball)

**Superior rectus muscle**

**Eyeball**

**Lacrimal nerve**
Sensory branch of the ophthalmic nerve, serving area around lacrimal gland

**Abducens nerve**

**Lateral rectus muscle**

**Oculomotor nerve**

**Optic nerve (CN II)**
Bundle of about 1 million nerve fibres originating from the retina; connects to the brain via an opening at the back of the orbit

**Trigeminal ganglion (CN V)**
A collection of nerve bodies, from which the nerve fibres emerge

**Abducens nerve (CN VI)**
Branches out to serve lateral rectus muscle, which pulls the eye away from the midline of the body

**Tendon of superior oblique muscle**

**Superior oblique muscle**

**Supra-orbital artery**
Branch of ophthalmic artery serving eyeball and forehead

**Medial rectus muscle**

**Ophthalmic artery**
Supplies the eyes, orbits, nose and forehead

**Superior oblique muscle**

**Levator palpebrae superioris muscle**

**Superior rectus muscle**

**Optic chiasma**
X-shaped, midline intersection at which some of the optic nerve fibres cross

**Carotid artery**
Passes into cranial cavity via carotid canal; gives off ophthalmic artery

**Trochlear nerve (CN IV)**
Innervates superior oblique muscle, moving the eye down and outwards

**Oculomotor nerve (CN III)**
Innervates all extrinsic eye muscles except the superior oblique and lateral rectus muscles; also responsible for elevating the upper eyelid and constricting the pupil

## Movement of the eye

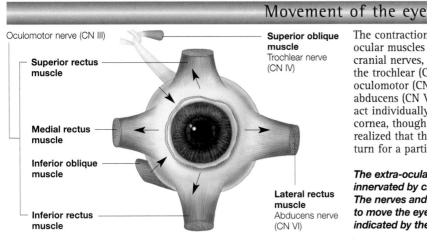

Oculomotor nerve (CN III)

**Superior rectus muscle**

**Medial rectus muscle**

**Inferior oblique muscle**

**Inferior rectus muscle**

**Superior oblique muscle**
Trochlear nerve (CN IV)

**Lateral rectus muscle**
Abducens nerve (CN VI)

The contraction of the extra-ocular muscles is controlled by cranial nerves, and specifically the trochlear (CN IV), oculomotor (CN III) and abducens (CN VI). The muscles act individually to turn the cornea, though it should be realized that the direction of turn for a particular muscle

*The extra-ocular muscles are innervated by cranial nerves. The nerves and muscles serve to move the eye in the directions indicated by the arrows.*

differs between right and left eyes; for example, in the right eye, lateral rectus will turn the cornea to the right, while in the left eye it would turn it to the left. Since eye movements normally occur in parallel, different muscles in each eye act together to turn the eyes.

For example, to look left, lateral rectus will turn the left eye and medial rectus the right eye. The eye movements of a single eye are usually the result of more than one of these muscles acting together.

# Eyelids and lacrimal apparatus

The eyelids are thin folds of skin that can close over the eye to protect it from injury and excessive light. The lacrimal apparatus is responsible for producing and draining lacrimal fluid.

Each lid is strengthened by a band of dense elastic connective tissue called a tarsal plate. These give the eyelids a curvature that matches that of the eye.

### EYELID STRUCTURE
The tarsal plate of the upper eyelid is larger than that of the lower. The inner and outer ends of both tarsal plates are attached to the underlying bone by tiny ligaments. Between the front surface of the tarsal glands and the overlying skin, lie fibres of the orbicularis oculi muscle.

The eyelashes project from the free edge of the eyelids. The follicles of the eyelashes, from which the hairs emerge, have nerve endings which can sense any movement of the lashes.

The tarsal plates contain glands, called meibomian glands, that secrete an oily liquid which prevents the eyelids sticking together. There are also other tiny ciliary glands associated with the eyelash follicles.

### EYELID MOVEMENT
The eye closes due to movement of the upper lid. The orbicularis oculi muscle contracts to close the eye, while the upper lid is opened by the levator palpebrae superioris muscle.

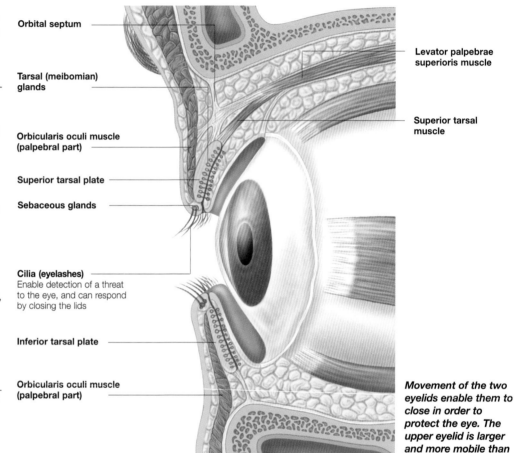

Orbital septum

Tarsal (meibomian) glands

Orbicularis oculi muscle (palpebral part)

Superior tarsal plate

Sebaceous glands

Cilia (eyelashes)
Enable detection of a threat to the eye, and can respond by closing the lids

Inferior tarsal plate

Orbicularis oculi muscle (palpebral part)

Levator palpebrae superioris muscle

Superior tarsal muscle

*Movement of the two eyelids enable them to close in order to protect the eye. The upper eyelid is larger and more mobile than the lower lid.*

## The conjunctiva

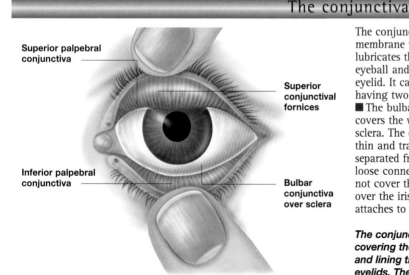

Superior palpebral conjunctiva

Inferior palpebral conjunctiva

Superior conjunctival fornices

Bulbar conjunctiva over sclera

The conjunctiva is a very thin membrane that lines and lubricates the surface of the eyeball and inner surfaces of the eyelid. It can be thought of as having two parts:
■ The bulbar conjunctiva – this covers the white of the eye, the sclera. The conjunctiva here is thin and transparent, and is separated from the sclera by loose connective tissue. It does not cover the cornea, which lies over the iris and pupil, but attaches to its periphery.

*The conjunctiva is a membrane covering the white of the eye and lining the inside of the eyelids. The conjunctiva over the eyeball is transparent.*

■ The palpebral conjunctiva – this lines the inside of the upper and lower eyelids. Deep recesses, known as conjunctival fornices, are formed where the bulbar and palpebral parts of the conjunctiva meet.

### INFECTION/IRRITATION
The bulbar conjunctiva, overlying the eyeball, is normally colourless. However, its tiny blood vessels can become dilated and congested as a response to local irritants such as smoke or dust. The conjunctiva may also be the site of viral or bacterial infections, where redness may be associated with a 'gritty' feeling and even pus formation.

# Lacrimal apparatus

The eyes are protected and lubricated by lacrimal fluid, our tears. The lacrimal system produces this fluid and drains the excess to the nasal cavity.

The eyes are kept moist by the continuous production of small amounts of lacrimal fluid by the lacrimal glands. This fluid also contains lysozyme, an antibacterial substance.

Most of the fluid, about 1 ml for each eye per day, is lost through evaporation. What is left is drained by the nasolacrimal ducts to the back of the nose.

### LACRIMAL GLAND

The lacrimal gland, which produces the thin, watery lacrimal fluid, lies above the outer side of the eye within a recess in the bony eye socket. It is about 2 cm long and roughly the shape of an almond.

The gland is divided into two parts; an upper orbital part and a lower palpebral part. There are also extra, accessory lacrimal glands which lie predominantly within the upper lid.

### LACRIMAL DUCTS

The lacrimal glands each have up to 12 tiny ducts. These lacrimal ducts carry the secretions away from gland and release them into the conjunctival sac through openings under the upper lid in the superior fornix.

### CANALICULI

After travelling across the eye during blinking, the lacrimal fluid collects in the lacrimal lake at the innermost corner.

The upper and lower eyelid both have a raised papilla at their inner ends, which has a tiny opening, the lacrimal punctum.

Excess lacrimal fluid enters these openings to be carried away by the underlying passages, the lacrimal canaliculi.

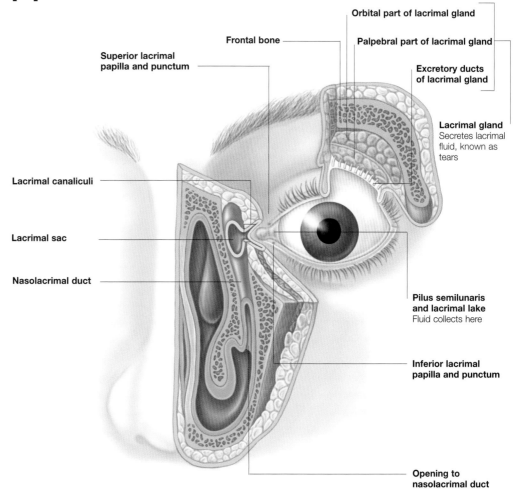

Superior lacrimal papilla and punctum

Frontal bone

Orbital part of lacrimal gland

Palpebral part of lacrimal gland

Excretory ducts of lacrimal gland

**Lacrimal gland**
Secretes lacrimal fluid, known as tears

Lacrimal canaliculi

Lacrimal sac

Nasolacrimal duct

**Pilus semilunaris and lacrimal lake**
Fluid collects here

Inferior lacrimal papilla and punctum

Opening to nasolacrimal duct

### LACRIMAL SAC AND NASOLACRIMAL DUCT

Lacrimal fluid passes from the canaliculi into a collecting area known as the lacrimal sac.

From here the lacrimal fluid is carried down to the back of the nasal cavity by the nasolacrimal duct.

The fluid leaving the

*The lacrimal apparatus is the system that produces fluid and drains it from the eye. The lacrimal gland secretes the fluid, which drains via the puncta.*

nasolacrimal duct normally evaporates within the nasal cavity, helping to humidify the air there.

---

## Disorders of the lacrimal glands

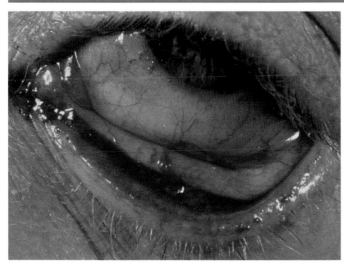

In normal circumstances the eye is slightly moist at all times. Disorders of the lacrimal system may lead to the eye being excessively wet or dry.

### WATERY EYE

A watery eye may be due to an excessive flow of fluid, for example where there is physical irritation. The drainage system cannot cope and tears may spill over the front of the lower lid. A watery eye may also be the

*Sjögren's syndrome affects the lacrimal glands. The condition causes an under-secretion of lacrimal fluid and results in dry, red eyes.*

result of blockage of the exit channels such as may occur if there is an infection in the lacrimal sac or nasolacrimal duct. These infections are usually passed up from the nasal cavity and may become chronic.

### DRY EYE

When the lacrimal glands do not produce enough secretions, the eye becomes dry. This can lead to irritation, with ulceration of the cornea in extreme cases.

Under-secretion of the lacrimal gland may be due to medicines taken, disruption of the nerve supply or hardening of the gland in a disease such as Sjögren's syndrome.

# Nose and nasal cavity

'Nose' commonly implies just the external structure, but anatomically it also includes the nasal cavity. The nose is the organ of smell and, as the opening of the respiratory tract, it serves to warm and filter air.

The external nose is a pyramid-shaped structure in the centre of the face, with the tip of the nose forming the apex of the pyramid. The underlying nasal cavity is a relatively large space and is the very first part of the respiratory tract (air passage).

The nasal cavity lies above the oral cavity (mouth) and is separated by a horizontal plate of bone called the hard palate. Both cavities open into the pharynx, a muscular, tube-like passageway.

## EXTERNAL STRUCTURE

The external nose is made up of bone in its upper part and cartilage and fibrous tissue in its lower part. The upper part of the skeleton of the nose is mainly made up of a pair of plate-like bones called the nasal bones. These join, by their upper edges, with the frontal bone (forehead). Joining the outer edge of each nasal bone is the frontal process of the maxilla – a projection from the cheekbone between the nasal bone and the inner wall of the orbit (eye socket).

The bridge of the nose consists almost entirely of the two nasal bones, and adjoins the forehead between the two orbits. Because of their location and their relative fragility, the nasal bones are vulnerable to fracturing.

The lower half of the external nose is made up of plates of cartilage on each side. These join each other, and the cartilages of the other side along the midline of the nose.

## Lateral view

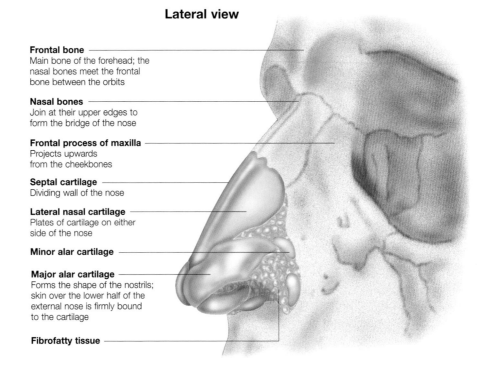

**Frontal bone**
Main bone of the forehead; the nasal bones meet the frontal bone between the orbits

**Nasal bones**
Join at their upper edges to form the bridge of the nose

**Frontal process of maxilla**
Projects upwards from the cheekbones

**Septal cartilage**
Dividing wall of the nose

**Lateral nasal cartilage**
Plates of cartilage on either side of the nose

**Minor alar cartilage**

**Major alar cartilage**
Forms the shape of the nostrils; skin over the lower half of the external nose is firmly bound to the cartilage

**Fibrofatty tissue**

## Inferior view

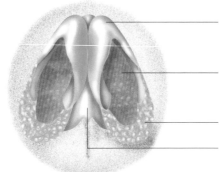

**Cartilage**
Lower structure of the nose is made up of plates of cartilage, a dense connective tissue

**Nostril**
One of two external openings of the nose; also known as the naris (*plural* nares)

**Fibrofatty tissue**

**Septal cartilage**
Separates the two nostrils; lined with mucous membrane

---

## Inside the nostrils

*Nosebleeds are common, particularly in children. This is because the blood-rich lining of the nose ruptures easily.*

The part of the nasal cavity immediately above the nostril is somewhat flared and is called the vestibule. It is lined with hair-bearing skin. Elsewhere, the nasal cavity has a more delicate inner lining – the mucous membrane.

The lining of the nasal cavity receives a generous blood flow due to the presence of a rich network of blood vessels. This ensures that inhaled air is adequately warmed and moistened in the nasal cavity before it reaches the lungs.

The delicate lining of the nasal cavity is prone to damage. The most common manifestation of this is bleeding from the membrane, known as a nosebleed (epistaxis).

The lining also contains an abundance of cells, which, when inflamed or infected, tend to secrete an excess of viscous fluid (with a cold, for example).

The roof of the nasal cavity has a lining – the olfactory epithelium – which is different from that of the rest of the nasal cavity. This contains specialized cells that are receptors for the sense of smell.

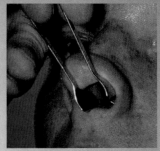

*The vestibule is lined with skin that grows hairs. These hairs filter dust and other particles from air entering the nose.*

# Inside the nasal cavity

The nasal cavity runs from the nostrils to the pharynx, and is divided in two by the septum. The roof forms part of the floor of the cranial cavity.

The nasal cavity is partitioned into two halves by a vertical plate called the nasal septum, which is part bone and part cartilage. Each half of the nasal cavity is open in front at the nostril, and opens into the pharynx at the back through an opening called the choana.

### NASAL CAVITY ROOF

The roof of the nasal cavity is arched from front to back. The central part of this roof is the cribriform plate of the ethmoid bone, a strip of bone perforated with a number of holes. This forms part of the floor of the cranial cavity, which contains the brain.

Running through the sieve-like cribriform plate from the nasal cavity to the brain is the olfactory nerve, which transmits the sensation of smell.

These anatomical features explain why head injuries involving fractures to the roof of the nasal cavity sometimes result in a leakage of cerebrospinal fluid (the clear fluid surrounding the brain) into the nose. If the head injury causes significant damage to the olfactory nerve, there may be a resultant loss of the ability to perceive smells. This is a condition called anosmia.

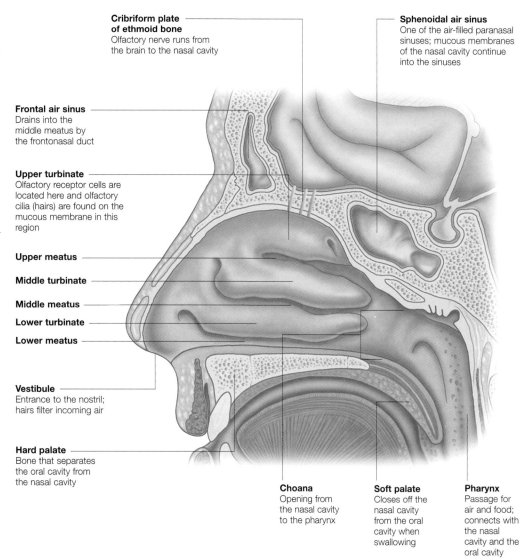

**Cribriform plate of ethmoid bone**
Olfactory nerve runs from the brain to the nasal cavity

**Sphenoidal air sinus**
One of the air-filled paranasal sinuses; mucous membranes of the nasal cavity continue into the sinuses

**Frontal air sinus**
Drains into the middle meatus by the frontonasal duct

**Upper turbinate**
Olfactory receptor cells are located here and olfactory cilia (hairs) are found on the mucous membrane in this region

**Upper meatus**

**Middle turbinate**

**Middle meatus**

**Lower turbinate**

**Lower meatus**

**Vestibule**
Entrance to the nostril; hairs filter incoming air

**Hard palate**
Bone that separates the oral cavity from the nasal cavity

**Choana**
Opening from the nasal cavity to the pharynx

**Soft palate**
Closes off the nasal cavity from the oral cavity when swallowing

**Pharynx**
Passage for air and food; connects with the nasal cavity and the oral cavity

## Side walls of the nasal cavity

The lateral (side) wall of the nasal cavity is made up of several bones, some of which partially overlap. However, the complexity of the bony architecture of the lateral wall of the nose is not readily apparent, as it is covered by the mucous membrane that lines the cavity.

When viewed from the inside, the side wall of the nasal cavity shows three horizontal, overhanging, inward projections; an upper, a middle and a lower. These projections are called turbinates, and each one is produced by an underlying curled plate of bone.

Below each turbinate is a space called a meatus. Thus there is an upper meatus, a middle meatus and a lower meatus, each situated below the corresponding turbinate.

Within the bones adjoining the nasal cavity are air-filled spaces – the paranasal sinuses. These communicate with the nasal cavity through tiny openings in the side wall of the nose, situated in one or other meatus. The mucosal lining of the nasal cavity continues through them to line the interior of the paranasal sinuses.

The nasolacrimal duct is an opening in the lower meatus. This is a tube that runs down from the lacrimal sac (within the orbit), allowing tears to drain into the nasal cavity.

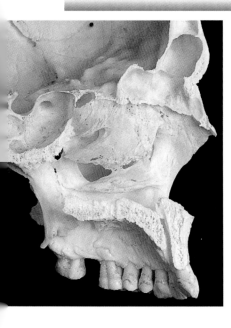

*The facial bones of the skull that form the lateral walls of the nose are reduced in density by air filled cavities - the paranasal sinuses.*

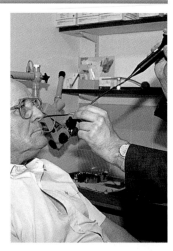

*Direct inspection of the nasal cavity is done using a fibre-optic endoscope. It is introduced into the cavity through the nostril.*

# Paranasal sinuses

The term 'paranasal' means 'by the side of the nose'. The paranasal sinuses are air-filled cavities in the bones around the nasal cavity.

The paranasal sinuses are paired structures, and the two members of each pair are related to opposite halves of the nasal cavity.

The four pairs of paranasal sinuses are named according to the bones in which they are situated. These four pairs are:
- Maxillary sinuses
- Ethmoidal sinuses
- Frontal sinuses
- Sphenoidal sinuses.

Each member of a pair of paranasal sinuses opens into its half of the nasal cavity through a tiny opening called an ostium on the side of the nasal cavity.

The paranasal sinuses are very small, or even absent, at the time of birth, and remain small until puberty. Thereafter, the sinuses enlarge fairly rapidly; this enlargement accounts partially for the distinctive change in the size and shape of the face that occurs during adolescence.

## FRONTAL SINUSES

The frontal sinuses are situated within the frontal bone (the bone of the forehead). Each is variable in size, corresponding to an area just above the inner part of the eyebrow.

The frontal sinuses are situated above the opening into the nasal cavity in the middle meatus. Drainage of mucous secretions is efficient and aided by gravity.

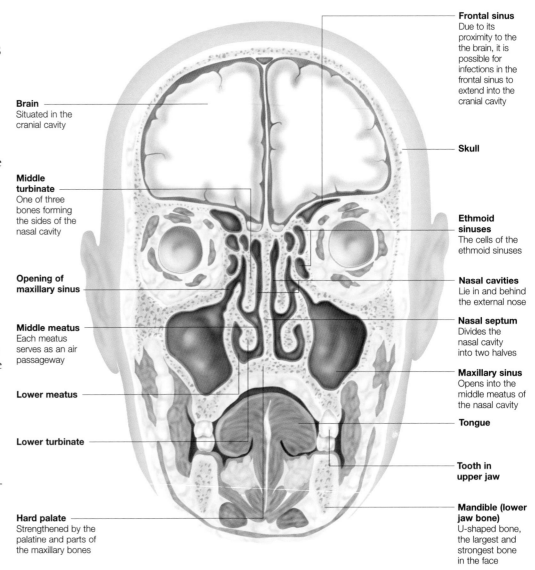

**Brain**
Situated in the cranial cavity

**Middle turbinate**
One of three bones forming the sides of the nasal cavity

**Opening of maxillary sinus**

**Middle meatus**
Each meatus serves as an air passageway

**Lower meatus**

**Lower turbinate**

**Hard palate**
Strengthened by the palatine and parts of the maxillary bones

**Frontal sinus**
Due to its proximity to the the brain, it is possible for infections in the frontal sinus to extend into the cranial cavity

**Skull**

**Ethmoid sinuses**
The cells of the ethmoid sinuses

**Nasal cavities**
Lie in and behind the external nose

**Nasal septum**
Divides the nasal cavity into two halves

**Maxillary sinus**
Opens into the middle meatus of the nasal cavity

**Tongue**

**Tooth in upper jaw**

**Mandible (lower jaw bone)**
U-shaped bone, the largest and strongest bone in the face

## Functions of the paranasal sinuses

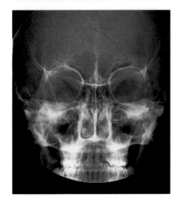

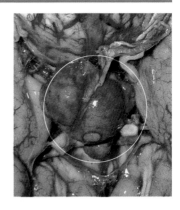

An important function of the paranasal sinuses is to help give the voice a warm, rich tone, as the sinuses act as resonators for sound. Patients with chronic sinusitis often have a noticeable lack of resonance in their voice. This strongly suggests that healthy sinuses have a role in modulating the quality of voice.

*The maxillary sinuses, under the eye sockets, can be seen on this X-ray. They are one of the four pairs of the paranasal sinuses.*

The paranasal sinuses are also believed to act as thermal insulators by preventing cold, inhaled air from cooling the surrounding structures. Another function of the paranasal sinuses is to lighten the weight of the skull.

They are also responsible for the production of mucus that flows into the nasal cavity.

*A pituitary gland tumour (circled) will often be surgically removed by approaching the gland through the sphenoidal sinus.*

# Inside the sinuses

The efficiency of mucous drainage from each of the pairs of sinuses depends on their location. Effective drainage lessens the risk of sinus infection.

### SPHENOIDAL SINUSES

The sphenoidal sinuses are behind the roof of the nasal cavity, within the sphenoid bone. The two sphenoidal sinuses lie side by side, separated by a thin, vertical, bony partition. Each sphenoidal sinus opens into the uppermost part of the side wall of the nasal cavity (immediately above the upper turbinate) and also drains fairly efficiently into the nasal cavity.

### ETHMOIDAL SINUSES

Each ethmoidal sinus is situated between the thin, inner wall of the orbit (eye socket) and the side wall of the nasal cavity. Unlike the other paranasal sinuses, these sinuses are made up of multiple communicating cavities called ethmoid air cells. These cells are subdivided into front, middle and back groups. The front and middle groups of air cells open into the middle meatus, while the back group opens into the upper meatus. The drainage into the nasal cavity is moderately efficient.

### MAXILLARY SINUSES

The largest of the pairs of sinuses are the maxillary sinuses, situated within the maxillae (cheekbones). Infections and inflammation are more common here than in any of the other paranasal sinuses. This is because the drainage of mucous secretions from this sinus to the nasal cavity is not very efficient.

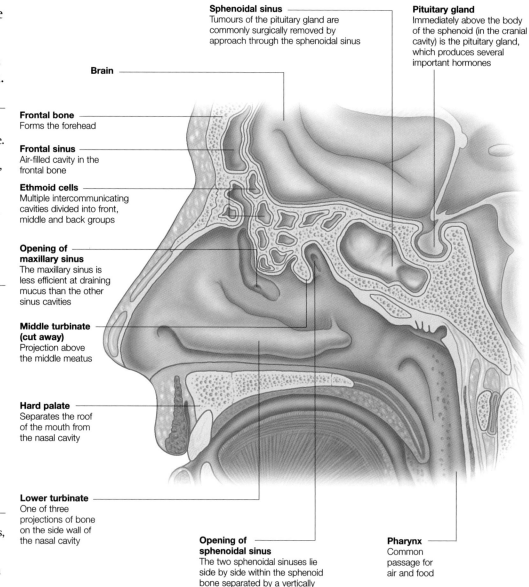

**Sphenoidal sinus**
Tumours of the pituitary gland are commonly surgically removed by approach through the sphenoidal sinus

**Pituitary gland**
Immediately above the body of the sphenoid (in the cranial cavity) is the pituitary gland, which produces several important hormones

**Brain**

**Frontal bone**
Forms the forehead

**Frontal sinus**
Air-filled cavity in the frontal bone

**Ethmoid cells**
Multiple intercommunicating cavities divided into front, middle and back groups

**Opening of maxillary sinus**
The maxillary sinus is less efficient at draining mucus than the other sinus cavities

**Middle turbinate (cut away)**
Projection above the middle meatus

**Hard palate**
Separates the roof of the mouth from the nasal cavity

**Lower turbinate**
One of three projections of bone on the side wall of the nasal cavity

**Opening of sphenoidal sinus**
The two sphenoidal sinuses lie side by side within the sphenoid bone separated by a vertically placed thin bony partition

**Pharynx**
Common passage for air and food

## Sinus problems

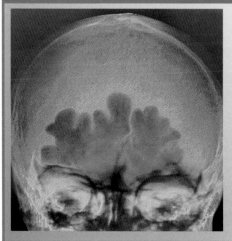

The paranasal sinuses have an inner lining of mucous membrane that is similar to the inner lining of the nasal cavity. As in the nasal cavity, the lining of each paranasal sinus contains many cells that constantly secrete fluid.

Other cells in the lining possess hair-like projections (cilia) on their surface. These projections, by their constant movement, help to propel the secretions into the nasal cavity through the ostia (openings).

Inflammation of the sinuses causes the mucous membrane lining to swell, resulting in

*A false-colour X-ray of a person suffering from sinusitis caused by infection reveals the mucus-filled paranasal sinus in the frontal bone. The space is normally air-filled, but is here enlarged and inflamed.*

the ostia becoming blocked. This in turn prevents the mucous secretions from draining into the nasal cavity as normal.

Because the lining of the nasal cavity continues through to the paranasal sinuses via the ostia, the paranasal sinuses may be regarded as extensions of the nasal cavity. This arrangement, however, may allow infections of the nasal cavity to spread to the paranasal sinuses.

Sinusitis – inflammation of the paranasal sinuses – is almost always preceded by an infection of the nasal cavity or throat. Symptoms include pain, purulent (pus-containing) discharge and nasal obstruction. The infection can sometimes spread to the meninges of the brain (meningitis), in which case it can be life-threatening.

# Oral cavity

Also known as the mouth, the oral cavity extends from the lips to the fauces, the opening leading to the pharynx.

The roof of the mouth, viewed from below, shows two distinct structures: the dental arch and the palate. The dental arch is the curved part of the maxilla bone at the front and sides of the roof, and the palate is a horizontal plate of tissue that separates the mouth from the nose.

The front two-thirds of the palate are bony and hard, and are formed by the maxillary bone. The hard palate is covered with a mucous membrane, beneath which run arteries, veins and nerves. These nourish and provide sensation to the palate and the overlying mucous glands, which often form fibrous ridges called rugae. The mucus secreted by these glands lubricates food to facilitate swallowing.

### SOFT PALATE

The rear third of the palate is composed of glandula mucosa, muscle and tendon. Forming much of the soft palate are the tensor and levator palati muscles. These muscles close off the nasal cavity from the mouth during swallowing by respectively tensing and elevating the soft palate. They also act with other muscles to open the auditory (Eustachian) tube, which equalizes pressure on either side of the eardrum.

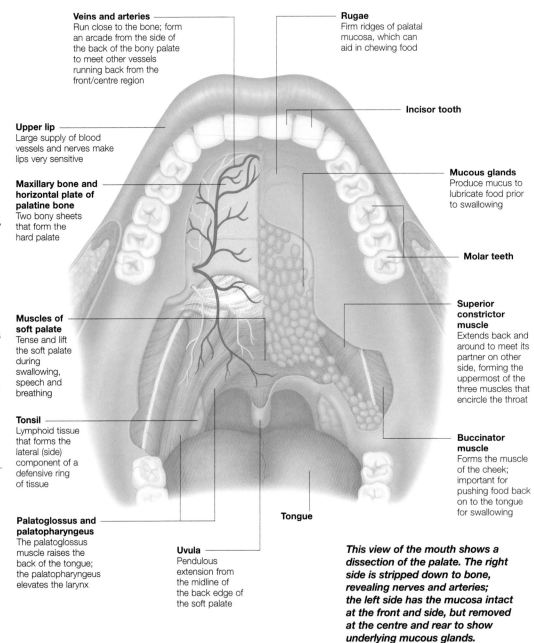

**Veins and arteries**
Run close to the bone; form an arcade from the side of the back of the bony palate to meet other vessels running back from the front/centre region

**Upper lip**
Large supply of blood vessels and nerves make lips very sensitive

**Maxillary bone and horizontal plate of palatine bone**
Two bony sheets that form the hard palate

**Muscles of soft palate**
Tense and lift the soft palate during swallowing, speech and breathing

**Tonsil**
Lymphoid tissue that forms the lateral (side) component of a defensive ring of tissue

**Palatoglossus and palatopharyngeus**
The palatoglossus muscle raises the back of the tongue; the palatopharyngeus elevates the larynx

**Uvula**
Pendulous extension from the midline of the back edge of the soft palate

**Rugae**
Firm ridges of palatal mucosa, which can aid in chewing food

**Incisor tooth**

**Mucous glands**
Produce mucus to lubricate food prior to swallowing

**Molar teeth**

**Superior constrictor muscle**
Extends back and around to meet its partner on other side, forming the uppermost of the three muscles that encircle the throat

**Buccinator muscle**
Forms the muscle of the cheek; important for pushing food back on to the tongue for swallowing

**Tongue**

*This view of the mouth shows a dissection of the palate. The right side is stripped down to bone, revealing nerves and arteries; the left side has the mucosa intact at the front and side, but removed at the centre and rear to show underlying mucous glands.*

## Cleft palate

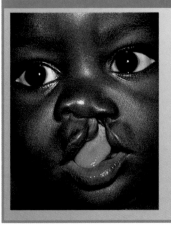

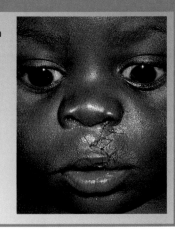

The term cleft palate refers to the condition in which the structures that form the palate do not fuse together properly. This results in a gap along the middle of the roof of the mouth and means that there is no plate to separate the nasal cavity from the oral cavity. If the condition affects the front of mouth, the top lip may be divided too, a deformity known as 'harelip'.

Although it can vary in severity and extent, any significant failure in palate development can lead to major problems with speech and swallowing. An infant with a cleft palate may also have significant problems when suckling from its mother's breast.

The defect can be largely repaired, often with very good cosmetic results, by surgery.

*This child has a cleft palate and a harelip. These congenital conditions can prevent the baby from feeding properly.*

*An operation may correct both conditions. Only a small scar on the outer lip will be visible afterwards.*

# Floor of the mouth

The floor of the mouth acts as the foundation for a network of muscles and glands that are essential to its function.

The tongue is situated over the mylohyoid muscle, which forms the muscular floor of the mouth. It is the hyoglossus muscle that anchors the tongue to the hyoid bone and provides extra strength, while the genioglossus muscle stops the tongue from moving back into the throat.

The temporalis muscles are muscles of mastication (chewing). The lingula is a small bony projection of the mandible. The mandibular nerve passes below this, through the mandibular foramen and runs within the body of the mandible to supply the lower teeth and lower lip with sensation.

### SALIVARY GLANDS

There are a pair each of the submandibular and sublingual salivary glands on either side of the oral floor and, together with the paired parotid glands, they make up the six salivary glands. Saliva flows along the submandibular gland duct on the mylohyoid muscle, and emerges in the front of the oral cavity on either side of the tongue, behind the lower front teeth.

Saliva from the sublingual glands either runs into the submandibular duct, or flows out through openings in the mucosa to the side of the tongue.

The lingual nerve provides taste and sensation to the front two-thirds of the tongue.

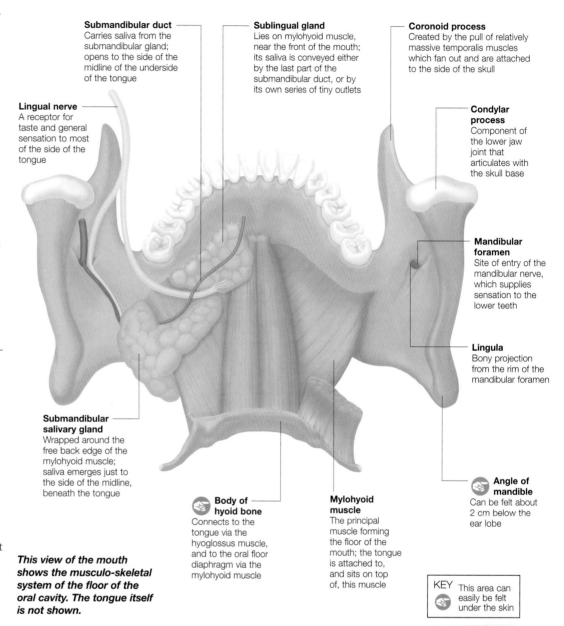

**Submandibular duct**
Carries saliva from the submandibular gland; opens to the side of the midline of the underside of the tongue

**Lingual nerve**
A receptor for taste and general sensation to most of the side of the tongue

**Sublingual gland**
Lies on mylohyoid muscle, near the front of the mouth; its saliva is conveyed either by the last part of the submandibular duct, or by its own series of tiny outlets

**Coronoid process**
Created by the pull of relatively massive temporalis muscles which fan out and are attached to the side of the skull

**Condylar process**
Component of the lower jaw joint that articulates with the skull base

**Mandibular foramen**
Site of entry of the mandibular nerve, which supplies sensation to the lower teeth

**Lingula**
Bony projection from the rim of the mandibular foramen

**Submandibular salivary gland**
Wrapped around the free back edge of the mylohyoid muscle; saliva emerges just to the side of the midline, beneath the tongue

**Body of hyoid bone**
Connects to the tongue via the hyoglossus muscle, and to the oral floor diaphragm via the mylohyoid muscle

**Mylohyoid muscle**
The principal muscle forming the floor of the mouth; the tongue is attached to, and sits on top of, this muscle

**Angle of mandible**
Can be felt about 2 cm below the ear lobe

*This view of the mouth shows the musculo-skeletal system of the floor of the oral cavity. The tongue itself is not shown.*

**KEY** This area can easily be felt under the skin

## Lips and cheeks

*The pinkish part normally thought of as the lips is called the 'free red margin'. The lips actually extend to just beneath the nose and above the chin.*

Strictly speaking, the lips and the cheeks form a portion of the oral cavity known as the vestibule. However, both work in close association with the dental arches, tongue and palate in activities such as speaking and eating.

The beginning of the digestive tract, the opening of the mouth, is surrounded by the lips. They are extremely sensitive and mobile, being abundantly supplied with nerves, blood and lymph vessels, and consist mainly of muscle fibres and elastic connective tissues. These tissues are covered with a thin, translucent outer layer which allows the small capillaries to show through, giving the lips their typical reddish colour.

Both the lips and the cheeks are involved in holding food in place so that the teeth can chew effectively. The lips also contain special nerves that help to identify various food textures.

The inner surface of the cheeks are lined with a mucous membrane made up of epithelial cells. These surface cells are rapidly worn away by abrasion with the teeth and are replaced by rapidly dividing cells underneath.

The mucus produced by the mucous membrane of the cheeks helps to lubricate the cheeks against the teeth and coats food, making it easier to swallow.

*The outer surface of the lips consists of skin which contains hair follicles and sweat glands. The red part has a translucent membrane.*

# Teeth

## Teeth are designed for biting and chewing up food, and each has a particular function.

The teeth are specialized hardened regions of gum tissue, partly embedded in the jaw bones. They break up solid foods by the actions of biting and chewing.

The visible part of a tooth is the crown. This is composed of a shell of hard, calcified material called dentine (similar to compact bone but without blood vessels), which is covered by a thin layer of even harder calcified material called enamel.

The hidden part (the root) is embedded in a socket of the jaw bone (the alveolus). It is also made of dentine, covered by a layer of cementum which, with dense, collagen-rich periodontal ligaments, anchors the root to the bone of the alveolar socket.

### INSIDE THE TEETH

Inside is an internal pulp cavity, containing soft connective tissue, blood vessels and nerves. The pulp is linked to the jaw via the root.

The layout of adult teeth is the same in the upper and lower jaws. Each side (quadrant) has eight teeth: two incisors, one canine, two premolars and three molars, making 32 in total. Children have 20 milk teeth, with only one molar in each quadrant.

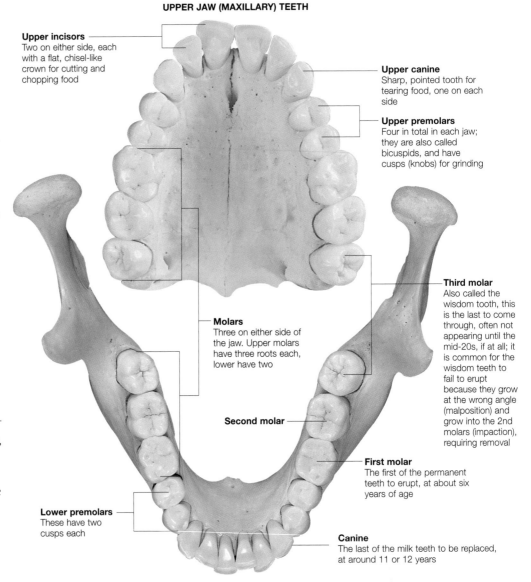

**UPPER JAW (MAXILLARY) TEETH**

**Upper incisors**
Two on either side, each with a flat, chisel-like crown for cutting and chopping food

**Upper canine**
Sharp, pointed tooth for tearing food, one on each side

**Upper premolars**
Four in total in each jaw; they are also called bicuspids, and have cusps (knobs) for grinding

**Third molar**
Also called the wisdom tooth, this is the last to come through, often not appearing until the mid-20s, if at all; it is common for the wisdom teeth to fail to erupt because they grow at the wrong angle (malposition) and grow into the 2nd molars (impaction), requiring removal

**Molars**
Three on either side of the jaw. Upper molars have three roots each, lower have two

**Second molar**

**First molar**
The first of the permanent teeth to erupt, at about six years of age

**Lower premolars**
These have two cusps each

**Canine**
The last of the milk teeth to be replaced, at around 11 or 12 years

**LOWER JAW (MANDIBULAR) TEETH**

## Tooth shape and function

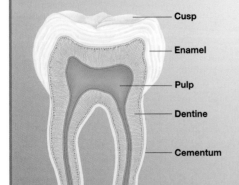

**Cusp**

**Enamel**

**Pulp**

**Dentine**

**Cementum**

*This cross-section of a lower molar shows typical tooth structure. The two large roots need secure support from the gums to remain snug in their jaw socket.*

The teeth are a variety of shapes, and each one is specialized for a particular function. The incisors at the front of the mouth have a flat, chisel-like crown for cutting. Behind them, the canines are sharp and pointed, and are used to tear tough food.

The surface of the crowns of the premolars and molars is broader, with cusps to aid grinding. The premolars (also known as the bicuspids) have two cusps each, and the molars have four or five cusps.

The arrangement of the teeth in the upper jaw (maxillary teeth) and the lower jaw (mandibular teeth) is essentially identical, although there are some differences in size and shape. The maxillary incisors, for instance, are typically wider than the mandibular incisors.

The roots of the teeth vary; incisors have one root, while lower molars have two roots and upper molars have three roots.

Human dentition, like that of other primates, is thought to have been originally suited to a diet of fruits, nuts and roots. It has, however, proved to be flexible, by adapting to a wider, omnivorous diet.

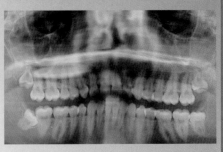

*This X-ray is an orthopantomograph, showing all the teeth of both jaws. Such images are taken using a special machine that moves horizontally around the face.*

# Development of teeth

There are two major phases of tooth development during childhood. This is to allow the head to grow and adult teeth to develop.

The teeth begin to develop in the human embryo around the sixth week of pregnancy. Six to eight months after birth, root growth pushes the tooth crown through the gum in the process of eruption called teething.

This first set are the primary or deciduous teeth (milk teeth). These erupt in a specific order, usually the lower central incisors first, then the upper central incisors. The deciduous teeth do not include premolars.

### ADULT TOOTH GROWTH

The tooth buds for the second wave of tooth production develop at the same time. These permanent teeth remain dormant until the ages of five to seven, when they begin to grow, causing the roots of the deciduous teeth to break down.

This breakdown, together with the pressure of the underlying permanent teeth, results in the shedding of the deciduous teeth. The new teeth then start to appear and continue to do so until the ages of 10 to 12.

Eruption of the permanent set follows a similar pattern to the earlier growth (although premolars erupt between the canines and the molars). The permanent set has additional, third molars (wisdom teeth) that tend to appear after between 15 and 25 years.

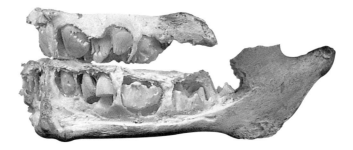

**Jaws of a newborn**
Unerupted deciduous (primary or milk) teeth can be be seen in the dental follicles (tooth-bearing capsules) of both jaws. They will start to emerge at about six months of age.

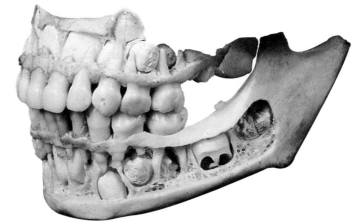

**Jaws of a six-year-old**
The deciduous teeth have all erupted. Beneath them in the alveoli (tooth sockets) are the permanent teeth ready to come through. This process continues until the early to mid teens.

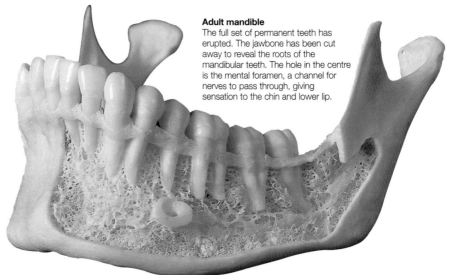

**Adult mandible**
The full set of permanent teeth has erupted. The jawbone has been cut away to reveal the roots of the mandibular teeth. The hole in the centre is the mental foramen, a channel for nerves to pass through, giving sensation to the chin and lower lip.

## Dental decay and other problems

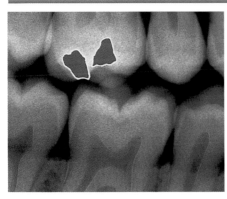

*This coloured X-ray of the teeth reveals two metal fillings in one of the upper premolars. The pink areas indicate the central pulp within each tooth.*

Dental caries (tooth decay) is caused by the formation of plaque, a combination of saliva, food residue and acid-producing bacteria that can eat into tooth enamel and dentine. Once the decay goes deep enough, infection and inflammation of the dental pulp inside may result. The pulp is living tissue, so this causes much pain. If untreated, the tooth will die. Infection can also result in a dentoalveolar abscess (gumboil), when the gum erupts.

Dentists can treat cavities by root canal work, removing the pulp (including the vessels and nerves), cleaning out the canal, and packing with a suitable material.

Gum disease is a major problem. Infections of the gum (gingivitis) can result in loosening or loss of teeth; there may even be a loss of bone from the jaws. This is probably due to a lack of mechanical force (chewing) on the bones.

Tartar (also known as calculus) is a chalky residue from saliva. If not regularly removed, it can harm the gums and shelter bacteria, increasing the likelihood of tooth decay.

*When the internal pulp is infected, the tooth can be saved by drilling out the root canal with a fine drill. The cavity is then filled, to avoid recurrence of the problem.*

# Tongue

The tongue is basically a mass of muscle, whose complex movement is essential for speech, mastication and swallowing. Its upper surface is lined with specialized tissue that contains taste buds.

The dorsal (upper) surface of the tongue is covered with an epithelium specialized for the sense of taste. The anterior two-thirds of the tongue at rest lies within the lower dental arcade. The posterior third slopes back and down to form part of the front wall of the oropharynx. Its musculature and movements are described in some detail overleaf.

## DORSAL SURFACE

The tongue's upper surface is characterized by filiform papillae, tiny protuberances which give the surface a rough feel. The filiform papillae have tufts of keratin which, when elongated, may give the surface a 'hairy' appearance and feel. These 'hairs' can be stained by food, medicine and nicotine. Scattered among them are the larger fungiform papillae. Larger still are the 8–12 circumvallate papillae, which form an inverse V at the junction of the anterior two-thirds and posterior third. These papillae are the major site of taste buds, although they do occur in other papillae and are scattered over the tongue surface, the cheek mucosa and the pharynx.

The posterior third of the dorsal surface has a cobbled appearance due to the presence of 40–100 nodules of lymphoid tissue, which together form the lingual tonsil.

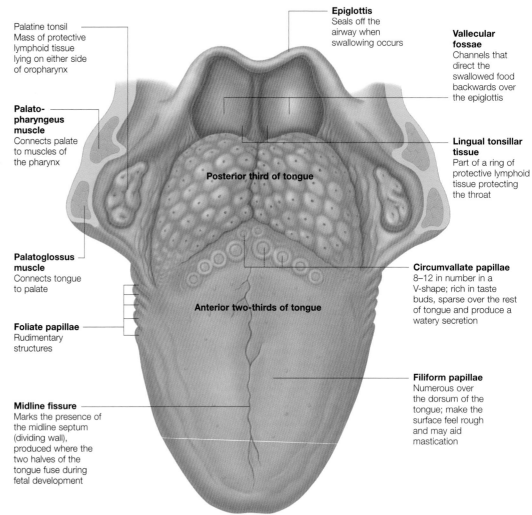

**Palatine tonsil**
Mass of protective lymphoid tissue lying on either side of oropharynx

**Palato-pharyngeus muscle**
Connects palate to muscles of the pharynx

**Palatoglossus muscle**
Connects tongue to palate

**Foliate papillae**
Rudimentary structures

**Midline fissure**
Marks the presence of the midline septum (dividing wall), produced where the two halves of the tongue fuse during fetal development

**Epiglottis**
Seals off the airway when swallowing occurs

**Vallecular fossae**
Channels that direct the swallowed food backwards over the epiglottis

**Lingual tonsillar tissue**
Part of a ring of protective lymphoid tissue protecting the throat

Posterior third of tongue

**Circumvallate papillae**
8–12 in number in a V-shape; rich in taste buds, sparse over the rest of tongue and produce a watery secretion

Anterior two-thirds of tongue

**Filiform papillae**
Numerous over the dorsum of the tongue; make the surface feel rough and may aid mastication

## Surface of the tongue

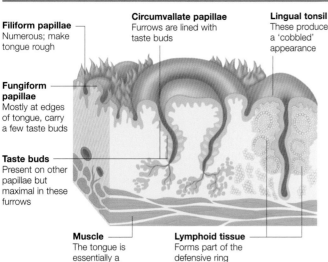

**Filiform papillae**
Numerous; make tongue rough

**Fungiform papillae**
Mostly at edges of tongue, carry a few taste buds

**Taste buds**
Present on other papillae but maximal in these furrows

**Circumvallate papillae**
Furrows are lined with taste buds

**Lingual tonsil**
These produce a 'cobbled' appearance

**Muscle**
The tongue is essentially a muscular organ

**Lymphoid tissue**
Forms part of the defensive ring against infection

The taste buds are nests of cells sensitive to flavoured substances in solution. It is traditional to describe tastes as either salt, sweet, bitter or sour, but the central processing of taste data by the brain is complex. It seems that when a nerve fibre is carrying data from a taste bud, it is responding to several or all four of these basic taste

*This illustration shows the structure in cross section through the tongue at the junction of the posterior third with the anterior two-thirds where the taste buds are concentrated in the furrows around the circumvallate papillae.*

sensations with differing sensitivities. Furthermore, the sense of taste is interrelated with the sense of smell, so food becomes relatively tasteless with a heavy cold.

The tongue also carries nerve endings for the 'common' sensations of touch, pressure, and pain.

Since the earliest days of medicine, the tongue has been used as a barometer of general health. Hippocrates, in the fifth century BC, correlated the dry, heavily coated, fissured tongue with fever and dehydration, and he gave a poor prognosis to patients with a red ulcerated tongue and mouth due to prolonged dysentery.

# Muscles of the tongue

The muscles within the tongue (intrinsic muscles) comprise three groups of fibre bundles running the length, breadth and depth of the organ.

The intrinsic muscles of the tongue alter the shape of the tongue to facilitate speech, mastication (chewing) and swallowing. The other muscles attached to the tongue (extrinsic muscles), move the organ as a whole. The names of the extrinsic muscles denote their attachments and the general direction of movement promoted.

Protrusion of the tongue (sticking it out), elevation of its sides and depression of its centre are functions of the intrinsic muscles. They also, together with an intact palate, the lips and the teeth, allow the formation of specific sounds in speech.

### SWALLOWING

When food has been chewed and mixed with lubricating saliva, it is forced up and back between the hard palate and the upper surface of the tongue by contraction of the styloglossus muscles which pull the tongue up and back. The palatoglossi then contract, squeezing the food bolus into the oral part of the pharynx. The levator palati muscles lift the soft palate to seal off the nasal passage, while the larynx and laryngopharynx are pulled up sealing the airway against the back of the epiglottis while the bolus passes over it.

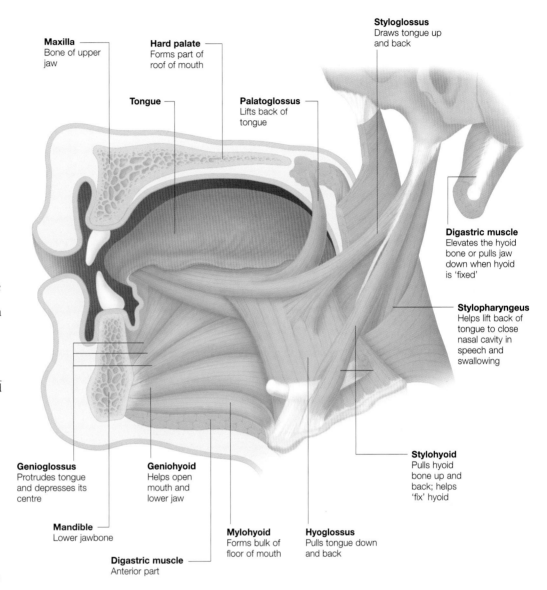

**Maxilla**
Bone of upper jaw

**Hard palate**
Forms part of roof of mouth

**Tongue**

**Styloglossus**
Draws tongue up and back

**Palatoglossus**
Lifts back of tongue

**Digastric muscle**
Elevates the hyoid bone or pulls jaw down when hyoid is 'fixed'

**Stylopharyngeus**
Helps lift back of tongue to close nasal cavity in speech and swallowing

**Genioglossus**
Protrudes tongue and depresses its centre

**Mandible**
Lower jawbone

**Geniohyoid**
Helps open mouth and lower jaw

**Digastric muscle**
Anterior part

**Mylohyoid**
Forms bulk of floor of mouth

**Hyoglossus**
Pulls tongue down and back

**Stylohyoid**
Pulls hyoid bone up and back; helps 'fix' hyoid

## Lesions on the tongue

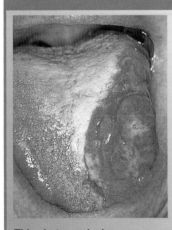

*This photograph shows an advanced carcinoma occupying most of the anterior two-thirds of the left side of the patient's tongue.*

The commonest mouth ulcers are apthous ulcers, which may be solitary or multiple. Major apthae are greater than 1 cm in diameter, last from weeks to months, and heal with scarring. Minor apthae are less than 1 cm, last for 10–14 days, and heal without leaving scars. Both types are painful, and occur on movable mucosa such as the tongue, lips and soft palate. Treatment is symptomatic and includes the use of oral rinses. Their aetiology (origin) is obscure, but may involve deficiencies in vitamin B12, iron, and folic acid, local trauma and stress.

Recurrent herpetic ulcers tend to arise in crops, and are due to the virus that causes cold sores on lips. In the mouth, unlike the apthae, they develop on mucosa that is bound to hard immovable surfaces such as the hard palate, gingivae and the mucosa covering the jaws. They are very painful, but usually last for less than 10 days. Relief may be obtained, and their course shortened, by using an antiviral, but it must be applied early on.

Cancer of the tongue, the commonest oral malignancy, may develop as an outgrowth or as a chronic ulcer. When treated early, the outlook is favourable, but when extensive disease is present even major surgery and/or radiotherapy do little to improve the poor prognosis. There is currently an extensive campaign to alert the population to the need for regular dental examinations to detect oral cancer early.

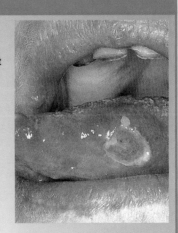

*A major apthous ulcer is easily visible here. Several smaller apthae are also present on the underside of the left of the tongue.*

# Salivary glands

The salivary glands produce about three-quarters of a litre of saliva a day. Saliva plays a major role in lubricating and protecting the mouth and teeth, as well as aiding swallowing and mastication.

There are three pairs of major salivary glands, which produce about 90 per cent of saliva; the remaining 10 per cent is produced by minor salivary glands located in the cheeks, lips, tongue and palate. The major role of saliva is lubrication, allowing mastication, swallowing and speech. It also has a protective function, keeping the mouth and gums moist and limiting bacterial activity.

The cells producing saliva are located in clusters at the end of a branching series of ducts. Two different types of saliva are produced by two distinctive cell types, called mucous and serous cells. The secretory products of mucous cells form a viscous mucin-rich product; the serous cells produce a watery fluid containing the enzyme amylase.

## PAROTID GLAND

The largest of salivary glands are the parotid glands, which secrete serous. Each parotid is superficial, lying just beneath the skin, situated between the mandible (lower jaw) and the ear.

Several important structures pass through the parotid gland. The deepest of these is the external carotid artery; the most superficial is the facial nerve, which supplies the muscles of facial expression.

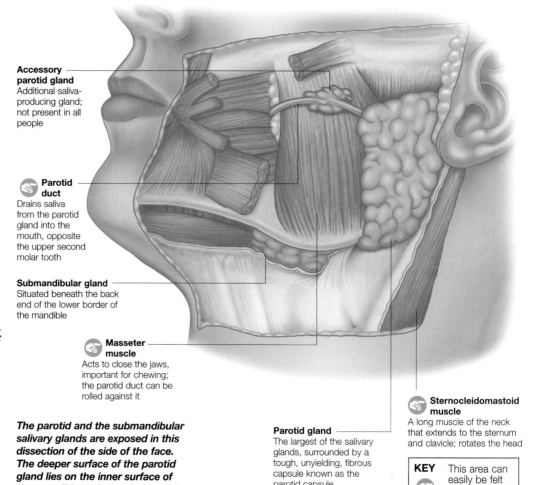

**Accessory parotid gland**
Additional saliva-producing gland; not present in all people

**Parotid duct**
Drains saliva from the parotid gland into the mouth, opposite the upper second molar tooth

**Submandibular gland**
Situated beneath the back end of the lower border of the mandible

**Masseter muscle**
Acts to close the jaws, important for chewing; the parotid duct can be rolled against it

**Parotid gland**
The largest of the salivary glands, surrounded by a tough, unyielding, fibrous capsule known as the parotid capsule

**Sternocleidomastoid muscle**
A long muscle of the neck that extends to the sternum and clavicle; rotates the head

**KEY** This area can easily be felt under the skin

*The parotid and the submandibular salivary glands are exposed in this dissection of the side of the face. The deeper surface of the parotid gland lies on the inner surface of the mandible and close to the wall of the pharynx.*

## Parotid enlargement

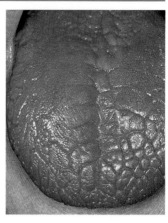

*The lump beside this woman's ear is evidence of a tumour of the parotid gland. If benign, this may be the only symptom.*

Slow-growing, benign tumours of the parotid gland may have no symptoms apart from an increase in gland size. However, rapidly growing malignant tumours may cause damage to the facial nerve within the gland, causing paralysis of facial muscles on one side – a condition similar to Bell's palsy.

If the majority of muscles are involved, the affected side of the face remains expressionless. The patient has difficulty with speaking and whistling, and cannot prevent food and saliva from leaking out of the corner of the mouth.

If the nerves supplying the muscle closing the eyelid – the orbicularis oris muscle – are also

involved, the ability to blink and spread a film of tears over the cornea is lost. This may result in ulceration of the cornea.

Sjögren's syndrome is a condition in which the parotid glands become enlarged as a result of infiltration by certain blood cells, called lymphocytes, causing destruction and loss of the serous secreting salivary cells. The reduction in saliva production results in a dry mouth (xerostomia). As a result of the lack of saliva cleansing the mouth there is severe gingivitis (inflammation and bleeding of the gums) and periodontitis (inflammation of the tooth-supporting structures), and considerable tooth decay.

*Sjögren's syndrome causes wasting of the salivary glands. Xerostomia (dry mouth) can be alleviated with mouthwashes.*

# Submandibular and sublingual glands

The two smaller pairs of salivary glands are the submandibular and the sublingual glands situated in the floor of the mouth.

The submandibular gland is situated beneath the lower border of the mandible towards the angle of the jaw. It is a mixed salivary gland containing serous cells (about 60 per cent) and mucous cells (about 40 per cent). About the size of a walnut, the gland has two parts: a large, superficial part and a smaller, deep part tucked behind the mylohyoid muscle which forms the floor of the mouth. The saliva produced by the submandibular gland is carried in the submandibular duct, which opens in the sublingual papilla (protuberance) underneath the tongue.

## SUBLINGUAL GLANDS

The sublingual gland is the smallest of the three major salivary glands and is almond-shaped. It is composed of about 60 per cent mucous cells and 40 per cent serous cell and lies under the tongue in the sublingual fossa. The two sublingual glands almost meet in the midline, and lie on the mylohyoid muscle.

Behind, the sublingual gland sits close to the deep part of the submandibular gland. Unlike the other glands, the sublingual gland does not have a single major collecting duct, but many smaller ones opening separately into the floor of the mouth or into the submandibular duct.

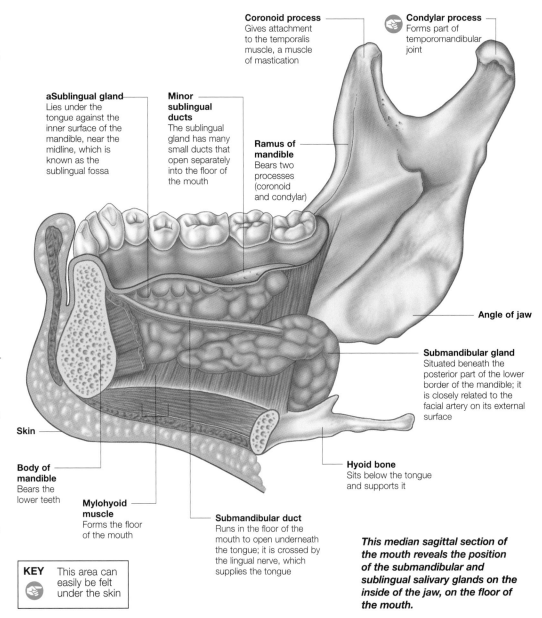

**Coronoid process**
Gives attachment to the temporalis muscle, a muscle of mastication

**Condylar process**
Forms part of temporomandibular joint

**aSublingual gland**
Lies under the tongue against the inner surface of the mandible, near the midline, which is known as the sublingual fossa

**Minor sublingual ducts**
The sublingual gland has many small ducts that open separately into the floor of the mouth

**Ramus of mandible**
Bears two processes (coronoid and condylar)

**Angle of jaw**

**Submandibular gland**
Situated beneath the posterior part of the lower border of the mandible; it is closely related to the facial artery on its external surface

**Skin**

**Body of mandible**
Bears the lower teeth

**Mylohyoid muscle**
Forms the floor of the mouth

**Submandibular duct**
Runs in the floor of the mouth to open underneath the tongue; it is crossed by the lingual nerve, which supplies the tongue

**Hyoid bone**
Sits below the tongue and supports it

**KEY** This area can easily be felt under the skin

*This median sagittal section of the mouth reveals the position of the submandibular and sublingual salivary glands on the inside of the jaw, on the floor of the mouth.*

## Salivary duct blockages

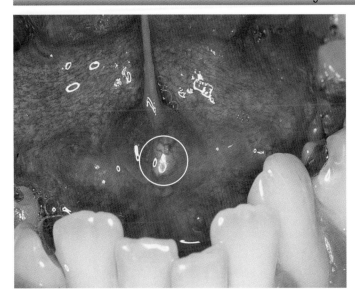

The submandibular duct is prone to blockage by the development of small calcified stones (calculi or sialoliths). This is partly due to the following factors:
■ Saliva is saturated with calcium and phosphate ions from mineralized calcium phosphate
■ The duct is somewhat twisted, leading to some stagnation of the saliva
■ Submandibular saliva is semi-viscous, and the saliva pools behind the lower incisor teeth near the opening of the duct.

Stones in the salivary duct

*A small calcified stone blocking a salivary duct is visible as a yellowish mass (circled) in the centre of the floor of the mouth.*

obstruct the flow of saliva, particularly the increased flow of saliva at mealtimes. A stone also predisposes the mouth to infection. The stone can be readily palpated and is evident on X-ray. Surgical removal is a simple procedure.

The submandibular gland, like the parotid, is subject to the development of tumours. To ensure total removal of all malignant material it is sometimes necessary to remove adjacent nerves that may be affected by the tumour. Removal of the hypoglossal nerve results in loss of movement of one half of the tongue on the affected side, and can lead to atrophy (wasting) of that side of the tongue.

# Infratemporal fossa

The infratemporal fossa (a fossa is a depression or hollow) is a region at the side of the head which contains a number of important nerves, blood vessels and muscles involved in mastication (chewing).

The infratemporal fossa is located below the base of the skull, between the pharynx and the ramus (side) of the mandible (lower jawbone). The region is of particular importance to dental surgeons, not only because many of its components are essential to the process of mastication, but also as many of the nerves and blood vessels supplying the mouth are transmitted through it.

### ANATOMY OF THE FOSSA
The region is largely defined by the skeletal boundaries of the infratemporal fossa. The anterior boundary is the posterior surface of the maxillary bone, and the posterior boundary is the styloid process of the temporal bone and the carotid sheath. The midline boundary is formed by the lateral pterygoid plate of the sphenoid bone; the lateral boundary is the ramus of the mandible and the roof is the base of the greater wing of the sphenoid bone. The infratemporal fossa has no floor, and is continuous with the neck.

### CONTENTS OF THE FOSSA
The fossa contains the pterygoid muscles, branches of the mandibular nerve, the chorda tympani branch of the facial nerve, the otic ganglion (part of the autonomic nervous system), the maxillary artery and the pterygoid venous plexus (vessels surrounding pterygoid muscles).

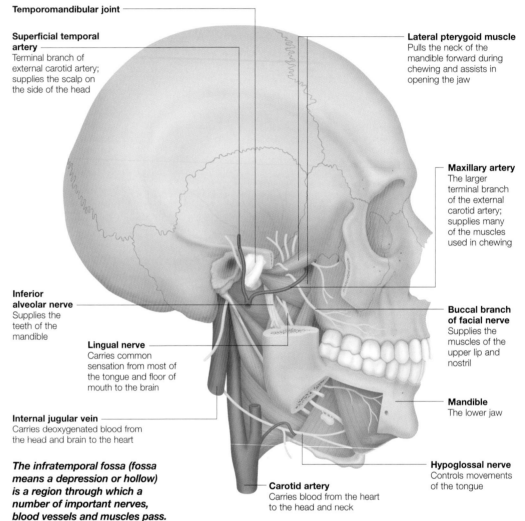

**Temporomandibular joint**

**Superficial temporal artery**
Terminal branch of external carotid artery; supplies the scalp on the side of the head

**Lateral pterygoid muscle**
Pulls the neck of the mandible forward during chewing and assists in opening the jaw

**Maxillary artery**
The larger terminal branch of the external carotid artery; supplies many of the muscles used in chewing

**Inferior alveolar nerve**
Supplies the teeth of the mandible

**Lingual nerve**
Carries common sensation from most of the tongue and floor of mouth to the brain

**Internal jugular vein**
Carries deoxygenated blood from the head and brain to the heart

**Buccal branch of facial nerve**
Supplies the muscles of the upper lip and nostril

**Mandible**
The lower jaw

**Hypoglossal nerve**
Controls movements of the tongue

**Carotid artery**
Carries blood from the heart to the head and neck

*The infratemporal fossa (fossa means a depression or hollow) is a region through which a number of important nerves, blood vessels and muscles pass.*

## Chorda tympani

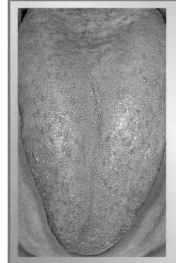

Most of the taste buds are located on the tongue. However, taste is a special sensation which is not in the repertoire of the trigeminal nerve.

A branch of the facial nerve, the chorda tympani, joins the lingual nerve in the infratemporal fossa to provide the sensation of taste. The chorda tympani also carries nervous information telling the submandibular and sublingual salivary glands when to secrete saliva.

*The chorda tympani is a branch of the facial nerve which carries the sensation of taste from the front of the tongue.*

## Pterygoid muscles

The pterygoid muscles, which are contained within the infratemporal fossa, are two of the four muscles known collectively as the muscles of mastication. All these muscles have the same developmental origin and therefore the same nerve supply, which is the mandibular nerve – a branch of the trigeminal nerve.

### CHEWING
Chewing involves movements of the mandible (lower jaw) relative to the cranium. Thus, the muscles of mastication have their origin in the cranial part of the skull and their insertions in the mandible or the joint between the two.

As the muscle fibres are directed backwards, contraction of the muscle (shortening of the fibres) on both sides of the head results in the the mandible protruding forwards.

Acting alternately, the left and right muscles will produce side to side motions of the jaws. Muscle fibres of the medial pterygoid insert into the medial surface of the angle of the mandible. Since the muscle fibres are orientated downwards and backwards, contraction of these fibres will result in elevation of the mandible and closing of the jaws. Acting alternately, the left and right muscles will produce a grinding action of the teeth.

# Mandibular nerve

The mandibular nerve leaves the skull (through the foramen ovale) to enter directly into the infratemporal fossa, where it divides into its many branches.

The mandibular nerve has motor branches which supply all of the muscles of mastication, allowing contractions of these muscles to take place. The nerve also supplies sensation to the skin of the temple and around the ear via the auriculotemporal nerve and to the skin on the outside of the cheek and the tissue lining the inside via the buccal nerve.

### BRANCHES OF THE MANDIBULAR NERVE

The branch called the inferior alveolar nerve (or inferior dental nerve) travels downwards and then forwards to enter the body of the mandible. It supplies sensation to all of the lower teeth, but it also has a branch called the mental nerve which leaves the mandible through a foramen in the lower premolar region. This supplies sensation to the lower lip.

The lingual nerve branch supplies common sensation (for example touch, temperature and pain) to most of the tongue and the floor of the mouth.

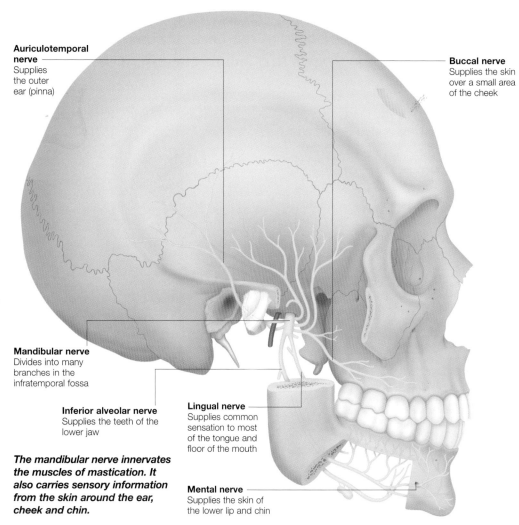

**Auriculotemporal nerve**
Supplies the outer ear (pinna)

**Buccal nerve**
Supplies the skin over a small area of the cheek

**Mandibular nerve**
Divides into many branches in the infratemporal fossa

**Inferior alveolar nerve**
Supplies the teeth of the lower jaw

**Lingual nerve**
Supplies common sensation to most of the tongue and floor of the mouth

**Mental nerve**
Supplies the skin of the lower lip and chin

*The mandibular nerve innervates the muscles of mastication. It also carries sensory information from the skin around the ear, cheek and chin.*

## Dental anaesthetics

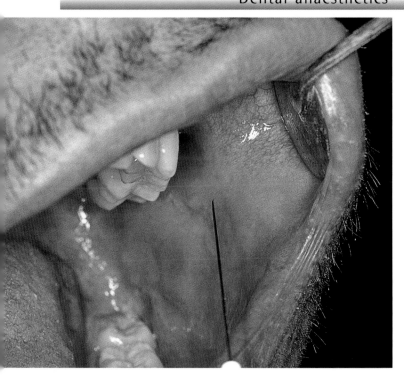

When a dentist needs to work on the teeth and gums of the lower jaw, it is common practice to use an inferior alveolar nerve block. The procedure involves injecting a local anaesthetic (LA) at the point where the nerve enters the body of the mandible on the side of interest. The anaesthetic desensitizes the nerve including its mental nerve branch and hence the lower lip becomes numb – often the first sign that the anaesthetic is working properly.

To desensitize the upper teeth, LA is injected either side of the individual tooth, and sometimes into the palate; the bone of the upper jaw is thin enough for the LA to filter through.

*Local anaesthetic (LA) is used to numb the area of the mouth that needs to be worked on. In order to desensitize the lower teeth and gums, the inferior alveolar nerve is numbed with an LA injection.*

## Tumours

Tumours affecting the infratemporal fossa are usually benign. The commonest are pleomorphic adenoma of the parotid salivary gland and schwannoma (tumour around a nerve). These often present as a fullness in the neck or a swelling at the back of the throat.

MR and CT scanning delineates the soft tissue extent of the mass and its relationship to the internal carotid artery. The scan images will also show any erosion of the skull base.

Treatment is by surgical removal. Small tumours may be approached from the neck and removed from behind the lower jaw. Larger or more vascular tumours may require some excision of bone to give better access to the internal carotid artery, thus preventing life-threatening haemorrhage.

# Pterygopalatine fossa

The pterygopalatine fossa is a funnel-shaped space between the bones of the head. It contains important nerves and blood vessels that supply the eye, mouth, nose and face.

The pterygopalatine fossa is an anatomical area that is difficult to find when the skull is intact, and furthermore disappears when the skull bones are separated. The easiest way of locating the fossa is via the pterygomaxillary fissure, which is a narrow triangular gap between the pterygoid plates of the sphenoid bone and the back of the upper jaw (maxilla). This leads to the lateral part of the fossa.

### LOCATION OF THE FOSSA

The fossa is a small funnel-shaped space that tapers downwards and lies below the back of the orbit. It is located behind the maxilla and its back wall is formed by the pterygoid plates and the greater wing of the sphenoid bone. The palatine bone forms its midline and its floor. It is a very important distribution centre as it communicates with all of the important regions of the head including the mouth, nose, eye and face, infratemporal fossa and also with the brain.

The main components of the pterygopalatine fossa are the maxillary artery and nerve (branch of the trigeminal nerve) and the pterygopalatine ganglion. These enter and exit the region through the spheno-palatine foramen (hole).

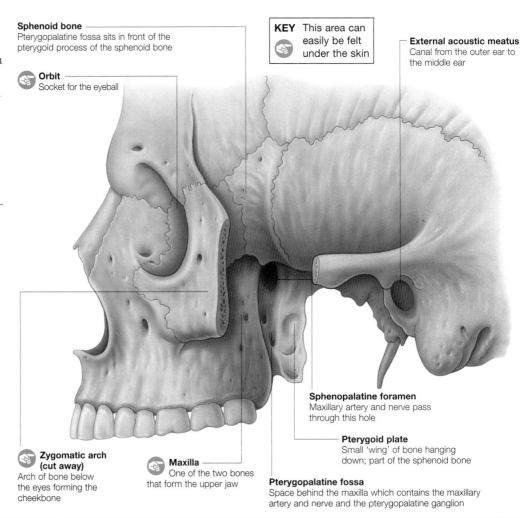

**Sphenoid bone**
Pterygopalatine fossa sits in front of the pterygoid process of the sphenoid bone

**Orbit**
Socket for the eyeball

**KEY** This area can easily be felt under the skin

**External acoustic meatus**
Canal from the outer ear to the middle ear

**Sphenopalatine foramen**
Maxillary artery and nerve pass through this hole

**Pterygoid plate**
Small 'wing' of bone hanging down; part of the sphenoid bone

**Pterygopalatine fossa**
Space behind the maxilla which contains the maxillary artery and nerve and the pterygopalatine ganglion

**Zygomatic arch (cut away)**
Arch of bone below the eyes forming the cheekbone

**Maxilla**
One of the two bones that form the upper jaw

## Maxillary artery

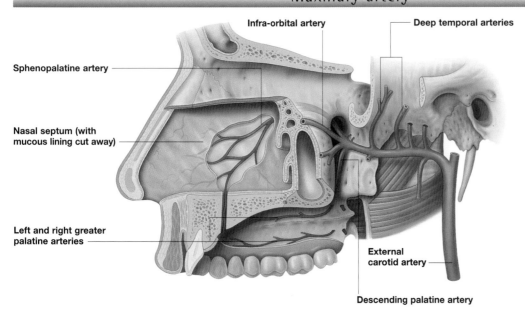

**Sphenopalatine artery**

**Nasal septum (with mucous lining cut away)**

**Left and right greater palatine arteries**

**Infra-orbital artery**

**Deep temporal arteries**

**External carotid artery**

**Descending palatine artery**

The maxillary artery is one of the terminal branches of the large external carotid artery. Within the infratemporal fossa, the artery divides into three parts and the pterygopalatine section is conventionally described as the third part.

### DIVISIONS OF THE MAXILLARY ARTERY

The maxillary artery enters the pterygopalatine fossa via the pterygomaxillary fissure. Within the fossa, the artery divides into numerous branches, which eventually supply oxygenated blood to all of the maxillary (upper) teeth, the hard and soft palate, the nasal cavity, the paranasal sinuses, the skin of the lower eyelid, the nose and the upper lip.

# Maxillary nerve

The maxillary nerve enters the pterygopalatine fossa before dividing into branches which supply sensation to large areas of the face.

The maxillary nerve leaves the cranial part of the skull to enter directly into the pterygopalatine fossa by the foramen rotundum. On entering the fossa, the nerve contains only fibres for common sensation including touch, pain and temperature. It divides within the fossa to supply these sensations to the nose, palate, tonsils and gums, skin of the cheeks, upper lip and upper molar teeth.

### BRANCHES OF THE MAXILLARY NERVE

The names of the main branches are the zygomaticotemporal and zygomaticofacial, greater and lesser palatine nerves, nasal nerves and posterior superior alveolar nerve. The main trunk of the maxillary nerve leaves the fossa through the inferior orbital fissure which is in the floor of the orbit.

As it leaves the pterygopalatine fossa, the maxillary nerve becomes the infra-orbital nerve. It travels in the floor of the orbit to emerge through a foramen in the maxilla, below the eye.

Branches from the infra-orbital nerve include the anterior superior alveolar nerve which supplies the front upper teeth.

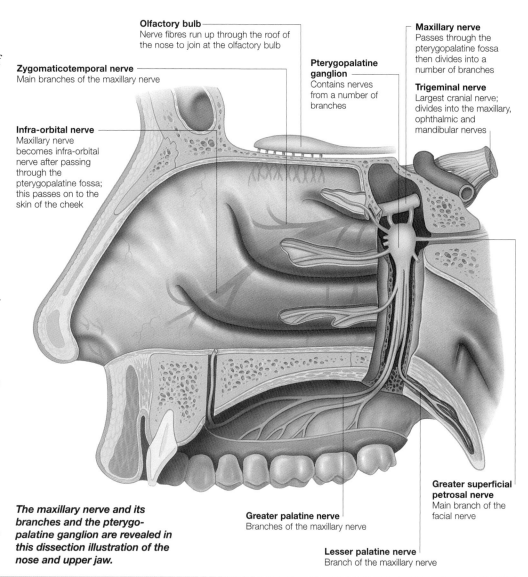

**Olfactory bulb**
Nerve fibres run up through the roof of the nose to join at the olfactory bulb

**Zygomaticotemporal nerve**
Main branches of the maxillary nerve

**Infra-orbital nerve**
Maxillary nerve becomes infra-orbital nerve after passing through the pterygopalatine fossa; this passes on to the skin of the cheek

**Pterygopalatine ganglion**
Contains nerves from a number of branches

**Maxillary nerve**
Passes through the pterygopalatine fossa then divides into a number of branches

**Trigeminal nerve**
Largest cranial nerve; divides into the maxillary, ophthalmic and mandibular nerves

**Greater superficial petrosal nerve**
Main branch of the facial nerve

**Greater palatine nerve**
Branches of the maxillary nerve

**Lesser palatine nerve**
Branch of the maxillary nerve

*The maxillary nerve and its branches and the pterygo-palatine ganglion are revealed in this dissection illustration of the nose and upper jaw.*

## 'Hay fever' ganglion

The pterygopalatine ganglion is a point of convergence for different nerves which communicate and unite within the pterygo-palatine fossa. Beyond common sensation, the fossa is also a relay station for nerve fibres which control glandular secretions. These are known as secretomotor fibres and are not natural components of the maxillary nerve as the trigeminal nerve is not capable of such functions.

### SECRETOMOTOR FIBRES

The main source of secretomotor fibres is the facial nerve. The main branch of the facial nerve carrying fibres into the

*The pterygopalatine ganglion contains nerve fibres which control secretions of tears and mucus. It is these fibres that are stimulated in hay fever.*

pterygopalatine fossa is called the greater superficial petrosal nerve. Just before entering the fossa it unites with a nerve from the sympathetic nervous system called the deep petrosal nerve. Fibres of this nerve are involved in vasoconstriction – reducing the blood flow to an area.

The combined nerve is known as the nerve of the pterygoid canal. Within the ganglion, secretomotor fibres and vasoconstrictor fibres unite with sensory fibres of branches of the maxillary nerve. In this way, secretomotor fibres are distributed to the lacrimal gland, which forms tears, and to the mucus-producing glands within the nose, palate and sinuses. For these reasons the pterygopalatine ganglion is often referred to by anatomists as the 'hay fever' ganglion.

# Ear

The ears are vital sensory organs of hearing and balance. Each ear is divided into three parts – outer, middle and inner ear – each of which is designed to respond to sound or movement in a different way.

The ear can be divided anatomically into three different parts: the external, middle and inner ear. The external and middle ear are important in the gathering and transmitting of sound waves. The inner ear is the organ of hearing and is also vital in enabling us to maintain our balance.

### TRANSMITTING INFORMATION

The external ear consists of the visible auricle or pinna (earlobe) and the canal that passes into the head – the external auditory meatus. At the inner end of the meatus is the tympanic membrane, or eardrum, which marks the border between the external and middle ear.

The middle ear is connected to the back of the throat via the auditory tube. Within the middle ear are three tiny bones called the ossicles. These bones are linked together in such a way that movements of the eardrum are transmitted via the footplate of the stapes to the oval window (the opening in between the middle and inner ear).

The inner ear contains the main organ of hearing, the cochlea, and the vestibular system that controls balance. Information from both these parts of the ear passes to specific areas within the brainstem via the vestibulocochlear nerve.

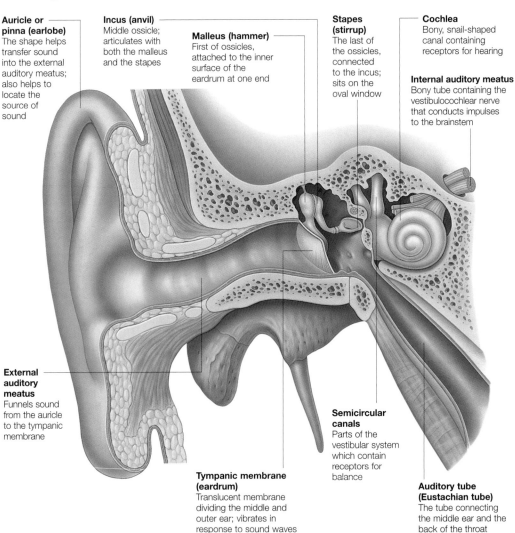

**Auricle or pinna (earlobe)**
The shape helps transfer sound into the external auditory meatus; also helps to locate the source of sound

**Incus (anvil)**
Middle ossicle; articulates with both the malleus and the stapes

**Malleus (hammer)**
First of ossicles, attached to the inner surface of the eardrum at one end

**Stapes (stirrup)**
The last of the ossicles, connected to the incus; sits on the oval window

**Cochlea**
Bony, snail-shaped canal containing receptors for hearing

**Internal auditory meatus**
Bony tube containing the vestibulocochlear nerve that conducts impulses to the brainstem

**External auditory meatus**
Funnels sound from the auricle to the tympanic membrane

**Tympanic membrane (eardrum)**
Translucent membrane dividing the middle and outer ear; vibrates in response to sound waves

**Semicircular canals**
Parts of the vestibular system which contain receptors for balance

**Auditory tube (Eustachian tube)**
The tube connecting the middle ear and the back of the throat

## Viewing the ear through an auriscope

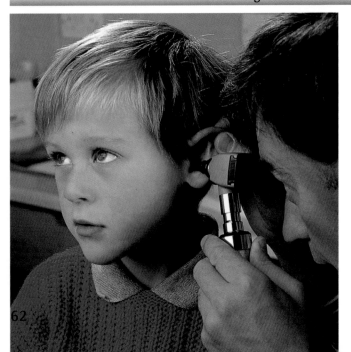

The tympanic membrane (eardrum) can be examined using an instrument called an auriscope, which is inserted into the external auditory meatus. The auriscope illuminates the eardrum, which appears pearly-grey in colour. A reflected cone of light can be seen originating at a small central depression, called the umbo, and radiating downwards and forwards. The umbo marks the site of attachment of the malleus on the other side of the membrane.

The majority of the membrane is thickened and taut (pars tensa)

*Before inserting an auriscope, the earlobe is pulled up and out. This is necessary as the external auditory meatus does not follow a straight course.*

but there is a small area at the top which is not so fibrous, called the pars flaccida. The membrane is well innervated (served by nerves) and inflammation due to infection may be extremely painful.

*A view of a healthy tympanic membrane (eardrum) as seen through an auriscope. The eardrum appears translucent.*

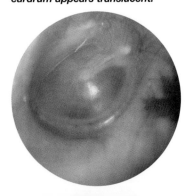

# External ear

The pinna is the skin and cartilage that make up the external ear. It serves to channel sound into the middle ear.

The pinna, or auricle, collects sound from the environment and channels it into the external auditory meatus. It consists of a thin sheet of elastic cartilage and a lower portion called the lobule, consisting mainly of fatty tissue, with a tight covering of skin.

The auricle is attached to the head by a series of ligaments and muscles, and the external ear has a complex sensory nerve supply involving three of the cranial nerves.

### PROTECTING THE EAR

The external auditory meatus is a tube extending from the lobule to the tympanic membrane and is about 2.5 cm long in adults. The outer third of the tube is made of cartilage (similar to that in the auricle), but the inner two thirds is bony (part of the temporal bone).

In the skin covering the cartilaginous part of the meatus, there are coarse hairs and ceruminous glands that secrete cerumen (earwax). Usually wax dries up and falls out of the ear, but it can build up and interfere with hearing. The combination of wax and hairs prevents dust and foreign objects from entering the ear.

The boundary between the outer and middle ear is the tympanic membrane, or eardrum. This is a translucent membrane which can be viewed using an auriscope. The tympanic membrane can sometimes be perforated due to middle ear infection or high-pressure sound waves.

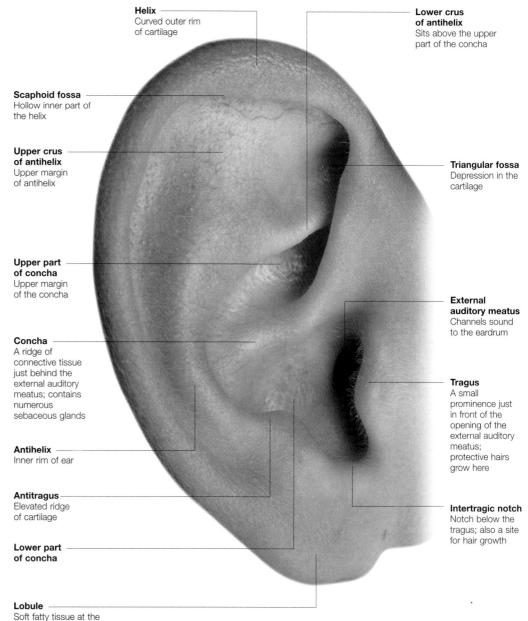

**Helix**
Curved outer rim of cartilage

**Lower crus of antihelix**
Sits above the upper part of the concha

**Scaphoid fossa**
Hollow inner part of the helix

**Upper crus of antihelix**
Upper margin of antihelix

**Triangular fossa**
Depression in the cartilage

**Upper part of concha**
Upper margin of the concha

**External auditory meatus**
Channels sound to the eardrum

**Concha**
A ridge of connective tissue just behind the external auditory meatus; contains numerous sebaceous glands

**Tragus**
A small prominence just in front of the opening of the external auditory meatus; protective hairs grow here

**Antihelix**
Inner rim of ear

**Antitragus**
Elevated ridge of cartilage

**Intertragic notch**
Notch below the tragus; also a site for hair growth

**Lower part of concha**

**Lobule**
Soft fatty tissue at the bottom of the earlobe, often the site for ear-piercing; contains no cartilage

## Ear deformities

Children with protruding ears, or 'bat' ears, are often self-conscious of their ears and suffer teasing. For this reason, some people choose to have their ears pinned back surgically. Children need to be over five years old to have the operation as before this age the ear cartilage has not yet hardened.

In some cases, protruding ears are caused by excess cartilage around the ear canal, pushing the ear out from the side of the head. To correct this, a surgeon cuts into the back of the ear and creates a fold in the cartilage. The ear is then stitched and allowed to heal.

Cauliflower ears are the result of repeated blows to the earlobe. They represent damage to the cartilage that makes up the earlobe. The problem arises because the cartilage has no blood supply of its own, but instead relies on the vessels within the skin that covers it. When the earlobe is struck, the cartilage may split into several layers. Blood collects within the split cartilage from the surrounding damaged blood vessels. The resultant scaring causes the ear to lose its normal shape.

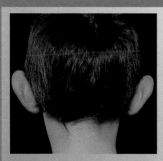

*Bat ears are a common minor cosmetic abnormality. The extent to which the ears protrude is variable.*

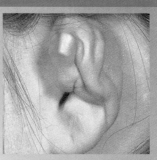

*Repeated trauma to the pinna causes cauliflower ear. Scar tissue forms as a result of the damage, deforming the shape.*

# Inside the ear

The middle ear is an air-filled cavity that contains the eardrum and three small bones that help transmit sound to the inner ear. It is also connected to the throat via the auditory tube.

The middle ear is an air-filled, box-shaped cavity within the temporal bone of the skull. It contains small bones or ossicles – the malleus, incus and stapes – that span the space between the tympanic membrane (the eardrum) and the medial wall of the cavity.

Two small muscles are also present: the tensor tympani, attached to the handle of the malleus; and the stapedius, attached to the stapes. Both help to modulate the movements of the ossicles. The medial wall divides the middle ear from the inner ear and contains two membrane-covered openings; the oval and round windows.

### AUDITORY TUBE

The middle ear is connected to the throat by the auditory (Eustachian) tube. This tube is a possible route of infection into the middle ear. If left untreated, infections can spread into the mastoid air cells that lie just behind the middle ear cavity, and may breach the roof of the temporal bone and infect the membranous covering of the brain (the meninges).

Just below the floor of the middle ear cavity is the bulb of the internal jugular vein, and just in front is the internal carotid artery.

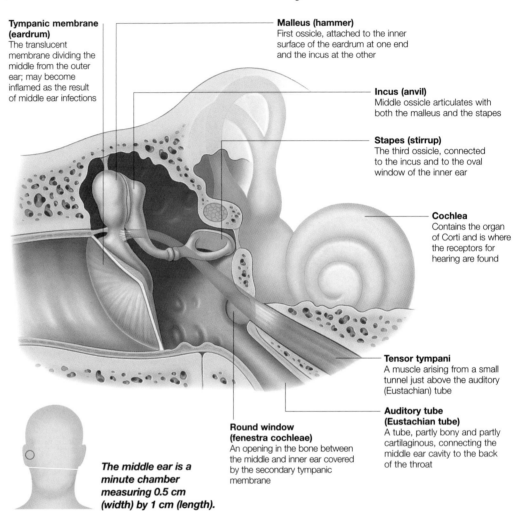

**Tympanic membrane (eardrum)**
The translucent membrane dividing the middle from the outer ear; may become inflamed as the result of middle ear infections

**Malleus (hammer)**
First ossicle, attached to the inner surface of the eardrum at one end and the incus at the other

**Incus (anvil)**
Middle ossicle articulates with both the malleus and the stapes

**Stapes (stirrup)**
The third ossicle, connected to the incus and to the oval window of the inner ear

**Cochlea**
Contains the organ of Corti and is where the receptors for hearing are found

**Tensor tympani**
A muscle arising from a small tunnel just above the auditory (Eustachian) tube

**Auditory tube (Eustachian tube)**
A tube, partly bony and partly cartilaginous, connecting the middle ear cavity to the back of the throat

**Round window (fenestra cochleae)**
An opening in the bone between the middle and inner ear covered by the secondary tympanic membrane

*The middle ear is a minute chamber measuring 0.5 cm (width) by 1 cm (length).*

## The ossicles

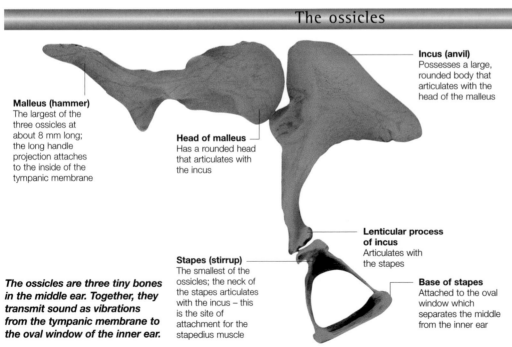

**Malleus (hammer)**
The largest of the three ossicles at about 8 mm long; the long handle projection attaches to the inside of the tympanic membrane

**Head of malleus**
Has a rounded head that articulates with the incus

**Incus (anvil)**
Possesses a large, rounded body that articulates with the head of the malleus

**Lenticular process of incus**
Articulates with the stapes

**Stapes (stirrup)**
The smallest of the ossicles; the neck of the stapes articulates with the incus – this is the site of attachment for the stapedius muscle

**Base of stapes**
Attached to the oval window which separates the middle from the inner ear

*The ossicles are three tiny bones in the middle ear. Together, they transmit sound as vibrations from the tympanic membrane to the oval window of the inner ear.*

The ossicles are arranged so that vibrations in the tympanic membrane are transmitted across the middle ear to the oval window and to the inner ear. All three bones are held in place by ligaments; in addition, there are two muscles that modulate movement.

Stapedius, the smallest skeletal muscle in the body, arises from a bony projection called the pyramid and attaches to the neck of the stapes. Contraction of this muscle helps to damp down loud sounds.

The other muscle, the tensor tympani, has a similar damping effect but it acts by increasing the tension in the tympanic membrane. People with damage to the facial nerve may suffer from hyperacusis, an abnormal sensitivity to sound.

# The inner ear

This part of the ear contains the organs of balance and hearing. It contains the labyrinth that helps us to orientate ourselves, and the cochlea, the organ of hearing.

The inner ear, also known as the labyrinth because of its contorted shape, contains the organ of balance (the vestibule) and of hearing (the cochlea). It can be divided into an outer bony labyrinth and an inner membranous labyrinth. The bony labyrinth is filled with perilymph and the membranous labyrinth contains a fluid called endolymph, with a different chemical composition.

## ORIENTATION

The membranous labyrinth contains the utricle and saccule – two linked, sac-like structures within the bony vestibule. They help detect orientation within the environment.

Related to these are the semicircular ducts lying within the bony semicircular canals. Where they are connected to the utricle, the semicircular canals enlarge to form ampullae, containing sensory receptors. Changes in the movement of the fluid in the ducts provides information about acceleration and deceleration of the head.

The cochlea is a bony spiral canal, wound around a central pillar – the modiolus. Within the cochlea are hair cells, the hearing receptors, that react to vibrations in the endolymph caused by the movement of the stapes on the oval window. They lie within the organ of Corti.

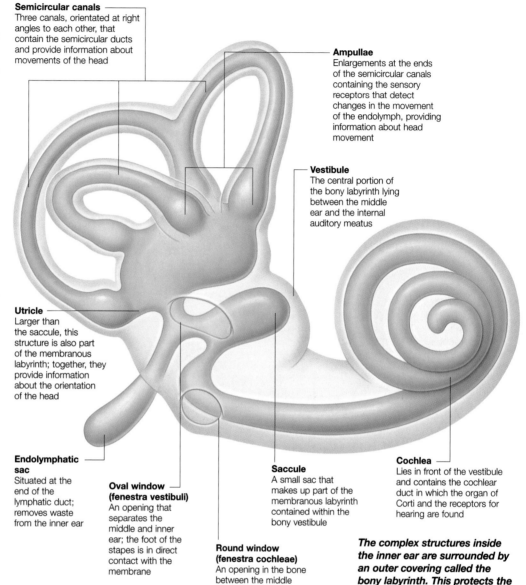

**Semicircular canals**
Three canals, orientated at right angles to each other, that contain the semicircular ducts and provide information about movements of the head

**Ampullae**
Enlargements at the ends of the semicircular canals containing the sensory receptors that detect changes in the movement of the endolymph, providing information about head movement

**Vestibule**
The central portion of the bony labyrinth lying between the middle ear and the internal auditory meatus

**Utricle**
Larger than the saccule, this structure is also part of the membranous labyrinth; together, they provide information about the orientation of the head

**Endolymphatic sac**
Situated at the end of the lymphatic duct; removes waste from the inner ear

**Oval window (fenestra vestibuli)**
An opening that separates the middle and inner ear; the foot of the stapes is in direct contact with the membrane

**Round window (fenestra cochleae)**
An opening in the bone between the middle and inner ear, covered by the secondary tympanic membrane

**Saccule**
A small sac that makes up part of the membranous labyrinth contained within the bony vestibule

**Cochlea**
Lies in front of the vestibule and contains the cochlear duct in which the organ of Corti and the receptors for hearing are found

*The complex structures inside the inner ear are surrounded by an outer covering called the bony labyrinth. This protects the receptors for hearing and the delicate organs that detect movements of the head.*

## Hearing aids and cochlear implants

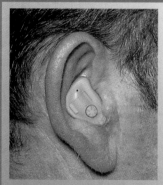

*This hearing aid fits in the outer ear. It improves hearing for partially deaf patients by amplifying sounds and transmitting them into the ear.*

There are two main forms of deafness. In conductive deafness, meaning a problem conducting sound, the problem is in the outer or middle ear. Sensori-neural deafness is when the problem lies with the cochlea or the pathway between the cochlea and the brain.

Conductive hearing loss can often be improved surgically, but can also be helped by using electrical hearing aids. These consist essentially of an amplifier, a microphone, a receiver and a battery, and can either be worn behind the earlobe or, with miniaturization, within the ear itself.

In those patients with sensori-neural loss, hearing aids need to be more complex. One approach is the cochlear implant or artificial ear. This requires a tiny microphone to be placed in the ear. This converts sound into electrical impulses which are then fed via electrodes to the cochlea, where they trigger nerve impulses in the vestibulocochlear nerve. This approach is used with patients in whom the hair cells of the organ of Corti have been destroyed. The hearing produced remains relatively crude but provides the patient with some perception of rhythm and intensity of sounds.

*The transmitter of a cochlear implant is attached to the scalp, underneath which is a receiver. Electrodes run from the receiver into the cochlea.*

# Inside the neck

The neck is one of the most anatomically complex areas of the body. Many vital structures, including the spinal cord and thyroid gland, are closely packed together within layers of connecting tissue and muscle.

The neck is defined as the region lying between the bottom of the lower jaw and the top of the clavicle (collar bone). Within this relatively small area there are numerous vital structures that are closely packed together between layers of connective tissue.

The outermost layer of the neck is the skin. The skin of the neck contains sensory nerve endings from the second, third and fourth cervical nerves. A number of natural stress lines can be seen on the skin that run around the neck horizontally. When the skin is cut during surgical procedures, the incisions are made along, rather than across, these stress lines in order to minimize scarring.

### EXTERNAL JUGULAR VEIN

Just beneath the skin is the thin layer of subcutaneous fat and connective tissue called the superficial fascia. Embedded in this layer are blood vessels, such as the external jugular vein and its tributaries. These veins drain blood from the face, scalp and neck. Closely associated with the external jugular vein are the superficial lymph nodes.

One other important structure that can be found in this layer, at the front of the neck, is the very thin platysma muscle that helps to depress the lower jaw.

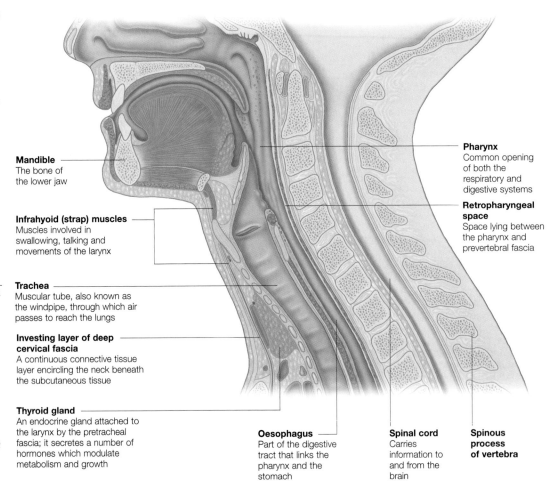

**Mandible**
The bone of the lower jaw

**Infrahyoid (strap) muscles**
Muscles involved in swallowing, talking and movements of the larynx

**Trachea**
Muscular tube, also known as the windpipe, through which air passes to reach the lungs

**Investing layer of deep cervical fascia**
A continuous connective tissue layer encircling the neck beneath the subcutaneous tissue

**Thyroid gland**
An endocrine gland attached to the larynx by the pretracheal fascia; it secretes a number of hormones which modulate metabolism and growth

**Pharynx**
Common opening of both the respiratory and digestive systems

**Retropharyngeal space**
Space lying between the pharynx and prevertebral fascia

**Oesophagus**
Part of the digestive tract that links the pharynx and the stomach

**Spinal cord**
Carries information to and from the brain

**Spinous process of vertebra**

## Lymph nodes

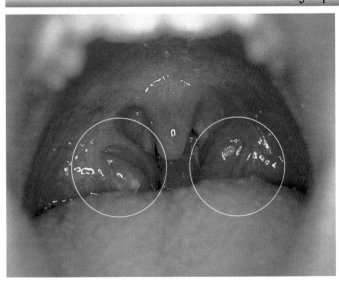

*The tonsils (circled) consist of lymphoid tissue, and are concerned with fighting infection. They are vulnerable to infection and inflammation.*

Within the neck are lymph nodes, which are essential for protecting the body from infection. Lymph nodes are embedded in connective tissue in various parts of the body, particularly the regions of the groin, the armpits and the neck. They are also present in lymph organs, such as the spleen and the tonsils.

The function of lymph nodes is to filter lymph fluid, which circulates specialized white blood cells (lymphocytes) throughout the body. Lymphocytes, located in the lymph nodes, are also essential to the body's defences, as they produce antibodies which play an important part in fighting infections.

Disorders of the lymphatic system are considered serious, and can include:

■ Lymphoedema – results from a blockage of lymphatic drainage, causing gross swelling. May be caused by some parasites, damage to the lymphatic system itself or hereditary abnormalities, such as Milroy's disease

■ Lymphangitis – acute inflammation of the lymphatic vessels caused by infection with streptococcal bacteria.

# Cross-section of the neck

**Deeper layers of the neck reveal interconnected sheets of tissue. These bind to and protect a variety of structures.**

Moving deeper into the neck, the connective tissue of the deep cervical fascia is arranged into a number of fibrous sheets. These fasciae surround different groups of muscles, blood vessels and nerves, allowing them to move relative to each other with minimal friction.

The first of these is the investing fascia. This encircles the neck and is anchored to the spinous processes of the cervical vertebrae. It encloses the large sternocleidomastoid muscle at the front and side of the neck, and the trapezius muscle at the back, both of which are important in the movements of the head and neck.

### LARYNX AND TRACHEA

The thin pretracheal fascia binds the thyroid gland to the larynx and trachea at the front of the neck. It is anchored to the cricoid cartilage, allowing movement during swallowing.

The pretracheal fascia is continuous with a sheet of tissue (the carotid sheath) which provides protection for the carotid artery, the internal jugular vein and the vagus nerve. Behind the trachea is the oesophagus (gullet), and behind the larynx is the pharynx, the muscular tube connecting the mouth and the oesophagus.

The last deep connective tissue layer is the prevertebral fascia, enclosing the remaining muscles of the neck, the vertebral column and the spinal cord, positioned in the centre of the neck for maximum protection.

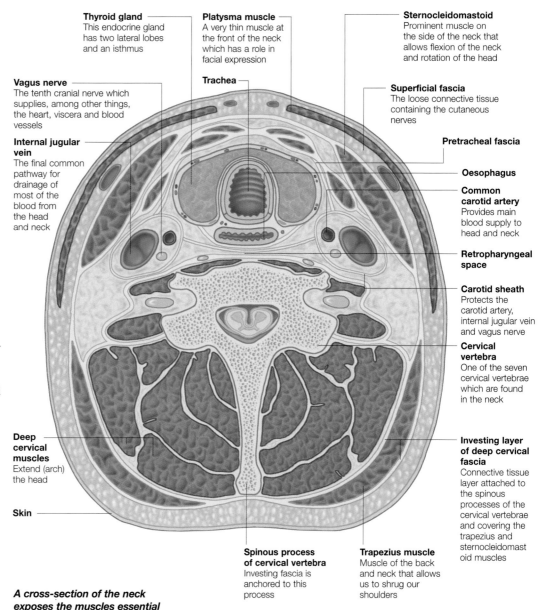

**Thyroid gland**
This endocrine gland has two lateral lobes and an isthmus

**Platysma muscle**
A very thin muscle at the front of the neck which has a role in facial expression

**Sternocleidomastoid**
Prominent muscle on the side of the neck that allows flexion of the neck and rotation of the head

**Vagus nerve**
The tenth cranial nerve which supplies, among other things, the heart, viscera and blood vessels

**Trachea**

**Superficial fascia**
The loose connective tissue containing the cutaneous nerves

**Internal jugular vein**
The final common pathway for drainage of most of the blood from the head and neck

**Pretracheal fascia**

**Oesophagus**

**Common carotid artery**
Provides main blood supply to head and neck

**Retropharyngeal space**

**Carotid sheath**
Protects the carotid artery, internal jugular vein and vagus nerve

**Cervical vertebra**
One of the seven cervical vertebrae which are found in the neck

**Deep cervical muscles**
Extend (arch) the head

**Skin**

**Investing layer of deep cervical fascia**
Connective tissue layer attached to the spinous processes of the cervical vertebrae and covering the trapezius and sternocleidomastoid muscles

**Spinous process of cervical vertebra**
Investing fascia is anchored to this process

**Trapezius muscle**
Muscle of the back and neck that allows us to shrug our shoulders

*A cross-section of the neck exposes the muscles essential for movement and facial expression. Among these are connecting tissues and vessels.*

## Retropharyngeal space

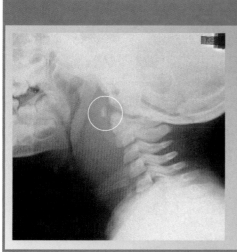

Between the different fascial layers there are areas of much looser connective tissue and spaces, such as the retropharyngeal space. This space lies between the back of the pharynx and the prevertebral fascia and extends from the base of the skull to the chest cavity.

These spaces are clinically important in terms of the spread of infection. An infection of the mouth or teeth may enter the retropharyngeal space and, due to the

*The retropharyngeal space can be a site of infection. This X-ray shows an abscess in the retropharyngeal space (circled). This may have been caused by infection spreading from the tonsils.*

sheet–like structure of the fascia, the infection may, rarely, spread into the chest.

Retropharyngeal abscesses arise due to spread of infection from areas such as the mouth and tonsils and are most common in children. They can also occur as the result of damage to the posterior (rear) wall of the pharynx that may be caused by objects such as lollipop-sticks.

Patients tend to be feverish and complain of pain when swallowing. Severe swelling can interfere with breathing. The abscess can be identified on a soft tissue X-ray of the side of the neck. Treatment involves making sure the patient has a clear airway, draining the abscess surgically and treating with antibiotics.

# Vertebral column

The vertebral column gives our bodies flexibility and keeps us upright. It also protects the delicate spinal cord.

The vertebral column forms the part of the skeleton commonly known as the backbone or spine. The spine supports the skull and gives attachment to the pelvic girdle, supporting the lower limbs. As well as its obvious role in posture and locomotion, the vertebral column surrounds and protects the spinal cord. Like all bones, its marrow is a source of blood cells, and it acts as a reservoir for calcium ions.

The spine exhibits four curvatures when viewed from the side. The cervical and lumbar curvatures are convex anteriorly (forward). The thoracic and sacral curvatures are convex posteriorly (backwards). The cervical curvature develops in infancy as the baby learns to hold its head upright; similarly, the lumbar curvature forms as the baby learns to walk.

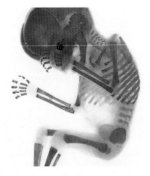

*In the fetus, the backbone has a single curvature in the thoracic and sacral regions. Other curvatures develop as the baby sits, stands and walks.*

**Frontal aspect**

**Lateral (side) view**

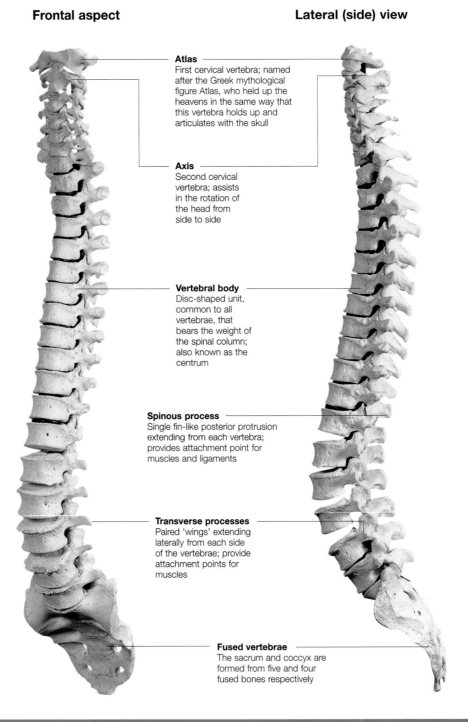

**Atlas**
First cervical vertebra; named after the Greek mythological figure Atlas, who held up the heavens in the same way that this vertebra holds up and articulates with the skull

**Axis**
Second cervical vertebra; assists in the rotation of the head from side to side

**Vertebral body**
Disc-shaped unit, common to all vertebrae, that bears the weight of the spinal column; also known as the centrum

**Spinous process**
Single fin-like posterior protrusion extending from each vertebra; provides attachment point for muscles and ligaments

**Transverse processes**
Paired 'wings' extending laterally from each side of the vertebrae; provide attachment points for muscles

**Fused vertebrae**
The sacrum and coccyx are formed from five and four fused bones respectively

## Intervertebral discs

Between the bodies of individual vertebrae are the intervertebral discs. Each disc is made of connective tissue with a soft central component (the jelly-like nucleus pulposus), and a tougher surrounding tissue known as the annulus fibrosus.

The intervertebral discs account for about 25 per cent of the total length of the vertebral column. The discs are elastic, and are compressed during the course of the day, meaning that we go to bed a few centimetres shorter than when we wake. The discs also allow for a wide range of different movements, and as the spinal column's natural shock absorbers, protect the vertebrae from excessive pressure.

A disc may be displaced (prolapse) backwards, irritating the spinal nerves and giving rise to the pain associated with prolapsed (also known as 'slipped') discs. Rest is often sufficient to relieve pain, but sometimes surgery is required.

With age, the discs become progressively thinner, partly accounting for the loss of height in older people.

*The cushion-like nature of the intervertebral discs is evident in this photograph. They are vital in ensuring the spine's flexibility.*

# Vertebral connections

The spinal column is divided into five main sections. Each section has a specific function and together they maintain the stability of the skeleton as a whole.

The vertebral column consists of 33 bones, known as the vertebrae. There are seven cervical vertebrae, twelve thoracic, five lumbar, five sacral and four coccygeal. Whereas the cervical, thoracic and lumbar vertebrae are separate bones, the sacral and coccygeal vertebrae are fused (inflexible). The vertebrae show differences along the column, and these will be featured on other sheets.

## STRUCTURE

Each vertebra conforms to the same basic plan, consisting of a body in front and a neural arch at the back, which surrounds and protects the spinal cord. From the neural arch arise the transverse processes and spines, which give attachment to muscles and ligaments. Adjacent vertebrae articulate at joints, allowing movement. Movements between adjacent vertebrae are relatively small but, when taken over the whole length of the vertebral column, give the trunk considerable mobility.

The nerves leaving and entering the spinal cord do so through gaps, the intervertebral foramina, between adjacent vertebrae.

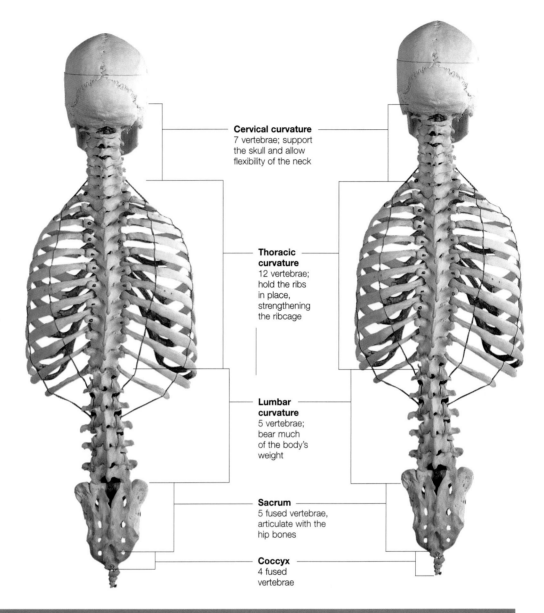

**Cervical curvature**
7 vertebrae; support the skull and allow flexibility of the neck

**Thoracic curvature**
12 vertebrae; hold the ribs in place, strengthening the ribcage

**Lumbar curvature**
5 vertebrae; bear much of the body's weight

**Sacrum**
5 fused vertebrae, articulate with the hip bones

**Coccyx**
4 fused vertebrae

## Disorders of the spinal column

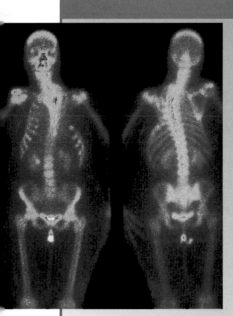

The vertebrae and their joints are affected by conditions common to other bones, such as osteoporosis, osteoarthritis and rheumatoid arthritis. The vertebrae are also commonly affected by fractures, which are considered extremely serious because of the presence of the spinal cord.

Spina bifida (meaning literally 'split spine') is a congenital condition in which the vertebral arches are incomplete and fail to unite at the midline. This causes the spinal cord and its covering to protrude through the vertebrae.

*Scoliosis is a congenital abnormal curvature of the thoracic spine. Treatment involves surgery or spinal immobilization with a brace.*

The condition results from a defect in fetal development, and is usually apparent on an ultrasound scan after week 16, but it may be unrecognized in mild cases, usually affecting the sacral and lumbar regions. The whole of the spinal column (and skull) may be affected in the most

severe cases. There may also be associated abnormalities of the brain, such as hydrocephalus.

*In spina bifida the spinal cord and surrounding meninges project through the skin. Paralysis of the lower limbs is a common symptom.*

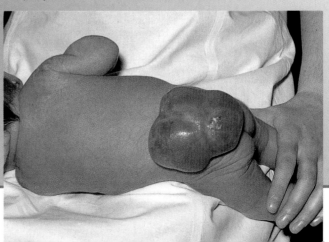

# Cervical vertebrae

There are seven cervical vertebrae, which together make up the skeletal structure of the neck. These vertebrae protect the spinal cord, support the skull and allow a range of movement.

Of the seven cervical vertebrae, the lower five appear similar, although the seventh has some distinctive features. The first cervical vertebra (atlas) and the second cervical vertebra (axis) show specializations related to the articulation of the vertebral column with the skull.

### TYPICAL CERVICAL VERTEBRA

The third to the sixth cervical vertebrae are comprised of two main components, a body towards the front and a vertebral arch at the rear. These surround the vertebral foramen (hole) which, as part of the vertebral column, forms the vertebral canal. The body is small compared with vertebrae in other regions, and is nearly cylindrical.

The vertebral arch can be subdivided in to two main elements. The pedicles, by which it is attached to the body, contain notches that allow the passage of spinal nerves. The laminae are thin plates of bone which are directed backwards and fuse in the midline, forming a bifid (divided) spine.

Associated with each vertebral arch are a pair of transverse processes. These are sites for muscle attachment, allowing movement and containing foramina through which blood vessels run.

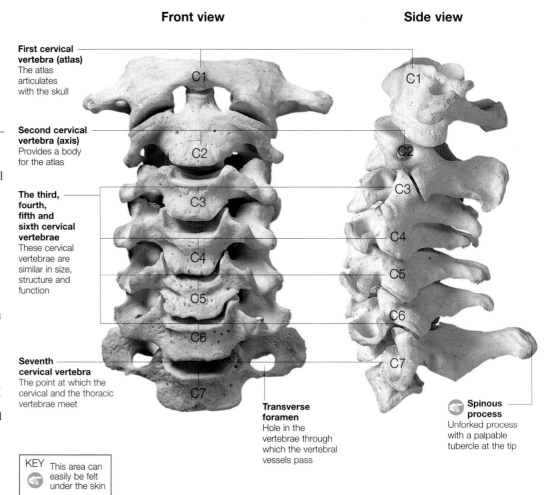

**Front view**

**Side view**

**First cervical vertebra (atlas)**
The atlas articulates with the skull

**Second cervical vertebra (axis)**
Provides a body for the atlas

**The third, fourth, fifth and sixth cervical vertebrae**
These cervical vertebrae are similar in size, structure and function

**Seventh cervical vertebra**
The point at which the cervical and the thoracic vertebrae meet

**Transverse foramen**
Hole in the vertebrae through which the vertebral vessels pass

**Spinous process**
Unforked process with a palpable tubercle at the tip

C1
C2
C3
C4
C5
C6
C7

**KEY** This area can easily be felt under the skin

## Damage to the cervical vertebrae

*After trauma, movement of the neck can be limited with a brace or collar. This reduces the risk of damage to the spinal cord.*

Dislocations of the cervical vertebrae are very serious, as any instability in this region may potentially lead to transection (severing) of the soft spinal cord by the sharp surface of the cervical vertebrae.

The muscles of the diaphragm, essential for breathing, are supplied chiefly by the fourth cervical spinal nerves, and transection above this level is fatal. Thus, where the site of the transection is concerned, distances of a few millimetres may mean the difference between life and death. For this

reason, it is essential at the scene of a traumatic accident that if injury to the cervical vertebrae cannot be excluded, the patient should not be moved until proper equipment and expertise is at hand.

The base of the dens (a toothlike projection of the axis which articulates with the atlas) may be fractured following severe head injuries and this must be checked using X-rays, as displacement of a fragment of bone may not occur immediately. If displacement does occur, it is usually fatal. Other dislocations may occur where the neck is most mobile – between the fourth and fifth or fifth and sixth vertebrae.

The synovial joints associated

with the cervical vertebrae, like similar joints elsewhere in the body, are susceptible to diseases such as rheumatoid arthritis. This is an auto-immune disease causing inflammation of the surface and lining of joints and leads to erosion of bones and deformities of the joint.

This may be extremely dangerous if the joint between the dens of the axis and the arch of the atlas is affected, as this can result in subluxation (dislocation of the joint such that the bones are still in contact but not aligned) of the dens. The dens may then compress the underlying medulla oblongata of the hindbrain, which contains vital brain centres, with disastrous consequences.

# Examining the cervical vertebrae

The first, second and seventh cervical vertebrae differ structurally from the others, in relation to their unique functions.

### FIRST CERVICAL VERTEBRA
The first cervical vertebra, the atlas, is the vertebra that articulates with the skull. Unlike the other vertebrae, it does not have a body, this being incorporated into the second cervical vertebra as the dens. It also has no spine. Instead, the atlas takes the form of a thin ring of bone with anterior and posterior arches, the surface of which show grooves related to the vertebral arteries before they enter the skull through the foramen magnum.

### SECOND CERVICAL VERTEBRA
The second cervical vertebra, the axis, can be distinguished from other cervical vertebrae by the presence of a tooth-like process called the dens (odontoid process). The dens articulates with the facet on the bottom surface of the anterior (front) arch of the atlas. Rotation of the head occurs at this joint.

The body of the axis resembles the bodies of the other cervical vertebrae.

### SEVENTH CERVICAL VERTEBRA
This vertebra has the largest spine of any cervical vertebra and, as the first to be readily palpated, it has been termed the vertebra prominens.

The transverse processes are also larger than those of the other cervical vertebrae and the oval foramen transversarium transmits an accessory vertebral vein.

## First cervical vertebra (atlas)

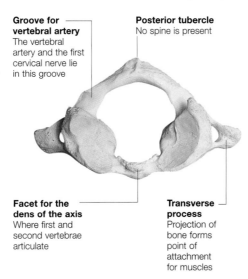

**Groove for vertebral artery**
The vertebral artery and the first cervical nerve lie in this groove

**Posterior tubercle**
No spine is present

**Facet for the dens of the axis**
Where first and second vertebrae articulate

**Transverse process**
Projection of bone forms point of attachment for muscles

## Second cervical vertebra (axis)

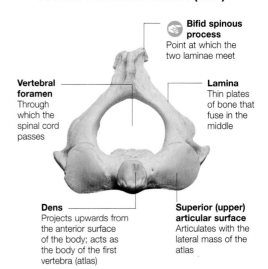

**Bifid spinous process**
Point at which the two laminae meet

**Vertebral foramen**
Through which the spinal cord passes

**Lamina**
Thin plates of bone that fuse in the middle

**Dens**
Projects upwards from the anterior surface of the body; acts as the body of the first vertebra (atlas)

**Superior (upper) articular surface**
Articulates with the lateral mass of the atlas

## Fifth (typical) cervical vertebra

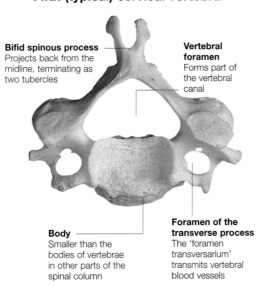

**Bifid spinous process**
Projects back from the midline, terminating as two tubercles

**Vertebral foramen**
Forms part of the vertebral canal

**Body**
Smaller than the bodies of vertebrae in other parts of the spinal column

**Foramen of the transverse process**
The 'foramen transversarium' transmits vertebral blood vessels

## Seventh cervical vertebra

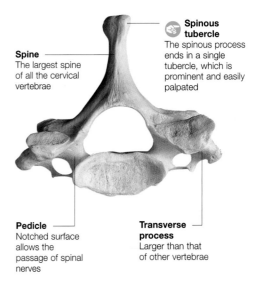

**Spinous tubercle**
The spinous process ends in a single tubercle, which is prominent and easily palpated

**Spine**
The largest spine of all the cervical vertebrae

**Pedicle**
Notched surface allows the passage of spinal nerves

**Transverse process**
Larger than that of other vertebrae

## Abnormalities in the neck

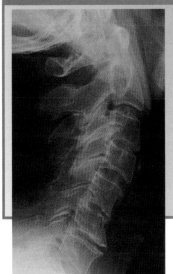

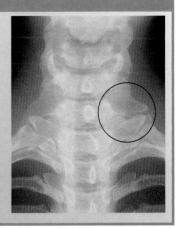

Bony outgrowths, or osteophytes, associated with the vertebra in the region of the spinal nerve pathway may compress the nerves. This may cause symptoms such as pain and numbness in the region supplied by that particular nerve. As the lower cervical spinal nerves contribute to the brachial plexus, this may give rise to symptoms experienced in the arm.

*Osteophytes usually occur as a result of osteoarthritis. They cause pain and restricted movement of the neck.*

In about 0.5 per cent of people, a small cervical rib may be found associated with the transverse process of (usually) the seventh cervical vertebra. Although usually symptomless, it can sometimes interfere with the blood flow in the subclavian artery. This artery supplies the arm and the condition may give rise to pain as a result of inadequate blood supply.

*Cervical ribs occur when the transverse process of a cervical vertebra continues to ossify towards the thoracic rib.*

# Muscles of the neck

The muscles running up the front of the neck are divided into the suprahyoid and infrahyoid muscle groups. They attach to the hyoid bone and act to raise and lower it and the larynx during swallowing.

Two groups of muscles run longitudinally within the front of the neck from the mandible (jaw) to the sternum (breastbone). These muscles are concerned with movements of the jaw, hyoid bone and larynx and are of particular importance during swallowing. The hyoid bone divides these two groups into the suprahyoid (above) and the infrahyoid (below).

### THE SUPRAHYOID MUSCLES

This is a group of paired muscles, lying between the jaw and the hyoid bone. The digastric muscle has two spindle-shaped bellies connected by a tendon in the middle. The anterior belly is attached to the mandible near the mid-line, while the posterior belly arises from the base of the skull. The connecting tendon slides freely through a fibrous 'sling' which is attached to the hyoid bone.

The stylohyoid is a small muscle which passes from the styloid process, a bony projection of the base of the skull, forward and downward to the hyoid bone. Arising from the back of the mandible, the mylohyoid muscles of each side unite in the mid-line to form the floor of the mouth. Posteriorly, they attach to the hyoid bone.

The geniohyoid is a narrow muscle that runs along the floor of the mouth from the back of the mandible in the mid-line to the hyoid bone below.

## Infrahyoid and suprahyoid muscles

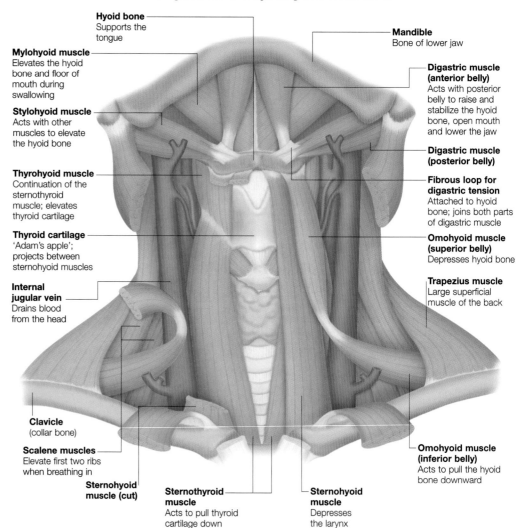

**Hyoid bone**
Supports the tongue

**Mylohyoid muscle**
Elevates the hyoid bone and floor of mouth during swallowing

**Stylohyoid muscle**
Acts with other muscles to elevate the hyoid bone

**Thyrohyoid muscle**
Continuation of the sternothyroid muscle; elevates thyroid cartilage

**Thyroid cartilage**
'Adam's apple'; projects between sternohyoid muscles

**Internal jugular vein**
Drains blood from the head

**Clavicle**
(collar bone)

**Scalene muscles**
Elevate first two ribs when breathing in

**Sternohyoid muscle (cut)**

**Sternothyroid muscle**
Acts to pull thyroid cartilage down

**Sternohyoid muscle**
Depresses the larynx

**Mandible**
Bone of lower jaw

**Digastric muscle (anterior belly)**
Acts with posterior belly to raise and stabilize the hyoid bone, open mouth and lower the jaw

**Digastric muscle (posterior belly)**

**Fibrous loop for digastric tension**
Attached to hyoid bone; joins both parts of digastric muscle

**Omohyoid muscle (superior belly)**
Depresses hyoid bone

**Trapezius muscle**
Large superficial muscle of the back

**Omohyoid muscle (inferior belly)**
Acts to pull the hyoid bone downward

## Infrahyoid muscles and platysma

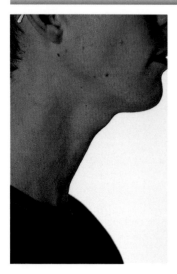 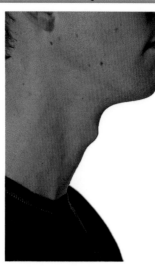

The infrahyoid group of muscles lies between the hyoid bone and the sternum, and comprises the sternohyoid and omohyoid, lying next to each other in the same plane and, more deeply, the thyrohyoid and sternothyroid muscles. Their flat shape leads to the common name of 'strap muscles'. After swallowing, the infrahyoid muscles act to return the hyoid bone and larynx to their previous positions.

*The larynx and the hyoid bone are raised during swallowing by the suprahyoid muscles (far left). The infrahyoid muscles then return these structures to their original positions (left).*

The platysma is a thin, flat sheet of muscle which lies just under the skin of the front of the neck in the subcutaneous connective tissue layer. It extends from the layer of deep fascia overlying the muscles of the upper chest to the mandible, with some fibres passing up to the corners of the mouth. At the lower end, the two sides are separate but they gradually converge as they ascend until they overlap beneath the chin.

Due to its action on the chin and mouth, the platysma plays a small role in facial expression. It is also the muscle which allows us to draw down the lower lip to show the teeth.

# Action of the neck muscles

The suprahyoid and infrahyoid groups of muscles have opposing actions on the larynx and hyoid bone. This enables us to swallow.

The mylohyoid, geniohyoid and the anterior belly of the digastric muscle act together to pull the hyoid and the larynx forward and up during swallowing. They also enable the mouth to be opened against resistance.

The stylohyoid and the posterior belly of the digastric muscle together lift and pull back the hyoid bone and the larynx. The suprahyoid muscles can be tested by asking the patient to open their mouth widely against resistance.

### OPPOSING ACTION

The infrahyoid group of muscles act together to pull the hyoid and the larynx back down to their normal positions, as at the end of the act of swallowing. When contracted, the infrahyoid muscles lower and fix the hyoid bone so that the suprahyoid muscles can pull against it to open the mouth.

The infrahyoid muscles can be tested by asking a patient to open their mouth against resistance while the doctor lightly holds the hyoid bone. The hyoid should move down as it is lowered and fixed by the muscles below. If there is weakness of the infrahyoid muscles the hyoid bone will rise up due to the unopposed action of the muscles above.

## Action of the infrahyoid and suprahyoid muscles

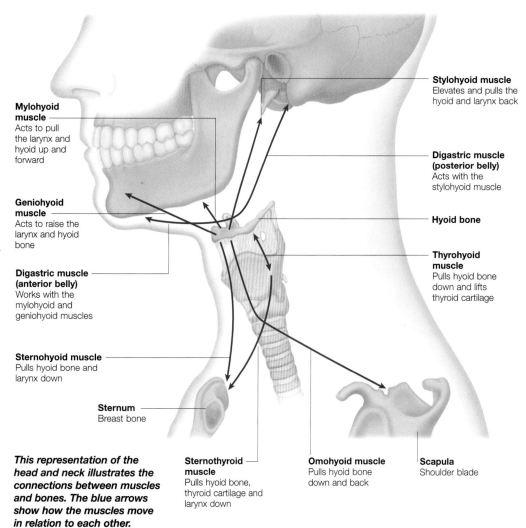

**Mylohyoid muscle**
Acts to pull the larynx and hyoid up and forward

**Geniohyoid muscle**
Acts to raise the larynx and hyoid bone

**Digastric muscle (anterior belly)**
Works with the mylohyoid and geniohyoid muscles

**Sternohyoid muscle**
Pulls hyoid bone and larynx down

**Sternum**
Breast bone

**Sternothyroid muscle**
Pulls hyoid bone, thyroid cartilage and larynx down

**Omohyoid muscle**
Pulls hyoid bone down and back

**Scapula**
Shoulder blade

**Stylohyoid muscle**
Elevates and pulls the hyoid and larynx back

**Digastric muscle (posterior belly)**
Acts with the stylohyoid muscle

**Hyoid bone**

**Thyrohyoid muscle**
Pulls hyoid bone down and lifts thyroid cartilage

*This representation of the head and neck illustrates the connections between muscles and bones. The blue arrows show how the muscles move in relation to each other.*

## The hyoid bone

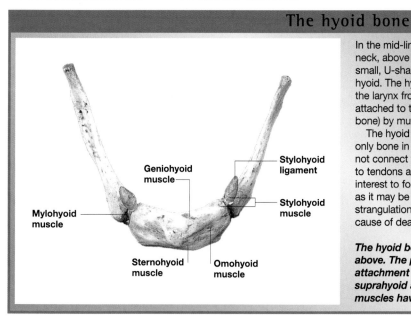

**Mylohyoid muscle**

**Geniohyoid muscle**

**Sternohyoid muscle**

**Omohyoid muscle**

**Stylohyoid ligament**

**Stylohyoid muscle**

In the mid-line of the front of the neck, above the larynx, lies a small, U-shaped bone called the hyoid. The hyoid bone supports the larynx from above and is itself attached to the mandible (jaw bone) by muscles and tendons.

The hyoid is unique as it is the only bone in the body which does not connect to another bone, only to tendons and muscles. It is of interest to forensic pathologists as it may be fractured during strangulation, a vital clue as to the cause of death.

*The hyoid bone as seen from above. The points of muscle attachment for some of the suprahyoid and infrahyoid muscles have been marked.*

Swallowing involves a rapid series of muscular movements in the back of the mouth, the pharynx and the neck. During the initial stages of swallowing, the suprahyoid muscles act to pull the hyoid bone upward and forward towards the mandible.

The hyoid bone is attached to the larynx by muscle and ligament and so the larynx is also pulled upward and forward. This can be seen in life by observing the 'Adam's apple' rising in the neck.

This movement of the larynx widens the pharynx (the gullet) behind it, thereby allowing food to pass. It also importantly helps to close off the respiratory passage, thus preventing the inhalation of any food.

# Brainstem

The brainstem lies at the junction of the brain and spinal cord.
It helps to regulate breathing and blood circulation as well as having
an effect upon a person's level of consciousness.

The brainstem is made up of three distinct parts: the midbrain, the pons, and the medulla oblongata. The midbrain connects with the higher brain above; the medulla is continuous with the spinal cord below.

### BRAINSTEM APPEARANCE

The three parts of the brainstem can be viewed from underneath:
■ The medulla oblongata – a bulge at the top of the spinal column. Pyramids, or columns, lie at either side of the midline. Nerve fibres within these columns carry messages from the cerebral cortex to the body. Raised areas known as the olives lie either side of the pyramids
■ The pons – contains a system of nerve fibres which originate in the nerve cell bodies deep within the substance of the pons
■ The midbrain – appears as two large columns, the cerebral crura, separated in the midline by a depression.

### CRANIAL NERVES

Also present in the brainstem are some of the cranial nerves which supply much of the head. These nerves carry fibres which are associated with the cranial nerve nuclei, collections of grey matter, that lie inside the brainstem.

*The brainstem connects the cerebral hemispheres with the spinal cord. There are three parts to the brain stem; the pons, medulla and the midbrain.*

**Ventral surface of the brainstem**

**Locator**

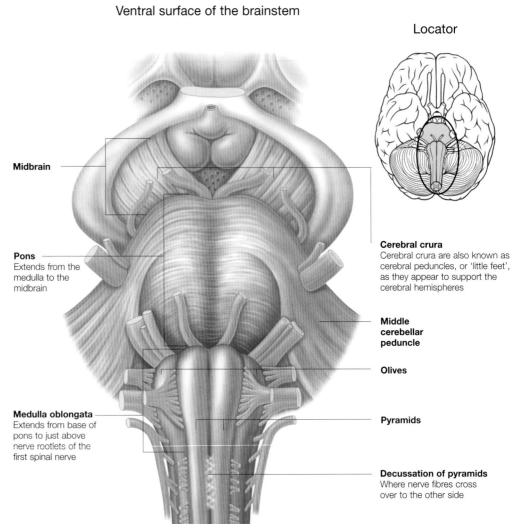

**Midbrain**

**Pons**
Extends from the medulla to the midbrain

**Medulla oblongata**
Extends from base of pons to just above nerve rootlets of the first spinal nerve

**Cerebral crura**
Cerebral crura are also known as cerebral peduncles, or 'little feet', as they appear to support the cerebral hemispheres

**Middle cerebellar peduncle**

**Olives**

**Pyramids**

**Decussation of pyramids**
Where nerve fibres cross over to the other side

## Relationships of the brainstem

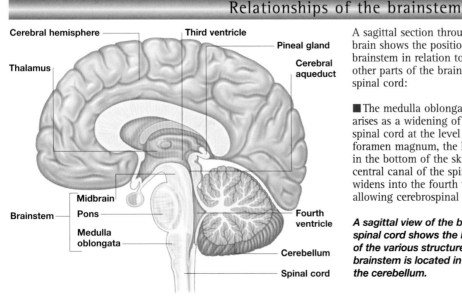

**Cerebral hemisphere**

**Thalamus**

**Third ventricle**

**Pineal gland**

**Cerebral aqueduct**

**Midbrain**

**Brainstem**

**Pons**

**Medulla oblongata**

**Fourth ventricle**

**Cerebellum**

**Spinal cord**

A sagittal section through the brain shows the position of the brainstem in relation to the other parts of the brain and spinal cord:

■ The medulla oblongata – arises as a widening of the spinal cord at the level of the foramen magnum, the large hole in the bottom of the skull. The central canal of the spinal cord widens into the fourth ventricle allowing cerebrospinal fluid

*A sagittal view of the brain and spinal cord shows the location of the various structures. The brainstem is located in front of the cerebellum.*

(CSF) to circulate between brain and spinal cord.

■ The pons – lies above the medulla, at the level of the cerebellum with which it makes many connections. Above the pons lies the midbrain, encircling the cerebral aqueduct which connects the fourth ventricle to the third ventricle.

■ The midbrain – is the shortest part of the the brainstem and lies under the thalamus, the central core of the brain, which is surrounded by the cerebral hemispheres. It thus lies below the thalamus and hypothalamus, and the tiny pineal gland.

# Internal structure of the brainstem

The brainstem contains many areas of neural tissue which have a variety of functions vital to life and health. Responses to visual and auditory stimuli that influence head movement are also controlled here.

Cross sections through the brainstem reveal its internal structure, the arrangement of white and grey matter, which differs according to the level at which the section is taken.

### MEDULLA

The features of a section through the medulla are:
■ The inferior olivary nucleus – a bag-like collection of grey matter which lies just under the olives. Other nuclei lying within the medulla include some belonging to the cranial nerves, such as the hypoglossal and the vagus nerves
■ The vestibular nuclear complex – an area that receives information from the ear and is concerned with balance and equilibrium
■ The reticular formation – a complex network of neurones, which is seen here and throughout the brainstem. It has a number of functions vital to life such as the control of respiration and circulation. The reticular formation is present in the midbrain as are several of the cranial nerve nuclei.

### MIDBRAIN

A section through the midbrain shows the presence of:
■ The cerebral aqueduct – the channel which connects the

Cross sections of the brainstem

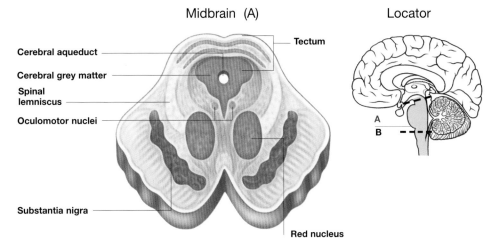

Midbrain (A)

Cerebral aqueduct
Cerebral grey matter
Spinal lemniscus
Oculomotor nuclei
Substantia nigra
Tectum
Red nucleus

Locator
A
B

Medulla (B)

Hypoglossal nuclei
Cuneate nucleus
Dorsal vagal nucleus
Vestibular nuclear complex
Reticular formation
Inferior olivary nucleus

third and fourth ventricles.
Above the aqueduct lies an area called the tectum, while below it lie the large cerebral peduncles
■ The cerebral peduncles – within these lie two structures on each side; the red nucleus and the substantia nigra.
The red nucleus is involved in control of movement, while

damage to the substantia nigra is associated with Parkinson's disease.

### PONS

The pons (not illustrated) is divided into upper and lower parts:
■ The lower part – mostly made up of transverse nerve fibres, running across from the nuclei

*The numerous nuclei and tracts that are within the brainstem can be seen in these cross sections. They are involved in most functions of the brain.*

of the pons to the cerebellum
■ The upper portion – contains a number of cranial nerve nuclei. The pons also contains part of the reticular formation.

## Brainstem death

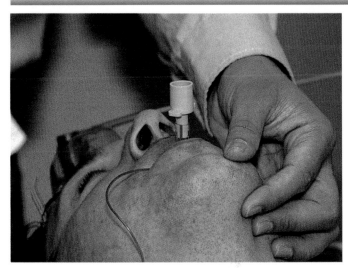

*Strict criteria exist when testing for brain stem death. One of these is the patient's ability to breathe independently when disconnected from a ventilator.*

It is possible in some cases for life-support machines in intensive care units to maintain breathing and blood circulation in a patient who has suffered brainstem death.

### CERTIFYING DEATH

In such cases doctors will certify death using a legally prescribed set of tests and observations. Many of these tests are designed to show death of the brainstem, that part of the brain which

controls the vital functions of consciousness, breathing and circulation.

### BRAIN STEM TESTING

Assessing the function of the brainstem includes looking for the following responses:
■ The ability to breathe without the help of a machine
■ Constriction of the pupil in response to light
■ Blinking of the eye when the cornea is touched
■ Eye movement when the ears are flushed with ice-water
■ Coughing or gagging when the airway is stimulated.
The responses are absent if the brainstem is non-functioning.

# Brachial plexus

Lying within the root of the neck and extending into the axilla,
the brachial plexus is a complicated network of nerves from which
arise the major nerves supplying the upper limb.

At the level of each vertebra of the spine there emerges a 'spinal nerve' which divides into dorsal and ventral parts, called 'rami'.

The brachial plexus is formed by the joining and intermixing of the ventral rami at the level of the fifth to the eighth cervical vertebrae and most of the ventral rami from the level of the first thoracic vertebra. These ventral rami are known as the 'roots' of the brachial plexus.

### STRUCTURE

The roots of the brachial plexus join to form three 'trunks': superior, middle and inferior.

As the complexity of the brachial plexus increases, each of the three trunks then divides into an anterior (front) and a posterior (back) 'division'. In general, the nerve fibres within the anterior divisions are those which will go on to supply the anterior structures of the upper limb, while the fibres of the posterior divisions will supply posterior upper limb structures.

From the six divisions, three 'cords' are formed, which are named for their positions in relation to the axillary artery to which they lie adjacent: lateral, medial and posterior.

The final part of the brachial plexus consists of the branches given off by the three cords, although other branches also arise at higher levels.

## Origins of the brachial plexus

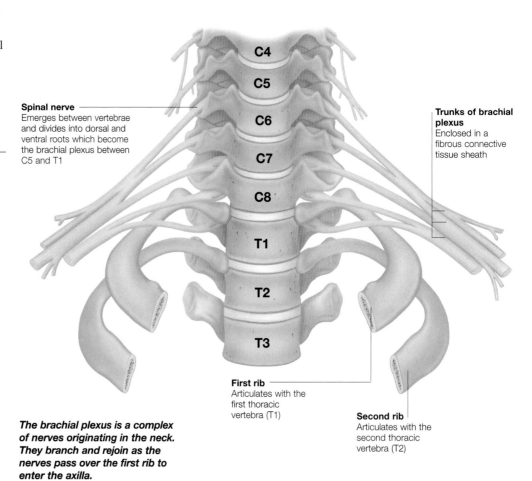

**Spinal nerve**
Emerges between vertebrae and divides into dorsal and ventral roots which become the brachial plexus between C5 and T1

C4
C5
C6
C7
C8
T1
T2
T3

**Trunks of brachial plexus**
Enclosed in a fibrous connective tissue sheath

**First rib**
Articulates with the first thoracic vertebra (T1)

**Second rib**
Articulates with the second thoracic vertebra (T2)

*The brachial plexus is a complex of nerves originating in the neck. They branch and rejoin as the nerves pass over the first rib to enter the axilla.*

## Parts of the brachial plexus

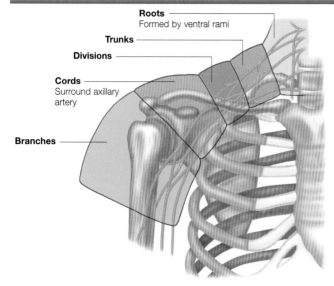

**Roots**
Formed by ventral rami

**Trunks**

**Divisions**

**Cords**
Surround axillary artery

**Branches**

Anatomically, the brachial plexus is divided into sections which, starting from the spine, are known as roots, trunks, divisions, cords and branches.

### ORIENTATION

■ Roots – the ventral rami of C5 to T1, lying within the neck to either side of the spinal column
■ Three trunks – lie above the clavicle
■ Divisions – arise from the trunks and pass behind the clavicle, entering the axilla

*The coloured blocks on this illustration indicate the anatomical levels of each different section of the brachial plexus.*

■ Three cords – lie alongside the second part of the axillary artery within the axilla and inside the protective covering of the connective tissue of the axillary sheath
■ The terminal branches of the brachial plexus leave the axilla as they pass into the upper limb.

### INJURIES TO THE BRACHIAL PLEXUS

If the brachial plexus is injured, the effect upon function of the upper limb will vary, according to the level of the plexus at which the damage occurs. The nearer the injury is to the spine, the more generalized the resulting damage will be.

# Dermatomes

A dermatome is an area of skin which receives its sensory nerve supply from a single spinal nerve (and therefore a single segment of the spinal cord); however, that nerve supply may actually be taken to the skin in two or more cutaneous branches.

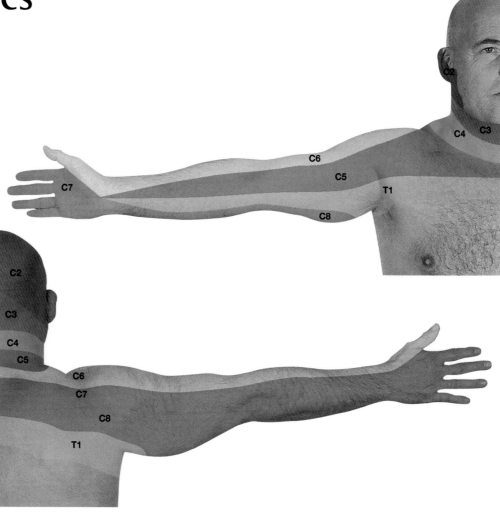

The nerve supply to the skin, and so the dermatomes, of the upper limb comes via the brachial plexus from the ventral rami of the spinal nerves of C5 to T1.

The segmental pattern of the dermatomes can most readily be seen by visualizing the arm held lifted to the side with the thumb uppermost. This pattern has arisen because, during fetal development, the limbs begin as 'buds' from the side of a segmentally arranged embryo which becomes elongated, stretching the dermatome bands as they grow outwards.

### ARRANGEMENT OF DERMATOMES

The exact arrangement of the dermatomes of the upper limb may vary but, in general:
■ C5 supplies a band of skin along the length of the front of the arm
■ C6 supplies the lateral surface down to and including the thumb
■ C7 supplies a band along the back of the arm which extends to the first two fingers
■ C8 supplies the last two fingers and a strip of skin along the back of the arm
■ T1 supplies a strip along the front of the arm but not extending to the hand.

This segmental pattern is continued down the length of the body, and is most striking over the thorax and abdomen.

*The arrangement of the dermatomes of the upper limb is variable between individuals but follows this basic pattern. They are numbered according to the spinal nerve of origin.*

---

## Clinical importance of dermatomes

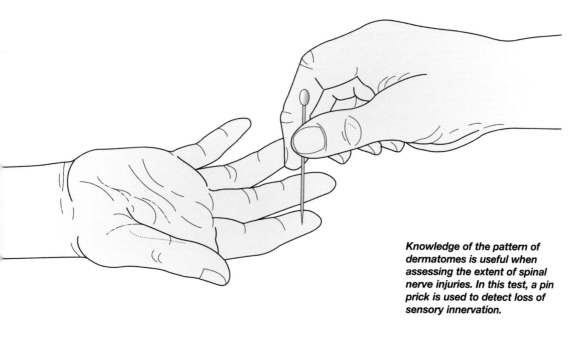

*Knowledge of the pattern of dermatomes is useful when assessing the extent of spinal nerve injuries. In this test, a pin prick is used to detect loss of sensory innervation.*

Awareness of the pattern of dermatomes over the body is of importance medically because it allows a doctor to test, with a pin prick, whether a particular segment of the spinal cord is working properly. This is of importance if a patient has a suspected spinal injury.

However, if there is a problem with just one spinal nerve or segment there may not be a loss of sensation in the dermatome it supplies as there is actually a good deal of overlap between dermatomes.

This means that even if there is damage to one spinal nerve or segment the skin it supplies may still receive a sensory supply from the adjacent nerves. There are, however, areas of skin over the upper limb which have no such overlap and so will be numb if the spinal nerve is damaged.

# Pharynx

The pharynx, situated at the back of the throat, is a passage both for food to the alimentary system and air to the lungs. It can be divided into three major parts, and the entrance is guarded by the tonsils.

The pharynx, a fibromuscular, 15 cm long tube at the back of the throat, is a passage for food and air. The constrictor muscles of the pharynx allow food to be squeezed into the oesophagus.

## NASOPHARYNX

The uppermost part of the pharynx, lying above the soft palate, is the nasopharynx. The most prominent feature on each side is the tubal elevation, the end of the auditory (Eustachian) tube that enables air pressure to be equalized between the nasopharynx and the middle ear cavity. Lymphoid (adenoid) tissue is found on the back wall.

## OROPHARYNX

The oropharynx lies at the back of the throat. Its roof is the undersurface of the soft palate; the floor is the back of the tongue. The palatine tonsil lies in the side wall, and is bounded by the palatoglossal fold in front and the palatopharyngeal fold behind.

## LARYNGOPHARYNX

The laryngopharynx extends from the upper border of the epiglottic cartilage (which covers the opening of the airway during swallowing) to the lower border of the cricoid cartilage, where it continues into the oesophagus. The inlet of the airway lies in the front section.

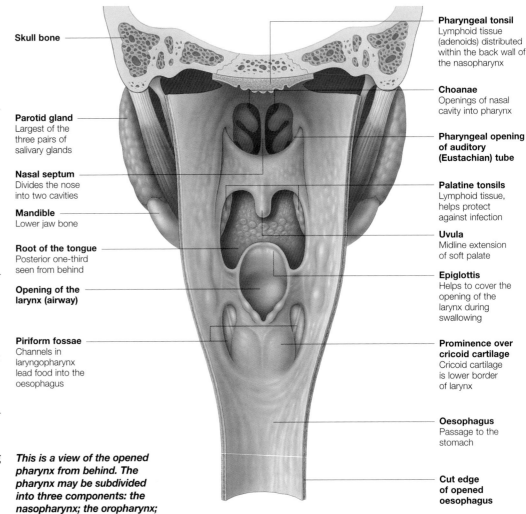

**Skull bone**

**Parotid gland**
Largest of the three pairs of salivary glands

**Nasal septum**
Divides the nose into two cavities

**Mandible**
Lower jaw bone

**Root of the tongue**
Posterior one-third seen from behind

**Opening of the larynx (airway)**

**Piriform fossae**
Channels in laryngopharynx lead food into the oesophagus

**Pharyngeal tonsil**
Lymphoid tissue (adenoids) distributed within the back wall of the nasopharynx

**Choanae**
Openings of nasal cavity into pharynx

**Pharyngeal opening of auditory (Eustachian) tube**

**Palatine tonsils**
Lymphoid tissue, helps protect against infection

**Uvula**
Midline extension of soft palate

**Epiglottis**
Helps to cover the opening of the larynx during swallowing

**Prominence over cricoid cartilage**
Cricoid cartilage is lower border of larynx

**Oesophagus**
Passage to the stomach

**Cut edge of opened oesophagus**

*This is a view of the opened pharynx from behind. The pharynx may be subdivided into three components: the nasopharynx; the oropharynx; and the laryngopharynx.*

---

## Infection and inflammation

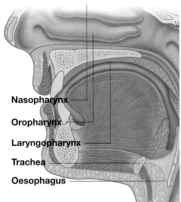

**Nasopharynx**

**Oropharynx**

**Laryngopharynx**

**Trachea**

**Oesophagus**

*The relative positions of the three major parts of the larynx, the trachea and the oesophagus are evident in this sagittal section.*

As the auditory (Eustachian) tube in the nasopharynx is connected with the middle ear cavity, upper respiratory tract infections can spread to cause inflammation of the middle ear (otitis media). Infection may cause blockage of the auditory tube and the middle ear cavity, which contains the three ear ossicles. The cavity may fill with fluid, causing difficulties with hearing. This condition is commonly called glue ear.

The palatine tonsil is a common site of bacterial infection. More seriously, an abscess can develop in and around the tonsil. This can cause swelling, fever and pain, especially during swallowing

and speech. There may be trismus (difficulty opening the mouth) caused by spasm of adjacent muscles. If the abscess is not drained, it can lead to blockage of the airway. This condition was formerly known as 'Vincent's angina', the term 'angina' indicating the constricting nature of the condition.

Inflammation of the epiglottic cartilage is more common in children under the age of two. This is potentially dangerous due to obstruction of the airway. It classically produces stridor (wheezing noises with each intake of breath). This is a sign of impending obstruction and needs prompt medical attention.

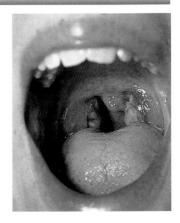

*The palatine tonsils are masses of lymphoid tissue on either side of the back of the mouth. The tonsil on the right is infected.*

# Muscles of the pharynx

There are six pairs of muscles which make up the pharynx. These muscles can be divided into two groups.

One group of pharyngeal muscles comprises three pairs of constrictor muscles that run across the pharynx: the superior, middle and inferior constrictors. These constrict the pharynx, squeezing food downward into the oesophagus.

The other group comprises three pairs of muscles running from above down into the pharynx: the salpingo-pharyngeus, stylopharyngeus and palatopharyngeus. These raise the pharynx during swallowing, elevating the larynx and protecting the airway.

The constrictor muscles overlap each other from below upwards (like three stacked plastic cups inside each other). Important structures enter the pharynx in the intervals between these muscles. The constrictor muscle fibres sweep backwards into a longitudinally running fibrous band in the midline, the pharyngeal raphé, which is attached to the base of the skull.

### NERVE SUPPLY

Most of the pharynx derives its sensory nerve supply from the glossopharyngeal (ninth cranial) nerve. Stimulation of the oropharynx at the back of the throat triggers the swallowing and gagging reflexes. The pharynx muscles are supplied chiefly by the 11th cranial (accessory) nerve.

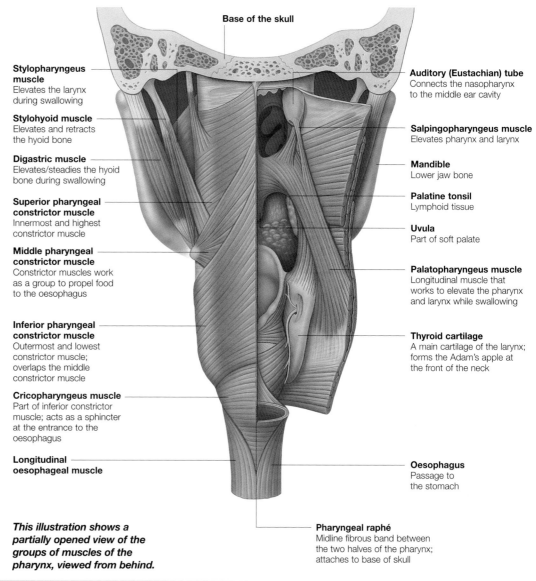

**Base of the skull**

**Stylopharyngeus muscle**
Elevates the larynx during swallowing

**Stylohyoid muscle**
Elevates and retracts the hyoid bone

**Digastric muscle**
Elevates/steadies the hyoid bone during swallowing

**Superior pharyngeal constrictor muscle**
Innermost and highest constrictor muscle

**Middle pharyngeal constrictor muscle**
Constrictor muscles work as a group to propel food to the oesophagus

**Inferior pharyngeal constrictor muscle**
Outermost and lowest constrictor muscle; overlaps the middle constrictor muscle

**Cricopharyngeus muscle**
Part of inferior constrictor muscle; acts as a sphincter at the entrance to the oesophagus

**Longitudinal oesophageal muscle**

**Auditory (Eustachian) tube**
Connects the nasopharynx to the middle ear cavity

**Salpingopharyngeus muscle**
Elevates pharynx and larynx

**Mandible**
Lower jaw bone

**Palatine tonsil**
Lymphoid tissue

**Uvula**
Part of soft palate

**Palatopharyngeus muscle**
Longitudinal muscle that works to elevate the pharynx and larynx while swallowing

**Thyroid cartilage**
A main cartilage of the larynx; forms the Adam's apple at the front of the neck

**Oesophagus**
Passage to the stomach

**Pharyngeal raphé**
Midline fibrous band between the two halves of the pharynx; attaches to base of skull

*This illustration shows a partially opened view of the groups of muscles of the pharynx, viewed from behind.*

## Inhaled objects

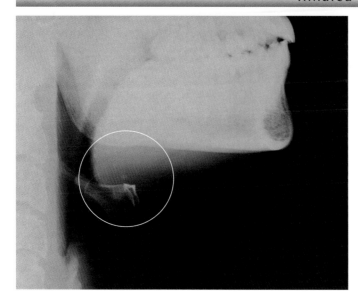

*If not removed, a lodged fishbone (circled) may become a site of inflammation, and even rupture the pharyngeal wall.*

The epiglottis helps to prevent entry of foreign bodies into the airway. However, it is possible to inhale food, stomach contents or a foreign body. This is more likely to happen if the patient is unconscious, under anaesthesia, drunk or suffering from diseases affecting the nerves or muscles of the pharynx, when there may be loss of the protective cough reflex. Blockage of the airway in such situations is life-threatening.

Between the inlet of the larynx and the side walls of the laryngopharynx lies a groove called the piriform fossa. During swallowing, particles of food may become stuck in the piriform fossa. This is particularly true of small fishbones. Certain fishbones, depending on size and degree of calcification, are more readily identified on X-rays than others.

Denture wearers may be more prone to swallowing foreign bodies as they have diminished palatal sensation due to shielding of the mucosa by the denture, and the tendency to chew food inefficiently. Such foreign bodies lodged in the pharynx can be retrieved by the use of a small, flexible viewing instrument (a naso-endoscope), through which tools can be passed under local anaesthesia.

# Larynx

The larynx is situated in the neck below and in front of the pharynx. It is the inlet protecting the lungs, and contains the vocal cords. In men, part of the larynx is visible as the Adam's apple.

The larynx is composed of five cartilages (three single and one paired), connected by membranes, ligaments and muscles. In adult men, the larynx lies opposite the third to sixth cervical vertebrae (slightly higher in women and children), between the base of the tongue and the trachea.

The larynx serves as an inlet to the airways, taking air from the nose and mouth to the trachea. Because air and food share a common pathway, the primary function of the larynx is to prevent food and liquid from entering the airway. This is achieved by three 'sphincters' and by elevation. The larynx has also evolved as an organ of phonation – the act of producing sounds – allowing vocalization.

### LARYNGEAL CARTILAGES

The laryngeal prominence (thyroid cartilage protrusion, or Adam's apple) is readily visible in most men. Its greater protrusion in men compared to women is due to the influence of the hormone testosterone.

The thyroid cartilage has two rear extensions, a superior and an inferior 'horn'. The cricoid cartilage, the only complete ring of cartilage in the airway, is partly overlapped above by the thyroid cartilage. Above it sit a pair of mobile, pyramid-shaped arytenoid cartilages.

**Midline sagittal view**

**Front view**

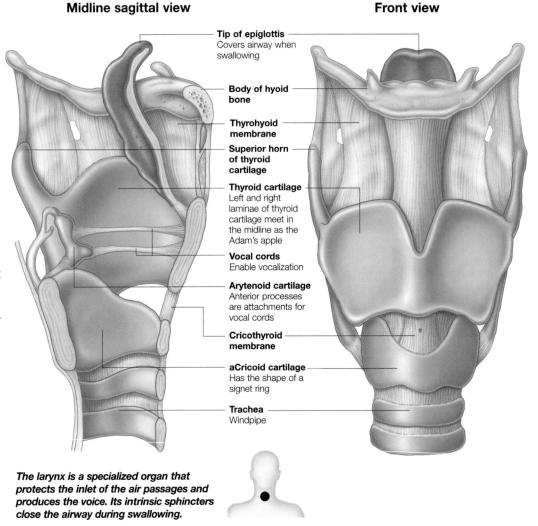

**Tip of epiglottis**
Covers airway when swallowing

**Body of hyoid bone**

**Thyrohyoid membrane**

**Superior horn of thyroid cartilage**

**Thyroid cartilage**
Left and right laminae of thyroid cartilage meet in the midline as the Adam's apple

**Vocal cords**
Enable vocalization

**Arytenoid cartilage**
Anterior processes are attachments for vocal cords

**Cricothyroid membrane**

**aCricoid cartilage**
Has the shape of a signet ring

**Trachea**
Windpipe

*The larynx is a specialized organ that protects the inlet of the air passages and produces the voice. Its intrinsic sphincters close the airway during swallowing.*

## Inside the larynx

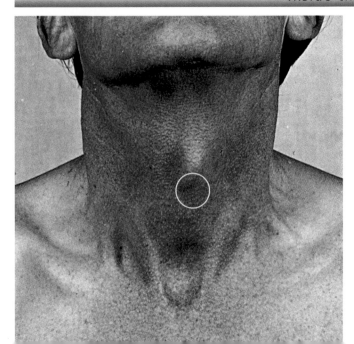

*The area where an emergency cricothyroidostomy would be performed (circled) is shown, just below the Adam's apple.*

The vocal cords run from the arytenoids to the inner surface of the thyroid cartilage. They can be seen by placing a mirror, or fibre-optic laryngoscope, into the pharynx. They appear white in colour.

The inside of the larynx is lined with mucosa. The mucosa extends from the free edge of the aryepiglottic folds (containing the aryepiglottic muscles) at the laryngeal inlet down over soft tissue masses (vestibular ligaments) that protrude medially, forming two mucosal folds (false cords or vestibular folds). It then extends laterally, into a recess (sinus) on either side before covering the vocal ligaments, to the vocal cords proper. The glottis is the gap between the vocal folds in front and the arytenoid cartilages behind.

If the glottis becomes obstructed by an inhaled foreign object, breathing is impeded. An emergency procedure may be necessary in such instances, whereby a small hole is made in the cricothyroid membrane to allow air into the larynx below the obstruction. This is called a cricothyroidostomy or laryngostomy, and it can be a life-saving procedure.

# Muscles of the larynx

The muscles of the larynx act to close the laryngeal inlet while swallowing and move the vocal cords to enable vocalization.

During swallowing, the epiglottis, along with the rest of the larynx, is raised. As the front surface hits the rear part of the tongue, it flips backwards over the laryngeal inlet.

### ARYEPIGLOTTIC FOLDS
The aryepiglottic folds of tissue are the free upper margins of the membranes that run between the epiglottis and the arytenoid cartilages. They contain a pair of transverse aryepiglottic and oblique aryepiglottic muscles. These arise from the muscular process of the opposite arytenoid cartilage, and attach to the sides of the epiglottis. They act like a 'purse-string', closing the laryngeal inlet. The lower ends of each of the quadrangular membranes form the vestibular folds, or 'false' vocal cords.

### MUCOUS GLANDS
The quadrangular membranes are covered by a mucosa, and a submucosa rich in mucous glands. These are connected to the inner walls of the thyroid and cricoid cartilages. They keep the vocal cords moist, as the vocal folds have no submucosa themselves, and therefore rely upon these secretions from above. A groove, the piriform fossae, slopes backwards and serves to channel liquids toward the oesophagus and away from the larynx.

**Rear view**

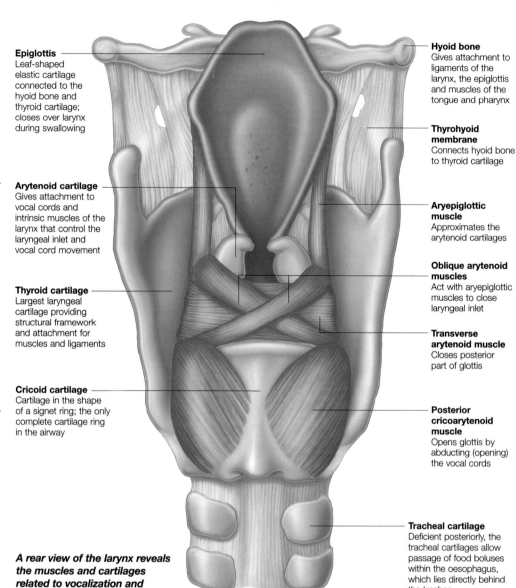

**Epiglottis**
Leaf-shaped elastic cartilage connected to the hyoid bone and thyroid cartilage; closes over larynx during swallowing

**Arytenoid cartilage**
Gives attachment to vocal cords and intrinsic muscles of the larynx that control the laryngeal inlet and vocal cord movement

**Thyroid cartilage**
Largest laryngeal cartilage providing structural framework and attachment for muscles and ligaments

**Cricoid cartilage**
Cartilage in the shape of a signet ring; the only complete cartilage ring in the airway

**Hyoid bone**
Gives attachment to ligaments of the larynx, the epiglottis and muscles of the tongue and pharynx

**Thyrohyoid membrane**
Connects hyoid bone to thyroid cartilage

**Aryepiglottic muscle**
Approximates the arytenoid cartilages

**Oblique arytenoid muscles**
Act with aryepiglottic muscles to close laryngeal inlet

**Transverse arytenoid muscle**
Closes posterior part of glottis

**Posterior cricoarytenoid muscle**
Opens glottis by abducting (opening) the vocal cords

**Tracheal cartilage**
Deficient posteriorly, the tracheal cartilages allow passage of food boluses within the oesophagus, which lies directly behind the trachea

*A rear view of the larynx reveals the muscles and cartilages related to vocalization and movement of the epiglottis.*

## Action of the vocal cords

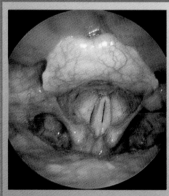

*This laryngoscopic image shows the vocal cords during speech. When the cords are in close proximity to each other, air causes them to vibrate, producing vocal noises.*

The size of the gap between the vocal cords, called the glottis, varies. Forced respiration requires a wide glottis, while speaking requires a narrow slit. Complete closure of the glottis is used during straining (for example, defecation or childbirth). The size of the glottis is controlled by movements of the arytenoid cartilages, since the vocal cords are attached to these.

These cartilages can be pulled apart (abducted), pulled together (adducted), and rotated by the crico-arytenoid and arytenoid groups of muscles supplied by the recurrent laryngeal nerve. The most important of these muscles is the posterior crico-arytenoid, which opens the glottis (abducts

the vocal folds to allow air into the airways). Paralysis of one posterior crico-arytenoid muscle may not produce any symptoms, as the other cord compensates. Paralysis of both muscles will produce acute breathing difficulties.

Speech is made by passing air over the vocal cords, and tension in these cords controls the pitch of the voice. Tilting the cricoid arch backwards causes an increase in tension, while bringing the thyroid and arytenoid cartilages together causes a relaxation. Fine tuning is accomplished via the vocalis muscle. The sounds that the larynx can produce are complex, and need to be learned. Accents are so acquired, and are often difficult to lose once mastered.

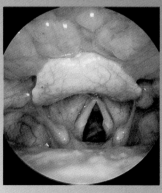

*The glottis is wider at rest, as the vocal cords sit apart from one another. The epiglottis, seen as the pale flap above the glottis and vocal cords, closes the larynx while swallowing.*

# Thyroid and parathyroid glands

The thyroid and parathyroid glands are situated in the neck. Together, they produce important hormones responsible for regulating growth, metabolism and calcium levels in the blood.

The thyroid gland is an endocrine gland situated in the neck, lying to the front and side of the larynx and trachea. It is similar to a bow-tie in shape, and it produces two iodine-dependent hormones: tri-iodothyronine and thyroxine. These are responsible for controlling metabolism through promotion of metabolic enzyme production.

In addition, the gland secretes calcitonin which is involved in the regulation of calcium levels in the blood. In children, growth is dependent upon this gland, through its stimulation of the metabolism of carbohydrates, proteins and fats.

## PYRAMIDAL LOBE

The gland has two conical-shaped lobes connected by an 'isthmus' (a band of tissue connecting the lobes), which usually lies in front of the second and third tracheal cartilage rings. The entire gland is surrounded by a thin connective tissue capsule and a layer of deep cervical fascia. There is often a small third lobe, the pyramidal lobe, which extends upwards from near the isthmus and lies over the cricothyroid membrane and median cricothyroid ligament.

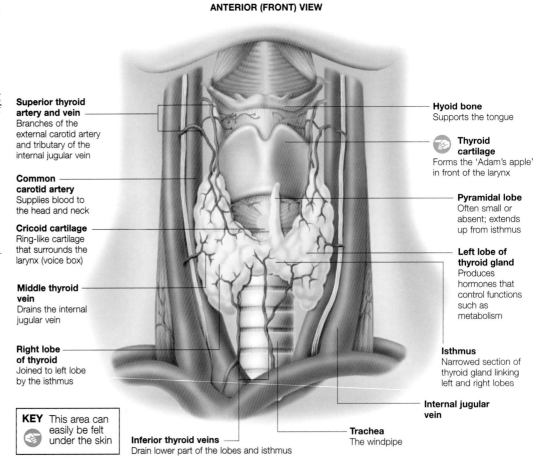

**ANTERIOR (FRONT) VIEW**

**Superior thyroid artery and vein**
Branches of the external carotid artery and tributary of the internal jugular vein

**Common carotid artery**
Supplies blood to the head and neck

**Cricoid cartilage**
Ring-like cartilage that surrounds the larynx (voice box)

**Middle thyroid vein**
Drains the internal jugular vein

**Right lobe of thyroid**
Joined to left lobe by the isthmus

**KEY** This area can easily be felt under the skin

**Inferior thyroid veins**
Drain lower part of the lobes and isthmus

**Hyoid bone**
Supports the tongue

**Thyroid cartilage**
Forms the 'Adam's apple' in front of the larynx

**Pyramidal lobe**
Often small or absent; extends up from isthmus

**Left lobe of thyroid gland**
Produces hormones that control functions such as metabolism

**Isthmus**
Narrowed section of thyroid gland linking left and right lobes

**Internal jugular vein**

**Trachea**
The windpipe

## Surface anatomy

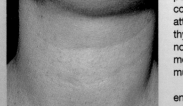

*Swelling of the thyroid gland and neck can be caused by a lack of iodine, the presence of tumours or thyrotoxicosis (over-production of hormones).*

The thyroid gland is held in position by an investing layer of connective tissue, which also attaches to the oblique line on the thyroid cartilage. The gland is not normally palpable, since it is mostly covered by the strap muscles of the neck.

However, should the gland enlarge, it may produce a noticeable swelling which moves upwards upon swallowing, because of its fascial attachments. This is a useful differential to other swellings which might appear in the neck, such as that caused by an enlargement of the pre-tracheal lymph nodes, which are not bound to the same extent.

The top margins of the thyroid lobes are limited by the attachment of the pre-tracheal strap muscles. Therefore, any enlargement of the gland must be downwards into the lower neck. This enlargement of the gland is referred to as a 'goitre'.

Enlargement of the gland can produce difficulty breathing (dyspnoea) due to compression of the trachea, and difficulty and pain on swallowing (dysphagia) due to compression of the oesophagus.

Enlargement may be associated with either under-production of thyroid hormones (hypothyroid goitre), or their over-production (hyperthyroid goitre).

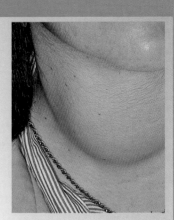

*Goitres – caused by the enlargement of the thyroid gland – can vary in size from a small lump to a large swelling.*

# Posterior view of thyroid

The posterior view of the thyroid reveals the small parathyroid glands, embedded within the lobes. A rich network of vessels supply the glands.

The thyroid gland is well supplied by blood vessels. The upper pole receives arterial blood from the superior thyroid artery, a branch of the external carotid artery. The lower pole is supplied by the inferior thyroid artery, a branch of the thyrocervical trunk. The lobes of the gland are directly related to the common carotid arteries. The hormones are distributed to the bloodstream via a network (plexus) of veins in and around the gland, which ultimately drain into the internal jugular and brachiocephalic veins.

### RELATION TO NERVES

In addition to the blood vessels, the gland is closely related to nerves. Posteriorly, the most important relation is the pair of recurrent laryngeal nerves from the vagus nerve. These ascend in the groove between the oesophagus and trachea, heading towards the larynx where they supply motor nerves to all laryngeal muscles (except the cricothyroid), and sensory nerves to the sub-glottic larynx. Hence, an enlarged thryoid may compress these nerves, causing a hoarseness in the voice.

**POSTERIOR (BACK) VIEW**

**Internal jugular vein**
Drains blood from the scalp, neck, thyroid and face

**Superior pharyngeal nerve**
External branch

**Vagus nerve**
Supplies motor and sensory fibres, especially recurrent laryngeal nerves

**Superior parathyroid gland**

**Left recurrent laryngeal nerve**
Supplies laryngeal muscles

**Left brachiocephalic vein**
Blood from gland drains into here

**Arch of aorta**
Supplies common carotid arteries

**Trachea**
Airway

**Right recurrent laryngeal nerve**
Supplies laryngeal muscles

**External carotid artery**
Gives rise to the superior thyroid artery

**Inferior pharyngeal constrictor muscle**

**Common carotid artery**
Supplies blood to the head and neck

**Right lobe of thyroid gland**

**Inferior thyroid artery**
Supplies lower pole of lobe

**Inferior parathyroid gland**

**Thyrocervical trunk**
Supplies inferior thyroid artery

## Parathyroid gland

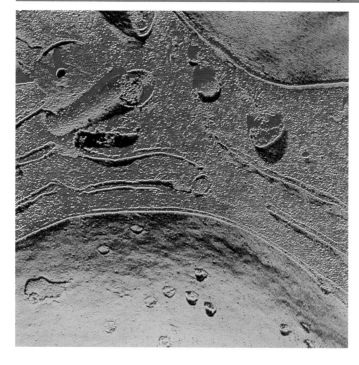

The pea-sized parathyroid glands (superior and inferior) are embedded within the rear tissue of the thyroid gland. They secrete parathormone which, together with calcitonin and vitamin D, controls calcium metabolism.

Disorders of the parathyroids cause problems associated with nerve, muscle and bone, since these tissues utilize calcium. A reduction in parathormone reduces levels of blood calcium, resulting in over-excitability of nerve and muscle. This may cause spasm or convulsions.

Hyperparathyroidism (over-production of parathormone) causes de-calcification of bone, increasing the chance of fractures. It also causes an

*This electron micrograph shows part of a parathyroid gland cell. These glands secrete chemicals vital for calcium metabolism.*

elevation of calcium excretion by the kidneys, making them prone to stone formation.

Rarely, the parathyroids may be found in a position independent of the thyroid gland. This is because the parathyroids, like the thyroid, develop from tissue in the floor of the embryonic pharynx, and migrate downwards. Thyroid gland cysts can be found anywhere along its embryonic route. The final location of the parathyroids is normally rear of the thyroid, but may be found anywhere between the hyoid bone and the upper chest cavity behind the sternum.

Such ectopic parathyroids are unlikely to cause problems, whereas an ectopic thyroid gland in the upper chest cavity is likely to block the thoracic inlet, causing difficulty and pain on swallowing (dysphagia), difficulty in breathing (dyspnoea), and swelling of the upper body.

# Thoracic vertebrae

The 12 thoracic vertebrae are the bones of the spinal column to which the ribs are attached. The thoracic vertebrae sit between the cervical vertebrae of the neck and the lumbar vertebrae of the lower back.

Each thoracic vertebrae has two components, a cylindrical body in front and a vertebral arch behind. The body and vertebral arch enclose a hole, called the vertebral foramen, which is rounded. When all the vertebrae are articulated together, the space formed by the linked vertebral foramina forms the vertebral canal. This houses the spinal cord surrounded by three protective layers, called the meninges.

### BONY PROCESSES

The part of the vertebral arch that attaches to the body on each side is called the pedicle and the arch is completed behind by two laminae that meet in the midline to form the spinous process. These processes project downwards (like the tiles of a roof), that of the eighth being the longest and most vertical. At the junction of the pedicles and laminae are the projecting transverse processes. These decrease in size from the top down.

### MUSCLE ATTACHMENTS

Muscles and ligaments are attached to the spines and transverse processes. The thoracic vertebrae articulate with each other at the intervertebral joints. Between the vertebral bodies are intervertebral discs acting as shock absorbers.

Each vertebra has four surfaces (facets), which form moveable synovial joints with the adjacent vertebra – one pair of facets articulates with the vertebra above, the other pair with the vertebra below. All of these joints are strengthened by ligaments.

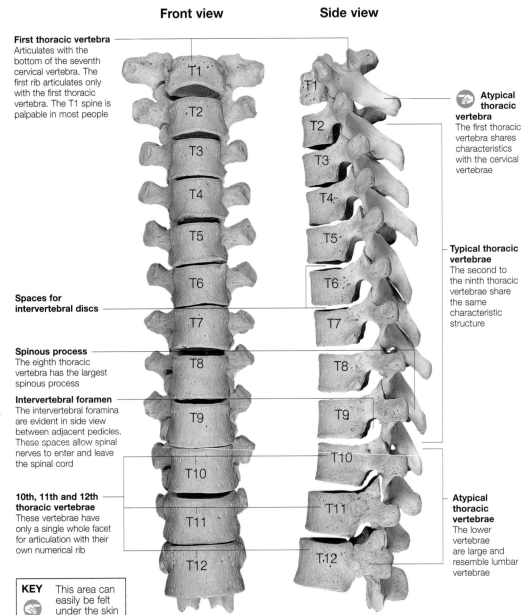

**Front view**

**Side view**

**First thoracic vertebra**
Articulates with the bottom of the seventh cervical vertebra. The first rib articulates only with the first thoracic vertebra. The T1 spine is palpable in most people

**Spaces for intervertebral discs**

**Spinous process**
The eighth thoracic vertebra has the largest spinous process

**Intervertebral foramen**
The intervertebral foramina are evident in side view between adjacent pedicles. These spaces allow spinal nerves to enter and leave the spinal cord

**10th, 11th and 12th thoracic vertebrae**
These vertebrae have only a single whole facet for articulation with their own numerical rib

**Atypical thoracic vertebra**
The first thoracic vertebra shares characteristics with the cervical vertebrae

**Typical thoracic vertebrae**
The second to the ninth thoracic vertebrae share the same characteristic structure

**Atypical thoracic vertebra**
The lower vertebrae are large and resemble lumbar vertebrae

T1, T2, T3, T4, T5, T6, T7, T8, T9, T10, T11, T12

**KEY** This area can easily be felt under the skin

---

## Vertebral deterioration

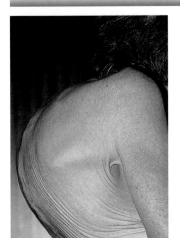

Osteoporosis is a condition which, if left untreated, results in a gradual loss of bone tissue. This particularly affects women following the menopause and may be related to the loss of particular sex hormones.

Osteoporosis results in the

*Kyphosis is an abnormal curvature of the spine, giving rise to the characteristic 'hunchback' appearance.*

bones becoming weaker and liable to fracture. In the case of the thoracic vertebrae, which help to support the weight of the body, osteoporosis may result in a compression fracture of the vertebral bodies. This causes 'wedging' and can result in kyphosis (curvature of the spine).

Tuberculosis is an infectious disease caused by the bacterium *Mycobacterium tuberculosis*. Although more commonly

affecting the lungs, it can affect any organ or tissue, including bone. Where bone is affected (as seen in Pott's disease), the symptoms may involve pain plus the constitutional symptoms of tuberculosis, including fever and weight loss. Pus (abscess) may form in and around the bone and intervertebral disc, resulting in destruction of much of the vertebra with deformity of posture.

# Examining the thoracic vertebrae

The thoracic vertebrae can be distinguished easily from the typical cervical vertebrae.

The thoracic vertebrae differ from the cervical vertebrae in several ways:
■ An absence of the transverse process foramen (the foramen transversarium, through which nerves and blood vessels pass in the cervical vertebrae)
■ A single, rather than bifid (two-part), spine
■ The vertebral canal, through which the spinal cord runs, is smaller and more circular.
■ The most distinguishing feature of the thoracic vertebrae, however, is the presence of facets enabling the ribs to articulate with the spine. Each typical thoracic vertebra has six facets for rib articulation – three on each side.

The head of the rib lies in the region of the intervertebral disc, at the back, and has two hemi- (half) facets that articulate with its own numbered vertebra (upper border) and the vertebra immediately above (lower border).

### ATYPICAL VERTEBRAE
The exceptions to the above rule are the first, 10th, 11th and 12th thoracic vertebrae. In the first thoracic vertebra, the facet on the upper border is a whole facet (rather than a half), as the first rib articulates only with its own vertebra.

Each of the 10th, 11th and 12th vertebrae has only one single whole facet to articulate with its own numerical rib. The 11th and 12th vertebrae have no articulation with the tubercle of the corresponding rib (and therefore no articular facet). The last two ribs are called 'floating ribs' as they have no connections to the ribs above.

## Fifth (typical) thoracic vertebra (front view)

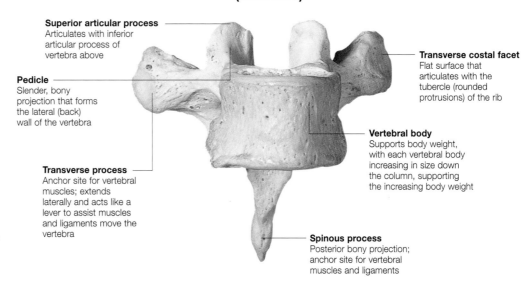

**Superior articular process**
Articulates with inferior articular process of vertebra above

**Pedicle**
Slender, bony projection that forms the lateral (back) wall of the vertebra

**Transverse process**
Anchor site for vertebral muscles; extends laterally and acts like a lever to assist muscles and ligaments move the vertebra

**Transverse costal facet**
Flat surface that articulates with the tubercle (rounded protrusions) of the rib

**Vertebral body**
Supports body weight, with each vertebral body increasing in size down the column, supporting the increasing body weight

**Spinous process**
Posterior bony projection; anchor site for vertebral muscles and ligaments

## First (atypical) thoracic vertebra (side view)

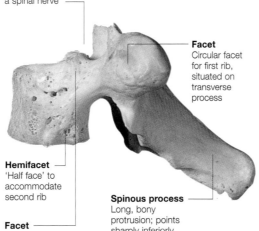

**Superior intervertebral notch**
Forms foramen with inferior notch below, providing passage for a spinal nerve

**Facet**
Circular facet for first rib, situated on transverse process

**Hemifacet**
'Half face' to accommodate second rib

**Facet**
Circular 'face' to accommodate head of first rib

**Spinous process**
Long, bony protrusion; points sharply inferiorly (downwards)

## 12th (atypical) thoracic vertebra (side view)

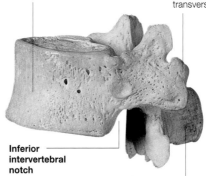

**Body of vertebra**
Structure of the lower thoracic vertebrae begins to resemble that of the lumbar vertebrae; only one round facet is present each side

**Transverse process**
11th and 12th thoracic vertebrae lack facet on transverse process

**Inferior intervertebral notch**
Forms the intervertebral foramen, though which a spinal nerve passes

**Spinous process**
At the base of the thoracic vertebrae, the spinous processes are small and rounded, resembling those of the lumbar vertebrae

## Bone cancers

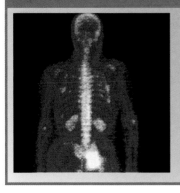

Cancers of bone may be primary, originating in bone, or secondary, when due to spread from another site. The most common cancers which spread to involve bone originate in organs such as the breast, lung, kidney, thyroid and prostate glands. When involving the vertebral column, this causes pain, but may present with varying degrees of weakness or paralysis in the legs due to compression of the spinal cord. Cancer can be seen on X-rays or by utilizing techniques such as radio-isotope bone scans.

*Coloured gamma-camera scans (scintigrams) show the 'hot spots' (bright areas) of tumours and cancers spreading to bone.*

*This scintigram reveals secondary cancer spreading to the thoracic and lumbar vertebral regions.*

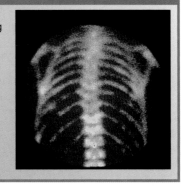

# Lumbar vertebrae

**The five lumbar vertebrae of the lower back are the strongest vertebrae of the spinal column.**

The individual lumbar vertebrae are the largest and strongest in the vertebral column. This is important, as the lower the position of the bones of the spinal column, the more body weight they must bear. The arrangement of the lumbar vertebral joints is designed to allow maximum flexion (allowing us to touch our toes), and some lateral flexion (allowing us to reach sideways), but little rotation (this occurs at the thoracic level).

### BASIC STRUCTURE

As with the cervical and thoracic vertebrae, each lumbar vertebra has the same basic plan, consisting of a cylindrical body in the front and a vertebral arch behind which enclose a space, called the vertebral foramen.

Each vertebral arch comprises a number of processes. There are two laterally projecting transverse processes, a centrally positioned spinous process and two pairs of articular facets, one pair above and one pair below. The transverse processes and spines are shorter and thicker than those of other vertebrae and are well adapted for the attachment of the large back muscles and strong ligaments.

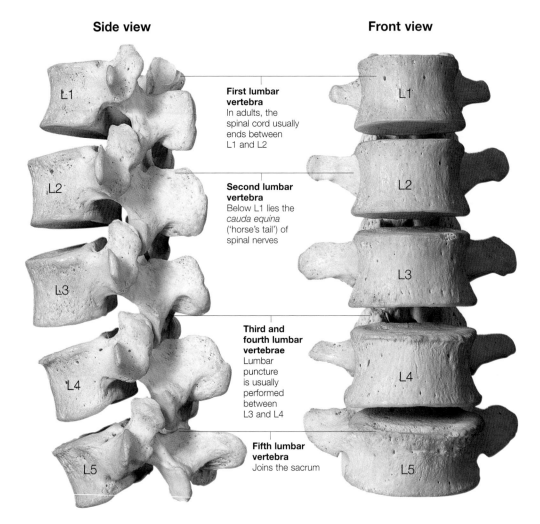

**Side view**

**Front view**

**First lumbar vertebra**
In adults, the spinal cord usually ends between L1 and L2

**Second lumbar vertebra**
Below L1 lies the *cauda equina* ('horse's tail') of spinal nerves

**Third and fourth lumbar vertebrae**
Lumbar puncture is usually performed between L3 and L4

**Fifth lumbar vertebra**
Joins the sacrum

*The front of the lumbar vertebrae form a convex curve when viewed from the side, known as lumbar lordosis. This increases strength and helps to absorb shock.*

*The five lumbar vertebrae are subject to greater vertical compression forces than the rest of the spine. For this reason, these vertebrae are large and strong.*

## Typical lumbar vertebrae

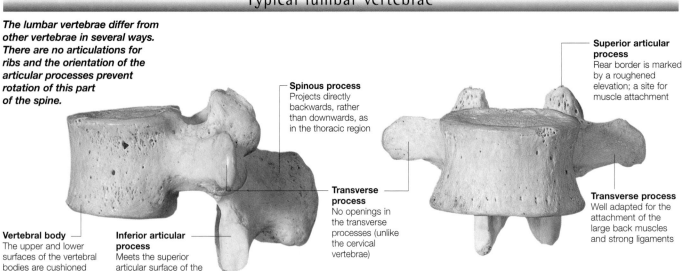

*The lumbar vertebrae differ from other vertebrae in several ways. There are no articulations for ribs and the orientation of the articular processes prevent rotation of this part of the spine.*

**Spinous process**
Projects directly backwards, rather than downwards, as in the thoracic region

**Transverse process**
No openings in the transverse processes (unlike the cervical vertebrae)

**Superior articular process**
Rear border is marked by a roughened elevation; a site for muscle attachment

**Transverse process**
Well adapted for the attachment of the large back muscles and strong ligaments

**Vertebral body**
The upper and lower surfaces of the vertebral bodies are cushioned by vertebral discs

**Inferior articular process**
Meets the superior articular surface of the lower lumbar vertebra

# Lumbar ligaments

The intervertebral discs and connecting ligaments support the bones of the spine. They act as shock absorbers, reducing wear on the vertebrae.

The intervertebral discs link the bones of adjacent vertebrae, prevent dislocation of the vertebral column and also act as shock absorbers between the vertebrae. Intervertebral discs contribute about one-fifth of the length of the vertebral column, and are thickest in the lumbar region where the vertical compression forces are greatest.

## STRENGTH AND STABILITY
To reinforce stability, the vertebral bodies are strengthened by tough, longitudinally running ligaments, consisting of fibrous tissue, in the front and rear. These ligaments are firmly attached to the intervertebral disc and adjacent edges of the vertebral body, but loosely attached to the rest of the body.

Movement between vertebrae is the result of the action of muscles attached to the processes of the vertebral arches. The joints associated with the articular processes are synovial joints, allowing the adjacent surfaces to glide smoothly over each other.

Each synovial joint is surrounded by a loose joint capsule. The joints of the vertebral arches are strengthened by various ligaments. The ligamenta flava join the laminae of the adjacent vertebra and contain elastic tissue.

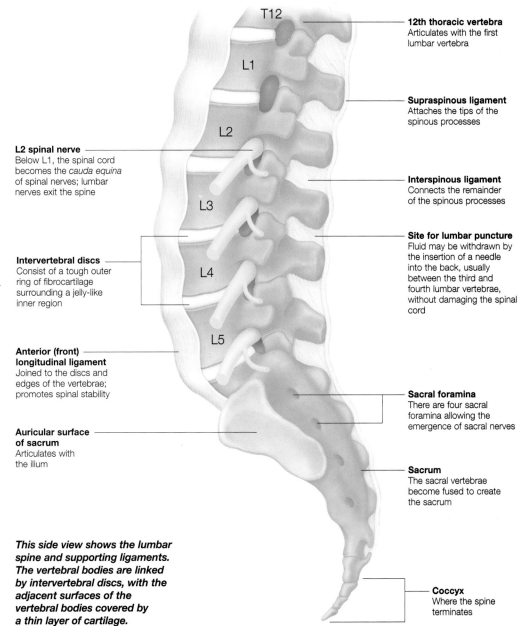

**T12**

**L1**

**L2**

**L3**

**L4**

**L5**

**L2 spinal nerve**
Below L1, the spinal cord becomes the *cauda equina* of spinal nerves; lumbar nerves exit the spine

**Intervertebral discs**
Consist of a tough outer ring of fibrocartilage surrounding a jelly-like inner region

**Anterior (front) longitudinal ligament**
Joined to the discs and edges of the vertebrae; promotes spinal stability

**Auricular surface of sacrum**
Articulates with the ilium

**12th thoracic vertebra**
Articulates with the first lumbar vertebra

**Supraspinous ligament**
Attaches the tips of the spinous processes

**Interspinous ligament**
Connects the remainder of the spinous processes

**Site for lumbar puncture**
Fluid may be withdrawn by the insertion of a needle into the back, usually between the third and fourth lumbar vertebrae, without damaging the spinal cord

**Sacral foramina**
There are four sacral foramina allowing the emergence of sacral nerves

**Sacrum**
The sacral vertebrae become fused to create the sacrum

**Coccyx**
Where the spine terminates

*This side view shows the lumbar spine and supporting ligaments. The vertebral bodies are linked by intervertebral discs, with the adjacent surfaces of the vertebral bodies covered by a thin layer of cartilage.*

## Disorders of the lumbar vertebrae

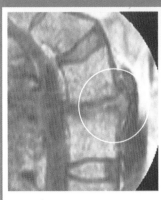

**This MR scan shows an intervertebral disc (circled) in the lumbar spine protruding from between the vertebrae. This can cause severe pain.**

Each intervertebral disc consists of a tough outer ring of fibrocartilage (the annulus fibrosus), surrounding a jelly-like inner region (the nucleus pulposus). The nucleus pulposus is under constant pressure in the upright position. Degeneration of the disc occurs with age and can allow the nucleus pulposus to protrude backwards through a split in the annulus fibrosus (a so-called slipped disc).

The whole disc does not slip out of place, but it can press on a spinal nerve root. This causes acute pain, known as 'sciatica', which radiates down the back of the thigh and calf, sometimes into the foot, along the sciatic nerve

(the main nerve supply to the leg).

Rarely, the herniated disc may press on the spinal cord itself, causing paralysis of the legs and disturbance of bladder function. Either of these occurrences is an emergency and usually results in surgery to remove the offending part of the herniated disc.

The most common cause of chronic back pain (spondylosis) is degenerative disease of the intervertebral discs and of the facet joints. Bone underlying the damaged cartilage develops ragged projections (osteophytes) that restrict joint movement, causing stiffness and secondary muscle spasm, and may press on nerve roots, causing pain.

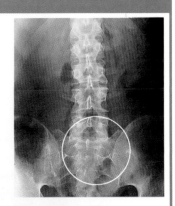

**Degeneration of the intervertebral discs (circled) can lead to compression of one vertebra against another. This can be caused by ageing.**

# Sacrum and coccyx

The sacrum and coccyx form the tail end of the spinal column.
Both are formed from fused vertebrae, allowing attachment for weight-bearing ligaments and muscles, and helping to protect pelvic organs.

The sacrum is a bony mass composed of five sacral vertebrae which fuse between puberty and the age of 30 years. It performs several functions: it attaches the vertebral column to the pelvic girdle, supporting the body's weight and transmitting it to the legs; it protects pelvic organs, such as the uterus and bladder; and it allows attachment of muscles that move the thigh.

The sacrum is shaped like an upside-down triangle, the five fused vertebral bodies diminishing in size from the wide base above (formed by the first sacral vertebra and the sacral alae, or 'wings') towards the apex below, where the coccyx is attached.

Centrally, horizontal bony ridges indicate the junctions between individual vertebrae; these are the remnants of intervertebral discs. On either side, sacral foramina (holes running through the bone) allow the passage of the ventral sacral motor nerve roots.

## THE COCCYX

The coccyx, attached to the base of the sacrum, is the remains of the tail seen in our primate relatives. It consists of a small, pyramid-shaped bone formed from four fused vertebrae, and allows the attachment of ligaments and muscles, forming the anal sphincter.

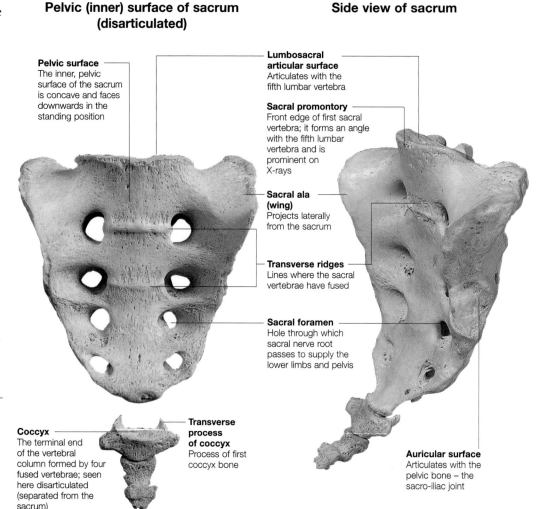

**Pelvic (inner) surface of sacrum (disarticulated)**

**Pelvic surface**
The inner, pelvic surface of the sacrum is concave and faces downwards in the standing position

**Coccyx**
The terminal end of the vertebral column formed by four fused vertebrae; seen here disarticulated (separated from the sacrum)

**Transverse process of coccyx**
Process of first coccyx bone

**Side view of sacrum**

**Lumbosacral articular surface**
Articulates with the fifth lumbar vertebra

**Sacral promontory**
Front edge of first sacral vertebra; it forms an angle with the fifth lumbar vertebra and is prominent on X-rays

**Sacral ala (wing)**
Projects laterally from the sacrum

**Transverse ridges**
Lines where the sacral vertebrae have fused

**Sacral foramen**
Hole through which sacral nerve root passes to supply the lower limbs and pelvis

**Auricular surface**
Articulates with the pelvic bone – the sacro-iliac joint

## Sacro-iliac joint

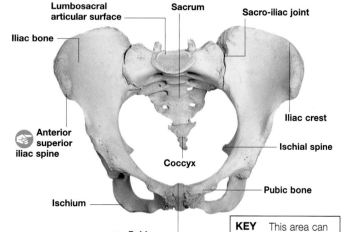

**Lumbosacral articular surface**

**Sacrum**

**Sacro-iliac joint**

**Iliac bone**

**Iliac crest**

**Anterior superior iliac spine**

**Ischial spine**

**Coccyx**

**Ischium**

**Pubic bone**

**Pubic symphysis**

**KEY** This area can easily be felt under the skin

On either side, the sacrum articulates with the pelvic bones at the sacro-iliac joints. The sacral joint surface is known as the auricular surface since it is vaguely ear-shaped.

The sacral joint surface is covered with hyaline cartilage (a type of cartilage typically found in free-moving joints) whereas the joint of the ilium is covered in tough fibrocartilage. The sacro-iliac joint is therefore a mixture of these two types.

*The relationship between the sacrum and the pelvis can be seen clearly in this anterior (front) view. The sacrum displays a convex (outwards) curvature, and terminates at the coccyx.*

In early life, the sacro-iliac joint is fairly mobile, but becomes progressively less so with age, although its mobility may still be significant. During delivery of a baby, it moves to enlarge the pelvic outlet.

There are sex differences between the male and female sacrum, often sufficient to allow identification of sex. The female sacrum is shorter and wider, allowing a larger pelvic cavity for the passage of an infant during childbirth. The diameter of the pelvic outlet also expands during birth due to the mobility of the coccyx, which moves backward for the baby's passage. The degree of curvature is greater in males than females.

# Spinal nerve roots

The genitals, buttocks and lower limbs are supplied by nerve roots that emerge from the lumbar and sacral spine.

The sensory and motor nerve supply to and from the pelvis and legs is derived from a network of nerve roots called the sacral plexus. This lies on the rear wall of the pelvic cavity in front of the piriformis muscle. Contributions to the sacral plexus come from the lumbosacral trunk, representing the 4th and 5th lumbar nerve roots and the sacral nerve roots.

At the sacral plexus these nerve roots exchange nerve fibres and re-form into major nerves. These include the superior and inferior gluteal nerves, supplying the buttocks, and the sciatic nerve, which supplies the muscles of the leg. The parasympathetic splanchnic nerves (S1, S2, S3) regulate urination and defecation by controlling the internal sphincters, and also erection by dilating penile arterioles.

### SACRAL FORAMINA

The convex outer sacral surface has a ridge called the median crest in the midline, where the spinous processes fuse. The four posterior sacral foramina transmit the dorsal nerve roots. Nerves pass down the sacrum through the sacral canal.

A normal defect in the fusion of the fifth sacral vertebra posteriorly causes the canal to open out at the sacral hiatus. This is useful to doctors, who can anaesthetize the lower spinal nerves by passing a needle through the open space.

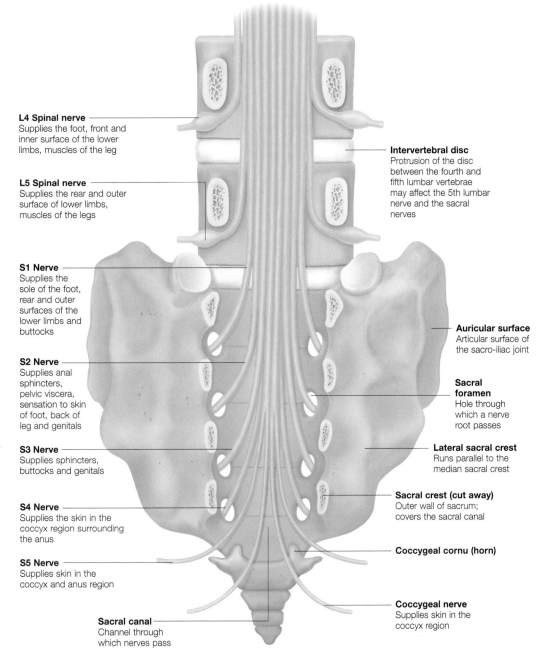

**L4 Spinal nerve**
Supplies the foot, front and inner surface of the lower limbs, muscles of the leg

**L5 Spinal nerve**
Supplies the rear and outer surface of lower limbs, muscles of the legs

**S1 Nerve**
Supplies the sole of the foot, rear and outer surfaces of the lower limbs and buttocks

**S2 Nerve**
Supplies anal sphincters, pelvic viscera, sensation to skin of foot, back of leg and genitals

**S3 Nerve**
Supplies sphincters, buttocks and genitals

**S4 Nerve**
Supplies the skin in the coccyx region surrounding the anus

**S5 Nerve**
Supplies skin in the coccyx and anus region

**Sacral canal**
Channel through which nerves pass

**Intervertebral disc**
Protrusion of the disc between the fourth and fifth lumbar vertebrae may affect the 5th lumbar nerve and the sacral nerves

**Auricular surface**
Articular surface of the sacro-iliac joint

**Sacral foramen**
Hole through which a nerve root passes

**Lateral sacral crest**
Runs parallel to the median sacral crest

**Sacral crest (cut away)**
Outer wall of sacrum; covers the sacral canal

**Coccygeal cornu (horn)**

**Coccygeal nerve**
Supplies skin in the coccyx region

## Clinical aspects of the sacrum and coccyx

Tumours and infections of the sacrum are rare. Fractures only occur with severe trauma since the sacrum is very strong.

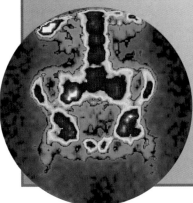

Coccydynia (literally 'pain at the coccyx') is a painful syndrome affecting the base of the spine, rectum, buttocks and lower back. Typically, the pain is worsened or precipitated by sitting down and relieved by standing or lying on the side.

Causes include a fracture or trauma of the coccyx, fibrositis, disc disease, local infection, or idiopathy (no cause identifiable).

*Sacro-iliitis, inflammation of the sacro-iliac joint, is revealed on this false-coloured scintigram of the pelvis. The inflammation appears as red and white areas.*

Treatment is difficult and consists of steroid and anaesthetic injections around the coccyx.

Sacro-iliitis is inflammation of the sacro-iliac joints. This is most commonly seen in a group of diseases known as the spondylo-arthropathies (literally 'diseases of the spinal joints').

The most common is ankylosing spondylitis. This affects men in their 20s to 40s

*This superior (above) MR image reveals a stress fracture in the right sacral ala (circled). Such fractures often result from falling on to hard surfaces.*

and causes back pain and stiffness and, in severe cases, a fixed, bent spine. On X-ray, there is irregular erosion, narrowing, and thickening at the sacro-iliac joint and vertebral joints. Other causes of sacro-iliitis are Crohn's disease, Reiter's syndrome and arthritis associated with ulcerative colitis.

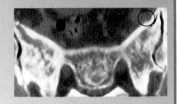

# Spinal cord

The spinal cord is the communication pathway between the brain and the body. It allows signals to pass down to control body function and up to inform the brain of what is happening in the body.

The spinal cord is a slightly flattened cylindrical structure of 42–45 cm length in adults, with an average diameter of about 2.5 cm. It begins as a continuation of the medulla oblongata, the lowest part of the brainstem, at the level of the foramen magnum, the largest opening in the base of the skull. It then runs down the length of the neck and back in the vertebral canal, protected by the bony vertebrae which make up the vertebral column.

### DEVELOPMENT

Up to the third month of development in the womb, the spinal cord runs the entire length of the vertebral column. Later on, however, the vertebral column outgrows the cord, which by birth ends at the level of the third lumbar vertebra. This more rapid growth of the vertebral column continues so that in the adult, the spinal cord ends at about the level of the disc between the first and second lumbar vertebrae.

### ANATOMY OF THE CORD

The cord is enlarged in the region of the neck and lower back. The lower end of the cord tapers off into a cone-shaped region – the conus medullaris. From this, the filum terminale – a thin strand of modified pia mater (one of the membranes that surround the brain and spinal cord) – continues downwards to be attached to the back of the coccyx, anchoring the spinal cord.

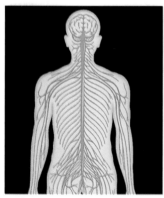

**The 31 pairs of spinal nerves that branch off the spinal cord transfer impulses between the brain and all parts of the body.**

**Posterior view of spinal cord**

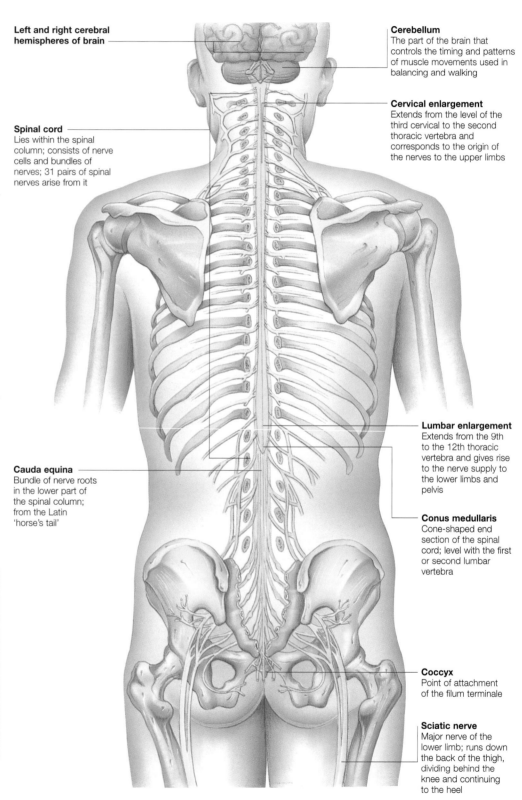

**Left and right cerebral hemispheres of brain**

**Spinal cord**
Lies within the spinal column; consists of nerve cells and bundles of nerves; 31 pairs of spinal nerves arise from it

**Cauda equina**
Bundle of nerve roots in the lower part of the spinal column; from the Latin 'horse's tail'

**Cerebellum**
The part of the brain that controls the timing and patterns of muscle movements used in balancing and walking

**Cervical enlargement**
Extends from the level of the third cervical to the second thoracic vertebra and corresponds to the origin of the nerves to the upper limbs

**Lumbar enlargement**
Extends from the 9th to the 12th thoracic vertebra and gives rise to the nerve supply to the lower limbs and pelvis

**Conus medullaris**
Cone-shaped end section of the spinal cord; level with the first or second lumbar vertebra

**Coccyx**
Point of attachment of the filum terminale

**Sciatic nerve**
Major nerve of the lower limb; runs down the back of the thigh, dividing behind the knee and continuing to the heel

# Cross-sections through the spinal cord

The appearance of the spinal cord varies at different levels, according to the amount of muscle supplied by the nerves that emanate from it.

The spinal cord is made up of an inner core of grey matter, which consists mainly of nerve cells and their supporting cells (neuroglia), surrounded by white matter, made up primarily of myelinated nerve fibres – nerves with an insulating sheath of the fatty substance myelin.

In cross-section, the grey matter typically has the shape of a letter H or a butterfly, with two anterior columns or horns, two posterior columns and a thin grey commissure connecting the grey matter in the two halves. There is a small central canal containing cerebrospinal fluid which at its uppermost limit runs into the fourth ventricle in the region of the lower brainstem and cerebellum.

There is some variation in the appearance of a cross-section of the spinal cord at different levels. The amount of grey matter corresponds to the bulk of muscle whose nerve supply comes off at that level.

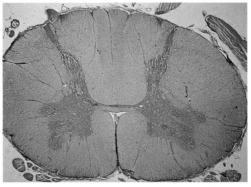

*Cervical: the cord is relatively large and has an oval shape. Grey matter (dark red) is prominent, corresponding to the cervical enlargement supplying the upper limbs.*

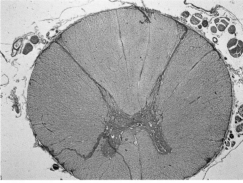

*Thoracic: the cord is almost circular and has a smaller diameter. There is an intermediate amount of white matter. The grey matter is not as prominent here.*

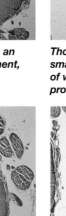

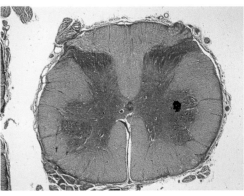

*Lumbar: the cord has a larger diameter, corresponding to the increased amount of grey matter in the lumbar enlargement supplying the lower limbs. The white matter is less prominent.*

*Sacral: in the region of the conus medullaris, the grey matter takes the form of two oval-shaped masses which occupy most of the cord with very little white matter.*

## Tracts in the spinal cord

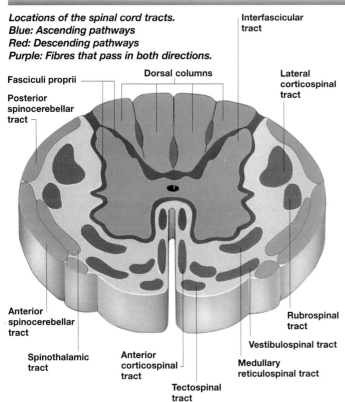

**Locations of the spinal cord tracts.**
**Blue: Ascending pathways**
**Red: Descending pathways**
**Purple: Fibres that pass in both directions.**

Fasciculi proprii
Posterior spinocerebellar tract
Dorsal columns
Interfascicular tract
Lateral corticospinal tract
Anterior spinocerebellar tract
Spinothalamic tract
Anterior corticospinal tract
Tectospinal tract
Medullary reticulospinal tract
Vestibulospinal tract
Rubrospinal tract

A tract is a collection of nerve axons which all have the same origin, destination and function.

### ASCENDING TRACTS

These carry sensory information from the body up to the brain:
**1** The dorsal columns carry information to the medulla in the brain about fine touch and pressure from receptors in the skin. They also allow position sense (proprioception) from receptors in the joints, tendons and muscles
**2** The anterior and lateral spinothalamic tracts carry information about poorly localized touch, deep pressure sensation, pain and temperature
**3** The anterior and posterior spinocerebellar tracts carry information about touch and pressure to the cerebellum to enable it to contribute to the control of voluntary movement.

### DESCENDING TRACTS

These carry signals from the brain to the body. They are particularly involved with the control of movement.

The pyramidal or corticospinal tract has its origin in the nerve cells of the cerebral cortex involved with initiating voluntary movement. The tract passes down into the spinal cord with impulses passing out through the ventral spinal nerve roots to skeletal muscles.

### EXTRAPYRAMIDAL TRACTS

**1** The tectospinal tract begins in the midbrain and passes down in the anterior white column. It contributes to the control of balance and co-ordination
**2** The rubrospinal tract originates in the red nucleus of the midbrain and descends in the lateral columns to help control posture and muscle tone
**3** The reticulospinal tract begins in the brainstem reticular formation and descends in the anterior and lateral columns. It is involved with muscle tone
**4** The vestibulospinal tract has its origin in the vestibular nuclei of the medulla and travels down in the anterior and lateral columns. It also contributes to the control of muscle tone.

# Spinal nerves

There are 31 pairs of spinal nerves, arranged on each side of the spinal cord along its length. The pairs are grouped by region: eight cervical, twelve thoracic, five lumbar, five sacral and one coccygeal.

Each spinal nerve has two roots. The anterior, or ventral root, contains the axons of motor nerves which send impulses to control muscle movement. The posterior or dorsal root contains the axons of sensory nerves which send sensory information from the body into the spinal cord on its way to the brain.

## SEGMENTS

Each root is formed by a series of small rootlets which attach it to the cord. The portion of the spinal cord which provides the rootlets for one dorsal root is referred to as a segment. In the lumbar and cervical regions, the rootlets are bunched closely, with the cord segments being only about 1 cm long. However, in the thoracic region they are more spread out, with segments more than 2 cm long.

## NERVE FORMATION

The ventral and dorsal roots come together to form a single spinal nerve within the intervertebral foramina – small openings between the vertebrae through which the spinal nerves pass.

Just before the point of fusion with the ventral root, there is an enlargement of each dorsal root. This enlargement is known as the dorsal root ganglion – this is a collection of cell bodies of sensory nerves.

**ANTERIOR VIEW**

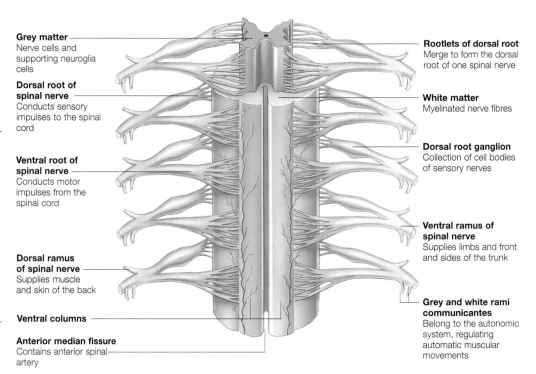

**Grey matter**
Nerve cells and supporting neuroglia cells

**Dorsal root of spinal nerve**
Conducts sensory impulses to the spinal cord

**Ventral root of spinal nerve**
Conducts motor impulses from the spinal cord

**Dorsal ramus of spinal nerve**
Supplies muscle and skin of the back

**Ventral columns**

**Anterior median fissure**
Contains anterior spinal artery

**Rootlets of dorsal root**
Merge to form the dorsal root of one spinal nerve

**White matter**
Myelinated nerve fibres

**Dorsal root ganglion**
Collection of cell bodies of sensory nerves

**Ventral ramus of spinal nerve**
Supplies limbs and front and sides of the trunk

**Grey and white rami communicantes**
Belong to the autonomic system, regulating automatic muscular movements

## RAMI

Shortly after passing through its intervertebral foramen, each spinal nerve divides into several branches, or rami, including:
■ Ventral ramus: supplies the limbs and front and sides of the trunk
■ Dorsal ramus: supplies the deep muscles and skin of the back
■ Rami communicantes: part of the autonomic nervous system.

## CAUDA EQUINA

Because the spinal cord is shorter than the vertebral column, the lower spinal nerve roots exit and travel downwards at quite an oblique angle. The lumbosacral nerve roots are bunched together and pass downwards almost vertically. This gives rise to the name *cauda equina* – Latin for horse's tail – which these lower nerve roots resemble.

---

## Lumbar puncture

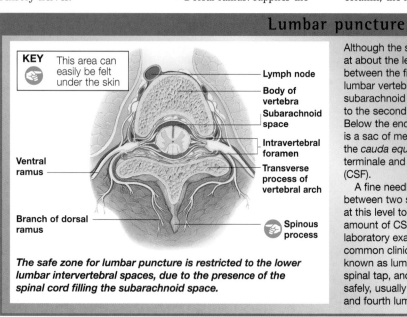

**KEY** This area can easily be felt under the skin

**Ventral ramus**

**Branch of dorsal ramus**

**Lymph node**

**Body of vertebra**

**Subarachnoid space**

**Intravertebral foramen**

**Transverse process of vertebral arch**

**Spinous process**

*The safe zone for lumbar puncture is restricted to the lower lumbar intervertebral spaces, due to the presence of the spinal cord filling the subarachnoid space.*

Although the spinal cord ends at about the level of the disc between the first and second lumbar vertebrae, the subarachnoid space continues to the second sacral vertebra. Below the end of the cord there is a sac of meninges containing the *cauda equina*, the filum terminale and cerebrospinal fluid (CSF).

A fine needle can be passed between two spinous processes at this level to allow a small amount of CSF to be taken for laboratory examination. This is a common clinical procedure known as lumbar puncture or spinal tap, and can be performed safely, usually between the third and fourth lumbar vertebrae.

*A lumbar puncture (spinal tap) is carried out to obtain CSF or to allow drugs to be given directly into the spine. The needle is passed into the subarachnoid space.*

# Blood supply of the spinal cord

The spinal cord is supplied by a complex arrangement of arteries. This blood supply is vital for the normal functioning of the nervous system.

The anterior spinal arteries originate from the two vertebral arteries at the base of the brain and join together to form a single artery which runs down the front of the spinal cord in the anterior median fissure. Segmental branches of this artery supplies the anterior two-thirds of the spinal cord.

The posterior spinal arteries also arise from the vertebral arteries and split into two descending branches which run either side of the cord, one behind and one in front of the attachment of the dorsal roots. These vessels supply the posterior third of the cord.

There is additional supply from radicular arteries which originate from the deep cervical arteries in the neck, the intercostal arteries in the chest and the lumbar arteries in the lower back. These vessels enter through the intervertebral foramina alongside the spinal nerves.

Usually, one of the anterior radicular arteries is larger than the others and is referred to as the artery of Adamkiewicz. It most commonly arises on the left-hand side from a branch of the descending aorta in the upper lumbar or lower thoracic region. This branch may be the main blood supply to the lower two-thirds of the spinal cord, and injury to it following trauma or during surgery may produce serious neurological damage.

*This cast of the aorta (red) and branches shows the rich supply of blood to the spinal column. All spinal nerve roots have associated arteries. The vessels show the segmental arrangement of the vertebrae.*

## Membranes that protect the spinal cord

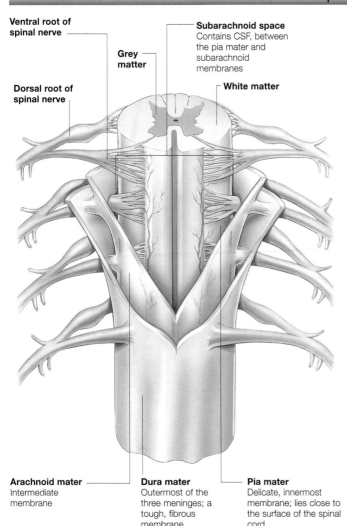

**Ventral root of spinal nerve**

**Grey matter**

**Dorsal root of spinal nerve**

**Subarachnoid space**
Contains CSF, between the pia mater and subarachnoid membranes

**White matter**

**Arachnoid mater**
Intermediate membrane

**Dura mater**
Outermost of the three meninges; a tough, fibrous membrane

**Pia mater**
Delicate, innermost membrane; lies close to the surface of the spinal cord

The bones of the vertebral column provide the major protection for the spinal cord, just as the skull does for the brain. However, like the brain, the cord has additional protection from three membranes, which continue down through the foramen magnum from inside the skull.

The dura mater is the tough, fibrous, outer membrane. The extradural or epidural space separates the dura from the bone of the vertebral bodies and contains fatty tissue and a plexus of veins.

The middle membrane is the arachnoid mater, which is much thinner and more delicate, with an arrangement of connective tissue fibres resembling a spider's web. There is a potential subdural space between the dura and the arachnoid, normally containing only a very thin film of fluid.

### PIA MATER
The innermost membrane is the fine pia mater, which is closely applied to the surface of the spinal cord. It is transparent and richly supplied with fine blood vessels, which carry oxygen and nutrients to the cord. Between the arachnoid and the pia is the subarachnoid space, which contains cerebrospinal fluid (CSF), which cushions the spinal cord, as well as helping to remove chemical waste products produced by nerve activity and metabolism. CSF is formed by the choroid plexuses inside the cerebral ventricles and circulates around the brain and spinal cord.

About 21 triangular extensions of the pia – the denticulate ligaments – pass outwards between the anterior and posterior nerve roots to join with the arachnoid and inner surface of the dura. The spinal cord is suspended by these in its dural sheath.

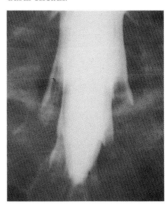

*Like the brain, the spinal cord is surrounded and protected by three membranes. These are the meninges – dura mater, arachnoid mater and pia mater.*

*The end of the spinal cord is shown on this myelogram (a specialized radiograph). Strands of the pia mater anchor the cord to the coccyx.*

# Muscles of the back

The muscles of the back give us our upright posture and allow flexibility and mobility of the spine. The superficial back muscles also act with other muscles to move the shoulders and upper arms.

The deep muscles of the back are concerned with support and movement of the spine, while the superficial muscles act to move the arm and shoulder.

## SUPERFICIAL MUSCLES

The trapezius is a large, fan-shaped muscle whose top edge forms the visible slope from neck to shoulder. It attaches to the skull and helps to hold up and rotate the head and enables us to brace the shoulders back. The latissimus dorsi, the largest and most powerful back muscle, is attached to the spine from above the lower edge of the trapezius and runs down to the back of the pelvis. The latissimus dorsi allows a lifted arm to be pulled back into line with the trunk, even against great force.

Smaller muscles also contribute to this superficial muscle layer. Levator scapulae, rhomboid major and rhomboid minor run between the spine and the scapula and act to move the scapula up and inwards.

The 'rotator cuff' is a group of muscles that run between the scapula and head of the humerus (bone of the upper arm) at the shoulder joint. Together, they hold the head of the humerus tightly into the shoulder joint. Serratus posterior runs from the vertebrae to the ribs and moves the ribcage up during breathing.

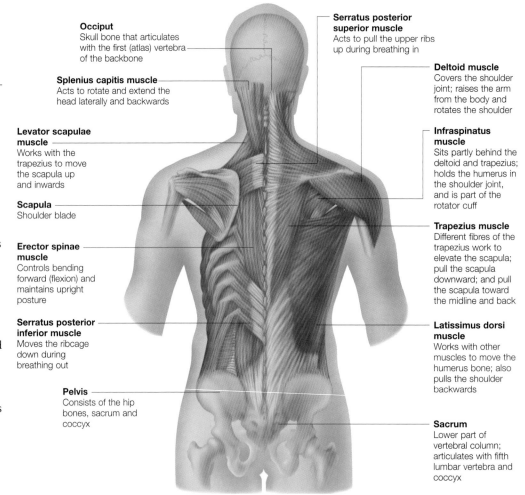

**Occiput**
Skull bone that articulates with the first (atlas) vertebra of the backbone

**Splenius capitis muscle**
Acts to rotate and extend the head laterally and backwards

**Levator scapulae muscle**
Works with the trapezius to move the scapula up and inwards

**Scapula**
Shoulder blade

**Erector spinae muscle**
Controls bending forward (flexion) and maintains upright posture

**Serratus posterior inferior muscle**
Moves the ribcage down during breathing out

**Pelvis**
Consists of the hip bones, sacrum and coccyx

**Serratus posterior superior muscle**
Acts to pull the upper ribs up during breathing in

**Deltoid muscle**
Covers the shoulder joint; raises the arm from the body and rotates the shoulder

**Infraspinatus muscle**
Sits partly behind the deltoid and trapezius; holds the humerus in the shoulder joint, and is part of the rotator cuff

**Trapezius muscle**
Different fibres of the trapezius work to elevate the scapula; pull the scapula downward; and pull the scapula toward the midline and back

**Latissimus dorsi muscle**
Works with other muscles to move the humerus bone; also pulls the shoulder backwards

**Sacrum**
Lower part of vertebral column; articulates with fifth lumbar vertebra and coccyx

## Movements of the spine

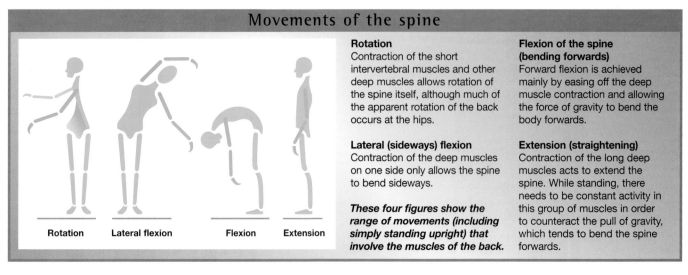

Rotation   Lateral flexion   Flexion   Extension

**Rotation**
Contraction of the short intervertebral muscles and other deep muscles allows rotation of the spine itself, although much of the apparent rotation of the back occurs at the hips.

**Lateral (sideways) flexion**
Contraction of the deep muscles on one side only allows the spine to bend sideways.

*These four figures show the range of movements (including simply standing upright) that involve the muscles of the back.*

**Flexion of the spine (bending forwards)**
Forward flexion is achieved mainly by easing off the deep muscle contraction and allowing the force of gravity to bend the body forwards.

**Extension (straightening)**
Contraction of the long deep muscles acts to extend the spine. While standing, there needs to be constant activity in this group of muscles in order to counteract the pull of gravity, which tends to bend the spine forwards.

# Deep muscles of the back

The deep muscles of the back attach to underlying bones of the spine, pelvis and ribs. They act together to allow smooth movements of the spine.

Muscles need to be attached to bone in order to give them the leverage they need to perform their functions. The bony attachments of the deep muscles of the back include the vertebrae, the ribs, the base of the skull and the pelvis.

### DEEP MUSCLE LAYERS

The deep muscles of the back are built up in layers; the most deeply located muscles are very short, running from each vertebra obliquely to the one above. Over these lie muscles which are longer and run vertically between several vertebrae and the ribs. More superficially, the muscles become longer and some are attached to the pelvic bones and the occiput (back of the base of the skull) as well as to the vertebrae.

There are numerous muscles in these layers. Although each muscle is individually named according to its position, in practice they act in varying combinations rather than individually. Together, they form the large group of deep muscles which lie on either side of the spine and act in conjunction to maintain the spine in an S-shaped curve, enabling the fluid movements of the spine.

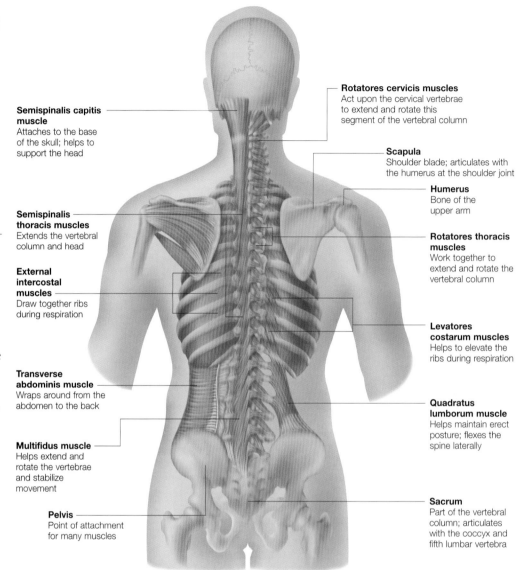

**Semispinalis capitis muscle**
Attaches to the base of the skull; helps to support the head

**Semispinalis thoracis muscles**
Extends the vertebral column and head

**External intercostal muscles**
Draw together ribs during respiration

**Transverse abdominis muscle**
Wraps around from the abdomen to the back

**Multifidus muscle**
Helps extend and rotate the vertebrae and stabilize movement

**Pelvis**
Point of attachment for many muscles

**Rotatores cervicis muscles**
Act upon the cervical vertebrae to extend and rotate this segment of the vertebral column

**Scapula**
Shoulder blade; articulates with the humerus at the shoulder joint

**Humerus**
Bone of the upper arm

**Rotatores thoracis muscles**
Work together to extend and rotate the vertebral column

**Levatores costarum muscles**
Helps to elevate the ribs during respiration

**Quadratus lumborum muscle**
Helps maintain erect posture; flexes the spine laterally

**Sacrum**
Part of the vertebral column; articulates with the coccyx and fifth lumbar vertebra

## Supporting the head and neck

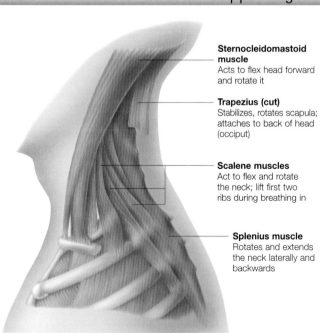

**Sternocleidomastoid muscle**
Acts to flex head forward and rotate it

**Trapezius (cut)**
Stabilizes, rotates scapula; attaches to back of head (occiput)

**Scalene muscles**
Act to flex and rotate the neck; lift first two ribs during breathing in

**Splenius muscle**
Rotates and extends the neck laterally and backwards

The deep muscles at the top of the spine, attached to the skull, also act to keep the neck extended and the head upright. The centre of gravity of the head is in front of the spine and so constant contraction of the muscles at the back of the neck is needed to prevent the head falling forward – hence the term 'nodding off' when the head nods forward as these muscles relax while falling asleep.

The sternocleidomastoid muscles are large muscles on either side of the neck. They act as the major muscles of flexion of the head and can be braced to support the head when it is

*A lateral view of the muscles of the neck reveals some of the major muscles responsible for supporting and flexing the head and neck.*

elevated – as happens when rising from a lying position. The sternocleidomastoid muscles are aided in these tasks by several other deep muscles.

The splenius muscles are broad sheets of muscle fibres that wrap around and over the deeper muscles of the neck. The splenius muscles originate in the cervical vertebrae (in the neck) and insert in the occipital bone at the back of the skull. When the muscles of one side of the neck are used alone, the neck and head is extended laterally or rotated; when used together and in collaboration with other muscles, the splenius muscles help to extend the neck backwards.

Extension of the neck is also aided by the action of the trapezius muscle which attaches to the occipital bone, thoracic vertebrae and scapula.

# Pectoral girdle

The pectoral, or shoulder, girdle is the bony structure that articulates with and supports the upper limbs. It consists of the clavicles at the front of the chest and the scapulae that lie flat against the back.

The upper limb is connected to the skeleton by the pectoral or shoulder girdle, made up of the clavicle (collar bone) and the scapula (shoulder blade). The pectoral girdle has only one joint with the central skeleton, at the inner end of the clavicle where it articulates with the sternum (breastbone). The stability of the pectoral girdle is provided by muscles and ligaments attached to the skull, ribs, sternum and vertebrae.

### THE CLAVICLE

The clavicle is an S-shaped bone that lies horizontally at the upper border of the chest. The front and upper surfaces of the clavicle are mostly smooth, while the under-surfaces are roughened and grooved by the attachments of muscles and ligaments.

The medial (inner) end of the clavicle has a large oval facet for connecting with the sternum at the sternoclavicular joint. A smaller facet lies at the other end where the clavicle articulates with the acromion (a bony prominence of the scapula) at the acromioclavicular joint.

The clavicle acts as a strut to brace the upper limb away from the body, thereby allowing a wide range of free movement. Along with the scapula and its muscular connections, it also transmits the force of impacts on the upper limb to the skeleton.

**Pectoral girdle from above**

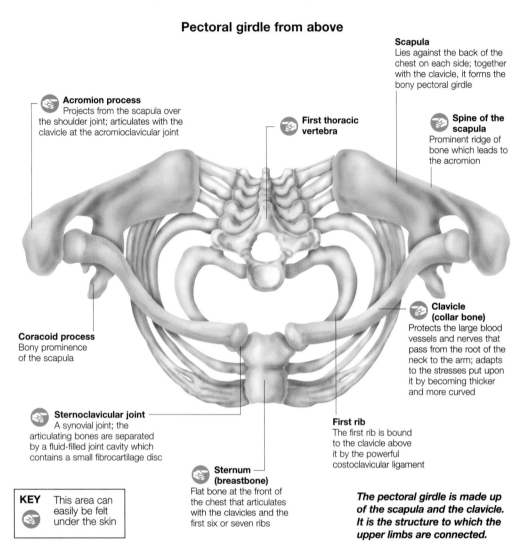

**Acromion process**
Projects from the scapula over the shoulder joint; articulates with the clavicle at the acromioclavicular joint

**First thoracic vertebra**

**Scapula**
Lies against the back of the chest on each side; together with the clavicle, it forms the bony pectoral girdle

**Spine of the scapula**
Prominent ridge of bone which leads to the acromion

**Coracoid process**
Bony prominence of the scapula

**Clavicle (collar bone)**
Protects the large blood vessels and nerves that pass from the root of the neck to the arm; adapts to the stresses put upon it by becoming thicker and more curved

**Sternoclavicular joint**
A synovial joint; the articulating bones are separated by a fluid-filled joint cavity which contains a small fibrocartilage disc

**First rib**
The first rib is bound to the clavicle above it by the powerful costoclavicular ligament

**Sternum (breastbone)**
Flat bone at the front of the chest that articulates with the clavicles and the first six or seven ribs

**KEY** This area can easily be felt under the skin

*The pectoral girdle is made up of the scapula and the clavicle. It is the structure to which the upper limbs are connected.*

## Joints of the clavicle

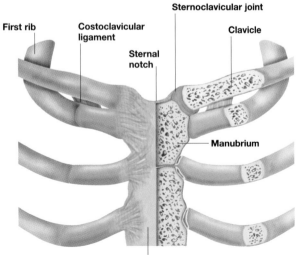

First rib

Costoclavicular ligament

Sternoclavicular joint

Clavicle

Sternal notch

Manubrium

Body of sternum

The sternoclavicular joint is the only bony connection between the pectoral girdle and the rest of the skeleton. It can be felt under the skin, as the sternal end of the clavicle is fairly large and extends above the top of the manubrium (the top of the sternum), both sides together forming the familiar 'sternal notch' at the base of the neck.

The cavity is divided into two by an articular disc made of fibrocartilage, which improves the fit of the bones and keeps the

*A tough fibrous capsule (sheath), together with strong surrounding ligaments, holds the sternoclavicular joint firmly in place.*

joint stable. The joint is further stabilized by the costoclavicular ligament, which anchors its underside to the first rib.

Only a small degree of movement is possible at the sternoclavicular joint; the outer end of the clavicle can move upward, as when shrugging the shoulders, or forward when the arm reaches out to pick up something in front of the body.

The acromioclavicular joint is formed between the outer end of the clavicle and the acromion of the scapula. The acromio-clavicular joint rotates the scapula on the clavicle under the influence of muscles which attach the scapula to the rest of the skeleton.

# Scapula

The scapula is a flat, triangular-shaped bone which lies against the back of the chest. With the clavicle, it forms the bony pectoral girdle.

The scapula, or shoulder blade, lies against the back of the chest on each side overlying the second to seventh ribs. As a rough triangle, the scapula has three borders: medial (inner), lateral (outer) and superior, with three angles between them.

### SURFACES

The scapula has two surfaces: anterior (front) and posterior (back). The anterior or costal (rib) surface lies against the ribs at the back of the chest and is concave, having a large hollow called the subscapular fossa that provides a large surface area for the attachment of muscles.

The posterior surface is divided by a prominent spine. The supraspinous fossa is the small area above the spine, while the infraspinous fossa lies below. These hollows also provide sites of attachment for muscles of the same name.

### BONY PROCESSES

The spine of the scapula is a thick projecting ridge, continuous with the bony outcrop called the acromion. This is a flattened prominence that forms the tip of the shoulder. The lateral angle, the thickest part of the scapula, contains the glenoid cavity, the depression into which the head of the humerus fits at the shoulder joint. The coracoid process – an important site of attachment of muscles and ligaments – is also palpable in this area.

**Rear view of scapula**

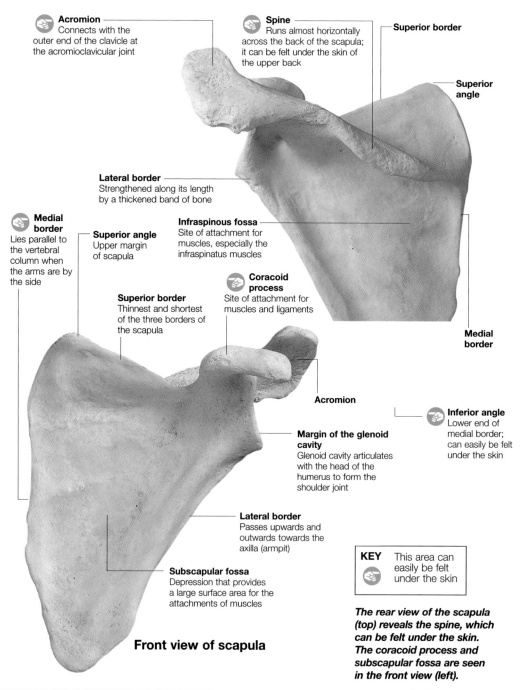

**Acromion**
Connects with the outer end of the clavicle at the acromioclavicular joint

**Spine**
Runs almost horizontally across the back of the scapula; it can be felt under the skin of the upper back

**Superior border**

**Superior angle**

**Lateral border**
Strengthened along its length by a thickened band of bone

**Infraspinous fossa**
Site of attachment for muscles, especially the infraspinatus muscles

**Medial border**
Lies parallel to the vertebral column when the arms are by the side

**Superior angle**
Upper margin of scapula

**Coracoid process**
Site of attachment for muscles and ligaments

**Superior border**
Thinnest and shortest of the three borders of the scapula

**Medial border**

**Acromion**

**Inferior angle**
Lower end of medial border; can easily be felt under the skin

**Margin of the glenoid cavity**
Glenoid cavity articulates with the head of the humerus to form the shoulder joint

**Lateral border**
Passes upwards and outwards towards the axilla (armpit)

**Subscapular fossa**
Depression that provides a large surface area for the attachments of muscles

**Front view of scapula**

**KEY** This area can easily be felt under the skin

*The rear view of the scapula (top) reveals the spine, which can be felt under the skin. The coracoid process and subscapular fossa are seen in the front view (left).*

## Winged scapula

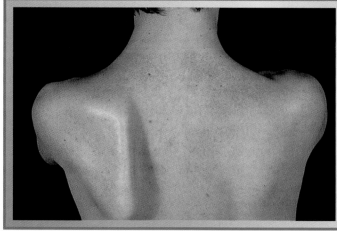

As it has no bony connections with the spine or the ribs, the scapula is held tightly against the posterior wall of the chest by the action of muscles, mainly the serratus anterior muscle.

Serratus anterior is supplied by the long thoracic nerve which descends from the axilla (armpit) on the surface of the muscle under

*The position of this patient's left scapula is the result of damage to the long thoracic nerve. This nerve supplies the serratus anterior muscle that holds the scapula to the chest.*

the skin, where it is vulnerable to injury. If this nerve is damaged, for instance by a penetrating wound, the muscle will be paralysed and the contraction within it that holds the scapula flat against the ribs will cease.

In this situation, the medial border and inferior angle of the scapula become more prominent and move away from the midline, the scapula jutting out like a wing. This gives rise to the name of 'winged scapula' for this condition, which is most obvious when the arm is pushed against a door or wall.

# Muscles of the pectoral girdle

The pectoral girdle consists of the scapulae and clavicles, and is responsible for attaching the upper limbs to the central skeleton. The pectoral girdle muscles hold the scapulae and clavicles in place.

The pectoral girdle is defined as the structure which attaches the upper limbs to the axial skeleton, namely the clavicles and scapulae, to which the muscles of the pectoral girdle attach; however, there are a few muscles which connect the upper limb directly to the central skeleton, and cause indirect movements of the pectoral girdle. This group of muscles lie superficially on the trunk; pectoralis major at the front and latissimus dorsi at the back.

### PECTORALIS MAJOR

Pectoralis major arises via two heads, one from the sternum (breastbone) and adjacent rib (costal) cartilages, and another from the middle third of the clavicle. Its tendon twists anti-clockwise as it courses towards the outer lip of the bicipital groove, on the upper end of the humerus. This twisting gives the clavicular head a greater mechanical advantage during flexion (bending) of the arm.

Pectoralis major derives its nerve supply and blood supply from a wide source. The sternocostal head of pectoralis major is a powerful adductor of the arm (pulling the limb towards the body), and is hence well-developed in climbers and weight-lifters. If the arm is kept fixed, this muscle can elevate the ribs as an accessory muscle of inspiration.

## Muscles of the pectoral girdle from the front

### Superficial

**Clavicle**
Collar bone; articulates with the scapula and sternum

**Deltoid muscle**
Covers the shoulder joint; gives the shoulder a rounded appearance

**Triceps brachii**
Extends the arm and forearm

**Latissimus dorsi**
Broad muscle of the back; powerful muscle of arm extension

**Pectoralis major**
Arises from the sternum, clavicle and the costal cartilages; pulls the arm toward the body

**Manubrium sterni**
Top section of the sternum

### Deep

**Sternocleidomastoid**
Enables flexion of the head and turning of the face sideways

**Subclavius**
Helps stabilize the pectoral girdle and protect underlying vessels

**Subscapularis**
Rotates the humerus and holds the shoulder joint in place

**Pectoralis minor**
Attaches to the coracoid process of scapula; assists in protraction (pushing the arm forwards)

**Serratus anterior**
Wraps around the ribcage; important in raising the arm and horizontal arm movements such as punching

**Sternum**
Breastbone; point of attachment for pectoralis major

## Beneath the pectoralis major

*If the arm is kept fixed, pectoralis major can elevate the ribs, and so act as an accessory muscle of inspiration. Exhausted sprinters, with hands on knees, exploit this feature.*

Deep to (lying beneath) the pectoralis major are subclavius and pectoralis minor. Subclavius is a rather insignificant muscle that probably helps to stabilize the clavicle during movements of the pectoral girdle. Following a clavicular fracture, the subclavius, together with deltoid and gravity, acts to pull downward on the outer fragment, while the medial fragment is pulled upwards by the unrestrained action of sternocleidomastoid. The separation of fragments may pose a particular threat to the subclavian vessels close by.

Sternocleidomastoid, which arises from the medial third of the clavicle and manubrium sterni, is mainly involved with movements of the head and neck.

Pectoralis minor arises from the second, third, fourth and fifth ribs, and attaches to the coracoid process of the scapula. It assists in pulling the scapula against and around the trunk wall. This action (protraction) is necessary to 'throw' a punch.

The main muscle which performs protraction is serratus anterior. This muscle wraps itself around the wall of the rib cage, to attach to the scapula's inner edge. The lower four digitations converge on the inferior angle of the scapula, and are involved in assisting trapezius during scapular rotations.

# Pectoral girdle from the back

The large trapezius and latissimus dorsi are superficial muscles of the back which attach to and influence the movement of the pectoral girdle.

Latissimus dorsi arises from the lower thoracic and the lumbar and sacral vertebrae. It also arises from the thoracolumbar fascia and posterior part of the iliac crest, with a few fibres attaching to the lower four ribs. From this broad base (latissimus means 'broadest' in Latin), it converges onto the floor of the bicipital groove at the upper end of the humerus.

This muscle assists pectoralis major in pulling the arm towards the body (adduction). Since the muscle wraps itself around the lower ribs, it assists during forceful expiration (breathing out), for example during coughing.

### TRAPEZIUS
Partly overlapping the latissimus dorsi is the lower part of the trapezius muscle. The trapezius also has a broad origin from the base of the skull (occipital protuberance) to the spines of the twelve thoracic vertebrae. The lower fibres attach to the spine of the scapula; intermediate fibres to the acromion process; and upper fibres to the outer third of the clavicle. The upper part serves to shrug the shoulders; the middle and lower parts serve to laterally rotate the scapula.

## Muscles of the pectoral girdle from the back

### Superficial

### Deep

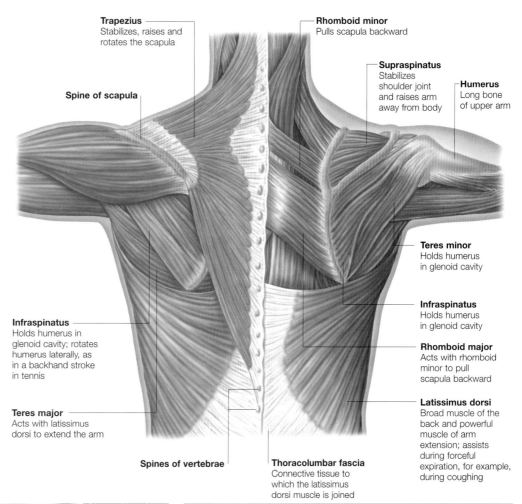

**Trapezius**
Stabilizes, raises and rotates the scapula

**Spine of scapula**

**Rhomboid minor**
Pulls scapula backward

**Supraspinatus**
Stabilizes shoulder joint and raises arm away from body

**Humerus**
Long bone of upper arm

**Teres minor**
Holds humerus in glenoid cavity

**Infraspinatus**
Holds humerus in glenoid cavity

**Infraspinatus**
Holds humerus in glenoid cavity; rotates humerus laterally, as in a backhand stroke in tennis

**Rhomboid major**
Acts with rhomboid minor to pull scapula backward

**Teres major**
Acts with latissimus dorsi to extend the arm

**Latissimus dorsi**
Broad muscle of the back and powerful muscle of arm extension; assists during forceful expiration, for example, during coughing

**Spines of vertebrae**

**Thoracolumbar fascia**
Connective tissue to which the latissimus dorsi muscle is joined

## Deep dissection

The scapula is pulled backwards (retracted) by the action of the rhomboids (rhomboid major and minor). They attach the inner edge of the scapula to the vertebral column. These muscles allow the shoulder to be 'braced'; as seen before a punch is thrown, or before a forceful push, since this maximizes the force in protraction (forwards).

Since these muscles lie deep to trapezius, they are difficult to see and feel. However, should they become paralysed on one side, the scapula on that side would be displaced further away from the midline.

*The rhomboids act together to retract the scapula to enable powerful protraction. This action can be seen before a boxer throws a punch.*

Rhomboid major and minor, together with the levator scapulae, also act to rotate the scapula medially, and hence counteract the actions of the trapezius and serratus anterior.

### MOVEMENT OF SCAPULA
Movements of the scapula are essential in providing the widest range of motion at the shoulder joint. Although there is no anatomical joint between the scapula and the trunk, clinicians often refer to a scapulothoracic 'joint', since there is a great deal of movement between the two.

These movements are also transferred to the sterno-clavicular joint through the clavicle. The sternoclavicular joint is the sole connecting link between the pectoral girdle and the trunk.

# Ribcage

The ribcage protects the vital organs of the thorax, as well as providing sites for the attachment of muscles of the back, chest and shoulders. It is also light enough to move during breathing.

The ribcage is supported at the back by the 12 thoracic vertebrae of the spinal column and is formed by the 12 paired ribs, the costal cartilages and the bony sternum, or breastbone, at the front.

## THE RIBS

Each of the 12 pairs of ribs is attached posteriorly (at the back) to the corresponding numbered thoracic vertebra. The ribs then curve down and around the chest towards the anterior (front) surface of the body.

The 12 ribs can be divided into two groups according to their anterior (front) site of attachment:

■ **True (vertebrosternal) ribs**
The first seven pairs of ribs attach anteriorly directly to the sternum via individual costal cartilages.

■ **False ribs**
These do not attach directly to the sternum. Rib pairs eight to 10 (vertebrochondral ribs) attach indirectly to the sternum via fused costal cartilages. Rib pairs 11 and 12 do not have attachments to bone or cartilage and so are known as 'vertebral' or 'floating' ribs. Their anterior ends lie buried within the musculature of the lateral abdominal wall.

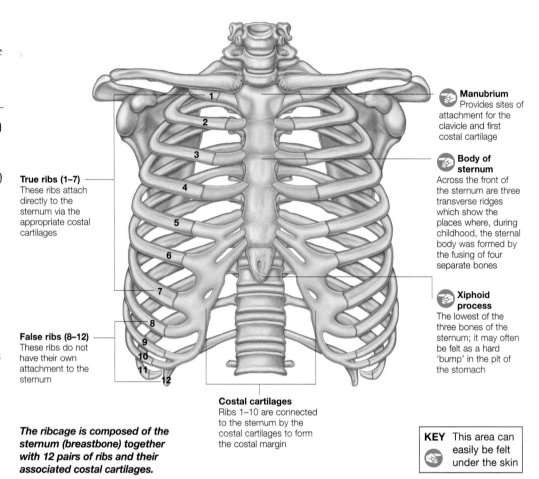

**Manubrium**
Provides sites of attachment for the clavicle and first costal cartilage

**Body of sternum**
Across the front of the sternum are three transverse ridges which show the places where, during childhood, the sternal body was formed by the fusing of four separate bones

**Xiphoid process**
The lowest of the three bones of the sternum; it may often be felt as a hard 'bump' in the pit of the stomach

**True ribs (1–7)**
These ribs attach directly to the sternum via the appropriate costal cartilages

**False ribs (8–12)**
These ribs do not have their own attachment to the sternum

**Costal cartilages**
Ribs 1–10 are connected to the sternum by the costal cartilages to form the costal margin

*The ribcage is composed of the sternum (breastbone) together with 12 pairs of ribs and their associated costal cartilages.*

**KEY** This area can easily be felt under the skin

## Rib structure

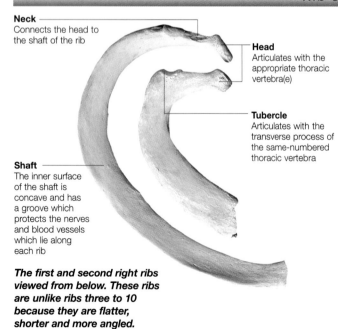

**Neck**
Connects the head to the shaft of the rib

**Head**
Articulates with the appropriate thoracic vertebra(e)

**Tubercle**
Articulates with the transverse process of the same-numbered thoracic vertebra

**Shaft**
The inner surface of the shaft is concave and has a groove which protects the nerves and blood vessels which lie along each rib

*The first and second right ribs viewed from below. These ribs are unlike ribs three to 10 because they are flatter, shorter and more angled.*

While they all vary slightly in their structure, ribs three to 10 are similar enough to be described as 'typical ribs'. They consist of the following parts:

■ **Head.** This connects with the thoracic vertebra with the same numeric value and the one immediately above that (for example the fourth rib attaches to both the third and fourth thoracic vertebrae)

■ **Neck.** This narrowed length of rib connects the head to the shaft or body

■ **Tubercle.** This raised, roughened area lies at the junction of neck and shaft and bears a facet for articulation with the transverse process of the thoracic vertebra

■ **Shaft.** The rib continues as a flattened, curved bone which bends around at the 'costal angle' to encircle the thorax.

### DISSIMILAR RIBS

■ **First rib.** This is the widest, shortest and most flattened rib; it has only one facet on its head for articulation with the first thoracic vertebra. On its upper surface it has a prominent 'scalene tubercle'

■ **Second rib.** This rib is thinner than the first, its shaft being more like that of a typical rib. Half-way down the shaft it has a second prominent tubercle for the attachment of muscles

■ **11th and 12th ribs (floating ribs).** These have only a single facet on their heads and do not have a point of articulation between their tubercle and the transverse process of the corresponding thoracic vertebrae. The ends of their shafts carry only a cap of cartilage and do not connect with any of the other ribs.

# The sternum

The sternum (breastbone) is a long, flat bone which lies vertically at the centre of the anterior (front) surface of the ribcage.

The sternum has three parts:
■ **The manubrium.** This bone forms the upper part of the sternum and is in the shape of a rough triangle with a prominent, and easily palpable, notch in the centre of its superior surface, the 'suprasternal notch'
■ **The body.** The manubrium and the body of the sternum lie in slightly different planes, angled so that their junction, the manubriosternal joint, projects forwards forming the 'sternal angle of Louis'. The body of the sternum is longer than the manubrium, forming the greater length of the breastbone
■ **The xiphoid process.** This is a small pointed bone which projects downwards and slightly backwards from the lower end of the body of the sternum. In young people it may be cartilaginous, but it usually becomes completely ossified (changed to bone) by 40–50 years of age.

*The sternum (breastbone) consists of three parts: the manubrium, the body and the xiphoid process.*

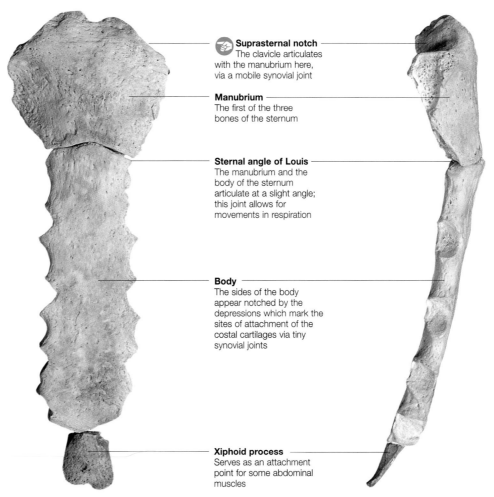

**Suprasternal notch**
The clavicle articulates with the manubrium here, via a mobile synovial joint

**Manubrium**
The first of the three bones of the sternum

**Sternal angle of Louis**
The manubrium and the body of the sternum articulate at a slight angle; this joint allows for movements in respiration

**Body**
The sides of the body appear notched by the depressions which mark the sites of attachment of the costal cartilages via tiny synovial joints

**Xiphoid process**
Serves as an attachment point for some abdominal muscles

---

## The costal cartilages

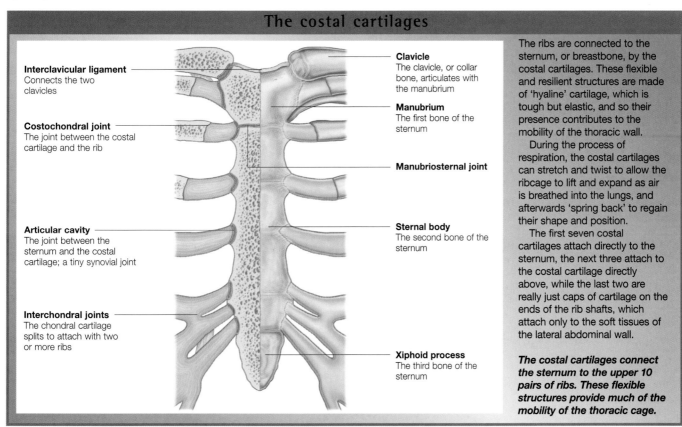

**Interclavicular ligament**
Connects the two clavicles

**Costochondral joint**
The joint between the costal cartilage and the rib

**Articular cavity**
The joint between the sternum and the costal cartilage; a tiny synovial joint

**Interchondral joints**
The chondral cartilage splits to attach with two or more ribs

**Clavicle**
The clavicle, or collar bone, articulates with the manubrium

**Manubrium**
The first bone of the sternum

**Manubriosternal joint**

**Sternal body**
The second bone of the sternum

**Xiphoid process**
The third bone of the sternum

The ribs are connected to the sternum, or breastbone, by the costal cartilages. These flexible and resilient structures are made of 'hyaline' cartilage, which is tough but elastic, and so their presence contributes to the mobility of the thoracic wall.

During the process of respiration, the costal cartilages can stretch and twist to allow the ribcage to lift and expand as air is breathed into the lungs, and afterwards 'spring back' to regain their shape and position.

The first seven costal cartilages attach directly to the sternum, the next three attach to the costal cartilage directly above, while the last two are really just caps of cartilage on the ends of the rib shafts, which attach only to the soft tissues of the lateral abdominal wall.

*The costal cartilages connect the sternum to the upper 10 pairs of ribs. These flexible structures provide much of the mobility of the thoracic cage.*

# Muscles and movements of the ribcage

The bony skeleton of the ribcage is sheathed in several layers of muscle which include many of the powerful muscles of the upper limb and back, as well as those which act upon the ribcage alone.

The integral muscles of the ribcage are concerned with respiration (breathing). They attach only to the ribcage and the thoracic spine. They form the structure of the thoracic wall, enclosing and protecting the vital internal organs of the thorax.

### INTERCOSTAL MUSCLES

The intercostal muscles fill the 11 intercostal spaces between the ribs. They lie in three layers, the external intercostals lying superficially, then the internal intercostals, with the innermost intercostals at the deepest level.

■ **External intercostal muscles**
The fibres of each external intercostal muscle run downwards and forwards to the rib below and their contraction acts to lift the ribs during inspiration (breathing in).

■ **Internal intercostal muscles**
The internal intercostal muscles lie just deep to the external intercostals and at right angles to them; that is, their fibres run downwards and backwards from the upper to the lower rib. Like the external intercostal muscles, they act to assist in inspiration.

■ **Innermost intercostal muscles**
These lie deep to the internal intercostal muscles, their fibres running in the same direction. They are separated from the internal intercostals by connective tissue containing the nerves and blood vessels.

## Internal view of the chest wall

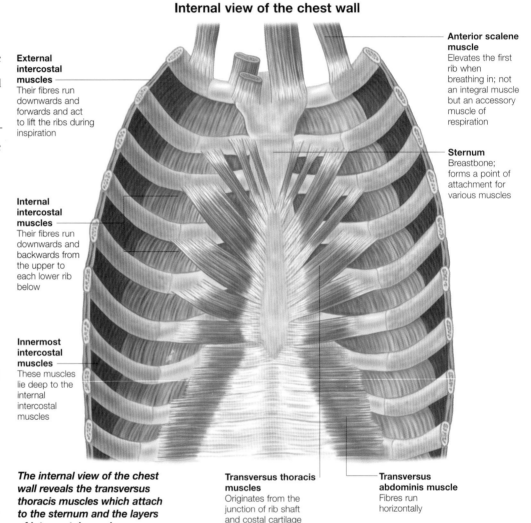

**External intercostal muscles**
Their fibres run downwards and forwards and act to lift the ribs during inspiration

**Internal intercostal muscles**
Their fibres run downwards and backwards from the upper to each lower rib below

**Innermost intercostal muscles**
These muscles lie deep to the internal intercostal muscles

**Anterior scalene muscle**
Elevates the first rib when breathing in; not an integral muscle but an accessory muscle of respiration

**Sternum**
Breastbone; forms a point of attachment for various muscles

**Transversus thoracis muscles**
Originates from the junction of rib shaft and costal cartilage

**Transversus abdominis muscle**
Fibres run horizontally

*The internal view of the chest wall reveals the transversus thoracis muscles which attach to the sternum and the layers of intercostal muscles.*

---

## Integral muscles of the ribcage

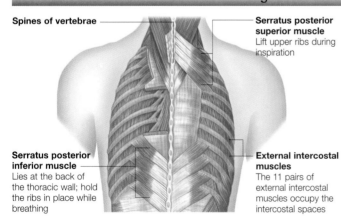

**Spines of vertebrae**

**Serratus posterior superior muscle**
Lift upper ribs during inspiration

**Serratus posterior inferior muscle**
Lies at the back of the thoracic wall; hold the ribs in place while breathing

**External intercostal muscles**
The 11 pairs of external intercostal muscles occupy the intercostal spaces

The integral muscles that form the structure of the ribcage include:

■ **Intercostal muscles**
These lie in three layers filling each intercostal space between the ribs.

■ **Subcostal muscles**
These are small muscles which run down on the inner surface of the posterior thoracic wall

*The view of the back of the thoracic wall reveals the external intercostal muscles and serratus inferior and superior muscles.*

between the lower ribs. Their fibres run in the same direction as those of the internal intercostal muscles and act to help in elevation of the ribs.

■ **Transversus thoracis muscles**
Small muscles which may vary in size and shape lying on the inside of the front of the chest.

■ **Serratus posterior**
These lie at the back of the thoracic wall in two parts: superior, which lifts the upper ribs during inspiration; and inferior, which holds the ribs in place during breathing.

# Movements of ribcage

During the action of breathing, the chest cavity expands and contracts, causing air to enter and leave. Expansion of the chest cavity is achieved by contraction of the diaphragm and movements of the ribcage.

Movements of the ribcage during quiet respiration are due to the action of the respiratory muscles, the most important being the intercostals. Contraction of the intercostal muscles causes the ribcage to expand both sideways and from front to back.

### EXPANDING THE CHEST
The lower ribs, especially, are lifted up and out to the sides in what had been described as a 'bucket handle' movement that increases the width of the ribcage. When the upper ribs are elevated, the sternum (breastbone) is also pulled up and rotated slightly so that its lower end moves forward. This action increases the depth of the ribcage and is described as a 'pump handle' movement.

Together, these movements act to increase the volume of the ribcage which, in turn, expands the underlying lungs and draws air in. When the intercostal muscles relax at the end of inspiration (breathing in), the ribcage descends again under the influence of gravity and the natural elasticity of the lungs.

## Ribcage when breathing in

**Lower ribs**
The lower ribs are moved out in a 'bucket handle' movement

**Upper ribs**
The first and second ribs may be elevated by the accessory muscles of respiration when a greater volume of air is required in the lungs

**Sternum**
The lower end of the sternum moves forward during inspiration, increasing the volume of the thorax in a 'pump handle' movement

*When breathing in, the ribcage can be seen to widen as the ribs are lifted up. The sternum also moves out, further expanding the chest.*

## Accessory muscles of respiration

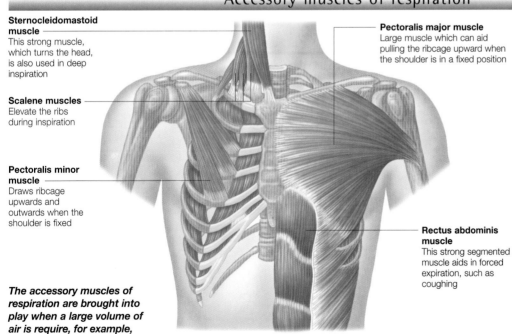

**Sternocleidomastoid muscle**
This strong muscle, which turns the head, is also used in deep inspiration

**Scalene muscles**
Elevate the ribs during inspiration

**Pectoralis minor muscle**
Draws ribcage upwards and outwards when the shoulder is fixed

**Pectoralis major muscle**
Large muscle which can aid pulling the ribcage upward when the shoulder is in a fixed position

**Rectus abdominis muscle**
This strong segmented muscle aids in forced expiration, such as coughing

*The accessory muscles of respiration are brought into play when a large volume of air is require, for example, after exercising.*

There are times when a much greater volume of air must enter the lungs or when, due to lung disease, there is more resistance to the entry of air. At these times, the accessory muscles of respiration are brought into play.

These are muscles with attachments both to the ribcage and to other parts of the upper skeleton, their normal function being to move the head, neck or upper limbs. If the origin of these powerful muscles is fixed at the other end, their contraction will lead to forcible movement and expansion of the ribcage.

This can be seen in the posture of an athlete after a race when the head is held back and the hands are held on hips or knees to brace the arms. This allows the muscles of the neck and shoulder girdle to expand the chest powerfully.

# Female breast

The breast undergoes structural changes throughout the life of a woman. The most obvious changes occur during pregnancy as the breast prepares for its function as the source of milk for the baby.

Men and women both have breast tissue, but the breast is normally a well-developed structure only in women. The two female breasts are roughly hemispherical and are composed of fat and glandular tissue which overlie the muscle layer of the front of the chest wall on either side of the sternum (breastbone).

### BREAST STRUCTURE

The base of the breast is roughly circular in shape and extends from the level of the second rib above to the sixth rib below. In addition, there may be an extension of breast tissue towards the axilla (armpit), known as the 'axillary tail'.

Breast size varies greatly between women; this is mainly due to the amount of fatty tissue present, as there is generally the same amount of glandular tissue in every breast.

The mammary glands consist of 15 to 20 lobules – clusters of secretory tissue from which milk is produced. Milk is carried to the surface of the breast from each lobule by a tube known as a 'lactiferous duct', which has its opening at the nipple.

The nipple is a protruding structure surrounded by a circular, pigmented area, called the areola. The skin of the nipple is very thin and delicate and has no hair follicles or sweat glands.

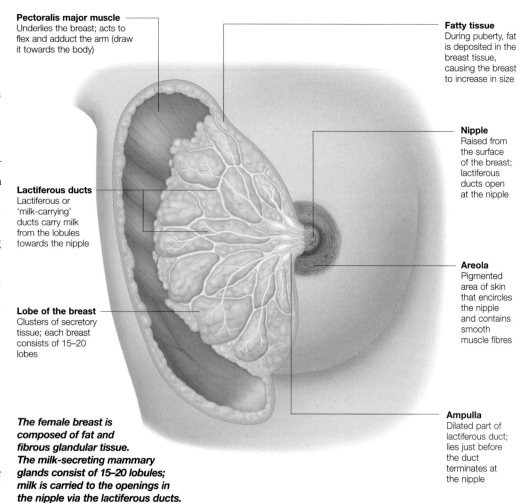

**Pectoralis major muscle**
Underlies the breast; acts to flex and adduct the arm (draw it towards the body)

**Fatty tissue**
During puberty, fat is deposited in the breast tissue, causing the breast to increase in size

**Nipple**
Raised from the surface of the breast; lactiferous ducts open at the nipple

**Lactiferous ducts**
Lactiferous or 'milk-carrying' ducts carry milk from the lobules towards the nipple

**Areola**
Pigmented area of skin that encircles the nipple and contains smooth muscle fibres

**Lobe of the breast**
Clusters of secretory tissue; each breast consists of 15–20 lobes

**Ampulla**
Dilated part of lactiferous duct; lies just before the duct terminates at the nipple

*The female breast is composed of fat and fibrous glandular tissue. The milk-secreting mammary glands consist of 15–20 lobules; milk is carried to the openings in the nipple via the lactiferous ducts.*

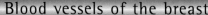

## Blood vessels of the breast

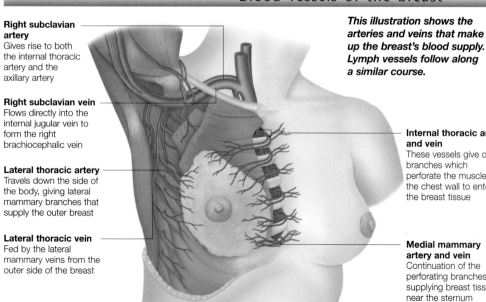

**Right subclavian artery**
Gives rise to both the internal thoracic artery and the axillary artery

**Right subclavian vein**
Flows directly into the internal jugular vein to form the right brachiocephalic vein

**Lateral thoracic artery**
Travels down the side of the body, giving lateral mammary branches that supply the outer breast

**Lateral thoracic vein**
Fed by the lateral mammary veins from the outer side of the breast

*This illustration shows the arteries and veins that make up the breast's blood supply. Lymph vessels follow along a similar course.*

**Internal thoracic artery and vein**
These vessels give off branches which perforate the muscles of the chest wall to enter the breast tissue

**Medial mammary artery and vein**
Continuation of the perforating branches supplying breast tissue near the sternum (breastbone)

The blood supply to the breast comes from a number of sources; these include the internal thoracic artery, which runs down the length of the front of the chest, and the lateral thoracic artery, which supplies the outer part of the breast and some of the posterior intercostal arteries.

A network of superficial veins underlies the skin of the breast, especially in the region of the areola, and these veins may become very prominent during pregnancy.

The blood collected in these veins drains in various directions, following a similar pattern to the arterial supply, travelling via the internal thoracic veins, the lateral thoracic veins and the posterior intercostal veins to the large veins that return blood to the heart.

# Lymphatic drainage of the breast

Lymph, the fluid which leaks out of blood vessels into the spaces between cells, is returned to the blood circulation by the lymphatic system. Lymph passes through a series of lymph nodes, which act as filters to remove bacteria, cells and other particles.

Tiny lymphatic vessels arise from the tissue spaces and converge to form larger vessels which carry the (usually) clear lymph away from the tissues and into the venous system.

Lymph drains from the nipple, areola and mammary gland lobules into a network of small lymphatic vessels, the 'subareolar lymphatic plexus'. From this plexus the lymph may be carried in several different directions.

### PATTERN OF DRAINAGE

About 75 per cent of the lymph from the subareolar plexus drains to the lymph nodes of the armpit, mostly from the outer quadrants of the breast. The lymph passes through a series of nodes in the region of the armpit draining into the subclavian lymph trunk, and ultimately into the right lymphatic trunk, which returns the lymph to the veins above the heart.

Most of the remaining lymph, mainly from the inner quadrants of the breast, is carried to the 'parasternal' lymph nodes, which lie towards the mid-line of the front of the chest. A small percentage of lymphatic vessels from the breast take another route and travel to the posterior intercostal nodes.

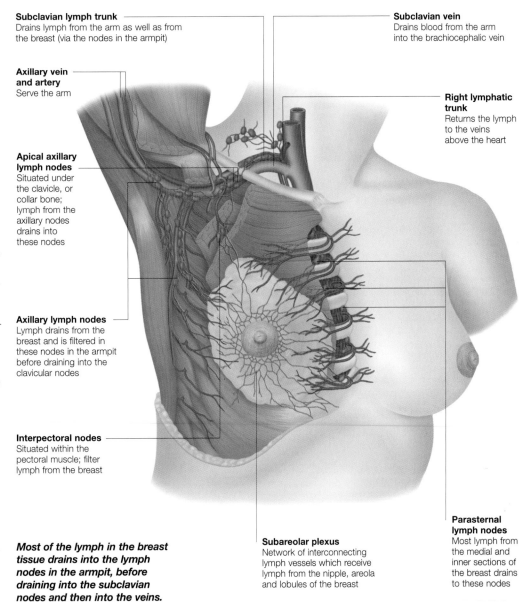

**Subclavian lymph trunk**
Drains lymph from the arm as well as from the breast (via the nodes in the armpit)

**Axillary vein and artery**
Serve the arm

**Apical axillary lymph nodes**
Situated under the clavicle, or collar bone; lymph from the axillary nodes drains into these nodes

**Axillary lymph nodes**
Lymph drains from the breast and is filtered in these nodes in the armpit before draining into the clavicular nodes

**Interpectoral nodes**
Situated within the pectoral muscle; filter lymph from the breast

**Subclavian vein**
Drains blood from the arm into the brachiocephalic vein

**Right lymphatic trunk**
Returns the lymph to the veins above the heart

**Parasternal lymph nodes**
Most lymph from the medial and inner sections of the breast drains to these nodes

**Subareolar plexus**
Network of interconnecting lymph vessels which receive lymph from the nipple, areola and lobules of the breast

*Most of the lymph in the breast tissue drains into the lymph nodes in the armpit, before draining into the subclavian nodes and then into the veins.*

---

## Lymphatic drainage and breast cancer

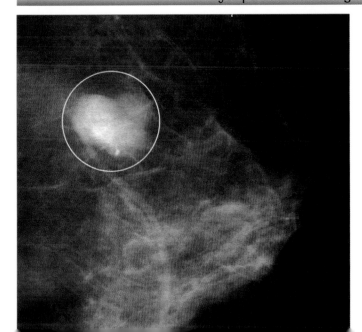

*This mammogram shows a malignant tumour in the breast. The tumour is apparent as the dense area (circled) within the breast tissue.*

Lymph fluid often contains particles such as cells which it has cleared from the tissue spaces. If the lymph has come from an area which contains a growing cancer, then it may contain cells which have broken off from that tumour. These cells will be filtered out by the lymph nodes where they may lodge and grow to form a secondary tumour, or 'metastasis'.

Knowledge of the pattern of lymph drainage of each area of the body, and especially of an area as prone to cancer as the breast, is therefore important to doctors. If a breast lump is found it is important for the doctor to check the associated lymph nodes for secondary spread of cancer cells.

### MAMMOGRAPHY

As well as examination of the breast by the doctor or the woman herself, mammography (X-ray examination of the breasts), can be used to check for breast cancer. Mammograms help to detect the presence of cancer of the breast at an early, and therefore more easily treatable, stage.

# Diaphragm

The diaphragm is a sheet of muscle that separates the thorax from the abdominal cavity. It is essential for breathing as its contraction expands the chest cavity, allowing air to enter.

The diaphragm is the main muscle involved in respiration and has several apertures for the passage of important structures which must pass between thorax and abdomen. It is made up of peripheral muscle fibres inserting into a central sheet of tendon which, unlike most tendons, does not have any attachment to bone.

## MUSCLE OF THE DIAPHRAGM

The muscle tissue of the diaphragm arises from three areas of the chest wall, merges to form a continuous sheet and converges on the central tendon, which acts as a site of muscular attachment.

The three areas of origin of the diaphragm give rise to three separately named parts: the sternal part, the costal part and the lumbar or vertebral part, which arises from the crus and arcuate ligaments.

## CENTRAL TENDON

Muscle fibres of the diaphragm insert into the central tendon, which has a three-leaved shape. The central part lies just beneath, and is depressed by, the heart. It is attached by ligaments to the pericardium, the membrane surrounding the heart. The two lateral leaves lie towards the back and help form the right and left domes (cupolae) of the diaphragm.

## Abdominal surface of the diaphragm

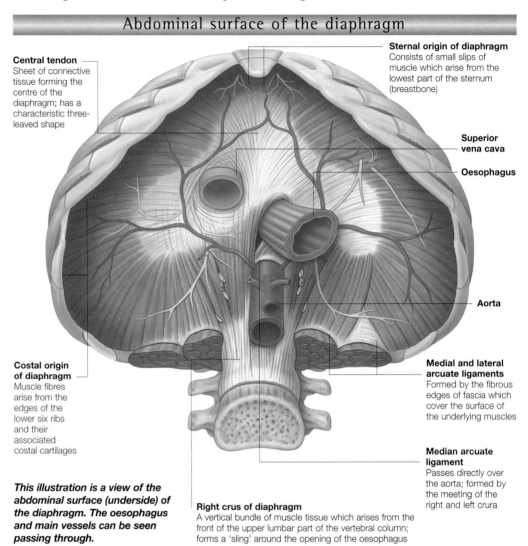

**Central tendon**
Sheet of connective tissue forming the centre of the diaphragm; has a characteristic three-leaved shape

**Sternal origin of diaphragm**
Consists of small slips of muscle which arise from the lowest part of the sternum (breastbone)

**Superior vena cava**

**Oesophagus**

**Aorta**

**Medial and lateral arcuate ligaments**
Formed by the fibrous edges of fascia which cover the surface of the underlying muscles

**Median arcuate ligament**
Passes directly over the aorta; formed by the meeting of the right and left crura

**Costal origin of diaphragm**
Muscle fibres arise from the edges of the lower six ribs and their associated costal cartilages

*This illustration is a view of the abdominal surface (underside) of the diaphragm. The oesophagus and main vessels can be seen passing through.*

**Right crus of diaphragm**
A vertical bundle of muscle tissue which arises from the front of the upper lumbar part of the vertebral column; forms a 'sling' around the opening of the oesophagus

## Nerve supply of the diaphragm

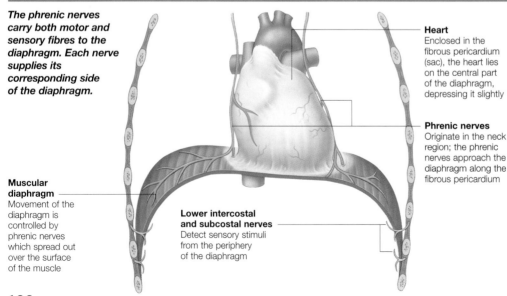

*The phrenic nerves carry both motor and sensory fibres to the diaphragm. Each nerve supplies its corresponding side of the diaphragm.*

**Muscular diaphragm**
Movement of the diaphragm is controlled by phrenic nerves which spread out over the surface of the muscle

**Lower intercostal and subcostal nerves**
Detect sensory stimuli from the periphery of the diaphragm

**Heart**
Enclosed in the fibrous pericardium (sac), the heart lies on the central part of the diaphragm, depressing it slightly

**Phrenic nerves**
Originate in the neck region; the phrenic nerves approach the diaphragm along the fibrous pericardium

The motor nerve supply of the diaphragm (which causes the muscle of the diaphragm to contract) comes entirely from a nerve on each side called the 'phrenic nerve'. These nerves originate from each side of the spinal cord in the neck, at the level of the third, fourth and fifth cervical vertebrae.

### SENSORY NERVE SUPPLY

The phrenic nerves also provide a sensory nerve supply, detecting pain and giving information on position, to the greater, central part of the diaphragm. The periphery of the diaphragm receives its sensory nerve supply from the lower intercostal nerves and the subcostal nerves.

# Thoracic surface of the diaphragm

The upper aspect of the diaphragm is convex and forms the floor of the thoracic (chest) cavity. It is perforated by major vessels and structures which must pass through the muscle sheet in order to reach the abdomen.

The central part of the surface of the diaphragm is covered by the pericardium, the membrane which surrounds the heart. To either side, the upper surface of the diaphragm is lined with the diaphragmatic part of the parietal pleura (the thin membrane which lines the chest cavity). This is continuous around the edges of the diaphragm with the costal pleura, which covers the inside of the chest wall.

## DIAPHRAGMATIC APERTURES

Although the diaphragm acts to separate the chest and abdominal cavities, certain structures do pass through 'diaphragmatic apertures'. The three largest of these are:

■ **The caval aperture**
This is an opening in the central tendon of the diaphragm which allows passage of the inferior vena cava, the main vein of the abdomen and lower limbs. As the opening is in the central tendon rather than the muscle of the diaphragm it will not close when the diaphragm contracts during inspiration; in fact the opening widens and blood flow increases. The opening also contains branches of the right phrenic nerve and lymphatic vessels.

### Diaphragm from above

**Diaphragmatic pleura**
Cut away here to show the underlying diaphragm

**Right leaflet of central tendon**
Non-muscular (fibrous) part of the diaphragm

**Aorta lying in the aortic aperture**
Not strictly an aperture as the aorta, thoracic duct and azygos vein actually lie against the vertebral column behind the diaphragm

**BACK**

**Caval aperture**
Opening in the central tendon, just to the right of the midline, through which the vena cava passes

**FRONT**

**Pericardium**
Sac containing the heart

**Left phrenic nerve**
Seen here travelling along the border of the pericardium

**Inferior vena cava**
Main vein of the abdomen and lower limbs

**Oesophagus**
Lies in the oesophageal aperture, just to the left of the midline within the right crus of the diaphragm

*This cross-section of the chest shows the diaphragm from above. The diaphragm provides a division between the thoracic and abdominal cavities.*

■ **The oesophageal aperture**
This allows the passage of the oesophagus (gullet) through the diaphragm to reach the stomach. The muscle fibres of the right crus act as a sphincter, closing off the oesophageal opening when the diaphragm contracts during inspiration. As well as the oesophagus, the aperture also gives passage to nerves (vagus), arteries and lymphatic vessels.

■ **The aortic aperture**
This opening lies behind the diaphragm rather than within it. As the aorta does not actually pierce the diaphragm, the flow of blood within it is not affected by diaphragmatic contractions while breathing. The aorta emerges under the median arcuate ligament, in front of the vertebral column. The aortic aperture also transmits the thoracic duct (major lymphatic channel) and the azygos vein.

### Position and function of the diaphragm

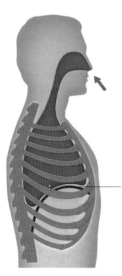

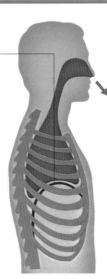

**Expiration**
As the diaphragm relaxes, the domes rise up, decreasing the volume of the chest resulting in air being exhaled

**Inspiration**
The diaphragm is pulled down as it is contracted (flattened), increasing the volume of the thorax; this results in air being taken into the lungs

The diaphragm lies across the body separating the thoracic cavity from the abdominal cavity. It curves upwards into two domes, right and left, separated by a central depression where the heart rests. The right dome is normally higher than the left because of the liver beneath.

The periphery of the diaphragm is at a constant level as it is attached to the thoracic wall, but the heights of the domes vary depending on the degree to which the muscle of

the diaphragm is contracted. The right dome can reach as high as the fifth rib, the left slightly lower.

## ACTIONS OF THE DIAPHRAGM

Contraction of the muscle fibres cause the domes to be pulled down, which expands the thoracic cavity above, and air enters. Relaxation of the diaphragmatic muscle allows the domes to rise and air is exhaled.

Contraction of the diaphragm also causes the abdominal cavity below to become smaller, putting the contents under greater pressure. Its contraction is thus used to help expel abdominal contents, such as in defecation.

*The diaphragm is the main muscle of respiration. By working in conjunction with the changing shape of the ribcage, air is inhaled and exhaled.*

107

# Lungs

The paired lungs are cone-shaped organs of respiration which occupy the thoracic cavity, lying to either side of the heart, great blood vessels and other structures of the central mediastinum.

The right and left lungs are separate entities, each enclosed within a bag of membranes, the right and left pleural sacs. Each lung lies free within the thoracic cavity, attached to the mediastinum only by a root made up of the main bronchus and large blood vessels.

The lung tissue is soft and spongy and has great elasticity. In children the lungs are pink in colour, but they usually become darkener and mottled later in life as they are exposed to dust which is taken in by the defence cells of the lining of the airways.

Each lung has:

■ An apex, which projects up into the base of the neck behind the clavicle (collarbone)

■ A base, with a concave surface, which rests on the superior surface of the diaphragm

■ A concave mediastinal surface, which lies against various structures of the mediastinum.

## LOBES AND FISSURES

The lungs are divided into sections known as lobes by deep fissures. The right lung has three lobes while the left lung, which is slightly smaller (due to the position of the heart), has two. Each lobe is independent of the others, receiving air via its own lobar bronchus and blood from lobar arteries.

The fissures are deep, extending right through the structure of the lung, and are lined by the pleural membrane.

### Anterior view of the lungs

Right lung      Left lung

**Horizontal fissure of right lung**
Lies anteriorly behind the fourth costal cartilage; extends back through the lung tissue to meet the oblique fissure about halfway along its length

**UPPER LOBE**

**MIDDLE LOBE**

**LOWER LOBE**

**Trachea**
Divides into the two bronchi

**UPPER LOBE**

**Hilum**
Area on the centre of the inner surface where the structures which form the root enter and leave the lung

**LOWER LOBE**

*The right lung consists of three lobes but the left lung has only two. This is to accommodate the heart which lies in the left chest.*

**Cardiac notch**
A 'cut-out' in the left lung which accommodates the heart

**Oblique fissure of right lung**
Lies between the middle and lower lobes of the right lung

**Oblique fissure of left lung**
Runs down and forward through the lung tissue from a point about 6 cm below the apex posteriorly

## Bronchopulmonary segments

Right lung

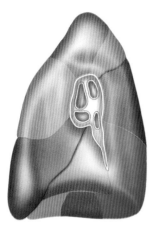

Left lung

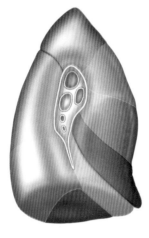

The lobes of the lung are further subdivided into units known as bronchopulmonary segments, which are separated from each other by a layer of connective tissue. Each segment is roughly pyramidal in shape, with its base on the pleural surface and its apex at the root of the lung, where the bronchus and major vessels enter and leave.

*The lobes of each lung are further divided into several distinct parts, known as the bronchopulmonary segments. Medial (inward-looking) views of the right and left lungs are illustrated here.*

### CLINICAL SIGNIFICANCE

Knowledge of the layout and structure of the bronchopulmonary segments is of particular importance to thoracic surgeons who may need to remove a lung tumour or abscess.

Like the whole lobe itself, each segment has its own blood supply and receives air from a segmental bronchus, thus making it independent from the others. For this reason, one or more segments may be surgically removed – because of disease or trauma, for instance – without adversely affecting the others.

# The pleura

The lungs are covered by a thin membrane known as the pleura. The pleura lines both the outer surface of the lung and the inner surface of the thoracic cage.

The layer of pleura covering the lung is called the visceral pleura, while that lining the thoracic cage is the parietal pleura.

### VISCERAL PLEURA

This thin membrane covers the lung surface, dipping down into the fissures between the lobes of the lung.

### PARIETAL PLEURA

This is continuous with the visceral pleura at the hilum of the lung. Here, the membrane reflects back and lines all the inner surfaces of the thoracic cavity. The parietal pleura is one continuous membrane divided into areas that are named after the surfaces they cover:

■ Costal pleura – lines the inside of the ribcage, the back of the sternum and the sides of the vertebral bodies of the spine
■ Mediastinal pleura – covers the mediastinum, the central area of the thoracic cavity
■ Diaphragmatic pleura – lines the upper surface of the diaphragm, except where it is covered by the pericardium
■ Cervical pleura – covers the tip of the lung as it projects up into the base of the neck.

## Position of the lungs and pleura

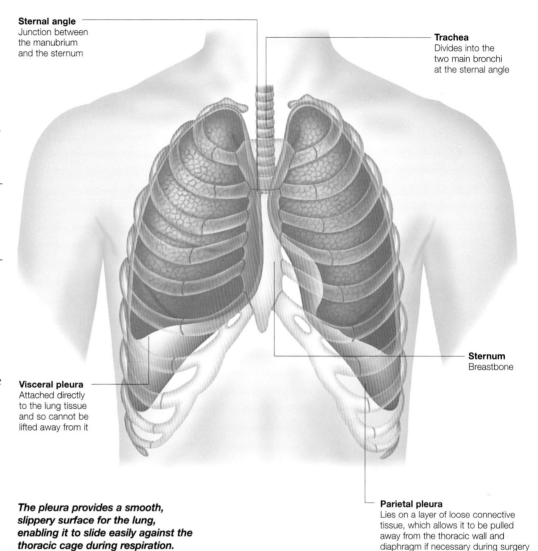

**Sternal angle**
Junction between the manubrium and the sternum

**Trachea**
Divides into the two main bronchi at the sternal angle

**Sternum**
Breastbone

**Visceral pleura**
Attached directly to the lung tissue and so cannot be lifted away from it

**Parietal pleura**
Lies on a layer of loose connective tissue, which allows it to be pulled away from the thoracic wall and diaphragm if necessary during surgery

*The pleura provides a smooth, slippery surface for the lung, enabling it to slide easily against the thoracic cage during respiration.*

## Pleural cavity and recesses of the pleura

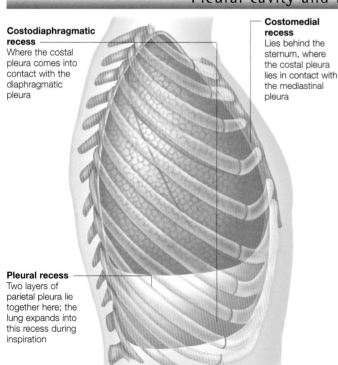

**Costodiaphragmatic recess**
Where the costal pleura comes into contact with the diaphragmatic pleura

**Costomedial recess**
Lies behind the sternum, where the costal pleura lies in contact with the mediastinal pleura

**Pleural recess**
Two layers of parietal pleura lie together here; the lung expands into this recess during inspiration

The pleural cavity, which lies between the visceral and parietal layers of pleura, is a narrow area filled with a small amount of pleural fluid. The fluid lubricates the movement of the lung within the thoracic cavity and also acts to provide a tight seal, holding the lung against the thoracic wall and diaphragm by surface tension. It is this seal that forces the elastic tissue of the lung to expand when the diaphragm contracts and the ribcage lifts during inspiration.

### PLEURAL RECESSES

During quiet breathing, the lungs do not completely fill the pleural sacs within which they lie. There is room for expansion

*This view from the right side of the chest shows how the lung does not entirely fill the pleural sac within which it lies.*

in the pleural recesses, areas where the sacs are empty and where parietal pleura comes into contact with itself rather than visceral pleura overlying lung tissue. The lungs only expand fully into these recesses during deep inspiration, when lung volume is at a maximum.

### PLEURAL EFFUSION

At the base of the thoracic cavity, the lowermost parts of the costal pleura come into contact with the diaphragmatic pleura in the costodiaphragmatic recess. This recess is of importance clinically because it provides a potential space that may become filled with fluid – a so-called pleural effusion – in certain medical conditions, such as heart failure.

The costomediastinal recess is smaller and of less clinical importance.

# Respiratory airways

The airways form a network along which air travels to, from and within the lungs. The airways branch repeatedly, each branch narrowing until the end terminals – the alveoli – are reached.

As a breath is taken, air enters through the nose and mouth, then passes down through the larynx to enter the trachea (windpipe). The air is carried down into the chest by the trachea, which then divides into smaller tubes – the bronchi – which take the air into the lungs.

The bronchi divide to form progressively smaller tubes that reach all areas of the lung. These tubes terminate in the alveolar sacs, which form the substance of the lung. It is in these thin-walled sacs that gas exchange with the blood occurs.

## TRACHEA

The trachea extends down from the cricoid cartilage just below the larynx in the neck to enter the chest. At the level of the sternal angle it ends by dividing into two branches, the right and left main bronchi.

The trachea is composed of strong fibroelastic tissue, within which are embedded a series of incomplete rings of hyaline cartilage, the tracheal cartilages. In adults the trachea is quite wide (approximately 2.5 cm), but it is much narrower in infants – about the width of a pencil.

The posterior (back) surface of the trachea has no cartilaginous support and instead consists of fibrous tissue and trachealis muscle fibres. This posterior wall lies in contact with the oesophagus, which is directly behind the trachea.

## The major airways

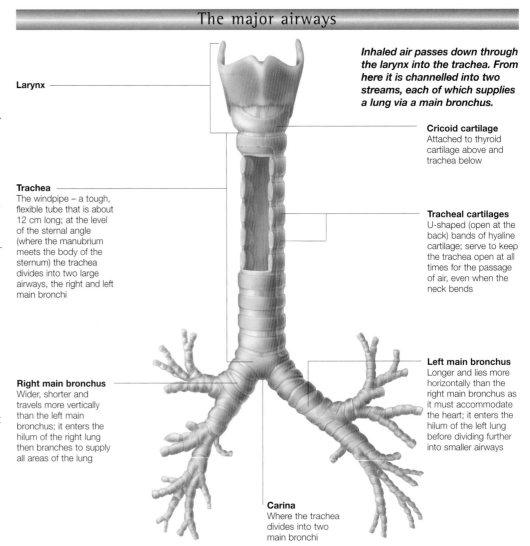

*Inhaled air passes down through the larynx into the trachea. From here it is channelled into two streams, each of which supplies a lung via a main bronchus.*

**Larynx**

**Trachea**
The windpipe – a tough, flexible tube that is about 12 cm long; at the level of the sternal angle (where the manubrium meets the body of the sternum) the trachea divides into two large airways, the right and left main bronchi

**Right main bronchus**
Wider, shorter and travels more vertically than the left main bronchus; it enters the hilum of the right lung then branches to supply all areas of the lung

**Cricoid cartilage**
Attached to thyroid cartilage above and trachea below

**Tracheal cartilages**
U-shaped (open at the back) bands of hyaline cartilage; serve to keep the trachea open at all times for the passage of air, even when the neck bends

**Left main bronchus**
Longer and lies more horizontally than the right main bronchus as it must accommodate the heart; it enters the hilum of the left lung before dividing further into smaller airways

**Carina**
Where the trachea divides into two main bronchi

## Cross-section through the trachea

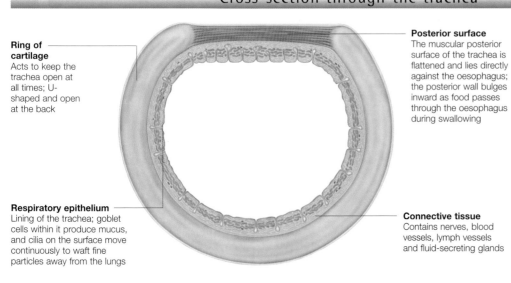

**Ring of cartilage**
Acts to keep the trachea open at all times; U-shaped and open at the back

**Respiratory epithelium**
Lining of the trachea; goblet cells within it produce mucus, and cilia on the surface move continuously to waft fine particles away from the lungs

**Posterior surface**
The muscular posterior surface of the trachea is flattened and lies directly against the oesophagus; the posterior wall bulges inward as food passes through the oesophagus during swallowing

**Connective tissue**
Contains nerves, blood vessels, lymph vessels and fluid-secreting glands

The trachea in cross-section is an incomplete ring. The epithelium (cellular lining) of the trachea contains goblet cells, which secrete mucus onto the surface, and tiny, brush-like cilia (hairs) which together help to catch dust particles and move them back up towards the larynx and away from the lung.

Between the epithelium and the rings of cartilage lies a layer of connective tissue containing small blood vessels, nerves, lymphatic vessels and glands that produce watery mucus which is secreted into the trachea. There are also many elastic fibres, which help to give the trachea its flexibility.

# Smaller airways and alveoli

On entering the lung the main bronchus divides again and again, forming the 'bronchial tree', which takes air to all parts of the lung.

The first division of the main bronchus gives rise to the lobar bronchi, three on the right and two on the left, which each supply one lobe of the lung. Each of these lobar bronchi divides to form the smaller bronchi, which supply each of the independent bronchopulmonary segments.

### BRONCHI STRUCTURE
The bronchi have a similar structure to the trachea, being very elastic and flexible, having cartilage in their walls and being lined with respiratory epithelium. There are also numerous muscle fibres, which allow for changes in diameter of these tubes.

### BRONCHIOLES
Within the bronchopulmonary segments the bronchi continue to divide, perhaps as many as 25 times, before they terminate in the blind-ended alveolar sacs.

At each division the tubes become smaller, although the total cross-sectional area increases. When the air tubes have an internal diameter of less than 1 mm they become known as bronchioles.

Bronchioles differ from bronchi in that they have no cartilage in their walls nor any mucus-secreting cells in their lining. They do, however, still have muscle fibres in their walls.

## Bronchioles and alveoli

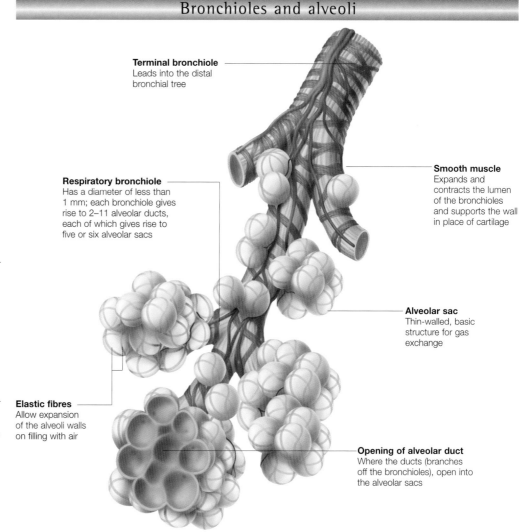

**Terminal bronchiole**
Leads into the distal bronchial tree

**Respiratory bronchiole**
Has a diameter of less than 1 mm; each bronchiole gives rise to 2–11 alveolar ducts, each of which gives rise to five or six alveolar sacs

**Elastic fibres**
Allow expansion of the alveoli walls on filling with air

**Smooth muscle**
Expands and contracts the lumen of the bronchioles and supports the wall in place of cartilage

**Alveolar sac**
Thin-walled, basic structure for gas exchange

**Opening of alveolar duct**
Where the ducts (branches off the bronchioles), open into the alveolar sacs

Further divisions lead to the formation of terminal bronchioles, which in turn divide to form a series of respiratory bronchioles, the smallest and finest air passages. Respiratory bronchioles are so named because they have a few alveoli (air sacs) opening directly into them. Most of the alveoli, however, arise in clusters from alveolar ducts, which are formed from division of the respiratory bronchioles.

*The branching of the bronchial tree ends in numerous terminal bronchioles from which arise the respiratory bronchioles, alveolar ducts and alveoli. The clusters of alveoli provide a large surface area for gaseous exchange.*

## Alveoli

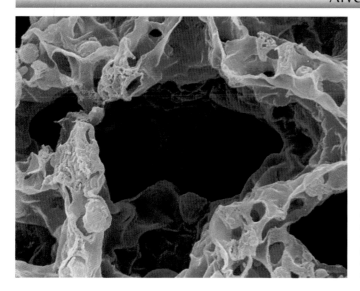

*Highly magnified image of alveolar sacs. It is across their thin walls that oxygen diffuses into the blood and waste gases are removed. Each adult lung contains about 300 million alveoli.*

The alveoli, tiny hollow sacs with extremely thin walls, are the sites of gaseous exchange within the lungs. It is through the alveolar walls that oxygen diffuses from the air into the pulmonary bloodstream, and waste carbon dioxide diffuses out.

There are many millions of alveoli in the human lung which together give a huge surface area (about 140 m$^2$) for this exchange to take place.

The alveoli lie in clusters like bunches of grapes around the alveolar ducts, each having a narrowed opening into a duct. They also have small holes, or pores, through which they connect with neighbouring alveoli. The alveolar walls are lined by flattened epithelial cells, and are supported by a framework of elastic and collagen fibres.

Two other types of cell are found in the alveoli: macrophages (defence cells), which engulf any foreign particles that get down the respiratory tract; and cells which produce surfactant, an important substance that lowers the surface tension in the fluid lining the alveoli, preventing their collapse.

# Vessels of the lung

The primary function of the lungs is to reoxygenate the blood used by the tissues of the body and to remove accumulated waste carbon dioxide. This is effected via the pulmonary blood circulation.

Blood from the body returns to the right side of the heart and from there passes directly to the lungs via the pulmonary arteries.

Having been oxygenated by its passage through the lungs, the blood returns to the left side of the heart in the pulmonary veins. The oxygen-rich blood is then pumped around the body. Collectively, the pulmonary arteries and veins and their branches are referred to as the pulmonary circulation.

## PULMONARY VESSELS

A large artery known as the pulmonary trunk arises from the heart's right ventricle carrying dark-red deoxygenated blood from the body into the lungs.

The pulmonary trunk divides into two smaller branches, the right and left pulmonary arteries, which run horizontally and enter the lungs at the hilum, alongside the bronchi (main airways).

Within the lungs the arteries divide to supply each lobe of their respective lung; two on the left and three on the right. The lobar arteries divide further to give the segmental arteries, which supply the bronchopulmonary segments (structural units of the lung). Each segmental artery ends in a network of capillaries.

Oxygenated blood returns to the left side of the heart through a system of pulmonary veins running alongside the arteries.

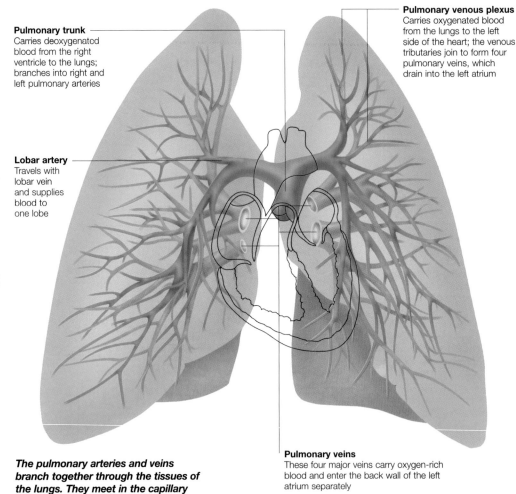

**Pulmonary trunk**
Carries deoxygenated blood from the right ventricle to the lungs; branches into right and left pulmonary arteries

**Lobar artery**
Travels with lobar vein and supplies blood to one lobe

**Pulmonary venous plexus**
Carries oxygenated blood from the lungs to the left side of the heart; the venous tributaries join to form four pulmonary veins, which drain into the left atrium

**Pulmonary veins**
These four major veins carry oxygen-rich blood and enter the back wall of the left atrium separately

*The pulmonary arteries and veins branch together through the tissues of the lungs. They meet in the capillary beds, where gas exchange occurs.*

## Alveolar capillary plexus

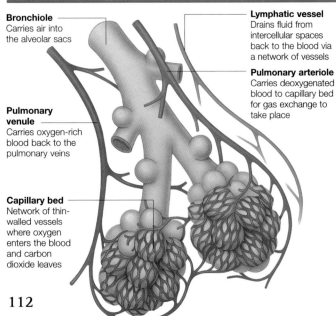

**Bronchiole**
Carries air into the alveolar sacs

**Pulmonary venule**
Carries oxygen-rich blood back to the pulmonary veins

**Capillary bed**
Network of thin-walled vessels where oxygen enters the blood and carbon dioxide leaves

**Lymphatic vessel**
Drains fluid from intercellular spaces back to the blood via a network of vessels

**Pulmonary arteriole**
Carries deoxygenated blood to capillary bed for gas exchange to take place

Within the lung, repeated division of the pulmonary arteries ultimately results in a network (plexus) of tiny blood vessels (capillaries), around each of the millions of alveolar sacs. The walls of the capillaries are extremely thin, which allows the blood within them to come into close contact with the walls of the alveoli, through which gas exchange takes place.

As oxygen enters and carbon dioxide leaves the pulmonary blood it changes from dark to

*Each alveolus is surrounded by a capillary plexus. Deoxygenated blood is oxygenated by gaseous exchange, which occurs through the walls of the alveoli.*

light red. The newly oxygenated blood is collected into venules which drain each capillary plexus, these venules ultimately joining to form the pulmonary veins, which complete the pulmonary circulation by returning the blood to the heart.

## INTRINSIC BLOOD SUPPLY

The tissues of the smallest airways can absorb oxygen from the air they contain, but this is not true for the larger airways, the supporting connective tissue of the lung and the pleura covering the lung. These structures receive their blood supply directly from two small bronchial arteries which arise from the thoracic aorta.

# Lymphatics of the lung

Lymphatic drainage of the lung originates in two main networks, or plexuses: the superficial (subpleural) plexus and the deep lymphatic plexus. These communicate freely with each other.

Lymph is a fluid which is collected from the spaces between cells and carried in lymphatic vessels back to the venous circulation. On its way, the lymph must pass through a series of lymph nodes, which act as filters to remove particulate matter and any invading micro-organisms.

### SUPERFICIAL PLEXUS
This network of fine lymphatic vessels extends over the surface of the lung, just beneath the visceral pleura (covering of the lung). The superficial plexus drains lymph from the lung towards the bronchi and trachea, where the main groups of lymph nodes are found.

Lymph from the superficial plexus arrives first at the bronchopulmonary group of lymph nodes, which lie at the hilum of the lung.

### DEEP PLEXUS
The lymphatic vessels of the deep plexus originate in the connective tissue surrounding the small airways, bronchioles and bronchi (the alveoli have no lymphatic vessels). There are also small lymphatic vessels within the lining of the larger airways.

These lymphatic vessels join and run back along the route of the bronchi and pulmonary blood vessels, passing through

**Trachea**
Airway through which air moves between the lungs and the atmosphere via the nose and mouth

**Right subclavian lymphatic trunk**
Drains lymph from upper limb and joins vessels draining right lung

**Interlobar fissure**
Separates adjacent lobes of the lung

**Tracheo-bronchial (carinal) lymph nodes**
Drain lymph from the nodes in the hilum

**Brachiocephalic vein**
Drains into left subclavian vein

**Thoracic duct**
Drains lymph from the left chest and most of the body below the diaphragm into the origin of the left brachiocephalic vein

**Paratracheal node**
Drains lymph from lung via carinal and hilar nodes

**Deep lymphatic vessels**
Drain lymph from within the substance of the lung

**Intrapulmonary lymph node**
Filters lymph in vessels of the deep lymphatic plexus

**Bronchopulmonary lymph nodes**
Lymph nodes at the hilum of the lung

intrapulmonary nodes which lie within the lung. From these nodes lymph passes through vessels which drain towards the hilum into the broncho-pulmonary lymph nodes.

The bronchopulmonary nodes at the hilum of the lung

therefore receive lymph from both superficial and deep lymphatic plexuses.

### LYMPH NODES OF THE BRONCHI AND TRACHEA
From the bronchopulmonary nodes, lymph drains to the

tracheobronchial (carinal) lymph nodes. From here, lymph passes up through the paratracheal nodes lying alongside the trachea, into the paired bronchomediastinal lymph trunks, which return the fluid to the venous system in the neck.

## Mottled lungs

Living in an urban environment where atmospheric pollution is high, or smoking cigarettes, will lead to the inhalation of air containing many particles of dust and carbon.

Specialized cells in the lungs, called phagocytes, are able to protect the delicate lung tissue from these potential irritants by ingesting them. The process of ingestion is known as phagocytosis.

*This post-mortem lung specimen shows the black discoloration of a smoker's lung. The air sacs are also abnormally enlarged due to emphysema.*

Phagocytes containing particles can be carried away in the lymphatics and become lodged in the superficial plexus just under the surface of the lung. This gives a darkly mottled, 'honeycomb' appearance to the lung surface. This dark staining may also be apparent in the various groups of lymph nodes throughout the lung.

An understanding of the layout of the lymphatic vessels and lymph nodes of the lung can be important clinically in the assessment of lung cancer, which can spread via the lymphatic system.

# Heart

The adult heart is about the size of a clenched fist and lies within
the mediastinum in the thoracic cavity. It rests on the central tendon
of the diaphragm and is flanked on either side by the lungs.

Surrounding the heart is a protective sac of connective tissue called the pericardium.

The heart is hollow and is composed almost entirely of muscle. The typical weight of the normal heart is only about 250 to 350 grams yet it has incredible power and stamina, beating over 70 times every minute to pump blood around the body.

### SURFACES OF THE HEART

Roughly the shape of a pyramid on its side, the heart is said to have a base, three surfaces and an apex:

■ The base of the heart lies posteriorly (at the back) and is formed mainly by the left atrium, the chamber of the heart that receives oxygenated blood from the lungs

■ The inferior or diaphragmatic surface lies on the underside and is formed by the left and right ventricles separated by the posterior interventricular groove. The right and left ventricles are the large chambers which pump blood around the lungs and the body respectively

■ The anterior, or sternocostal, surface lies at the front of the heart just behind the sternum and the ribs and is formed mainly by the right ventricle

■ The left, or pulmonary, surface is formed mainly by the large left ventricle, which lies in a concavity of the left lung.

## Position of the heart

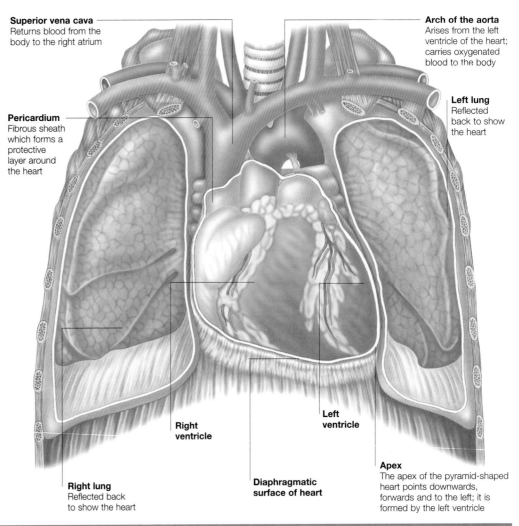

**Superior vena cava**
Returns blood from the body to the right atrium

**Arch of the aorta**
Arises from the left ventricle of the heart; carries oxygenated blood to the body

**Pericardium**
Fibrous sheath which forms a protective layer around the heart

**Left lung**
Reflected back to show the heart

**Right ventricle**

**Left ventricle**

**Right lung**
Reflected back to show the heart

**Diaphragmatic surface of heart**

**Apex**
The apex of the pyramid-shaped heart points downwards, forwards and to the left; it is formed by the left ventricle

## Position of the heart

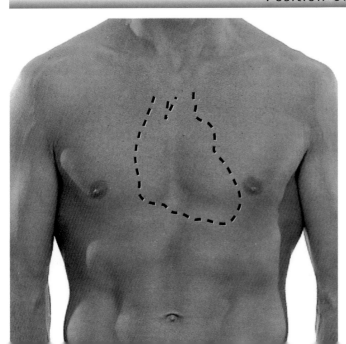

The heart lies behind the body of the sternum (breastbone), extending from the second rib above to the fifth intercostal space below. About two-thirds of the heart lies to the left of the midline of the chest, with the remaining third to the right.

### BORDERS

The heart has four borders. The right border is formed by the right atrium and is slightly convex. The left border is formed mainly by the left ventricle and **The heart fills the central part of the thorax, with the apex extending to the left. The heart's shape and position vary as it beats and also with respiration.**

slopes upwards and inwards to merge with the superior border, which is formed by the atria and great blood vessels. The inferior border, which lies nearly horizontally, is formed mainly by the right ventricle.

### APEX OF THE HEART

The apex of the heart normally lies behind the fifth intercostal space a hand's breadth from the midline. The pulsations of the heart can usually be felt, and often observed, at this point.

As it is attached only to other soft tissues the heart is quite mobile within the thoracic cavity and can change position as the diaphragm, on which it lies, contracts and relaxes.

# The pericardium

The heart is enclosed within a protective triple-walled bag of connective tissue called the pericardium. The pericardium is composed of two parts, the fibrous pericardium and the serous pericardium.

### FIBROUS PERICARDIUM

The fibrous pericardium forms the outer part of the bag and is composed of tough fibrous connective tissue. It has three main functions:

■ **Protection.** The fibrous pericardium is strong enough to provide some protection from trauma for such a vital structure as the heart

■ **Attachment.** There are fibrous attachments between this part of the pericardium and both the sternum and the diaphragm. In addition, the fibrous pericardium fuses with the strong walls of the arteries which pass through it from the heart. These attachments help to anchor the heart to its surrounding structures

■ **Prevention of overfilling of the heart.** Because the fibrous pericardium is non-elastic, it does not allow the heart to expand with blood beyond a certain safe limit.

### SEROUS PERICARDIUM

The serous pericardium covers and surrounds the heart in the same way as the pleura does the lungs. This part of the pericardium is a thin membrane which has two parts that are continuous with each other, the parietal and the visceral layers.

**The pericardial sac with the heart removed**

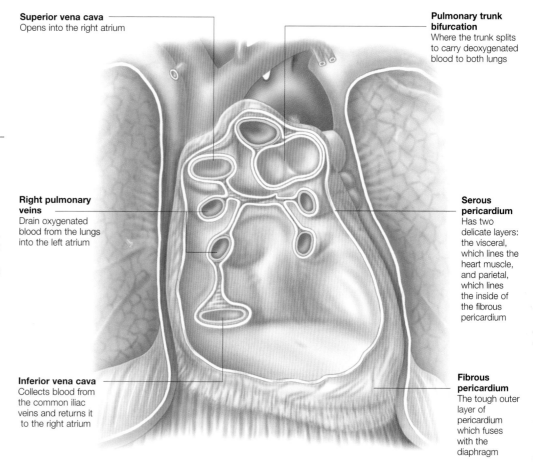

**Superior vena cava**
Opens into the right atrium

**Pulmonary trunk bifurcation**
Where the trunk splits to carry deoxygenated blood to both lungs

**Right pulmonary veins**
Drain oxygenated blood from the lungs into the left atrium

**Serous pericardium**
Has two delicate layers: the visceral, which lines the heart muscle, and parietal, which lines the inside of the fibrous pericardium

**Inferior vena cava**
Collects blood from the common iliac veins and returns it to the right atrium

**Fibrous pericardium**
The tough outer layer of pericardium which fuses with the diaphragm

The parietal pericardium lines the inner surface of the fibrous pericardium and reflects back onto the surface of the heart at the roots of the large blood vessels to form the visceral pericardium.

Between the two layers of serous pericardium lies a slit-like cavity, the pericardial cavity, which is filled with a very small amount of fluid. The presence of this fine fluid layer, together with the slipperiness of the layers of serous pericardium, allows the chambers of the heart to move freely within the pericardium as the heart beats.

If the pericardial cavity becomes filled with an abnormally large amount of fluid, as may happen in infection or inflammation, the heart becomes compressed within the confines of the fibrous pericardium and is unable to function properly. In extreme cases, when it is known as 'cardiac tamponade', this is life-threatening.

## Layers of the heart wall

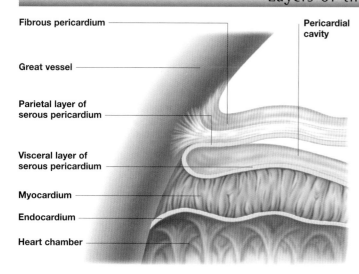

**Fibrous pericardium**

**Great vessel**

**Parietal layer of serous pericardium**

**Visceral layer of serous pericardium**

**Myocardium**

**Endocardium**

**Heart chamber**

**Pericardial cavity**

Inside the pericardial cavity, the heart wall is made up of three layers: the epicardium, the myocardium and the endocardium.

■ The epicardium is the visceral layer of the serous pericardium, which covers the outer surface of the heart and is attached firmly to it

■ The myocardium makes up the bulk of the heart wall and is

*A section taken through the heart at the junction of a typical great vessel reveals the different layers of pericardium and heart wall.*

composed of specialized cardiac muscle fibres. This type of muscle occurs only in the heart and is adapted for the special role it plays there. The muscle fibres of the myocardium are supported and held together by interlocking fibres of connective tissue

■ The endocardium is a smooth, delicate membrane, formed by a very thin layer of cells, and lines the inner surface of the heart chambers and valves. The blood vessels entering and leaving the heart are lined by a similar layer – the endothelium – which is a continuation of the endocardium.

# Chambers of the heart

The heart is divided into four chambers: two thin-walled atria, which receive venous blood, and two larger, thick-walled ventricles, which pump blood into the arterial system.

The heart is divided into left and right sides, each having an atrium and ventricle.

### THE VENTRICLES

The two ventricles make up the bulk of the muscle of the heart, the left being larger and more powerful than the right. The right ventricle lies in front, forming much of the anterior surface of the heart, while the left lies behind and below, comprising the greater part of the inferior surface. The apex of the heart is formed by the tip of the left ventricle.

The right ventricle receives blood from the right atrium, back flow being prevented by the tricuspid valve. Blood is then pumped by contraction of the ventricular muscle up through the pulmonary valve into the pulmonary trunk and from there into the lungs.

The left ventricle receives blood from the left atrium through the left atrioventricular orifice, which bears the mitral valve. Powerful contractions of the left ventricle then pump the blood up through the aortic valve into the aorta, the main artery of the body.

*This illustration shows the internal structure of the heart when opened along a plane connecting the root of the aorta and the apex of the heart.*

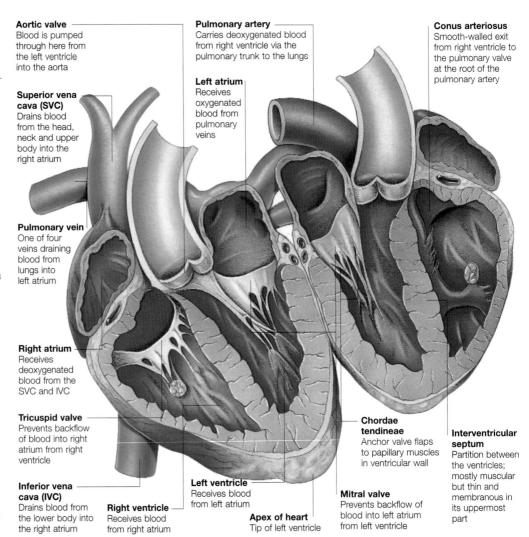

**Aortic valve**
Blood is pumped through here from the left ventricle into the aorta

**Superior vena cava (SVC)**
Drains blood from the head, neck and upper body into the right atrium

**Pulmonary vein**
One of four veins draining blood from lungs into left atrium

**Right atrium**
Receives deoxygenated blood from the SVC and IVC

**Tricuspid valve**
Prevents backflow of blood into right atrium from right ventricle

**Inferior vena cava (IVC)**
Drains blood from the lower body into the right atrium

**Pulmonary artery**
Carries deoxygenated blood from right ventricle via the pulmonary trunk to the lungs

**Left atrium**
Receives oxygenated blood from pulmonary veins

**Right ventricle**
Receives blood from right atrium

**Left ventricle**
Receives blood from left atrium

**Apex of heart**
Tip of left ventricle

**Conus arteriosus**
Smooth-walled exit from right ventricle to the pulmonary valve at the root of the pulmonary artery

**Chordae tendineae**
Anchor valve flaps to papillary muscles in ventricular wall

**Mitral valve**
Prevents backflow of blood into left atrium from left ventricle

**Interventricular septum**
Partition between the ventricles; mostly muscular but thin and membranous in its uppermost part

## Architecture of the ventricular walls

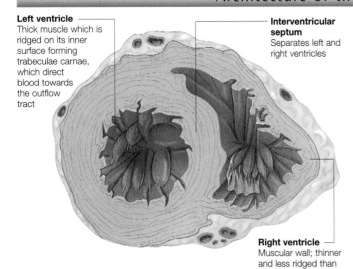

**Left ventricle**
Thick muscle which is ridged on its inner surface forming trabeculae carnae, which direct blood towards the outflow tract

**Interventricular septum**
Separates left and right ventricles

**Right ventricle**
Muscular wall; thinner and less ridged than that of the left ventricle

The muscular walls of the left ventricle are twice as thick as those of the right, and form a rough circle in cross-section. The right ventricle forms a crescent in cross-section as it is deformed by the more muscular left ventricle.

The difference in muscle thickness between the chambers reflects the pressure required to empty the relevant chamber when the muscle contracts.

Arising from the walls of both ventricles are the papillary

*A cross-section of the heart through the ventricles shows the difference in thickness of the muscular walls of the left and right ventricles.*

muscles, which taper to a point and bear tendinous chords (chordae tendineae) that attach to the tricuspid and mitral valves to stabilize them during pumping.

The inner surfaces of the ventricular walls, especially where blood enters, are roughened by irregular ridges of muscle, the trabeculae carnae, which give way to smoother walls near the outflow tracts through which blood is pumped out. There is only a small area of smooth wall in the left ventricle, just before the aortic valve. The right ventricle has a larger, funnel-shaped area of smooth wall below the pulmonary valve known as the conus arteriosus, or infundibulum.

# The atria

The atria are the two smaller, thin-walled chambers of the heart. They sit above the ventricles separated by the atriovbentricular valves.

All the venous blood from the body is delivered to the right atrium by the two great veins, the superior and inferior vena cavae (SVC and IVC respectively). The coronary sinus, the vessel which collects venous blood from the heart tissues, also drains into the right atrium.

The interior has a smooth-walled posterior part and a rough-walled anterior section. These two areas are separated by a ridge of tissue known as the crista terminalis.

The roughened anterior wall is thicker than the posterior part, being composed of the pectinate muscles, which give a comb-like appearance to the inner surface. The fossa ovalis is a depression on the wall adjoining the left atrium.

The pectinate muscles extend into a small, ear-like outpouching of the right atrium called the auricle. This conical chamber wraps around the outside of the main artery from the heart – the aorta – and acts to increase the capacity of the right atrium.

## OPENINGS INTO THE RIGHT ATRIUM

The SVC, which receives blood from the upper half of the body, opens into the upper part of the smooth area of the right atrium.

The IVC, which receives blood from the lower half of the body, enters the lower part of the right atrium. The SVC has no valve to prevent backflow of blood; the IVC only bears a rudimentary non-functional valve.

The opening of the coronary sinus lies between the IVC opening and the opening that allows blood through into the right ventricle (the right atrioventricular orifice).

## Right atrium of the heart

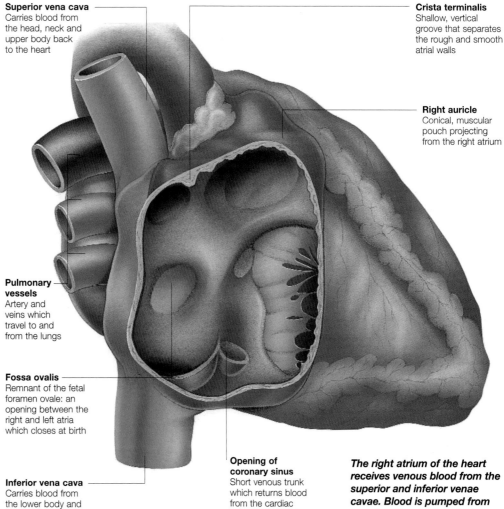

**Superior vena cava**
Carries blood from the head, neck and upper body back to the heart

**Pulmonary vessels**
Artery and veins which travel to and from the lungs

**Fossa ovalis**
Remnant of the fetal foramen ovale: an opening between the right and left atria which closes at birth

**Inferior vena cava**
Carries blood from the lower body and legs back to the heart

**Crista terminalis**
Shallow, vertical groove that separates the rough and smooth atrial walls

**Right auricle**
Conical, muscular pouch projecting from the right atrium

**Opening of coronary sinus**
Short venous trunk which returns blood from the cardiac veins to the heart

*The right atrium of the heart receives venous blood from the superior and inferior venae cavae. Blood is pumped from here into the right ventricle.*

## THE LEFT ATRIUM

The left atrium is smaller than the right, and forms the main part of the base of the heart. It is roughly cuboid in shape and has smooth walls, except for the lining of the left auricle, which is roughened by muscle ridges. The four pulmonary veins, which bring oxygenated blood back from the lungs, open into the posterior part of the left atrium. There are no valves in these orifices.

In the wall adjoining the right atrium lies the oval fossa, which corresponds to the oval fossa on the right side.

## The fetal heart

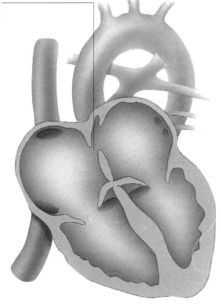

**Foramen ovale**
Gap between the two atria through which blood can flow before birth

In the fetus, the route of bloodflow through the heart is different from that after birth. Instead of being passed into the right ventricle to be pumped into the lungs, blood passes from the right atrium directly into the left atrium to be pumped around the body.

The blood passes through the foramen ovale, a hole in the wall which divides the two atria and has a flap-like valve to prevent backflow.

*The circulation within the fetal heart is different from that of the postnatal heart. Blood flows directly between the atria via the foramen ovale.*

### CHANGES AFTER BIRTH

After birth the foramen ovale closes and blood is pumped into the lungs from the right ventricle. The site of the foramen ovale is marked by a depression in the wall (septum) between the atria, known as the fossa ovalis.

### ATRIAL SEPTAL DEFECTS

In about 15 to 25 per cent of adults a small opening may still be present at this site although it may be found only incidentally during investigations of the heart and does not usually cause problems. Openings of this kind are known as atrial septal defects, or 'holes in the heart'.

# Valves of the heart

The heart is a powerful muscular pump through which blood flows
in a forward direction only. Backflow is prevented by the four heart
valves, which have a vital role in maintaining the circulation.

Each of the two sides of the
heart has two valves. On the
right side of the heart, the
tricuspid valve lies between the
atrium and the ventricle, and
the pulmonary valve lies at the
junction of the ventricle and
the pulmonary trunk. On the left
side, the mitral valve separates
the atrium and ventricle while
the aortic valve lies between
the ventricle and the aorta.

### THE TRICUSPID AND MITRAL VALVES

The tricuspid and mitral valves
are also known as the
atrioventricular valves as they
lie between the atria and the
ventricles on each side. They are
composed of tough connective
tissue covered with endocardium,
the thin layer of cells which lines
the entire heart. The upper
surface of the valves is smooth
whereas the lower surface carries
the attachments of the chordae
tendineae.

The tricuspid valve has three
cusps, or flaps. In contrast, the
mitral valve has only two and is
consequently also known as the
bicuspid valve; the name 'mitral'
comes from its supposed likeness
to a bishop's mitre.

### THE HEARTBEAT

During its contraction, the
normal heart makes a two-
component sound (often
described as 'lub-dup')
which can be heard using
a stethoscope. The first of
these sounds comes from
the closure of the
atrioventricular valves while the
second is due to the closure of
the pulmonary and aortic valves.

## Diastolic heart with the atria removed

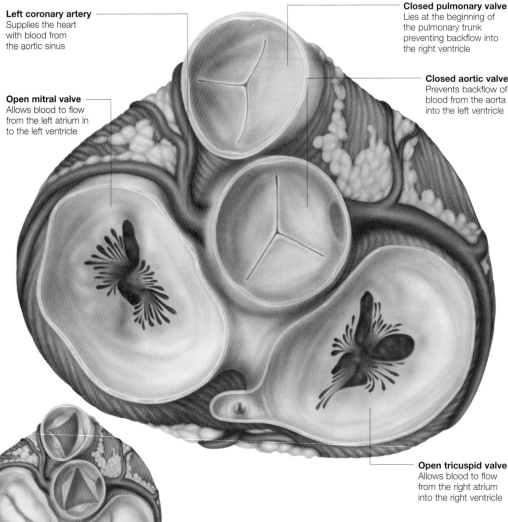

**Left coronary artery**
Supplies the heart
with blood from
the aortic sinus

**Open mitral valve**
Allows blood to flow
from the left atrium in
to the left ventricle

**Closed pulmonary valve**
Lies at the beginning of
the pulmonary trunk
preventing backflow into
the right ventricle

**Closed aortic valve**
Prevents backflow of
blood from the aorta
into the left ventricle

**Open tricuspid valve**
Allows blood to flow
from the right atrium
into the right ventricle

*When the heart is in systole the
ventricles are contracting and
the aortic and pulmonary valves
open, allowing blood to be
pumped out of the heart.*

*During diastole the heart muscle
of the ventricles is relaxing. The
tricuspid and mitral valves are
open allowing blood to flow from
the atria to fill the ventricles.*

## The chordae tendineae

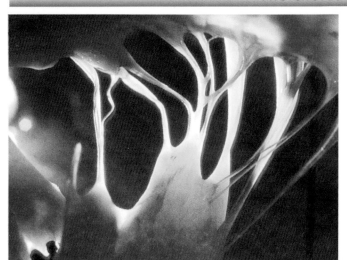

Attached to the edges and lower
surfaces of the tricuspid and
mitral valves are many thin
tendinous chords of collagen –
the chordae tendineae – which
pass down to the papillary
muscles which project into the
cavity of the ventricle from the
muscular walls.

*The chordae tendineae of the
mitral valve attach the cusps of
the valve to papillary muscles,
which in turn are attached to
the wall of the ventricle.*

### ACTION OF THE CHORDS

These chords act like guy ropes
to anchor the valves and prevent
the cusps of the valves from
giving way or being blown
inside out like an umbrella
under the high pressure of blood
during contraction of the
ventricles. Chords attached to
neighbouring cusps also act to
keep those cusps held tightly
together during the ventricular
contraction so that no blood can
leak between them when they
are closed.

# Aortic and pulmonary valves

The pulmonary and aortic valves are also known as the semilunar valves. They guard the route of exit of blood from the heart, preventing backflow of blood into the ventricles as they relax after a contraction.

Each of these two valves is composed of three semilunar pocket-like cusps, which have a core of connective tissue covered by a lining of endothelium. This lining ensures a smooth surface for the passage of blood.

### AORTIC VALVE
The aortic valve lies between the left ventricle and the aorta, the main artery that carries oxygenated blood to the body. It is stronger and more robust than the pulmonary valve as it has to cope with the higher pressures of the systemic circulation (to the body).

Above each cusp of the valve, formed by bulges of the aortic wall, lie the aortic sinuses. From two of these sinuses arise the right and left coronary arteries, which carry blood to the muscle and coverings of the heart itself.

### PULMONARY VALVE
The pulmonary valve separates the ventricle from the pulmonary trunk, the large artery that carries blood from the heart towards the lungs. Just above each cusp of the valve the pulmonary trunk bulges slightly to form the pulmonary sinuses, blood-filled spaces that prevent the cusps from sticking to the arterial wall behind them when they open.

**View of the left ventricle opened up**

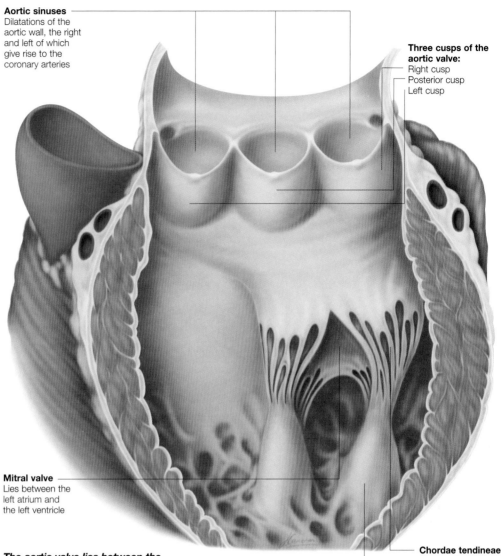

**Aortic sinuses**
Dilatations of the aortic wall, the right and left of which give rise to the coronary arteries

**Three cusps of the aortic valve:**
Right cusp
Posterior cusp
Left cusp

**Mitral valve**
Lies between the left atrium and the left ventricle

**Papillary muscle**
Larger in the left ventricle than in the right due to having a greater force to overcome

**Chordae tendineae**
Fibrous strands that attach the cusps to the anchoring papillary muscles

*The aortic valve lies between the left ventricle and the aorta. The three cusps of the valve prevent blood expelled from the ventricle from re-entering.*

## Action of the valves

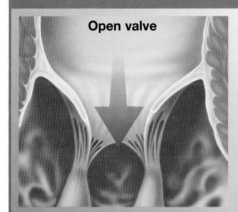

**Open valve**

*When an atrioventricular valve is open, the papillary muscles are relaxed and the cusps flap downwards. Blood from the atrium can flow into the ventricle.*

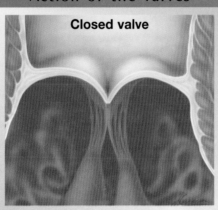

**Closed valve**

*As the ventricle fills with blood the atrioventricular valve snaps shut, tensing the chordae tendineae. When the ventricle contracts the blood is thus pushed forwards.*

When the atria contract, blood passes through the open and relaxed tricuspid and mitral valves into the ventricles.

As the ventricles contract in turn, the sudden rising pressure of blood within each ventricle causes the valves to close, so preventing backflow of that blood into the atria. The pull of the chordae tendineae steadies the valves and enables them to withstand the pressure of the blood within the ventricle.

As the atrioventricular valves are now closed the blood must travel up and out through the semilunar valves into the pulmonary trunk and the aorta. The semilunar valves are forced open by the high-pressure flow of blood from the ventricles, but snap shut again as soon as the ventricles stop contracting and start to relax.

# Vessels of the heart

Blood is delivered to the heart by two large veins – the superior and inferior venae cavae – and pumped out into the aorta. The venae cavae and aorta are collectively known as the great vessels.

## THE VENAE CAVAE

The superior vena cava is the large vein that drains blood from the upper body to the right atrium of the heart. It is formed by the union of the right and left brachiocephalic veins which, in turn, have been formed by smaller veins that receive blood from the head, neck and upper limbs.

The inferior vena cava is the widest vein in the body, but only its last part lies within the thorax as it passes up through the diaphragm to deliver blood to the right atrium.

## THE AORTA

The aorta is the largest artery in the body, having an internal diameter of about 2.5 cm in adults. Its relatively thick walls contain elastic connective tissue which allows the vessel to expand slightly, as blood is pumped into it under pressure, and then recoil, thus maintaining blood pressure between heart beats.

The aorta passes upwards initially, then curves around to the left and travels down into the abdomen. It consists of the ascending aorta, the arch of the aorta and the descending (thoracic) aorta. The various sections of the aorta are named for their shape or the positions in which they lie, and each has branches which carry blood to the tissues of the body.

## The heart and great vessels

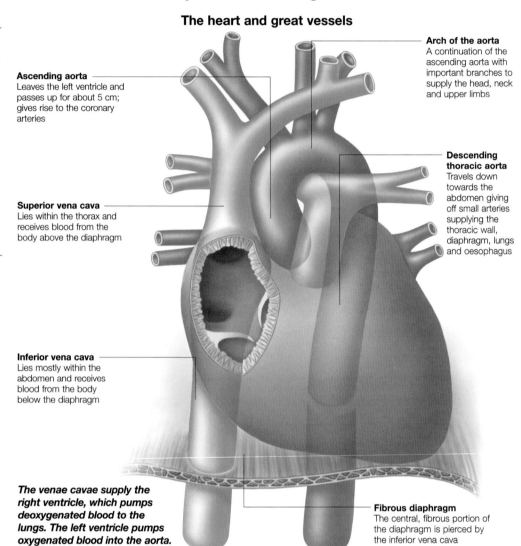

**Ascending aorta**
Leaves the left ventricle and passes up for about 5 cm; gives rise to the coronary arteries

**Superior vena cava**
Lies within the thorax and receives blood from the body above the diaphragm

**Inferior vena cava**
Lies mostly within the abdomen and receives blood from the body below the diaphragm

**Arch of the aorta**
A continuation of the ascending aorta with important branches to supply the head, neck and upper limbs

**Descending thoracic aorta**
Travels down towards the abdomen giving off small arteries supplying the thoracic wall, diaphragm, lungs and oesophagus

**Fibrous diaphragm**
The central, fibrous portion of the diaphragm is pierced by the inferior vena cava

*The venae cavae supply the right ventricle, which pumps deoxygenated blood to the lungs. The left ventricle pumps oxygenated blood into the aorta.*

## How the fetal heart changes after birth

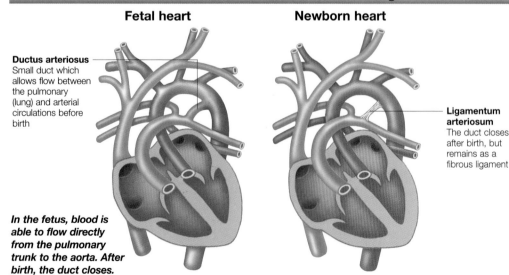

**Fetal heart**

**Newborn heart**

**Ductus arteriosus**
Small duct which allows flow between the pulmonary (lung) and arterial circulations before birth

**Ligamentum arteriosum**
The duct closes after birth, but remains as a fibrous ligament

*In the fetus, blood is able to flow directly from the pulmonary trunk to the aorta. After birth, the duct closes.*

In the fetus, there is a connecting blood vessel which allows blood to travel from the pulmonary trunk to the aorta, bypassing the lungs. This vessel, known as the ductus arteriosus, closes after birth. Then, blood from the right ventricle only passes into the pulmonary circulation.

The site of this fetal blood vessel is marked by the ligamentum arteriosum, a fibrous band that passes from the pulmonary trunk to the arch of the aorta. Sometimes, the ductus arteriosus does not close at birth and high pressure aortic blood will enter the relatively low pressure pulmonary system. Surgical closure is then required.

# Supplying blood to the heart

The heart muscle itself
and the coverings of
the heart need their own
blood supply, which is
provided by the
coronary arteries.

There are two coronary arteries:
right and left. These arise from
the ascending aorta just above
the aortic valve and run around
the heart just beneath the
epicardium, embedded in fat.

■ **The right coronary artery**
This arises within the right aortic
sinus, a small outpouching of the
arterial wall just behind the aortic
valve. It runs down and to the
right, along the groove between
the right atrium and the right
ventricle until it lies along the
inferior surface of the heart. Here
it terminates in an anastomosis
(connecting network) with
branches of the left coronary
artery. The right coronary artery
gives off several branches.

■ **The left coronary artery**
This arises from the coronary
sinus above the aortic valve
and runs down towards the
apex of the heart. The left
coronary artery divides early
on into two branches.

### VENOUS DRAINAGE

The main vein of the heart is the
coronary sinus. It receives blood
from the cardiac veins and
empties into the right atrium. In
general, cardiac veins follow the
routes of the coronary arteries.

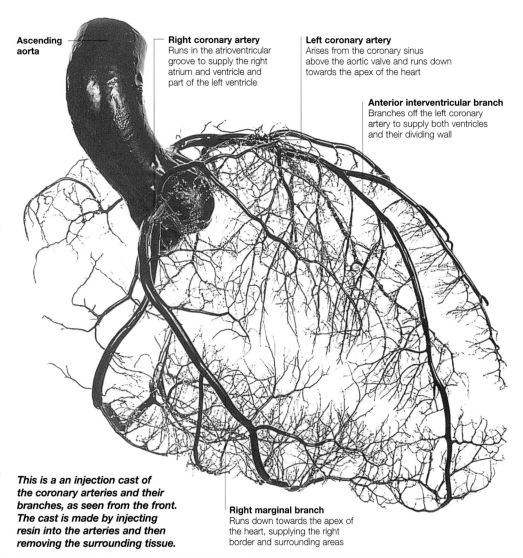

**Ascending aorta**

**Right coronary artery**
Runs in the atrioventricular
groove to supply the right
atrium and ventricle and
part of the left ventricle

**Left coronary artery**
Arises from the coronary sinus
above the aortic valve and runs down
towards the apex of the heart

**Anterior interventricular branch**
Branches off the left coronary
artery to supply both ventricles
and their dividing wall

**Right marginal branch**
Runs down towards the apex of
the heart, supplying the right
border and surrounding areas

*This is a an injection cast of
the coronary arteries and their
branches, as seen from the front.
The cast is made by injecting
resin into the arteries and then
removing the surrounding tissue.*

## Variations in the coronary arteries

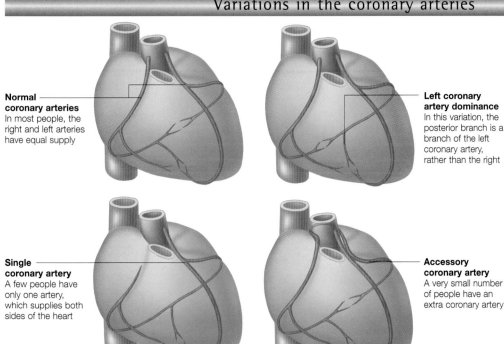

**Normal coronary arteries**
In most people, the
right and left arteries
have equal supply

**Single coronary artery**
A few people have
only one artery,
which supplies both
sides of the heart

**Left coronary artery dominance**
In this variation, the
posterior branch is a
branch of the left
coronary artery,
rather than the right

**Accessory coronary artery**
A very small number
of people have an
extra coronary artery

In most people, the right and
left coronary arteries are equally
responsible for the blood supply
to the heart; however, there may
be great variation in the
branching patterns of the
coronary arteries between
individuals.

### VARIATIONS

However, in about 15 per cent of
people, the left coronary artery
provides a greater supply as it
gives rise to the large posterior
interventricular artery (normally
a branch of the right coronary
artery). Very occasionally, there
may be only one coronary artery
or sometimes an extra, accessory
coronary artery. There are many
other possible variations.

*The blood supply of the heart
can vary; either the left or right
coronary artery can be
dominant, an artery can be
missing or an extra one present.*

121

# Conducting system of the heart

When the body is at rest, the heart beats at a rate of about 70 to 80 beats per minute. Within its muscular walls, a conducting system sets the pace and ensures that the muscle contracts in a co-ordinated way.

## SINO-ATRIAL NODE

The sino-atrial (SA) node is a collection of cells within the wall of the right atrium.

Each contraction of the cells of the SA node generates an electrical impulse, which is passed to the other muscle cells of the right and left atria and then to the atrio-ventricular (AV) node.

## ATRIOVENTRICULAR NODE

The cells of the AV node will initiate contractions of their own, and pass on impulses at a slower rate, if not stimulated by the SA node. Impulses from the AV node are passed to the ventricles through the next stage of conducting tissue.

## ATRIOVENTRICULAR BUNDLE

The AV bundle passes from the atria to the ventricles through an insulating layer of fibrous tissue. It then divides into two parts, the right and left bundle branches, which supply the right and left ventricles respectively.

*The intrinsic conduction system of the heart carries a wave of nerve impulses, which create synchronized contraction of the heart muscle.*

### The intrinsic conduction system of the heart

**Conducting fibre**
Branches from the sinoatrial node and reaches the left atrium

**Right atrium**
Area of the heart where contraction impulses are initiated

**Sino-atrial node (pacemaker)**
Acts as a pacemaker for the heart by contracting at a faster rate than other cardiac muscle cells

**Atrioventricular bundle**
Divides into right and left bundle branches, which supply first the papillary muscles, and then the rest of the ventricular myocardium

**Atrioventricular node**
Oval-shaped collection of nodal tissue; lies within the floor of the right atrium

**Purkinje fibres**
Smaller divisions of the bundle branches

## Nerve supply of the heart

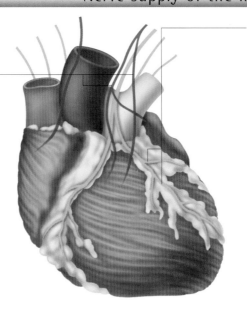

**Parasympathetic nerves**
These nerves have a 'braking' effect and slow the heart

**Sympathetic nerves**
Impulses from these nerves increase both the rate and force of the heartbeat

*The nerve supply to the heart is from the autonomic nervous system. This is the system of nerves that regulates the internal organs of the body without our conscious control.*

The heart beats regularly without external stimulation; its nerve supply affects its rate and force of contraction.

## EXTERNAL NERVE SUPPLY

The autonomic nerve supply is carried to the heart from the cardiac plexuses, networks of nervous tissue that lie just behind the ascending aorta above the heart.

Autonomic nerves are divided into two groups: sympathetic fibres, which arise from the cervical and upper thoracic parts of the sympathetic trunks (which lie alongside the spine); and parasympathetic fibres, which come via the vagus (10th cranial) nerves.

# The cardiac cycle

The cardiac cycle is the series of changes within the heart which causes blood to be pumped around the body. It is divided into a period when heart muscle contracts, known as systole and a period when it is relaxed, known as diastole.

### VENTRICULAR FILLING
During diastole the tricuspid and mitral valves are open. Blood from the great veins fills the atria and then passes through these open valves to fill the relaxing ventricles.

### ATRIAL CONTRACTION
As diastole ends and systole begins, the SA node sparks off a contraction of the atrial muscle which forces more blood into the ventricles.

### VENTRICULAR CONTRACTION
The wave of contraction reaches the ventricles via the AV bundles and the Purkinje fibres. The tricuspid and mitral valves snap shut as pressure increases. The blood pushes against the closed pulmonary and aortic valves and causes them to open.

As the wave of contraction dies away, the ventricles relax. The cycle begins again with the next SA node impulse about a second later.

*The movements of the heart cause the circulation of blood. The sequence of contraction is repeated, in normal adults, about 70 to 90 times a minute.*

## Events of the cardiac cycle

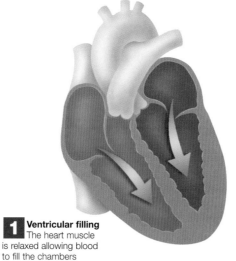

**1** **Ventricular filling**
The heart muscle is relaxed allowing blood to fill the chambers

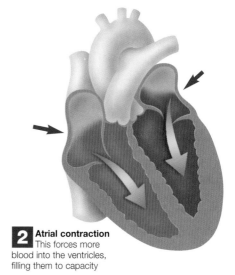

**2** **Atrial contraction**
This forces more blood into the ventricles, filling them to capacity

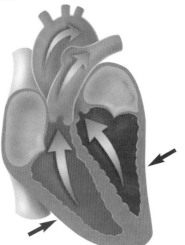
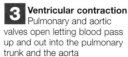

**3** **Ventricular contraction**
Pulmonary and aortic valves open letting blood pass up and out into the pulmonary trunk and the aorta

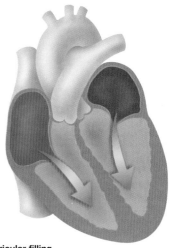

**4** **Ventricular filling**
As the wave of contraction dies away the ventricles relax and allow blood to enter again

## Fibrous skeleton of the heart

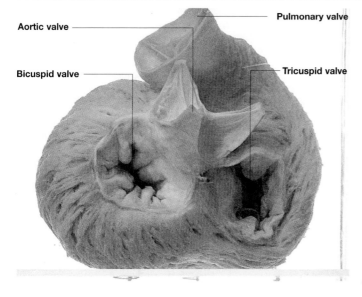

Aortic valve

Bicuspid valve

Pulmonary valve

Tricuspid valve

Like the muscles of the bony skeleton, when the muscle of the heart wall contracts it needs something to pull against to be effective. There are no bones or solid structures in the heart, but it does have a skeleton of tough fibrous connective tissue, which performs a similar function in that it offers a site for attachment of the cardiac muscle fibres.

### SUPPORT
The fibrous skeleton of the heart also helps to support the heart

*The skeleton of the heart is made of tough fibrous connective tissue. It forms the rigid framework that the heart pulls against when it contracts.*

valves and prevent them from becoming pulled out of shape by the great pressure of blood during systole. It also provides a base for the cusps of those valves.

### INSULATION
Another vital function of the fibrous skeleton is to separate and insulate the myocardium (the middle of the three layers forming the wall of the heart) of the atria from that of the ventricles so that the wave of contraction during systole can only pass via the AV bundle.

This ensures that the ventricles will contract slightly after the atria contract, which gives time for them to be filled as a result of atrial contraction.

# Shoulder joint

The glenohumeral, or shoulder joint, is a ball-and-socket joint at the point of articulation of the humerus and the scapula. The construction of this joint allows the arm a wide range of movement.

The glenohumeral, or shoulder joint, is the point of articulation between the glenoid cavity of the scapula (shoulder blade) and the head of the humerus (bone of the upper arm). It is a ball-and-socket synovial (fluid-filled) joint constructed to allow the upper limb a very wide range of movement.

### ARTICULAR SURFACE

To permit a wide range of movement, the head of the humerus provides a large articular surface. The glenoid cavity of the scapula, deepened by a ring of tough fibrocartilage (the glenoid labrum), offers only a shallow socket. The resulting ball-and-socket is so shallow that the joint needs to be held firmly together by the surrounding muscles and ligaments.

A thin layer of smooth articular (or hyaline) cartilage allows the bones to slip over each other with minimum friction.

### JOINT CAPSULE

The shoulder joint is surrounded by a loose capsule of fibrous tissue. This capsule is lined by the synovial membrane which covers all the inner surfaces of the joint except those covered with articular cartilage.

The cells of this synovial membrane secrete synovial fluid, a viscous liquid which lubricates and nourishes the joint.

## Shoulder joint viewed from the front

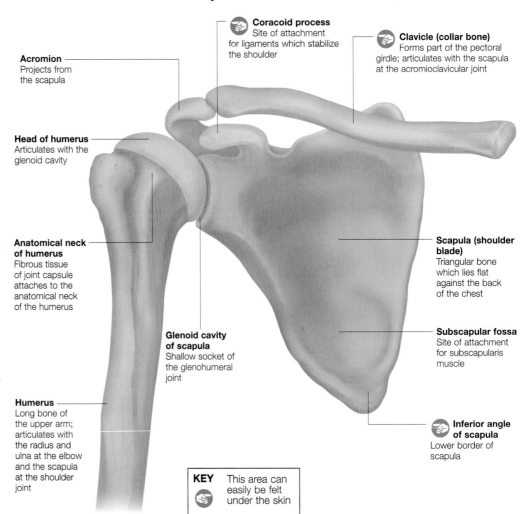

**Coracoid process**
Site of attachment for ligaments which stabilize the shoulder

**Clavicle (collar bone)**
Forms part of the pectoral girdle; articulates with the scapula at the acromioclavicular joint

**Acromion**
Projects from the scapula

**Head of humerus**
Articulates with the glenoid cavity

**Anatomical neck of humerus**
Fibrous tissue of joint capsule attaches to the anatomical neck of the humerus

**Glenoid cavity of scapula**
Shallow socket of the glenohumeral joint

**Humerus**
Long bone of the upper arm; articulates with the radius and ulna at the elbow and the scapula at the shoulder joint

**Scapula (shoulder blade)**
Triangular bone which lies flat against the back of the chest

**Subscapular fossa**
Site of attachment for subscapularis muscle

**Inferior angle of scapula**
Lower border of scapula

**KEY** This area can easily be felt under the skin

## Bursae of the shoulder joint

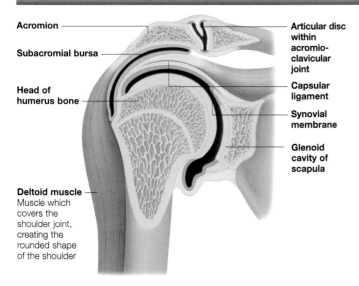

**Acromion**

**Subacromial bursa**

**Head of humerus bone**

**Deltoid muscle**
Muscle which covers the shoulder joint, creating the rounded shape of the shoulder

**Articular disc within acromio-clavicular joint**

**Capsular ligament**

**Synovial membrane**

**Glenoid cavity of scapula**

*A coronal section through the glenohumeral joint shows the position of the bursa of the shoulder joint.*

A bursa (*plural*: bursae) is a flattened fibrous sac lined with synovial membrane which contains a small amount of viscous synovial fluid. Bursae act to reduce the friction between structures which necessarily rub against each other during normal movement. Bursae are located at various points around the body where ligaments, muscle and tendons rub against bone.

Bursae may become abnormally enlarged at a point of unusual pressure, such as occurs with a bunion at the base of the big toe where a shoe rubs.

The shoulder joint has several important bursae:

■ **Subscapular bursa**
This protects the tendon of the subscapularis muscle as it passes over the neck of the scapula. It usually has an opening which leads into the joint cavity and so may actually be thought of as an outpouching of that cavity.

■ **Subacromial bursa**
This lies above the glenohumeral joint beneath the acromion and the coraco-acromial ligament. It allows free movement of the muscles which pass beneath it. It is usually a true bursa, with no connection to the joint cavity of the shoulder.

# Ligaments of the shoulder joint

The ligaments of the shoulder joint, along with the surrounding muscles, are crucial for the stability of this shallow ball-and-socket joint.

The ligaments around any joint contribute to its stability by holding the bones firmly together. In the shoulder joint, the main stabilizers are the surrounding muscles, but ligaments also play a role.

### STABILIZING LIGAMENTS
The fibrous joint capsule has ligaments within it which help to strengthen the joint:
■ The glenohumeral ligaments are three weak, fibrous bands which reinforce the front of the capsule
■ The coracohumeral ligament is a strong, broad band which strengthens the upper aspect of the capsule. Although not actually part of the glenohumeral joint itself, the coraco-acromial ligament is important as it spans the gap between the acromion and the coracoid process of the scapula. The arch of bone and ligament is so strong that even if the humerus is forcibly pushed up, it will not break; the clavicle or the humerus will give way first
■ The transverse humeral ligament runs from the greater to the lesser tuberosity of the humerus, creating a tunnel for the passage of the biceps brachii tendon in its synovial sheath.

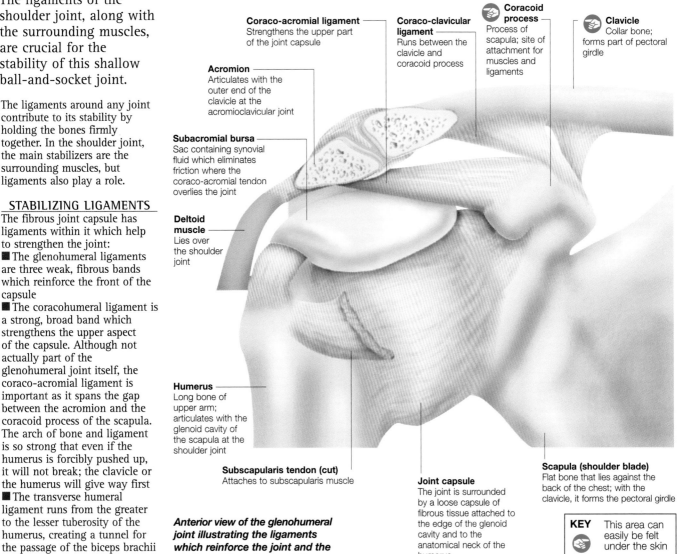

**Coraco-acromial ligament**
Strengthens the upper part of the joint capsule

**Coraco-clavicular ligament**
Runs between the clavicle and coracoid process

**Coracoid process**
Process of scapula; site of attachment for muscles and ligaments

**Clavicle**
Collar bone; forms part of pectoral girdle

**Acromion**
Articulates with the outer end of the clavicle at the acromioclavicular joint

**Subacromial bursa**
Sac containing synovial fluid which eliminates friction where the coraco-acromial tendon overlies the joint

**Deltoid muscle**
Lies over the shoulder joint

**Humerus**
Long bone of upper arm; articulates with the glenoid cavity of the scapula at the shoulder joint

**Subscapularis tendon (cut)**
Attaches to subscapularis muscle

**Joint capsule**
The joint is surrounded by a loose capsule of fibrous tissue attached to the edge of the glenoid cavity and to the anatomical neck of the humerus

**Scapula (shoulder blade)**
Flat bone that lies against the back of the chest; with the clavicle, it forms the pectoral girdle

*Anterior view of the glenohumeral joint illustrating the ligaments which reinforce the joint and the position of the subacromial bursa.*

**KEY** This area can easily be felt under the skin

## Instability of the shoulder joint

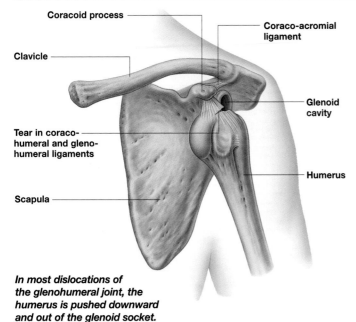

**Coracoid process**

**Clavicle**

**Tear in coraco-humeral and gleno-humeral ligaments**

**Scapula**

**Coraco-acromial ligament**

**Glenoid cavity**

**Humerus**

*In most dislocations of the glenohumeral joint, the humerus is pushed downward and out of the glenoid socket.*

A wide range of movement is one of the characteristics of the shoulder joint, but this is achieved at the expense of stability. The features which allow such free movement cause the joint to be relatively unstable; the fibrous capsule is lax, the ligaments are weak and loose and the socket of this ball-and-socket joint is shallow.

The shoulder joint is stabilized primarily by the action of the short muscles that surround it, holding the head of the humerus into the glenoid cavity, the so-called rotator cuff.

### DISLOCATED SHOULDER
Of all the joints in the body, the shoulder is the most likely to dislocate. Dislocation of the shoulder joint most commonly occurs in a downward direction as the top and sides of the joint are supported by the rotator cuff and the coraco-acromial ligament, leaving the under side supported only by the lax fibrous capsule.

Dislocation of the shoulder may occur in athletes and is usually the result of a sudden force being applied along the length of the humerus when the arm is lifted high to one side. The head of the humerus is pushed down over the lip of the glenoid cavity and, under the influence of the muscles which act upon it, usually comes to rest just beneath the coracoid process of the scapula.

After dislocation, the arm cannot be used until the bones are returned to the correct alignment. Once a dislocation has occurred, damage to the joint may leave the shoulder susceptible to future dislocations.

# Movements of the shoulder joint

The shoulder joint is a ball-and-socket joint which allows 360° of movement to give maximum flexibility. In addition to enabling these movements, the muscles of the pectoral girdle add stability.

The movements of the shoulder joint take place around three axes: a horizontal axis through the centre of the glenoid fossa; axis perpendicular to this (front-back) through the humeral head; and a third axis running vertically through the shaft of the humerus. These give the axes of flexion and extension, adduction (movement towards the body) and abduction (movement away from the body), and medial (internal) and lateral (external) rotation respectively. A combination of these movements can allow a circular motion of the limb called circumduction.

## MUSCLES OF SHOULDER MOVEMENT

Many of the muscles involved in these movements are attached to the pectoral girdle (the clavicles and scapulae). The scapula has muscles attached to its rear and front surfaces and the coracoid process, a bony projection. Some muscles arise directly from the trunk (pectoralis major and latissimus dorsi). Other muscles influence the movement of the humerus even though they are not attached to it directly (such as trapezius). They do this by moving the scapula, and hence the shoulder joint.

### Front view of muscles of the shoulder

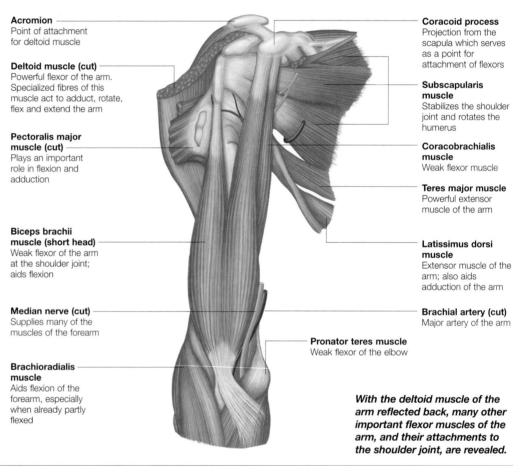

**Acromion**
Point of attachment for deltoid muscle

**Deltoid muscle (cut)**
Powerful flexor of the arm. Specialized fibres of this muscle act to adduct, rotate, flex and extend the arm

**Pectoralis major muscle (cut)**
Plays an important role in flexion and adduction

**Biceps brachii muscle (short head)**
Weak flexor of the arm at the shoulder joint; aids flexion

**Median nerve (cut)**
Supplies many of the muscles of the forearm

**Brachioradialis muscle**
Aids flexion of the forearm, especially when already partly flexed

**Coracoid process**
Projection from the scapula which serves as a point for attachment of flexors

**Subscapularis muscle**
Stabilizes the shoulder joint and rotates the humerus

**Coracobrachialis muscle**
Weak flexor muscle

**Teres major muscle**
Powerful extensor muscle of the arm

**Latissimus dorsi muscle**
Extensor muscle of the arm; also aids adduction of the arm

**Brachial artery (cut)**
Major artery of the arm

**Pronator teres muscle**
Weak flexor of the elbow

*With the deltoid muscle of the arm reflected back, many other important flexor muscles of the arm, and their attachments to the shoulder joint, are revealed.*

## Movements of the shoulder joint

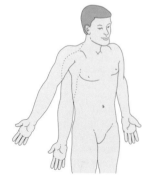

*Adduction (towards the body) of the arm is brought about by pectoralis major and latissimus dorsi muscles; abduction (away from the body) by supraspinatus and the deltoid.*

*Muscles which bring about lateral rotation are infraspinatus, teres minor and the posterior fibres of the deltoid muscle. Medial rotators form the 'rotator cuff' group of muscles.*

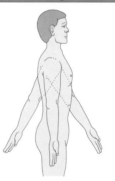

*Flexion (forward movement) is due to biceps, coracobrachialis, deltoid and pectoralis major. Extension (backward movement) is due to rear fibres of deltoid, latissimus dorsi and teres major.*

*Circumduction is a combination of these movements. It is dependent on the clavicle holding the shoulder joint in the glenoid cavity and contractions of different muscle groups.*

# Rotation of the arm and 'rotator cuff'

The rotator cuff muscles include subscapularis, supraspinatus, infraspinatus and teres minor. These muscles act to strengthen and increase the stability of the shoulder joint. They also act individually to move the humerus and upper arm.

The pectoralis major, anterior fibres of deltoid, teres major and latissimus dorsi muscles also cause medial rotation of the humerus. The most powerful medial rotator, however, is subscapularis. This muscle occupies the entire front surface of the scapula, and attaches to the joint capsule around the lesser tuberosity of the humerus.

## ROTATOR CUFF

Subscapularis is one of a set of four short muscles, collectively called the 'rotator cuff', which attach to and strengthen the joint capsule. In addition, they pull the humerus into the socket of the joint (glenoid fossa), increasing contact of the bony elements. This is the most important factor contributing to the stability of the joint.

The other muscles of the group are supraspinatus, infraspinatus and teres minor. These latter three muscles attach to the three facets on the greater tuberosity of the humerus. Infraspinatus and teres minor are lateral rotators of the shoulder joint, together with the posterior fibres of the deltoid.

Injury to the rotator cuff muscles is disabling, because the stability of the humerus in the joint is lost. The other muscles of the arm lose the ability to move the humerus correctly, resulting in dislocation of the joint.

### Muscles of shoulder movement (front)

**Coracoid process**
Site of muscle attachment

**Clavicle**
Collar bone

**Deltoid (reflected)**
Prime mover of abduction; also acts to flex the arm

**Subscapularis**
A rotator cuff muscle; holds the humerus in the joint cavity

**Pectoralis major (reflected)**
Acts to flex the arm; adducts the arm against resistance

**Coracobrachialis**
Acts to flex the arm and adducts the humerus

**Pectoralis minor**
Draws the scapula forward and downward

*The rotator cuff muscles and surrounding muscles that act to move the shoulder and arm are seen viewed from the front (left) and behind (right).*

### Muscles of shoulder movement (back)

**Supraspinatus muscle**
Rotator cuff muscle which stabilizes the shoulder joint

**Spine of scapula**
Ridge of bone on outer surface of the scapula (shoulder blade)

**Greater tubercle of humerus**
Point of attachment for infraspinatus muscle

**Infraspinatus**
Rotator cuff muscle; holds the humerus in the glenoid cavity

**Teres minor**
Rotator cuff muscle; rotates the humerus laterally

**Teres major**
Extends and rotates the humerus medially

**Triceps brachii**
Forearm extensor; also stabilizes the shoulder joint

**Latissimus dorsi muscle**
Important in extension and adduction; used in movements such as hammering or swimming

**Olecranon process of ulna**
Triceps brachii tendon inserts in the olecranon process

**Humerus**
Bone of the upper arm

## Abduction of the arm

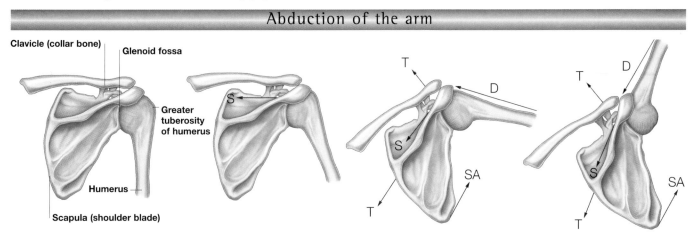

**Clavicle (collar bone)**

**Glenoid fossa**

**Greater tuberosity of humerus**

**Humerus**

**Scapula (shoulder blade)**

*Abduction (movement away from the body) is a weak action performed by supraspinatus (S) and the acromial (middle) part of deltoid (D) muscle.*

| KEY | S | = Supraspinatus |
| | D | = Deltoid |
| | T | = Trapezius |
| | SA | = Serratus anterior |

*From the resting position, the deltoid muscle can pull the humerus upwards but not outwards. Thankfully, the supraspinatus muscle is in a much better mechanical position to initiate abduction. Once the motion has started, the deltoid muscle takes over the movement and continues the movement.*

*The next major obstacle to full abduction is the bony contact of the greater tuberosity of the humerus and the acromion process of the scapula. This bony contact would prevent raising of the arm higher than horizontal (for example, arms held straight outwards at shoulder height).*

*We are able to put raise our hands above our heads by rotating the scapula using the trapezius muscle (T). The scapula rotates so that the glenoid fossa points upwards, taking the acromion process with it. The humerus also rotates so that articular contact of the joint is maintained.*

127

# Axilla

The axilla, or armpit, is a roughly pyramidal space where the upper arm joins the thorax. It contains a number of important structures, such as blood vessels and nerves passing to and from the upper limb.

Vessels, nerves and lymphatics serving the upper limb all pass through the axilla. The structures lie embedded in fatty connective tissue, which occupies the axillary space.

### THE AXILLARY ARTERY
The axillary artery and its branches supply oxygenated blood to the upper limb.

As it passes through the axilla this artery gives off several branches which supply the surrounding structures of the shoulder and pectoral regions.

### THE AXILLARY VEIN
The axillary vein runs through the axilla on the medial side of the axillary artery.

The pattern of veins and venous drainage is variable but the axillary vein, in general, receives blood from tributary veins which correspond to the branches of the axillary artery.

### NERVES IN THE AXILLA
The nerves which lie in the axilla are part of a complex network known as the 'brachial plexus'.

### LYMPHATICS
Within the fatty connective tissue of the axilla lie a series of groups of lymph nodes which are connected by lymphatic vessels. Lymph nodes are scattered throughout the fat of the axilla.

**Front view of the shoulder showing the structures of the axilla**

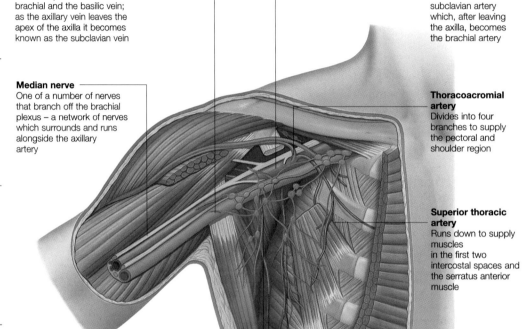

**Axillary vein**
Formed by the union of the brachial and the basilic vein; as the axillary vein leaves the apex of the axilla it becomes known as the subclavian vein

**Median nerve**
One of a number of nerves that branch off the brachial plexus – a network of nerves which surrounds and runs alongside the axillary artery

**Subscapular artery**
Largest branch of the axillary artery; runs down the outer edge of the subscapularis muscle

*The axilla is an important site of intersection for the major structures supplying the upper limb, containing a dense network of blood vessels, nerves and lymphatics.*

**Axillary artery**
A continuation of the subclavian artery which, after leaving the axilla, becomes the brachial artery

**Thoracoacromial artery**
Divides into four branches to supply the pectoral and shoulder region

**Superior thoracic artery**
Runs down to supply muscles in the first two intercostal spaces and the serratus anterior muscle

**Lymph nodes**
Lymph is collected from the upper arm, the breast and the thoracic wall and passes through these nodes to be filtered

**Lateral thoracic artery**
Runs along the lower border of pectoralis minor and gives off branches to supply the outer side of the mammary gland

## Passage of vessels and nerves

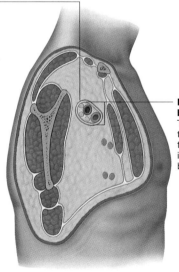

**Axillary sheath**
Formed from deep fascia in the neck, the sheath extends to enclose important structures of the axilla

**Neurovascular bundle**
The vein lies on the inner side of the artery, which is surrounded by nerves

*This section of the axilla shows muscles, vessels, bones and lymph nodes. The nerves and vessels can be seen travelling in the axillary sheath.*

Throughout the body it is a common pattern for arteries, veins and nerves to travel together in 'neurovascular bundles' and, indeed, the blood vessels and nerves of the upper limb pass through the axilla together in such an arrangement.

### THE AXILLARY SHEATH
Within the axilla (which is vulnerable to trauma, especially from below), these important structures are protected and enclosed by a tube of strong connective tissue, the 'axillary sheath'. Within the axillary sheath the vein lies on the medial (inner) side of the artery, with the nerves (parts of the brachial plexus) surrounding the artery.

The artery, vein and nerves supplying the upper limb all lie within the protection of the axillary sheath.

Because of the situation of the sheath, it is an important site for administration of general anaesthesia. If the lower end of the sheath is occluded (blocked) with finger pressure, the anaesthetic injected into the proximal sheath causes brachial plexus nerve block.

# The clavipectoral fascia

This is a sheet of strong connective tissue, which is attached at its upper border to the coracoid process of the scapula and the clavicle.

The clavipectoral fascia descends to enclose the subclavius muscle and the pectoralis minor muscle and then joins with the overlying axillary fascia in the base of the axilla.

The part of the clavipectoral fascia that lies above the pectoralis minor muscle is known as the 'costocoracoid membrane' and is pierced by the nerve which supplies the overlying pectoralis minor muscle.

Below the pectoralis minor muscle, the fascia becomes the 'suspensory ligament of the axilla', which attaches to the skin of the armpit and is responsible for pulling that skin up when the arm is raised.

The clavipectoral fascia is continuous with the brachial fascia, which envelops the arm like a sleeve.

The fascia is pierced by a number of veins, arteries and nerves. These are the cephalic vein, the thoracoacromial artery (a branch of the axillary artery) and the lateral pectoral nerve.

## Front view of the axilla showing the clavipectoral fascia

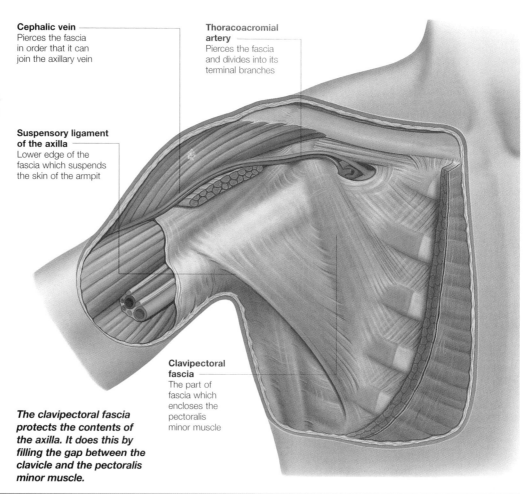

**Cephalic vein**
Pierces the fascia in order that it can join the axillary vein

**Thoracoacromial artery**
Pierces the fascia and divides into its terminal branches

**Suspensory ligament of the axilla**
Lower edge of the fascia which suspends the skin of the armpit

**Clavipectoral fascia**
The part of fascia which encloses the pectoralis minor muscle

*The clavipectoral fascia protects the contents of the axilla. It does this by filling the gap between the clavicle and the pectoralis minor muscle.*

## Borders of the axilla

*The shape of the axilla varies according to the position of the arm. When the arm is raised the axilla is a wide-based pyramid, and when the arm is lowered it is a narrow, compressed space.*

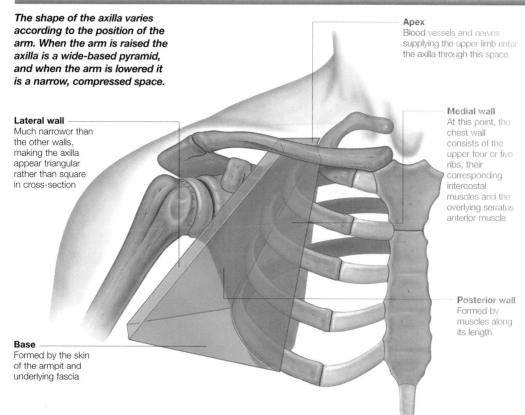

**Lateral wall**
Much narrower than the other walls, making the axilla appear triangular rather than square in cross-section

**Base**
Formed by the skin of the armpit and underlying fascia

**Apex**
Blood vessels and nerves supplying the upper limb enter the axilla through this space

**Medial wall**
At this point, the chest wall consists of the upper four or five ribs, their corresponding intercostal muscles and the overlying serratus anterior muscle

**Posterior wall**
Formed by muscles along its length

The axilla is said to have an apex, a base, and four walls:

■ The apex, or top point of the axilla, is a space between the clavicle (collarbone) at the front, the first rib on the medial (inner) side and the top of the scapula (shoulder blade) behind
■ The base is formed by the skin of the armpit and underlying axillary fascia, a layer of strong connective tissue
■ The anterior wall is formed by the pectoral and subclavius muscles and by the clavipectoral fascia
■ The posterior wall is formed by the subscapularis muscle lying on the scapula, and, lower down, by the latissimus dorsi and teres major muscles
■ The medial (inner) wall of the axilla is formed by the chest wall
■ The lateral (outer) wall is formed by the muscles attached to the bone of the upper arm, the humerus. These muscles are the coracobrachialis and biceps brachii.

# Structure of the humerus

The humerus, a typical 'long bone', is found in the upper arm. It has a long shaft with expanded ends that connect with the scapula at the shoulder joint and the radius and ulna at the elbow.

At the top of the humerus (the proximal end) lies the smooth, hemispherical head that fits into the glenoid cavity of the scapula at the shoulder joint. Behind the head is a shallow constriction known as the 'anatomical neck' of the humerus, which separates the head from two bony prominences, the greater and the lesser tuberosities. These are sites for muscle attachment and are separated by the intertubercular (or bicipital) groove.

## THE SHAFT

At the upper end of the shaft is the slightly narrowed 'surgical neck' of the humerus – a common site for fractures. The relatively smooth shaft has two distinctive features. About half way down the shaft, on the lateral (outer) side, lies the deltoid tuberosity, a raised site of attachment of the deltoid muscle. The second feature is the radial (or spiral) groove which runs across the back of the middle part of the shaft. This depression marks the path of the radial nerve and the profunda brachii artery.

Ridges at each side of the lower shaft pass down to end in the prominent medial (inner) and lateral epicondyles. There are two main parts to the articular surface: the trochlea, which articulates with the ulna; and the capitulum, which articulates with the radius.

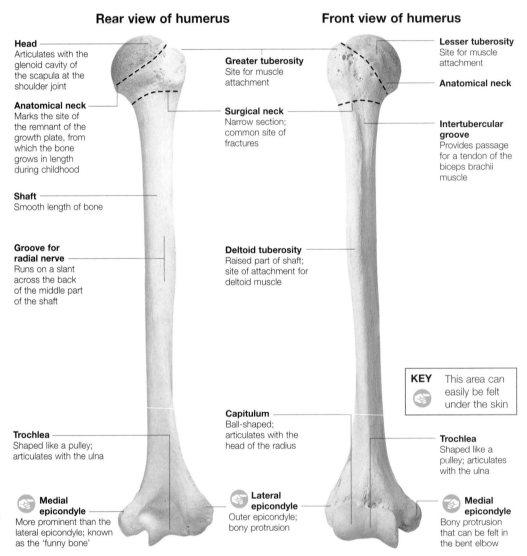

**Rear view of humerus**

**Head**
Articulates with the glenoid cavity of the scapula at the shoulder joint

**Anatomical neck**
Marks the site of the remnant of the growth plate, from which the bone grows in length during childhood

**Shaft**
Smooth length of bone

**Groove for radial nerve**
Runs on a slant across the back of the middle part of the shaft

**Trochlea**
Shaped like a pulley; articulates with the ulna

**Medial epicondyle**
More prominent than the lateral epicondyle; known as the 'funny bone'

**Greater tuberosity**
Site for muscle attachment

**Surgical neck**
Narrow section; common site of fractures

**Deltoid tuberosity**
Raised part of shaft; site of attachment for deltoid muscle

**Capitulum**
Ball-shaped; articulates with the head of the radius

**Lateral epicondyle**
Outer epicondyle; bony protrusion

**Front view of humerus**

**Lesser tuberosity**
Site for muscle attachment

**Anatomical neck**

**Intertubercular groove**
Provides passage for a tendon of the biceps brachii muscle

**KEY** This area can easily be felt under the skin

**Trochlea**
Shaped like a pulley; articulates with the ulna

**Medial epicondyle**
Bony protrusion that can be felt in the bent elbow

## Fractures of the humerus

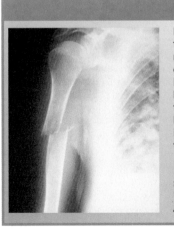

Most fractures of the upper end of the humerus occur at the surgical neck, and often happen as a result of a fall onto an outstretched hand. Fractures of the shaft of the humerus may cause damage to the radial nerve as it lies along the bone in the radial groove, resulting in the condition 'wrist drop', where the muscles at the back of the forearm which are innervated by the radial nerve become paralysed.

In children, fractures of the humerus are often supracondylar (at the lower end just above the elbow joint) and occur when the child falls on an outstretched hand with the elbow slightly bent. In these cases, there may be damage to the nearby nerves and arteries.

*This X-ray shows a fracture of the upper part of the humerus. This may occur after falling onto an outstretched hand.*

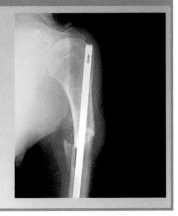

*Some fractures of the humerus may need to be stabilized with a metal pin. This holds the broken ends of bone together.*

# Inside the humerus

The structure of the humerus is typical of the long bones. The bone is divided into the diaphysis (shaft) and the epiphysis (head) at either end.

Long bones are elongated in shape and longer than they are wide. Most of the bones of the limbs are long bones, even the small bones of the fingers, and as such they have many features in common with the humerus.

The humerus consists of a diaphysis, or shaft, with an epiphysis (expanded head) at each end. The diaphysis is of tubular construction with an outer layer of dense, thick bone surrounding a central medulla (inner region) containing fat cells. The epiphyses of the humerus are, at the upper end, the head and at the lower end the condylar region. These are composed of a thin layer of compact bone covering cancellous (spongy) bone which makes up the greater volume.

## BONE SURFACE

The surface of the humerus (and all long bones) is covered by a thick membrane, the periosteum. The articular surfaces at the joints are the only parts of the bone not covered by the periosteum. These surfaces are covered by tough articular (or hyaline) cartilage which is smooth, allowing the bones to glide over each other.

The outer compact bone receives its blood supply from the arteries of the periosteum, and will die if that periosteum is stripped off, while the inner parts of the bone are supplied by occasional nutrient arteries which pierce the compact bone.

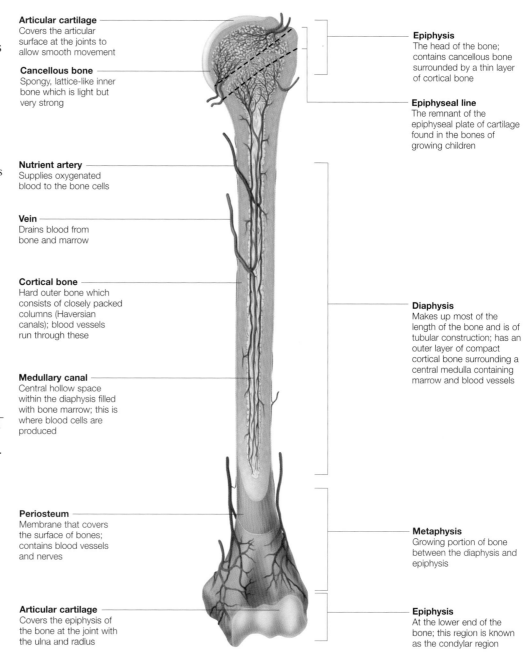

**Articular cartilage**
Covers the articular surface at the joints to allow smooth movement

**Cancellous bone**
Spongy, lattice-like inner bone which is light but very strong

**Nutrient artery**
Supplies oxygenated blood to the bone cells

**Vein**
Drains blood from bone and marrow

**Cortical bone**
Hard outer bone which consists of closely packed columns (Haversian canals); blood vessels run through these

**Medullary canal**
Central hollow space within the diaphysis filled with bone marrow; this is where blood cells are produced

**Periosteum**
Membrane that covers the surface of bones; contains blood vessels and nerves

**Articular cartilage**
Covers the epiphysis of the bone at the joint with the ulna and radius

**Epiphysis**
The head of the bone; contains cancellous bone surrounded by a thin layer of cortical bone

**Epiphyseal line**
The remnant of the epiphyseal plate of cartilage found in the bones of growing children

**Diaphysis**
Makes up most of the length of the bone and is of tubular construction; has an outer layer of compact cortical bone surrounding a central medulla containing marrow and blood vessels

**Metaphysis**
Growing portion of bone between the diaphysis and epiphysis

**Epiphysis**
At the lower end of the bone; this region is known as the condylar region

## Types of bone tissue found in the body

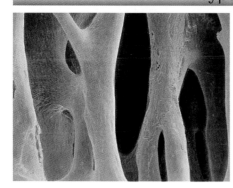

*Cancellous (or spongy) bone. This tissue, seen on this electron micrograph, fills the interior of bones. Cancellous bone is lattice-like in structure and has a low density.*

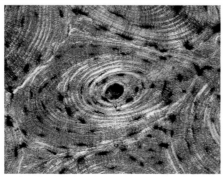

*Cortical bone. This is made up of parallel columns called Haversian canals. These consist of concentric layers around channels containing blood vessels and nerves.*

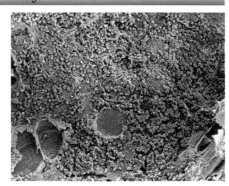

*Bone marrow. This is found within the spaces of the cancellous bone in the centre of long bones. Bone marrow contains stem cells which produce several types of blood cells.*

# Ulna and radius

The ulna and the radius are the long bones of the forearm. They articulate with the humerus and the wrist bones and are uniquely adapted to enable rotation of the hand and forearm.

The ulna and radius are the two parallel long bones of the forearm and lie between the elbow and wrist joints. The ulna lies on the same side as the little finger (medially), while the radius lies on the same side as the thumb (laterally).

The radio-ulnar joints allow the ulna and radius to rotate around each other in the movements peculiar to the forearm known as 'pronation' (rotating the forearm so that the palm faces down), and 'supination' (rotating the forearm so that the palm faces up).

### THE ULNA

The ulna is longer than the radius and is the main stabilizing bone of the forearm. It has a long shaft with two expanded ends. The upper end of the ulna has two prominent projections, the olecranon and the coronoid process, which are separated by the deep trochlear notch, which articulates with the trochlea of the humerus.

On the lateral (outer) side of the coronoid process, there is a small, rounded recess (the radial notch), which is the site of articulation of the upper end of the ulna with the neighbouring head of the radius. The head of the ulna is separated from the wrist joint by an articular disc and does not play much part in the wrist joint itself.

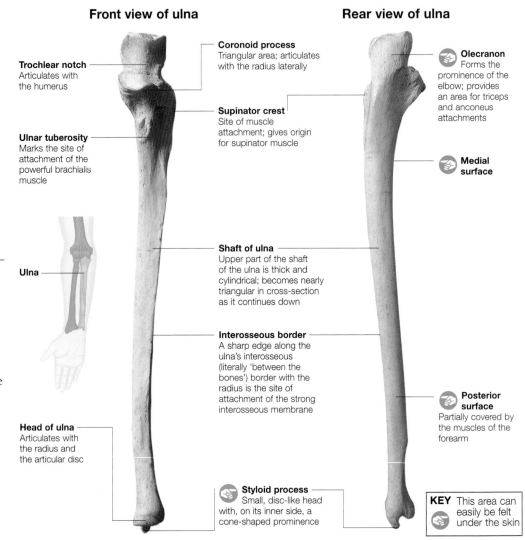

**Front view of ulna**

**Trochlear notch**
Articulates with the humerus

**Ulnar tuberosity**
Marks the site of attachment of the powerful brachialis muscle

**Ulna**

**Head of ulna**
Articulates with the radius and the articular disc

**Coronoid process**
Triangular area; articulates with the radius laterally

**Supinator crest**
Site of muscle attachment; gives origin for supinator muscle

**Shaft of ulna**
Upper part of the shaft of the ulna is thick and cylindrical; becomes nearly triangular in cross-section as it continues down

**Interosseous border**
A sharp edge along the ulna's interosseous (literally 'between the bones') border with the radius is the site of attachment of the strong interosseous membrane

**Styloid process**
Small, disc-like head with, on its inner side, a cone-shaped prominence

**Rear view of ulna**

**Olecranon**
Forms the prominence of the elbow; provides an area for triceps and anconeus attachments

**Medial surface**

**Posterior surface**
Partially covered by the muscles of the forearm

**KEY** This area can easily be felt under the skin

---

## The interosseous membrane

### Cross-section through the bones of the forearm

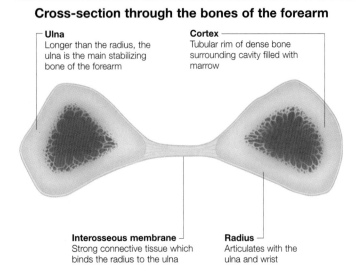

**Ulna**
Longer than the radius, the ulna is the main stabilizing bone of the forearm

**Cortex**
Tubular rim of dense bone surrounding cavity filled with marrow

**Interosseous membrane**
Strong connective tissue which binds the radius to the ulna

**Radius**
Articulates with the ulna and wrist

The radius and the ulna are connected by a thin sheet of tough, fibrous connective tissue which ties them tightly together, called the interosseous membrane. This membrane is broad enough to enable a good deal of movement between the bones during the actions of supination and pronation (turning the palm up and then down). The interosseous membrane is also strong enough to provide sites for the attachment of some of the deep muscles of the forearm.

*The interosseous membrane, composed of tough connective tissue, binds the radius and ulna together. It also divides the forearm into two compartments.*

The interosseous membrane has an important role to play in the transmission of force through the forearm. If force were to be applied to the wrist – as in breaking a fall onto an outstretched hand – that force would be received first by the end of the radius as it makes up the greater part of the wrist joint.

The tough fibres of the interosseous membrane lie in such a direction that the force is then transmitted effectively to the ulna, which makes up the greater part of the elbow joint. The transmission of this force via the interosseous membrane to the ulna allows the impact to be further absorbed by the bone of the upper arm, the humerus.

# The radius

The radius is the shorter of the two bones of the forearm and articulates with the wrist. It is joined firmly to the ulna by a tough layer of connective tissue.

Like the ulna, the radius has a long shaft with upper and lower expanded ends. While the ulna is the forearm bone which contributes most to the elbow, the radius plays a major part in the wrist joint.

### HEAD OF THE RADIUS

The disc-like head of the radius is concave above, where it articulates with the capitulum of the humerus in the elbow joint. The cartilage that covers this concavity continues down over the head, especially on the side nearest the ulna, to allow the smooth articulation of the head of the radius with the radial notch at the upper end of the ulna.

### THE SHAFT

The shaft of the radius becomes progressively thicker as it continues down to the wrist. It also has a sharp edge for attachment of the interosseous membrane. On the inner side, next to the ulna, there is a concavity (the ulnar notch), which is the site for articulation with the head of the ulna.

Extending from the opposite side is the radial styloid process, a blunt cone which projects a little further down than the ulnar styloid process. At the back of the end of the radius, and easily felt at the back of the wrist, is the dorsal tubercle.

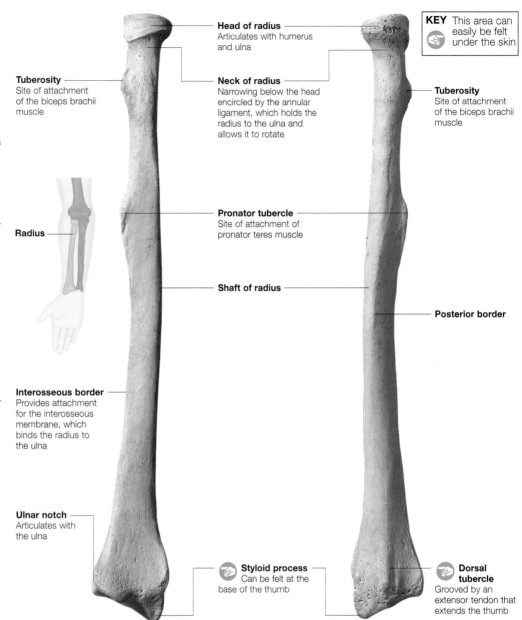

**Front view of radius**

**Rear view of radius**

**KEY** This area can easily be felt under the skin

**Head of radius**
Articulates with humerus and ulna

**Tuberosity**
Site of attachment of the biceps brachii muscle

**Neck of radius**
Narrowing below the head encircled by the annular ligament, which holds the radius to the ulna and allows it to rotate

**Tuberosity**
Site of attachment of the biceps brachii muscle

**Radius**

**Pronator tubercle**
Site of attachment of pronator teres muscle

**Shaft of radius**

**Posterior border**

**Interosseous border**
Provides attachment for the interosseous membrane, which binds the radius to the ulna

**Ulnar notch**
Articulates with the ulna

**Styloid process**
Can be felt at the base of the thumb

**Dorsal tubercle**
Grooved by an extensor tendon that extends the thumb

## Colles' fracture

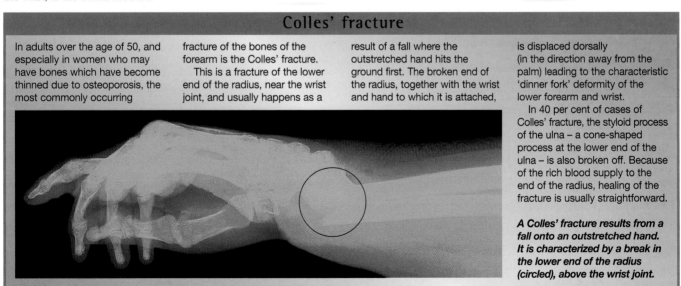

In adults over the age of 50, and especially in women who may have bones which have become thinned due to osteoporosis, the most commonly occurring fracture of the bones of the forearm is the Colles' fracture.

This is a fracture of the lower end of the radius, near the wrist joint, and usually happens as a result of a fall where the outstretched hand hits the ground first. The broken end of the radius, together with the wrist and hand to which it is attached, is displaced dorsally (in the direction away from the palm) leading to the characteristic 'dinner fork' deformity of the lower forearm and wrist.

In 40 per cent of cases of Colles' fracture, the styloid process of the ulna – a cone-shaped process at the lower end of the ulna – is also broken off. Because of the rich blood supply to the end of the radius, healing of the fracture is usually straightforward.

*A Colles' fracture results from a fall onto an outstretched hand. It is characterized by a break in the lower end of the radius (circled), above the wrist joint.*

# Elbow

The elbow is the fluid-filled joint where the humerus of the upper arm and the radius and ulna of the forearm articulate. The joint structure only allows hinge-like movement but is extremely stable.

The elbow is a synovial (fluid-filled) joint between the lower end of the humerus and the upper ends of the ulna and radius. It is the best example of a 'hinge' joint, where the only movements permitted are flexion (bending) and extension (straightening). Its structure gives the joint great stability and in adults dislocation rarely occurs.

### STRUCTURE OF THE ELBOW

At the elbow, the pulley-shaped trochlea of the lower end of the humerus articulates with the deep trochlear notch of the ulna, while its hemispherical capitulum articulates with the head of the radius. All the opposing joint surfaces are covered by smooth articular cartilage (hyaline) to reduce friction between the bony surfaces during movement.

The whole joint is surrounded by a fibrous capsule which extends down from the articular surfaces of the humerus to the upper end of the ulna. The capsule is loose at the back of the elbow to allow flexion and extension. The capsule is lined with synovial membrane which secretes thick synovial fluid filling the joint cavity. This fluid nourishes the joint and acts as a lubricant. The joint cavity is continuous with that of the superior radioulnar joint below.

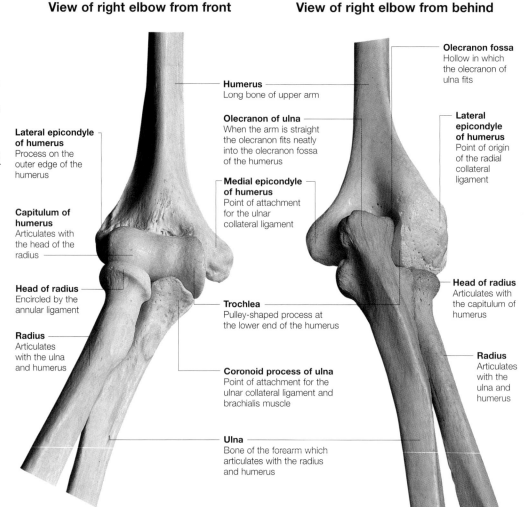

**View of right elbow from front**

**Lateral epicondyle of humerus**
Process on the outer edge of the humerus

**Capitulum of humerus**
Articulates with the head of the radius

**Head of radius**
Encircled by the annular ligament

**Radius**
Articulates with the ulna and humerus

**Humerus**
Long bone of upper arm

**Olecranon of ulna**
When the arm is straight the olecranon fits neatly into the olecranon fossa of the humerus

**Medial epicondyle of humerus**
Point of attachment for the ulnar collateral ligament

**Trochlea**
Pulley-shaped process at the lower end of the humerus

**Coronoid process of ulna**
Point of attachment for the ulnar collateral ligament and brachialis muscle

**Ulna**
Bone of the forearm which articulates with the radius and humerus

**View of right elbow from behind**

**Olecranon fossa**
Hollow in which the olecranon of ulna fits

**Lateral epicondyle of humerus**
Point of origin of the radial collateral ligament

**Head of radius**
Articulates with the capitulum of humerus

**Radius**
Articulates with the ulna and humerus

## Stability and movement of the elbow

### Bending the elbow joint

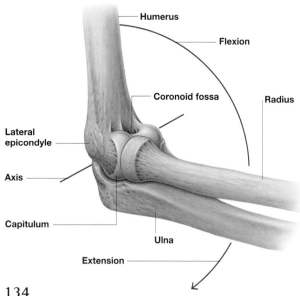

**Humerus**

**Flexion**

**Coronoid fossa**

**Radius**

**Lateral epicondyle**

**Axis**

**Capitulum**

**Ulna**

**Extension**

*The elbow joint is capable of two movements: flexion (bending) and extension (straightening), as indicated by the purple arrow.*

The elbow performs only two movements, bending and straightening, so the structure is very stable. The main stability of the elbow comes from the size and depth of the trochlear notch of the ulna, which effectively grips the lower end of the humerus like a wrench.

The depth of this bony notch is increased by the presence of a band of the medial collateral ligament. Because of the shape of this joint, and the presence of the strong collateral ligaments on each side, the elbow can move only as a hinge.

### FLEXION AND EXTENSION

Flexion (bending) of the elbow is achieved by contraction of the powerful muscles at the front of the upper arm such as brachialis and the well-known biceps brachii. The movement is limited at its fullest extent by the coming together of the forearm and the upper arm.

Extension of the elbow is mainly achieved by contraction of the triceps muscle at the back of the upper arm, assisted by gravity. At full extension, with the arm straight, the olecranon of the ulna fits neatly into the olecranon fossa (hollow) of the lower end of the back of the humerus. This fitting together of the two bones prevents over-extension of the elbow, and so adds to its stability.

# Ligaments of the elbow

The elbow is supported and strengthened at each side by the strong collateral ligaments. These are thickenings of the joint capsule.

The radial collateral ligament is a fan-shaped ligament that originates from the lateral epicondyle – a bony prominence on the outer side of the lower end of the humerus – and runs down to blend with the annular ligament, which encircles the head of the radius. It is not attached to the radius itself so does not restrict movement of the radius during pronation (when the forearm is rotated so that the palm faces down) and supination (when the forearm is rotated so the palm faces up).

The ulnar collateral ligament runs between the medial (inner) epicondyle of the humerus and the upper end of the ulna and is in three parts, which form a rough triangle.

### CARRYING ANGLE

When the arm is fully extended downwards with the palm facing forwards, the long axis of the forearm is not in line with the long axis of the upper arm, but deviates slightly outwards.

The angle so formed at the elbow is known as the 'carrying angle' and is greater in women than in men (by about 10 degrees), possibly to accommodate the wider hips of the female body. The carrying angle disappears when the forearm is pronated (turned so the palm faces in to the body).

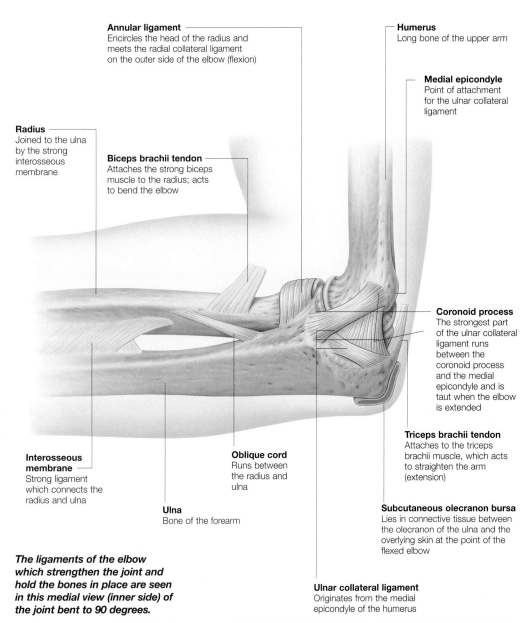

**Annular ligament**
Encircles the head of the radius and meets the radial collateral ligament on the outer side of the elbow (flexion)

**Humerus**
Long bone of the upper arm

**Medial epicondyle**
Point of attachment for the ulnar collateral ligament

**Radius**
Joined to the ulna by the strong interosseous membrane

**Biceps brachii tendon**
Attaches the strong biceps muscle to the radius; acts to bend the elbow

**Coronoid process**
The strongest part of the ulnar collateral ligament runs between the coronoid process and the medial epicondyle and is taut when the elbow is extended

**Interosseous membrane**
Strong ligament which connects the radius and ulna

**Oblique cord**
Runs between the radius and ulna

**Ulna**
Bone of the forearm

**Triceps brachii tendon**
Attaches to the triceps brachii muscle, which acts to straighten the arm (extension)

**Subcutaneous olecranon bursa**
Lies in connective tissue between the olecranon of the ulna and the overlying skin at the point of the flexed elbow

**Ulnar collateral ligament**
Originates from the medial epicondyle of the humerus

*The ligaments of the elbow which strengthen the joint and hold the bones in place are seen in this medial view (inner side) of the joint bent to 90 degrees.*

## Clinical features

### Cross-section through elbow joint

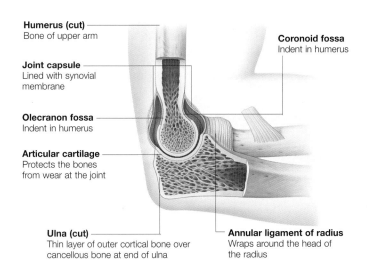

**Humerus (cut)**
Bone of upper arm

**Joint capsule**
Lined with synovial membrane

**Olecranon fossa**
Indent in humerus

**Articular cartilage**
Protects the bones from wear at the joint

**Coronoid fossa**
Indent in humerus

**Ulna (cut)**
Thin layer of outer cortical bone over cancellous bone at end of ulna

**Annular ligament of radius**
Wraps around the head of the radius

### DISLOCATION

The bones which stabilize the elbow joint are incompletely developed in children and dislocations of the elbow, where the ulna and radius move posteriorly (backwards with respect to the humerus) may occur when a child falls onto an outstretched, partially flexed arm. There is often tearing of the ulnar collateral ligament and sometimes a fracture of the upper parts of the radius and ulna associated with this dislocation.

*A cross-section through the elbow joint reveals the articular surfaces and the positions of the overlying joint capsules in front of and behind the humerus.*

### TENNIS ELBOW

Despite the name, tennis elbow is not a condition of the elbow joint itself but is a painful inflammation of the site of attachment of muscles to the lateral epicondyle of the humerus. The muscles concerned are those which extend the wrist and the fingers and so are used when, for instance, hitting a ball with a backhand stroke in tennis.

The condition occurs as a result of acute trauma to the area or normal but excessively repetitive actions involving those muscles. Pain is felt over the lateral epicondyle and down the back of the forearm, especially when the hand is being used.

135

# Muscles of the upper arm

The musculature of the upper arm is divided into two distinct compartments. The muscles of the anterior compartment act to flex the arm and the muscles of the posterior compartment extend it.

The muscles of the anterior (front) compartment of the upper arm are all flexors:

■ Biceps brachii. This muscle arises from two heads, which join together to form the body of the muscle. The bulging body then tapers as it runs down to form the strong tendon of insertion.

When the elbow is straight, biceps acts to flex the forearm. However, when the elbow is already bent the biceps muscle is a powerful supinator of the forearm, rotating the forearm so that the hand is palm up.
■ Brachialis. This arises from the lower half of the anterior surface of the humerus and passes down to cover the front of the elbow joint, its tendon inserting into the coronoid process and tuberosity of the ulna.

Brachialis is the main flexor muscle of the elbow, whatever the position of the forearm.
■ Coracobrachialis. This muscle arises from the tip of the coracoid process of the scapula and runs down and outwards to insert into the inner surface of the humerus. This muscle helps to flex the upper arm at the shoulder and to pull it back into line with the body (adduction).

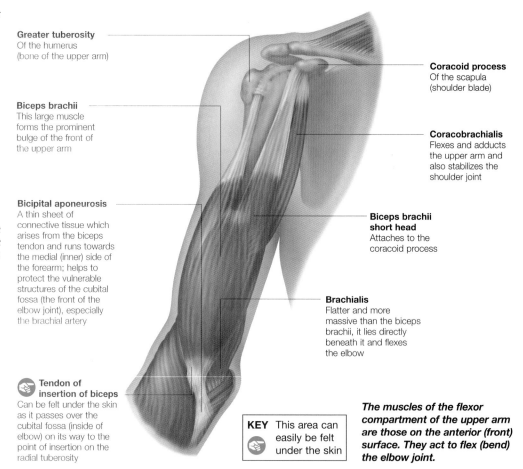

**Greater tuberosity**
Of the humerus
(bone of the upper arm)

**Biceps brachii**
This large muscle forms the prominent bulge of the front of the upper arm

**Bicipital aponeurosis**
A thin sheet of connective tissue which arises from the biceps tendon and runs towards the medial (inner) side of the forearm; helps to protect the vulnerable structures of the cubital fossa (the front of the elbow joint), especially the brachial artery

**Tendon of insertion of biceps**
Can be felt under the skin as it passes over the cubital fossa (inside of elbow) on its way to the point of insertion on the radial tuberosity

**Coracoid process**
Of the scapula
(shoulder blade)

**Coracobrachialis**
Flexes and adducts the upper arm and also stabilizes the shoulder joint

**Biceps brachii short head**
Attaches to the coracoid process

**Brachialis**
Flatter and more massive than the biceps brachii, it lies directly beneath it and flexes the elbow

**KEY** This area can easily be felt under the skin

*The muscles of the flexor compartment of the upper arm are those on the anterior (front) surface. They act to flex (bend) the elbow joint.*

## The long head of biceps

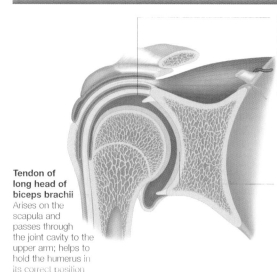

**Synovial membrane**
Sheath of fluid-secreting tissue that lubricates the tendon, reducing friction on movement

**Tendon of long head of biceps brachii**
Arises on the scapula and passes through the joint cavity to the upper arm; helps to hold the humerus in its correct position

**Glenoid fossa**
Depression of bone, lined with cartilage, into which the head of the humerus fits at the shoulder joint

*This section through the shoulder joint is angled to show the tendon of the long head of biceps. The name biceps means 'having two heads'.*

The long head of biceps brachii arises from a point on the scapula just above the glenoid fossa. The rounded tendon crosses the head of the humerus actually within the cavity of the shoulder joint before emerging in the upper arm.

As it passes out of the shoulder joint cavity, the tendon of the long head runs in the 'bicipital groove' between the lesser and greater tubercles of the humerus, surrounded by a sheath of synovial membrane (fluid-secreting connective tissue). The fluid acts to lubricate the tendon, reducing friction on movement. The position of attachment of this head of the biceps muscle allows it to help in stabilizing the shoulder joint, as well as in flexing the arm.

### RUPTURE OF THE TENDON
Very occasionally, and usually after inflammation, the tendon of the long head of biceps may rupture as it passes within the bicipital groove. On flexing the elbow, a large 'lump' will appear, which is the bunched-up body and long head of the biceps muscle, with a depression above it showing that the long head is not in its usual position.

# Muscles of the posterior compartment

The muscles of the back of the upper arm act to extend the elbow, so straightening the forearm with the upper arm.

The posterior compartment has only one major muscle, the triceps brachii, which is a powerful extensor (straightens the arm). The only other muscle in this compartment is the small, relatively insignificant anconeus.

### TRICEPS BRACHII

This is a large, bulky muscle which lies posterior to the humerus and, as its name implies, has three heads:

- The long head
- The lateral head
- The medial head.

The three heads converge in the middle of the upper arm on a wide, flattened tendon which passes down, over a small bursa, to attach to the olecranon process of the ulna.

The main action of triceps is to extend (straighten) the elbow joint. In addition, because of its position, the long head of the triceps muscle helps to stabilize the shoulder joint.

### ANCONEUS

The small anconeus muscle lies behind and below the elbow joint and is triangular in shape. As with the triceps, it extends the elbow and also has a function in the stabilization of the elbow joint.

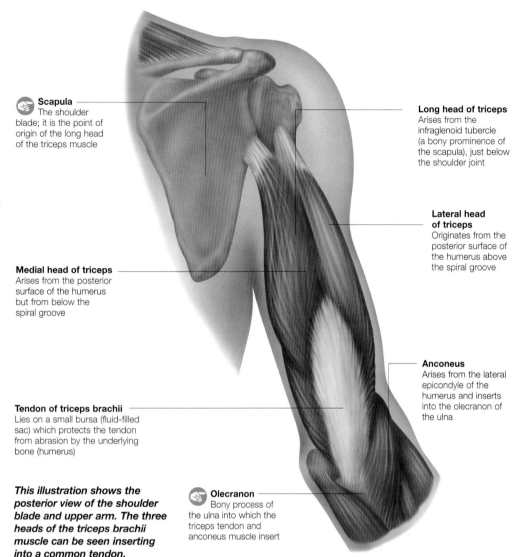

**Scapula**
The shoulder blade; it is the point of origin of the long head of the triceps muscle

**Medial head of triceps**
Arises from the posterior surface of the humerus but from below the spiral groove

**Tendon of triceps brachii**
Lies on a small bursa (fluid-filled sac) which protects the tendon from abrasion by the underlying bone (humerus)

**Long head of triceps**
Arises from the infraglenoid tubercle (a bony prominence of the scapula), just below the shoulder joint

**Lateral head of triceps**
Originates from the posterior surface of the humerus above the spiral groove

**Anconeus**
Arises from the lateral epicondyle of the humerus and inserts into the olecranon of the ulna

**Olecranon**
Bony process of the ulna into which the triceps tendon and anconeus muscle insert

*This illustration shows the posterior view of the shoulder blade and upper arm. The three heads of the triceps brachii muscle can be seen inserting into a common tendon.*

## Cross-section of the upper arm

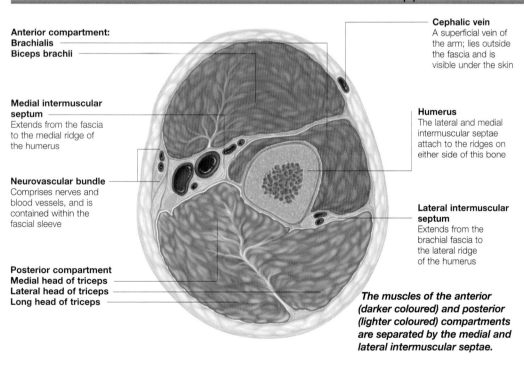

**Anterior compartment:**
**Brachialis**
**Biceps brachii**

**Medial intermuscular septum**
Extends from the fascia to the medial ridge of the humerus

**Neurovascular bundle**
Comprises nerves and blood vessels, and is contained within the fascial sleeve

**Posterior compartment**
**Medial head of triceps**
**Lateral head of triceps**
**Long head of triceps**

**Cephalic vein**
A superficial vein of the arm; lies outside the fascia and is visible under the skin

**Humerus**
The lateral and medial intermuscular septae attach to the ridges on either side of this bone

**Lateral intermuscular septum**
Extends from the brachial fascia to the lateral ridge of the humerus

*The muscles of the anterior (darker coloured) and posterior (lighter coloured) compartments are separated by the medial and lateral intermuscular septae.*

Viewing the upper arm in cross-section illustrates the fact that the arm is divided into distinct compartments, surrounded and enclosed by sheets of connective tissue known as fascia.

The brachial fascia is like a sleeve under the skin within which the major structures of the arm lie. Further fascial divisions, the lateral and medial intermuscular septae, arise from this brachial fascia and attach to the ridges on either side of the humerus, dividing the upper arm into the anterior and posterior muscular compartments.

### NEUROVASCULAR BUNDLES

Also contained within the fascial 'sleeve' are the nerves and blood vessels of the upper arm. Nerves and blood vessels often travel together in the body within 'neurovascular bundles' and this is apparent in the case of the upper arm.

137

# Muscles of the forearm

The flexor muscles of the front compartment of the forearm act to flex the hand, wrist and fingers. They are divided into superficial and deep muscles of the flexor and extensor compartments.

## Superficial flexor muscles

This compartment, or section, of the forearm lies in the front of the forearm and contains muscles which flex the wrist and fingers as well as some which pronate the forearm (turn the hand palm down). They are sub-divided into superficial and deep layers according to position.

The superficial group contains five muscles which all originate at the medial epicondyle of the humerus, where their fibres merge to form the 'common flexor tendon':

■ Pronator teres – pronates the forearm and flexes the elbow
■ Flexor carpi radialis – acts to produce flexion and abduction (bending away from the midline of the body) of the wrist

■ Palmaris longus – this small muscle is absent in 14 per cent of people; it acts to flex the wrist
■ Flexor carpi ulnaris – this muscle flexes and adducts the wrist (bends away from the midline of the body); unlike the other muscles of the flexor compartment, this muscle is innervated by the ulnar nerve
■ Flexor digitorum superficialis – this is the largest superficial muscle of the forearm and it acts, as its name suggests, to flex the fingers, or digits.

*The five main superficial flexor muscles of the forearm are shown in this illustration. These muscles originate from the humerus bone of the upper arm.*

## Superficial flexor muscles

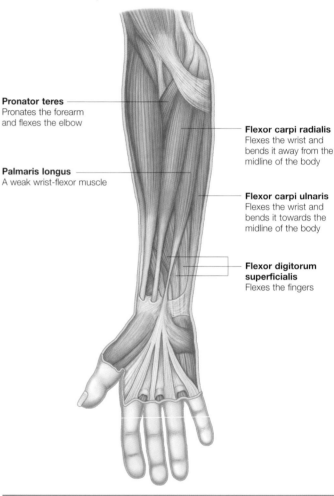

**Pronator teres**
Pronates the forearm and flexes the elbow

**Palmaris longus**
A weak wrist-flexor muscle

**Flexor carpi radialis**
Flexes the wrist and bends it away from the midline of the body

**Flexor carpi ulnaris**
Flexes the wrist and bends it towards the midline of the body

**Flexor digitorum superficialis**
Flexes the fingers

## Deep flexor muscles

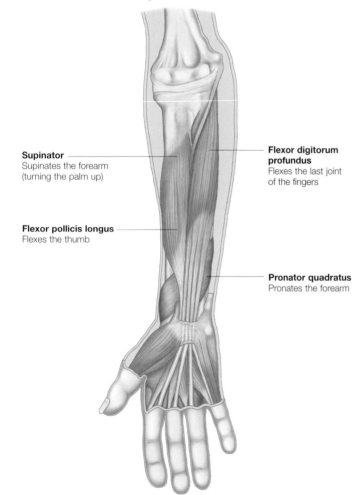

**Supinator**
Supinates the forearm (turning the palm up)

**Flexor pollicis longus**
Flexes the thumb

**Flexor digitorum profundus**
Flexes the last joint of the fingers

**Pronator quadratus**
Pronates the forearm

## Deep flexor muscles

The deep layer of the flexor compartment consists of three muscles:

■ **Flexor digitorum profundus**
This bulky muscle originates from a wide area of the ulna and neighbouring interosseous membrane (a strong sheet of tissue connecting the radius and ulna). It is the only muscle which flexes the last joint of the fingers and so acts with its more superficial counterpart to curl the fingers. Like the flexor digitorum superficialis muscle, this deeper muscle divides into four tendons, which pass

*The deep flexor muscles lie close to the bones of the forearm (the ulna and radius). These act to flex the hand, wrist and fingers.*

through the carpal tunnel within the same synovial sheath. The tendons insert into the bases of the distal (far end) phalanges of the four fingers.

■ **Flexor pollicis longus**
This muscle flexes the thumb. Its long, flat tendon passes through the carpal tunnel within its own synovial sheath and inserts into the base of the distal phalanx of the thumb (which, unlike the fingers, has only two phalanges).

■ **Pronator quadratus**
The deepest muscle of the anterior compartment, the pronator quadratus acts to pronate the forearm and is the only muscle which attaches solely to the radius and ulna. It also assists the interosseous membrane in binding the radius and ulna tightly together.

# Flexing the hand

The muscles of the forearm are divided into front and rear compartments. The front flexor muscles bend the wrist and fingers and the rear extensor muscles act to straighten them again.

The muscles of the forearm are roughly divided into two groups, according to their function. These two groups are isolated from each other by the radius and ulna bones and by fascial layers (sheets of connective tissue) to form the 'anterior flexor compartment' and the 'posterior extensor compartment' of the forearm.

### OPPOSING ACTIONS

The flexor muscles act to flex (bend) the wrist joint and the fingers, while the extensors act to extend (straighten) the same joints. Within these two groups are both deep and superficial muscles which act together to give the wide range of movements characteristic of the wrist and hand.

### FOREARM TENDONS

So that the wrist and hand may move flexibly, the bulk of muscle around the lower end of the upper limb is kept to a minimum. This is achieved by using long tendons from muscles higher up in the forearm to work the wrist, and the fingers.

The muscles concerned are forearm muscles and need to be longer than the forearm will allow to work at maximum efficiency and thus many originate from the lower end of the humerus. The humerus has developed two projections called the medial (inner) and lateral (outer) epicondyles. The flexor muscles are attached to the medial epicondyle while the extensor muscles are attached to the lateral epicondyle.

## Cross-section through the forearm

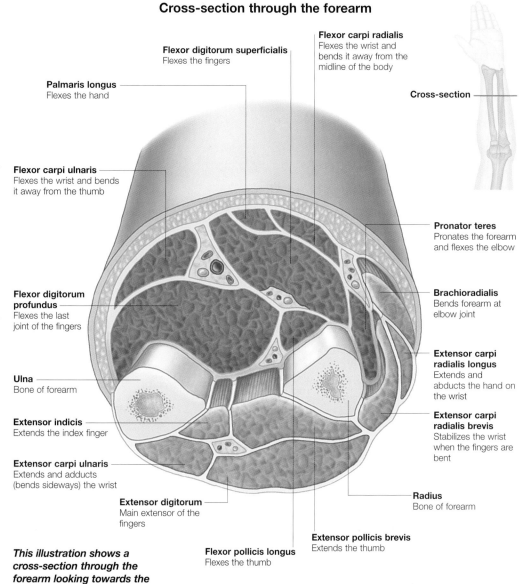

**Flexor carpi radialis**
Flexes the wrist and bends it away from the midline of the body

**Flexor digitorum superficialis**
Flexes the fingers

**Palmaris longus**
Flexes the hand

**Cross-section**

**Flexor carpi ulnaris**
Flexes the wrist and bends it away from the thumb

**Pronator teres**
Pronates the forearm and flexes the elbow

**Brachioradialis**
Bends forearm at elbow joint

**Flexor digitorum profundus**
Flexes the last joint of the fingers

**Extensor carpi radialis longus**
Extends and abducts the hand on the wrist

**Ulna**
Bone of forearm

**Extensor carpi radialis brevis**
Stabilizes the wrist when the fingers are bent

**Extensor indicis**
Extends the index finger

**Radius**
Bone of forearm

**Extensor carpi ulnaris**
Extends and adducts (bends sideways) the wrist

**Extensor digitorum**
Main extensor of the fingers

**Extensor pollicis brevis**
Extends the thumb

**Flexor pollicis longus**
Flexes the thumb

*This illustration shows a cross-section through the forearm looking towards the hand with the palm upturned.*

## Compression of the forearm tissues

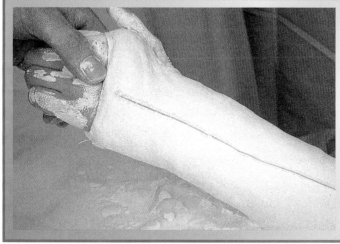

The strong fascial layers, together with the bones and interosseous membrane which surrounds and encloses the compartments of the forearm, can be of clinical significance after a fracture to the forearm bones, especially if a plaster cast is applied too tightly.

In this situation, the bleeding and swelling of the tissues that accompanies any fracture can cause a rise in pressure within the

*It is important that plaster casts applied to the forearm are not overtight. If the dressing is too constricting, the underlying tissues may become damaged.*

forearm compartments. The soft veins within the compartment are compressed, preventing blood from leaving the area and increasing the swelling.

As the pressure rises, the walled arteries are compressed, decreasing the blood supply and oxygen available to the nerves and muscles, and the cells of these structures begin to die. Dead tissues are replaced with fibrous scar tissue, which causes the damaged muscle to shorten permanently, leaving a deformity of the hand and sometimes the wrist. This deformity is known as Volkmann's ischaemic contracture.

# Blood vessels of the arm

The arteries of the arm supply blood to the soft tissues and bones. The main arteries divide to form many smaller vessels which communicate at networks – anastomoses – at the elbow and wrist.

The main blood supply to the arm is provided by the brachial artery, a continuation of the axillary artery, which runs down the inner side of the upper arm. It gives rise to many smaller branches that supply surrounding muscles and the humerus (upper bone of the arm). The largest of these is the profunda brachii artery, which supplies the muscles that straighten the elbow.

The profunda brachii artery and the other, smaller arteries given off by the lower part of the brachial artery run down around the elbow joint. They then form a network of connecting arteries before rejoining the main arteries of the forearm.

### FOREARM AND HAND
The brachial artery divides below the elbow joint into the radial and the ulnar arteries. The radial artery runs from the cubital fossa along the length of the radius (bone of the forearm). At the lower end of the radius, it lies under the skin and connective tissue; pulsations can be felt here. The ulnar artery runs towards the base of the ulna (the other bone of the forearm).

The hand has a profuse blood supply from the end branches of the radial and ulnar arteries. Branches of the two arteries join together in the palm to form the deep and the superficial palmar arches, from which small arteries arise to supply the fingers.

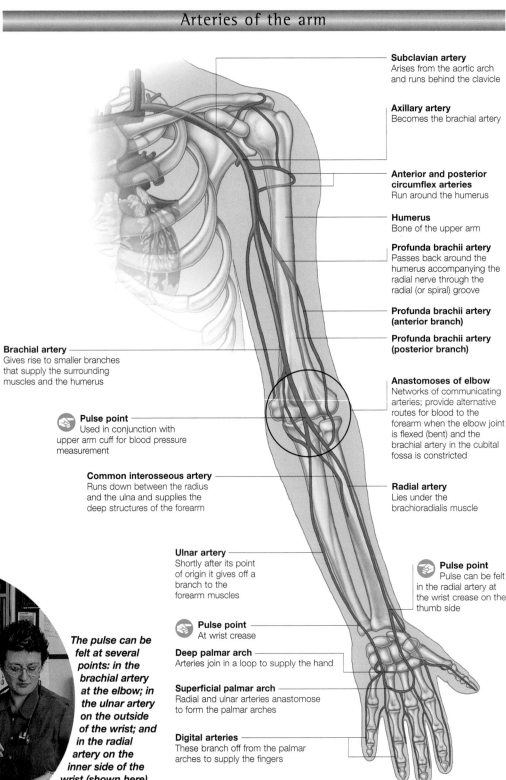

## Arteries of the arm

**Subclavian artery**
Arises from the aortic arch and runs behind the clavicle

**Axillary artery**
Becomes the brachial artery

**Anterior and posterior circumflex arteries**
Run around the humerus

**Humerus**
Bone of the upper arm

**Profunda brachii artery**
Passes back around the humerus accompanying the radial nerve through the radial (or spiral) groove

**Profunda brachii artery (anterior branch)**

**Profunda brachii artery (posterior branch)**

**Anastomoses of elbow**
Networks of communicating arteries; provide alternative routes for blood to the forearm when the elbow joint is flexed (bent) and the brachial artery in the cubital fossa is constricted

**Radial artery**
Lies under the brachioradialis muscle

**Brachial artery**
Gives rise to smaller branches that supply the surrounding muscles and the humerus

**Pulse point**
Used in conjunction with upper arm cuff for blood pressure measurement

**Common interosseous artery**
Runs down between the radius and the ulna and supplies the deep structures of the forearm

**Ulnar artery**
Shortly after its point of origin it gives off a branch to the forearm muscles

**Pulse point**
At wrist crease

**Deep palmar arch**
Arteries join in a loop to supply the hand

**Superficial palmar arch**
Radial and ulnar arteries anastomose to form the palmar arches

**Digital arteries**
These branch off from the palmar arches to supply the fingers

**Pulse point**
Pulse can be felt in the radial artery at the wrist crease on the thumb side

*The pulse can be felt at several points: in the brachial artery at the elbow; in the ulnar artery on the outside of the wrist; and in the radial artery on the inner side of the wrist (shown here).*

# Veins of the arm

The veins of the upper limb are divided into deep and superficial veins. The superficial veins lie close to the skin's surface and are often easily visible.

Venous drainage of the upper limb is achieved by two interconnecting series of veins, the deep and the superficial systems. Deep veins run alongside the arteries, while superficial veins lie in the subcutaneous tissue. The layout of the veins is very variable but usually resembles the pattern detailed below.

### DEEP VEINS

In most cases, the deep veins are paired or double veins (venae comitantes) that lie on either side of the artery they accompany, making frequent anastomoses and forming a network surrounding the artery. The pulsations of blood within the artery alternately compress and release the surrounding veins, helping blood return to the heart.

The radial and ulnar veins arise from the palmar venous arches of the hand and run up the forearm to merge at the elbow, forming the brachial vein. This, in turn, merges with the basilic vein to form the large axillary vein.

### SUPERFICIAL VEINS

There are two main superficial veins of the arm, the cephalic and the basilic veins, which originate at the dorsal venous arch of the hand. The cephalic vein runs under the skin along the radial side of the forearm.

The basilic vein runs up the ulnar side of the forearm, crossing the elbow to lie along the border of the biceps muscle. About halfway up the upper arm it turns inwards to become a deep vein.

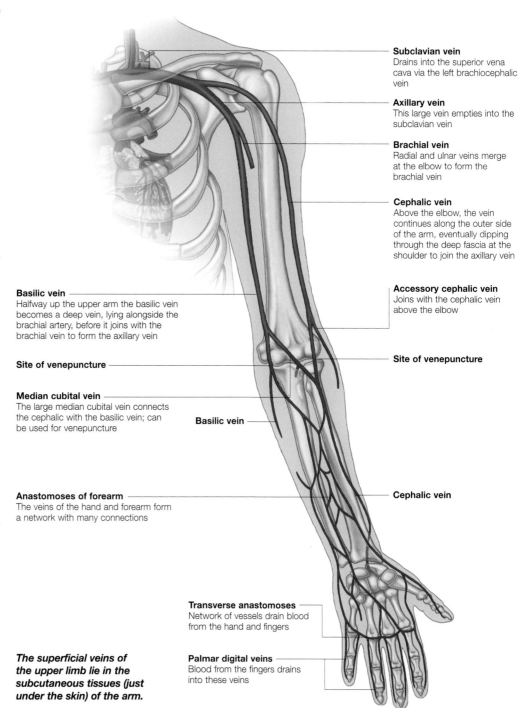

**Subclavian vein**
Drains into the superior vena cava via the left brachiocephalic vein

**Axillary vein**
This large vein empties into the subclavian vein

**Brachial vein**
Radial and ulnar veins merge at the elbow to form the brachial vein

**Cephalic vein**
Above the elbow, the vein continues along the outer side of the arm, eventually dipping through the deep fascia at the shoulder to join the axillary vein

**Accessory cephalic vein**
Joins with the cephalic vein above the elbow

**Site of venepuncture**

**Cephalic vein**

**Basilic vein**
Halfway up the upper arm the basilic vein becomes a deep vein, lying alongside the brachial artery, before it joins with the brachial vein to form the axillary vein

**Site of venepuncture**

**Median cubital vein**
The large median cubital vein connects the cephalic with the basilic vein; can be used for venepuncture

**Basilic vein**

**Anastomoses of forearm**
The veins of the hand and forearm form a network with many connections

**Transverse anastomoses**
Network of vessels drain blood from the hand and fingers

**Palmar digital veins**
Blood from the fingers drains into these veins

*The superficial veins of the upper limb lie in the subcutaneous tissues (just under the skin) of the arm.*

## Venepuncture

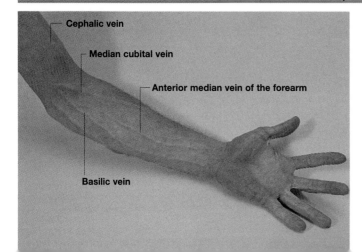

**Cephalic vein**

**Median cubital vein**

**Anterior median vein of the forearm**

**Basilic vein**

The presence of the large median cubital vein in the cubital fossa makes this an ideal site for the removal of a sample of venous blood for laboratory analysis. This large vein is usually easy to see or feel but may be difficult to find if the patient is obese.

*The superficial veins in men's arms are often quite visible. This is because men tend to have less cutaneous fat covering their veins than women.*

There are, however, some risks associated with using the median cubital vein to take a blood sample. The biceps tendon and the brachial artery lie deep to the median cubital vein and care must therefore be taken to not penetrate the tissues too deeply.

In some cases, it may be necessary to place a tourniquet around the upper arm to engorge the veins of the forearm making them more prominent.

# Nerves of the arm

The nerves of the arm supply the skin and muscles of the forearm and hand. There are four main nerves in the arm: the radial, musculocutaneous, median and ulnar nerves.

The nerve supply to the upper limb is provided by four main nerves and their branches. These receive sensory information from the hand and arm, and also innervate the numerous muscles of the upper limb. The radial and musculocutaneous nerves supply muscles and skin of all parts of the arm, while the median and ulnar nerves only supply structures below the elbow.

### RADIAL NERVE

The radial nerve is of great importance as it is the main supplier of innervation to the extensor muscles which straighten the bent elbow, wrist and fingers. It arises as the largest branch of the 'brachial plexus', a network of nerves from the spinal cord in the neck.

Near the lateral epicondyle, the radial nerve divides into its two terminal branches:
■ The superficial terminal branch – sensory nerve supply to the skin over the back of the hand, thumb and adjoining two and a half fingers
■ The deep terminal branch – motor nerve supply to all of the extensor muscles of the forearm.

### MUSCULOCUTANEOUS NERVE

The musculocutaneous nerve supplies both muscles and skin in the front of the upper arm. Below the elbow it becomes the lateral cutaneous nerve of the forearm, a sensory nerve which supplies a large area of forearm skin.

## Radial nerve damage

The radial nerve is most vulnerable as it passes along the bone through the radial groove at the back of the humerus. Here, it may be damaged during fracture of the shaft of the humerus or may be compressed against the bone, and thus bruised, by a direct blow to the back of the arm.

Damage to the radial nerve may paralyse all of the extensor muscles of the wrist and fingers. This leads to the characteristic clinical sign of 'wrist drop', when the wrist is held flexed due to the unopposed action of the flexor muscles and gravity.

## Rear view of the nerves of the arm

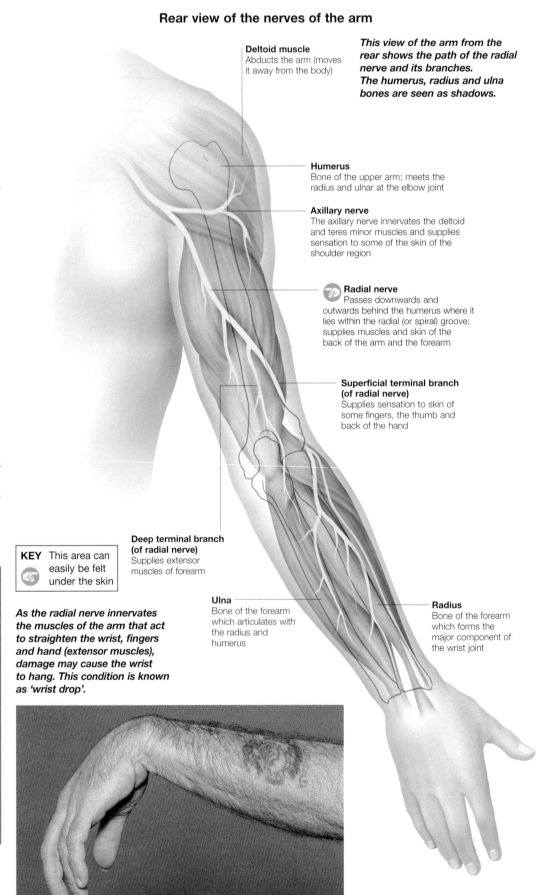

*This view of the arm from the rear shows the path of the radial nerve and its branches. The humerus, radius and ulna bones are seen as shadows.*

**Deltoid muscle**
Abducts the arm (moves it away from the body)

**Humerus**
Bone of the upper arm; meets the radius and ulnar at the elbow joint

**Axillary nerve**
The axillary nerve innervates the deltoid and teres minor muscles and supplies sensation to some of the skin of the shoulder region

**Radial nerve**
Passes downwards and outwards behind the humerus where it lies within the radial (or spiral) groove; supplies muscles and skin of the back of the arm and the forearm

**Superficial terminal branch (of radial nerve)**
Supplies sensation to skin of some fingers, the thumb and back of the hand

**Deep terminal branch (of radial nerve)**
Supplies extensor muscles of forearm

**Ulna**
Bone of the forearm which articulates with the radius and humerus

**Radius**
Bone of the forearm which forms the major component of the wrist joint

**KEY** This area can easily be felt under the skin

*As the radial nerve innervates the muscles of the arm that act to straighten the wrist, fingers and hand (extensor muscles), damage may cause the wrist to hang. This condition is known as 'wrist drop'.*

# Median and ulnar nerves

The median nerve supplies the forearm muscles enabling the actions of flexion and pronation. The ulnar nerve passes behind the elbow – where it may be felt if the 'funny bone' is knocked – to supply some of the small muscles of the hand.

The median nerve of the upper limb arises from the brachial plexus and runs downwards centrally to the elbow. It is the main nerve of the front of the forearm, which contains the muscles of flexion and pronation.

At the wrist, the median nerve passes through the carpal tunnel. The median nerve ends in branches that supply some of the small muscles of the hand, as well as the skin over the thumb and some neighbouring fingers.

### ULNAR NERVE

The ulnar nerve passes down along the humerus to the elbow where it loops behind the medial epicondyle, beneath the skin where it can easily be felt. It gives off branches to supply the elbow, two of the muscles of the forearm and several areas of overlying skin before entering the hand. In the hand, the ulnar nerve divides into deep and superficial branches.

### MEDIAN NERVE DAMAGE

The median nerve can be damaged by fractures of the lower end of the humerus or compressed by swollen muscle tendons within the carpal tunnel (carpal tunnel syndrome). Median nerve injury can make it difficult to use the 'pincer grip' of the thumb and fingers, as the nerve supplies the small muscles of the thenar eminence (the fleshy prominence below the base of the thumb).

The ulnar nerve is most vulnerable to injury as it passes behind the medial epicondyle of the humerus. The feeling from hitting the 'funny bone' occurs when the nerve is compressed against the underlying bone. Severe damage can lead to sensory loss, paralysis and wasting of the muscles it supplies.

*If the ulnar nerve is damaged, the first dorsal interosseus muscle – at the back of the thumb – may atrophy. Wasting of this muscle can be seen circled below.*

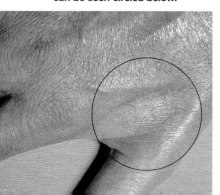

## Front view of the nerves of the arm

*The paths of the ulnar, median and musculocutaneous nerves can be seen in this dissected illustration of the arm from the front.*

**KEY** This area can easily be felt under the skin

**Humerus**
Bone of the upper arm

**Musculocutaneous nerve**
This nerve supplies both muscles and skin in the arm; it is protected by muscles along its course, and is rarely injured

**Median nerve**
Innervates the flexor muscles of the front of the forearm as well as muscles of the outer wrist and first two fingers; also supplies sensation to the thumb and two-and-a-half fingers on the front of the hand

**Ulnar nerve**
Innervates the elbow and some flexor muscles of the forearm; lies close to the surface of the elbow and, if knocked, causes a 'funny bone' sensation; it can be palpated just behind the medial epicondyle

**Branch of ulnar nerve**
Innervates many of the intrinsic muscles of the hand as well as sensation to one-and-a-half fingers on the front and back of the hand

*The marked section of this hand corresponds to the area of skin supplied by the ulnar nerve. The radial and median nerves supply other parts of the hand.*

# Bones of the wrist

The wrist lies between the radius and ulna of the forearm and the bones of the fingers. It is made up of eight marble-sized bones which move together to allow flexibility of the wrist joint and the hand.

The area that we commonly think of as the wrist is the end area of the forearm overlying the lower ends of the radius and ulna bones of the forearm. The wrist, in fact, lies in the base of the hand, and comprises eight bones held together by ligaments. They move in relation to each other, thus allowing the wrist to be flexible.

The carpal bones form two rows of four bones each – the proximal row (nearer the forearm) and the distal row (nearer the fingers). The main joint of the wrist is between the first of these two rows and the lower end of the radius.

### THE PROXIMAL ROW

The proximal row of the wrist consists of the following bones:
■ Scaphoid – a 'boat-shaped' bone which has a large facet for articulation with the lower end of the radius; it articulates with three bones of the distal row
■ Lunate – this is a moon-shaped bone that articulates with the lower end of the radius
■ Triquetral – this pyramid-shaped bone articulates with the disc of the inferior radioulnar joint and the pisiform bone
■ Pisiform – although usually considered part of the proximal row, this small bone plays no part in the wrist joint. It is about the size and shape of a pea and is a 'sesamoid' bone, a bone that lies within a muscle tendon.

*The way that the bones of the wrist sit in relation to each other is seen in this image. The top (distal) bones – closest to the fingers – are tinted orange; the bottom (proximal) bones – closest to the forearm are purple.*

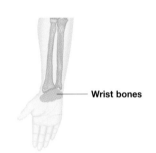
Wrist bones

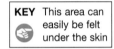 **KEY** This area can easily be felt under the skin

## Bones of the left wrist viewed from above

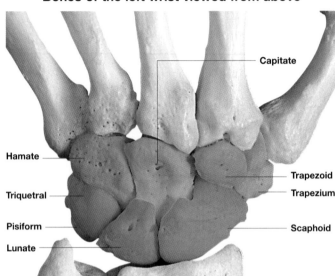

Capitate

Hamate

Triquetral

Pisiform

Lunate

Trapezoid

Trapezium

Scaphoid

## Bottom (proximal) row of wrist bones

*The proximal row of carpal bones includes two bones that can be easily felt: the pisiform and scaphoid bones.*

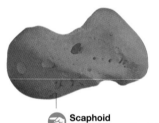

**Triquetral**
Has a small facet which is the site of articulation with the pisiform bone

**Pisiform**
Lies within the tendon of the flexor carpi ulnaris muscle

**Lunate**
Articulates with the lower end of the radius

**Scaphoid**
Has a narrowed 'waist' which is of importance clinically as it may be the site of a fracture

## The distal row

### Top (distal) row of wrist bones

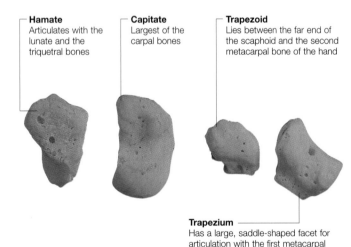

**Hamate**
Articulates with the lunate and the triquetral bones

**Capitate**
Largest of the carpal bones

**Trapezoid**
Lies between the far end of the scaphoid and the second metacarpal bone of the hand

**Trapezium**
Has a large, saddle-shaped facet for articulation with the first metacarpal

The distal row of the bones of the wrist include the:
■ **Trapezium**
This four-sided bone lies between the scaphoid and the first metacarpal (the lowest bone of the thumb). It has a large, saddle-shaped facet for articulation with the first metacarpal and a prominent tubercle (bump) on its palmar side.
■ **Trapezoid**
A small, wedge-shaped bone which lies between the far end of the scaphoid and the second

*The top (distal) row of carpal bones lies between the bones of the hand and the bottom (proximal) row. Both of these rows are held together by ligaments.*

metacarpal, the bone of the hand which runs up to the base of the index finger.
■ **Capitate**
The largest of the carpal bones, the capitate is named after its large, rounded head, which lies in the cup-shaped hollow formed by the scaphoid and the lunate bones. It articulates at its far end with the third metacarpal and also the second and fourth metacarpal bones.
■ **Hamate**
A triangular bone which is much wider at its far end than at the proximal end. It articulates with the lunate and the triquetral bones. This bone has a hook-like process on its palmar surface, the 'hook of the hamate'.

# The wrist joint

The bones of the wrist are covered in cartilage and enclosed by a synovial membrane. This secretes a viscous fluid which allows the bones to move in relation to one another with minimum friction.

The wrist, or radiocarpal, joint is a synovial (fluid-filled) joint. On one side lie the lower end of the radius and the articular disc of the inferior radioulnar joint; while on the other are three bones of the first row of carpal (wrist) bones: the scaphoid, lunate and triquetral bones. The fourth bone of this first row, the pisiform, plays no part in the wrist joint.

### THE RADIOCARPAL JOINT
The radiocarpal joint is made up of three areas, which are separated by two low ridges:
■ A lateral area (outer, on the same side as the thumb), which is formed by the lateral half of the end of the radius as it articulates with the scaphoid bone
■ A middle area, where the medial (inner) half of the end of the radius articulates with the lunate bone
■ A medial area (inner, on the side of the little finger), where the articular disc which separates the wrist joint from the inferior radioulnar joint articulates with the triquetral bone.

All the articular surfaces are covered with smooth, articular (hyaline) cartilage for reduction of friction during movement. The joint is lined with synovial membrane which secretes thick, lubricating synovial fluid, and is surrounded by a fibrous

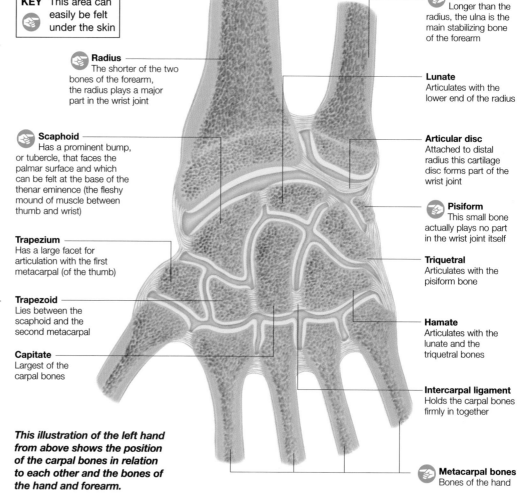

**KEY** This area can easily be felt under the skin

**Radius**
The shorter of the two bones of the forearm, the radius plays a major part in the wrist joint

**Scaphoid**
Has a prominent bump, or tubercle, that faces the palmar surface and which can be felt at the base of the thenar eminence (the fleshy mound of muscle between thumb and wrist)

**Trapezium**
Has a large facet for articulation with the first metacarpal (of the thumb)

**Trapezoid**
Lies between the scaphoid and the second metacarpal

**Capitate**
Largest of the carpal bones

**Ulna**
Longer than the radius, the ulna is the main stabilizing bone of the forearm

**Lunate**
Articulates with the lower end of the radius

**Articular disc**
Attached to distal radius this cartilage disc forms part of the wrist joint

**Pisiform**
This small bone actually plays no part in the wrist joint itself

**Triquetral**
Articulates with the pisiform bone

**Hamate**
Articulates with the lunate and the triquetral bones

**Intercarpal ligament**
Holds the carpal bones firmly in together

**Metacarpal bones**
Bones of the hand

*This illustration of the left hand from above shows the position of the carpal bones in relation to each other and the bones of the hand and forearm.*

capsule that is strengthened by ligaments.

The articular surfaces as a whole form an ellipsoid shape, with the long axis of the ellipse lying across the width of the wrist. The shape of the articular surfaces of a joint helps to determine the range of movements; an ellipsoid shape

does not allow rotation of that joint. The joint is convex towards the hand.

### THE INTERCARPAL JOINTS
As well as the joint between the lower end of the forearm and the first row of carpal bones, there is articulation between the carpal bones themselves.

There is a large, irregular, 'midcarpal' joint which lies between the two rows of carpal bones. It is a synovial joint with a joint cavity which extends into the gaps between the eight bones and allows them to glide over one another, giving the flexibility which is needed in the wrist.

## Fracture of the scaphoid

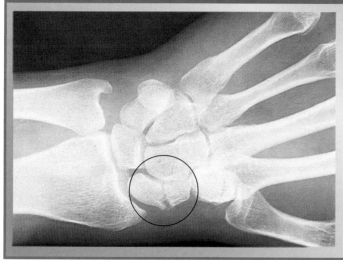

The most frequently fractured carpal bone is the scaphoid bone; fractures of this bone are one of the most common types of wrist injury. The fracture is often the result of a fall onto the outstretched hand and is usually across the narrowed 'waist' of the bone.

Fracture of the scaphoid is important clinically as the pattern of arteries around the bone is such that after a fracture across

*The scaphoid is prone to fracture through the narrow waist in the centre of the bone. This X-ray reveals the fracture (circled) but it is not always visible.*

the middle region, part of the bone may be left without a blood supply and may undergo avascular necrosis (tissue death due to lack of a blood supply). This may lead to damage and loss of function of the whole wrist.

Clinical suspicion of a scaphoid fracture is aroused by the presence of pain when pressure is applied by the doctor to the 'anatomical snuffbox', a depression at the back of the wrist near the base of the thumb; the scaphoid bone lies at the base of this depression. Diagnosis is complicated as there may be no obvious changes on an X-ray of the wrist.

# Carpal tunnel

The strong ligaments of the wrist bind together the carpal bones, allowing stability and flexibility. Within the wrist is a fibrous band through which important tendons and nerves run – the carpal tunnel.

The eight carpal bones fit together in the wrist to form the shape of an arch. The back of the wrist, the dorsal surface, is gently convex upwards while the palmar surface is concave. The arch is deepened on the palmar aspect of the wrist by the presence of the prominent tubercles of the scaphoid and trapezium bones on one side and the hook of the hamate and the pisiform bone on the other.

## STRUCTURE OF THE WRIST

This bony arch is converted into a tunnel by a tough band of fibrous tissue, the flexor retinaculum, which lies across the palmar surface and is attached on each side to the bony projections. This is called the carpal tunnel; through it run the long tendons of the muscles which flex (bend) the fingers. The presence of this band ensures that these tendons are held close to the wrist even when the wrist is bent, so allowing flexion of the fingers at every position of the wrist.

*The flexor retinaculum holds the tendons tightly together, allowing flexion in all positions. This is called the carpal tunnel.*

### Tendons of the wrist

**Radius**
Bone of the forearm

**Interosseous membrane**
Binds the radius and ulna firmly together

**Flexor carpi radialis tendon**
Flexes the wrist and bends it away from the body

**Radial artery**
Major artery of the forearm

**Flexor pollicis longus tendon**
Flexes the thumb

**Median nerve**
Main nerve supplying the hand

**Flexor retinaculum**
Tough band of fibrous tissue which hold the tendons in place

**Metacarpal bones**
Bones of the fingers

**Ulnar artery and nerve**

**Flexor carpi ulnaris tendon**
Flexes the wrist

**Flexor digitorum profundus tendons**
Flexes the last joint of the fingers

**Flexor digitorum superficialis tendons**
Flexes the fingers

### Cross-section of the right wrist

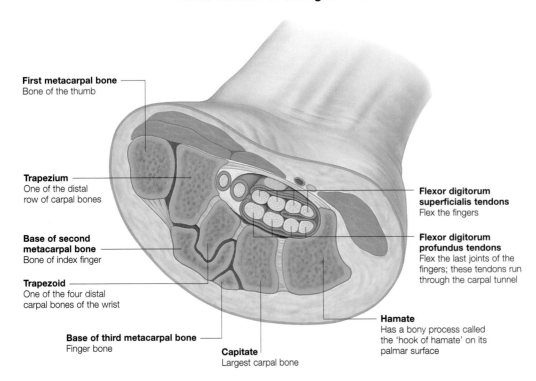

**First metacarpal bone**
Bone of the thumb

**Trapezium**
One of the distal row of carpal bones

**Base of second metacarpal bone**
Bone of index finger

**Trapezoid**
One of the four distal carpal bones of the wrist

**Base of third metacarpal bone**
Finger bone

**Capitate**
Largest carpal bone

**Flexor digitorum superficialis tendons**
Flex the fingers

**Flexor digitorum profundus tendons**
Flex the last joints of the fingers; these tendons run through the carpal tunnel

**Hamate**
Has a bony process called the 'hook of hamate' on its palmar surface

## NERVE SUPPLY

As well as the long flexor tendons, the carpal tunnel also contains the median nerve, one of the main nerves supplying the hand. If there is any swelling within the confined space of the carpal tunnel, the median nerve will be constricted. Such swelling may occur due to inflammation of the long flexor tendons caused by repetitive strain injuries, or due to general fluid retention such as is occasionally seen in pregnancy.

This leads to the condition known as 'carpal tunnel syndrome' whereby constriction of the median nerve causes 'pins and needles' or a burning pain in the skin of the side of the hand. There may also be weakness of the muscles at the base of the thumb as these are supplied from the median nerve as well.

*Compression of the carpal tunnel (blue) may affect the median nerve and therefore the functioning of the fingers.*

# Ligaments of the wrist

The ligaments of the wrist joint are thickenings of the joint capsule which help tie the wrist strongly to the lower ends of the radius and ulna.

The wrist joint itself cannot rotate and so rotation of the hand is achieved by pronation and supination of the forearm. The strong ligaments between the carpal bones and the radius are important as they 'carry' the hand round with the forearm during these actions. These ligaments include:

■ Palmar radiocarpal ligaments
Run from the radius to the carpal bones on the palm side of the hand. The fibres are directed so that the hand will go with the forearm during supination.
■ Dorsal radiocarpal ligaments
Run at the back of the wrist from the radius to the carpal bones and carry the hand back during pronation.

## COLLATERAL LIGAMENTS
Strong collateral ligaments run down each side of the wrist to strengthen the joint capsule and add to the stability of the wrist. These limit the movements of the wrist joint when it is bent.
■ Radial collateral ligament
Runs between the styloid process of the radius and the scaphoid bone in the wrist.
■ Ulnar collateral ligament
Runs between the styloid process of the ulna and the triquetral bone.

## Dorsal view of the ligaments of the wrist

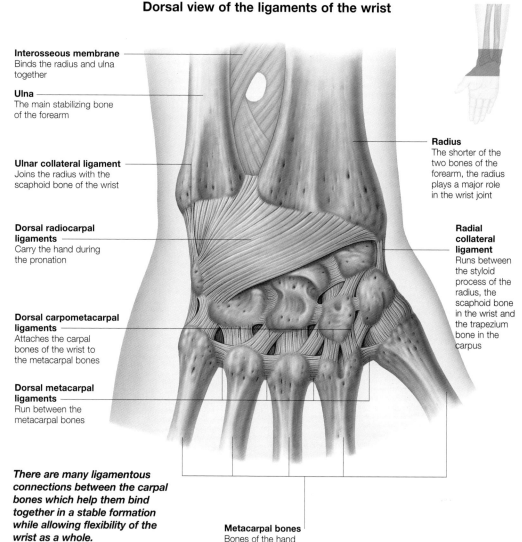

**Interosseous membrane**
Binds the radius and ulna together

**Ulna**
The main stabilizing bone of the forearm

**Ulnar collateral ligament**
Joins the radius with the scaphoid bone of the wrist

**Dorsal radiocarpal ligaments**
Carry the hand during the pronation

**Dorsal carpometacarpal ligaments**
Attaches the carpal bones of the wrist to the metacarpal bones

**Dorsal metacarpal ligaments**
Run between the metacarpal bones

**Radius**
The shorter of the two bones of the forearm, the radius plays a major role in the wrist joint

**Radial collateral ligament**
Runs between the styloid process of the radius, the scaphoid bone in the wrist and the trapezium bone in the carpus

**Metacarpal bones**
Bones of the hand

*There are many ligamentous connections between the carpal bones which help them bind together in a stable formation while allowing flexibility of the wrist as a whole.*

## Movements of the wrist

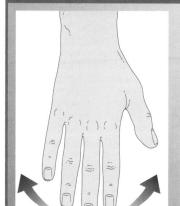

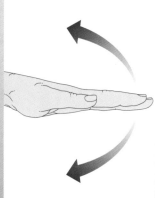

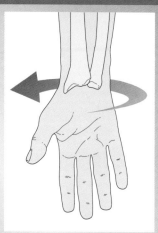

*Abduction is the the action of bending the wrist sideways towards the side of the thumb. This is limited to about 15 degrees. Adduction is the action of bending the wrist away from the thumb.*

*Flexion (bending) of the wrist is limited by the pull of the tendons at the back of the hand. The wrist can normally flex about 80 degrees, whereas extension (bending back) can usually only achieve 60 degrees.*

*The wrist is rotated by the action of the forearm in pronation (turning the palm face down) and supination (turning the palm face up). This is possible due to the strong ligaments of the wrist.*

Movements at the wrist joint are added to by smaller movements between the carpal bones themselves. The movements possible at the wrist joint are flexion and extension (bending forwards and backward), abduction (bending toward the thumb) and adduction (bending away from the thumb). Put together, these actions can bring about circumduction which is a complete circular movement of the hand at the wrist.

The most stable position of the wrist, when the bones are held most firmly together, is when it is in full extension, with the hands bent back. In this position the strong anterior radiocarpal ligaments are stretched taut. This is the position of the wrist that is naturally used when we push a heavy load, or put out the hand to break a fall.

# Bones of the hand

The bones of the hand are divided into the metacarpal bones which support the palm and the phalanges or finger bones. The joints of these bones allow the fingers and the thumb great mobility.

The skeleton of the hand is made up of eight carpal bones of the wrist, the five metacarpal bones, which support the palm, and the 14 phalanges, or finger bones.

### THE METACARPALS

Five slender bones radiate out from the wrist bones towards the fingers to form the support of the palm of the hand. They are numbered from one to five, starting at the thumb.

Each of the metacarpals is made up of a body, or shaft, and two slightly bulbous ends. The proximal end (near to the wrist) or base articulates with one of the carpal bones. The distal end (away from the wrist), or head, articulates with the first phalanx of the corresponding finger. In a clenched fist, the heads of the metacarpals are the knuckles.

### THE THUMB

The first metacarpal, at the base of the thumb, is the shortest and thickest of the five bones and is rotated slightly out of line. It is extremely mobile, allowing a wider range of movement to the thumb than to the fingers, including the action of opposition whereby the thumb can touch the tips of each of the fingers.

## The metacarpal bones

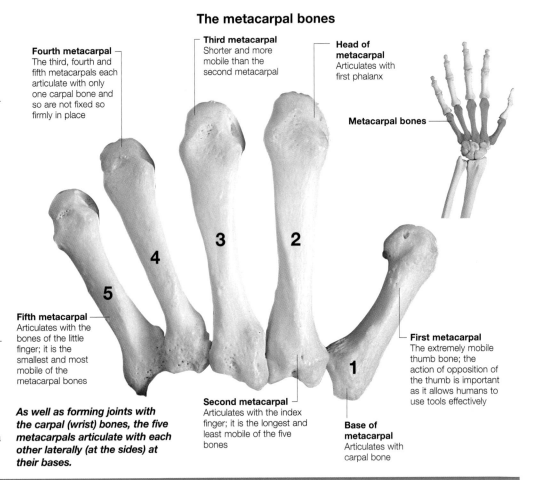

**Fourth metacarpal**
The third, fourth and fifth metacarpals each articulate with only one carpal bone and so are not fixed so firmly in place

**Third metacarpal**
Shorter and more mobile than the second metacarpal

**Head of metacarpal**
Articulates with first phalanx

**Metacarpal bones**

**Fifth metacarpal**
Articulates with the bones of the little finger; it is the smallest and most mobile of the metacarpal bones

*As well as forming joints with the carpal (wrist) bones, the five metacarpals articulate with each other laterally (at the sides) at their bases.*

**Second metacarpal**
Articulates with the index finger; it is the longest and least mobile of the five bones

**First metacarpal**
The extremely mobile thumb bone; the action of opposition of the thumb is important as it allows humans to use tools effectively

**Base of metacarpal**
Articulates with carpal bone

## The phalanges

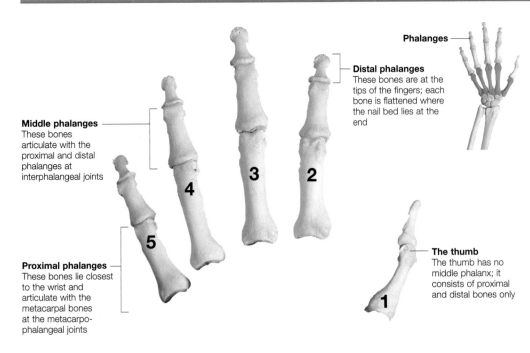

**Middle phalanges**
These bones articulate with the proximal and distal phalanges at interphalangeal joints

**Proximal phalanges**
These bones lie closest to the wrist and articulate with the metacarpal bones at the metacarpo-phalangeal joints

**Phalanges**

**Distal phalanges**
These bones are at the tips of the fingers; each bone is flattened where the nail bed lies at the end

**The thumb**
The thumb has no middle phalanx; it consists of proximal and distal bones only

The phalanges (singular: 'phalanx') are the bones of the fingers, or digits. The digits are numbered one to five, with the thumb being number one. The first digit, the thumb, has only two phalanges, the other four digits each have three.

Each phalanx is a miniature long bone with a slender shaft, or body, and two expanded ends. In each digit the first, or proximal, phalanx is the largest while the end, or distal, phalanx is the smallest. The phalanges of the thumb are shorter and thicker than those in the other digits.

Each of the small distal phalanges is characteristically flattened at the tip to form the skeletal support of the nail bed.

*Each of the fingers, with the exception of the thumb, consists of three bones. These articulate with each other and with the metacarpal bones.*

# Finger joints

The joints between the phalanges are surrounded by fibrous capsules, lined with synovial membrane and supported by strong collateral ligaments.

The joints of the metacarpal bones with the carpal bones of the wrist – the carpometacarpal joints – are synovial (fluid-filled). The thumb has a saddle-shaped joint with the trapezium allowing a wide range of movement while the other metacarpals form 'plane' joints where the articulating surfaces are flat; they therefore have a limited range of movements.

The carpometacarpal joints are surrounded by fibrous joint capsules lined with synovial membrane. This secretes the lubricating synovial fluid which fills the joint cavity. In most people there is a single, continuous joint cavity for the second to fifth carpometacarpal joints. The joint of the first metacarpal with the trapezium has its own separate joint cavity.

### METACARPOPHALANGEAL JOINTS

The joints between the metacarpals and the proximal phalanges are 'condyloid' synovial joints – this shape allows movement in two planes. The fingers may flex and extend (bend and straighten), or abduct and adduct (move apart and together sideways, spreading the fingers). This adds to the mobility and versatility of the hand, as the fingers can be placed in a wide variety of positions.

### INTERPHALANGEAL JOINTS

The joints between each phalanx and the next are simple hinge-shaped joints which allow flexion and extension only.

**Synovial membrane**
Secretes the lubricating synovial fluid which fills the joint cavity

**Metacarpal bone**
The five metacarpal bones support the palm; the head of each metacarpal articulates with the first phalanx of the corresponding finger to form a 'knuckle'

**Metacarpophalangeal joint**
Synovial joint where the metacarpal bone of the hand and the proximal phalanges meet

**Joint capsule**
Each joint is surrounded by a fibrous capsule which is lined by synovial membrane and supported by a strong collateral ligament on each side

**Middle phalanx**
Found only in the second to fifth digits and is absent in the thumb

**Interphalangeal joint**
Hinge-shaped joint connects the individual phalanges; these joints allow flexion and extension alone

**Distal phalanges**
Bone of the tip of the finger which is flattened under the nail bed

*Each finger has two inter-phalangeal joints, where the phalanges articulate with each other. These joints allow flexion and extension.*

*The hinge-shaped joints of the fingers – the interphalangeal joints – enable flexion and extension. The fingers may be flexed without flexing the hand.*

## Dislocated fingers

Dislocation is an injury to a joint which results in the bones of that joint becoming misaligned with respect to each other. Dislocation may be accompanied by damage to soft tissues surrounding the joint, the synovial membrane lining the joint cavity, the ligaments, and to muscles, nerves and blood vessels.

Dislocation of the interphalangeal joints is relatively common. Typically the finger is bent backwards so forcibly that the ligaments surrounding the joint are unable to keep the bones aligned. Another cause of finger dislocation is rheumatoid arthritis where tissues surrounding the joint are softened by inflammation.

The dislocated finger joint may be bruised, swollen and painful on trying to bend it. There may be obvious deformity of the finger, with a corresponding loss of function.

Treatment involves returning the finger bones to their correct alignment, a process known as 'reduction'. Damage to surrounding tissues may require surgical intervention.

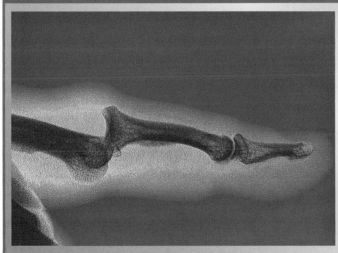

*This false-colour X-ray shows a dislocation of the finger at the proximal interphalangeal joint. It is treated by manipulating the bones back into position.*

# Muscles of the hand

The human hand is an exceptionally versatile structure, capable of powerful and delicate movements. These are produced by the actions and interactions of the numerous muscles which act upon it.

Many powerful movements of the hand, which need the contractile strength of a large bulk of muscle tissue, are controlled by the action of muscles in the forearm via tendons, rather than the hand.

Precise and delicate actions are produced by small, or 'intrinsic', muscles. These can be divided into three groups:
■ The muscles of the thenar eminence (the bulge of muscle which lies between the base of the thumb and the wrist), which move the thumb
■ The muscles of the hypothenar eminence (muscle between the little finger and the wrist), which move the little finger
■ The short muscles that run deep in the palm of the hand.

There are two groups of muscles which run longitudinally deep within the hand – the lumbricals and the interossei.

## THE LUMBRICALS

There are four lumbrical muscles arising in the palm from the tendons of the flexor digitorum profundus, a powerful muscle of the forearm. The four lumbrical muscles pass around the thumb side of the corresponding digit and insert into the area on the back of the finger which contains the extensor tendons (extensor expansion, or hood).

## The lumbrical muscles

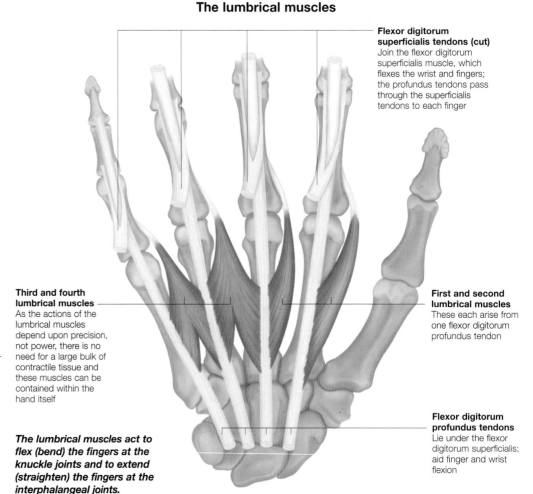

**Flexor digitorum superficialis tendons (cut)**
Join the flexor digitorum superficialis muscle, which flexes the wrist and fingers; the profundus tendons pass through the superficialis tendons to each finger

**Third and fourth lumbrical muscles**
As the actions of the lumbrical muscles depend upon precision, not power, there is no need for a large bulk of contractile tissue and these muscles can be contained within the hand itself

**First and second lumbrical muscles**
These each arise from one flexor digitorum profundus tendon

**Flexor digitorum profundus tendons**
Lie under the flexor digitorum superficialis; aid finger and wrist flexion

*The lumbrical muscles act to flex (bend) the fingers at the knuckle joints and to extend (straighten) the fingers at the interphalangeal joints.*

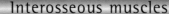

## Interosseous muscles

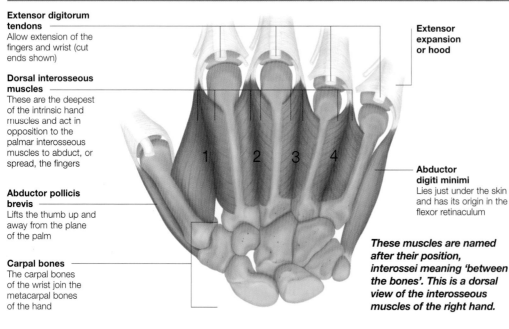

**Extensor digitorum tendons**
Allow extension of the fingers and wrist (cut ends shown)

**Dorsal interosseous muscles**
These are the deepest of the intrinsic hand muscles and act in opposition to the palmar interosseous muscles to abduct, or spread, the fingers

**Abductor pollicis brevis**
Lifts the thumb up and away from the plane of the palm

**Carpal bones**
The carpal bones of the wrist join the metacarpal bones of the hand

1   2   3   4

**Extensor expansion or hood**

**Abductor digiti minimi**
Lies just under the skin and has its origin in the flexor retinaculum

*These muscles are named after their position, interossei meaning 'between the bones'. This is a dorsal view of the interosseous muscles of the right hand.*

The interosseous muscles lie in two layers, those near the palm, the 'palmar interossei', and the deeper layer, the 'dorsal interossei'.
■ Palmar interossei
These small muscles arise from the palmar surface of the metacarpals (excluding the third). The first two pass round the medial side of each digit before inserting into the dorsal (back) surface. Those which pass to digits four and five pass around the lateral (thumb) side. Contraction of these muscles pulls the fingers in together to give the action of adduction.
■ Dorsal interossei
These larger muscles lie between the metacarpal bones of the hand, deep to the palmar interossei. Each arises from the sides of the metacarpal bones and act to spread the fingers.

# Moving the thumb and little finger

The muscles that move the thumb are contained in the thenar eminence, at the base of the thumb; those that move the little finger are found in the hypothenar eminence, between the little finger and the wrist.

The four small muscles of the thenar eminence act together to allow the thumb to move in the manner that is so important to humans. This action is known as 'opposition' and is the action whereby the tip of the thumb is brought around to touch the tip of any of the fingers.

The muscles of the thenar eminence that move the thumb include:

■ **Abductor pollicis brevis**
Abductor pollicis brevis literally means the short muscle which abducts the thumb (lifts the thumb up away from the palm).
■ **Flexor pollicis brevis**
Flexor pollicis brevis (which flexes the thumb) lies near to the centre of the palm.
■ **Opponens pollicis**
Opponens pollicis (the muscle that opposes the thumb) originates in the flexor retinaculum and the trapezium bone of the wrist, and it inserts into the outer border of the first metacarpal bone.

## Palmar view of the right hand

*The muscles which activate the thumb and little finger are seen in this illustration of the palm of the right hand.*

**Opponens digiti minimi**
Opposes the little finger

**Flexor digiti minimi**
Short flexor muscle that bends the little finger

**Abductor digiti minimi**
Abducts the little finger; lies just under the skin and has its origin in the flexor retinaculum

**Flexor retinaculum**
Band of strong connective tissue which lies across the front of the wrist to prevent 'bowstringing' of long tendons

**Flexor pollicis brevis**
Flexes the thumb

**Abductor pollicis brevis**
Lifts the thumb up away from the plane of the palm; originates from the scaphoid and trapezium bones of the wrist and from the flexor retinaculum

**Opponens pollicis**
Opposes the thumb; originates in the flexor retinaculum; this lies deep to the flexor and abductor pollicis brevis muscles

## Section through the hand

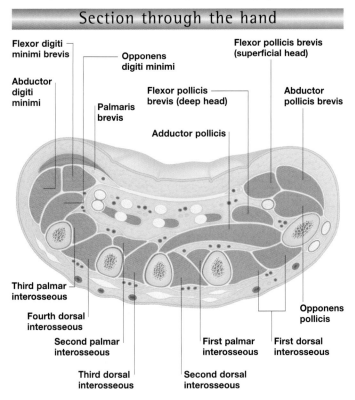

**Flexor digiti minimi brevis**

**Abductor digiti minimi**

**Opponens digiti minimi**

**Palmaris brevis**

**Flexor pollicis brevis (deep head)**

**Adductor pollicis**

**Flexor pollicis brevis (superficial head)**

**Abductor pollicis brevis**

**Third palmar interosseous**

**Fourth dorsal interosseous**

**Second palmar interosseous**

**Third dorsal interosseous**

**First palmar interosseous**

**Second dorsal interosseous**

**First dorsal interosseous**

**Opponens pollicis**

■ **Adductor pollicis**
Adductor pollicis brings the abducted thumb back in line with the palm. This is a deeply placed muscle which has two heads of origin, separated by the radial artery, which join to form a tendon. This tendon often contains a 'sesamoid' bone, a small bone which lies completely within the tendon and makes no connections with other bones.

### THE HYPOTHENAR EMINENCE

The muscles of the smaller hypothenar eminence form the swelling which lies between the little finger and the wrist. These muscles act together to move the little finger around towards the thumb in the action of cupping the hand, or when gripping the lid of a jar to twist it off.

*This illustration of a cross-section of the hand seen palm-up reveals the position of many of the hand muscles in relation to one another.*

■ **Abductor digiti minimi**
This muscle lies just under the skin and has its origin in the flexor retinaculum and the pisiform bone of the wrist. It inserts into the side of the base of the little finger.
■ **Flexor digiti minimi**
This short flexor muscle lies alongside the previous muscle but nearer to the centre of the palm. It originates in the flexor retinaculum and the hamate bone of the wrist, and inserts into the base of the little finger.
■ **Opponens digiti minimi**
This muscle, which opposes the little finger, lies underneath the more superficial muscles of the hypothenar eminence.
■ **Palmaris brevis muscle**
This short muscle has no attachments to bone, but originates in the palmar aponeurosis (connective tissue sheet which lies in the palm) and inserts into the skin overlying the hypothenar eminence. It acts to wrinkle the skin, which is believed to aid grip.

151

# Nerves and blood vessels of the hand

The hand is supplied with numerous arteries and veins. These join to form networks of small, interconnecting blood vessels which ensure a good blood supply to all fingers, even if one artery is damaged.

The hand has a plentiful blood supply from the ulnar and radial arteries. These have many interconnections (anastomoses), maintaining the blood supply even if one artery is damaged.

■ **Superficial palmar arch**
The ulnar artery enters the hand on the same side as the little finger and crosses the palm to join with the radial artery to form the 'superficial palmar arch'. This gives off small digital arteries which supply blood to the little, ring and middle fingers.

■ **Deep palmar arch**
The deep palmar arch is formed by a continuation of the radial artery. This enters the palm from below the base of the thumb and gives off small arteries which supply the thumb and index finger as well as metacarpal branches which anastomose with the digital arteries.

■ **Back of the hand**
An irregular network of small arteries lies over the back of the wrist, which supplies the back of the hand and fingers.

## Palmar view of arteries of the left hand

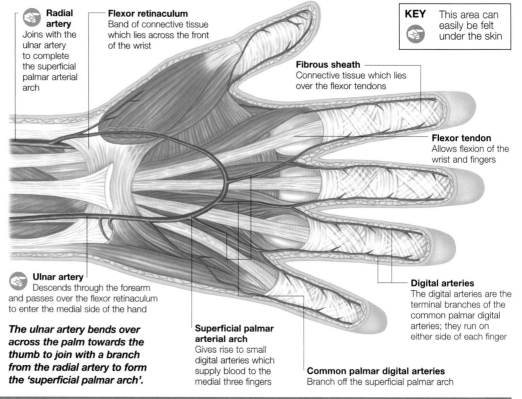

**Radial artery**
Joins with the ulnar artery to complete the superficial palmar arterial arch

**Flexor retinaculum**
Band of connective tissue which lies across the front of the wrist

**KEY** This area can easily be felt under the skin

**Fibrous sheath**
Connective tissue which lies over the flexor tendons

**Flexor tendon**
Allows flexion of the wrist and fingers

**Ulnar artery**
Descends through the forearm and passes over the flexor retinaculum to enter the medial side of the hand

*The ulnar artery bends over across the palm towards the thumb to join with a branch from the radial artery to form the 'superficial palmar arch'.*

**Superficial palmar arterial arch**
Gives rise to small digital arteries which supply blood to the medial three fingers

**Digital arteries**
The digital arteries are the terminal branches of the common palmar digital arteries; they run on either side of each finger

**Common palmar digital arteries**
Branch off the superficial palmar arch

## Veins of the hand

### Dorsal view of the veins of the left hand

*The small veins of the hand join together to form the larger veins of the arm, which carry the blood back to the heart.*

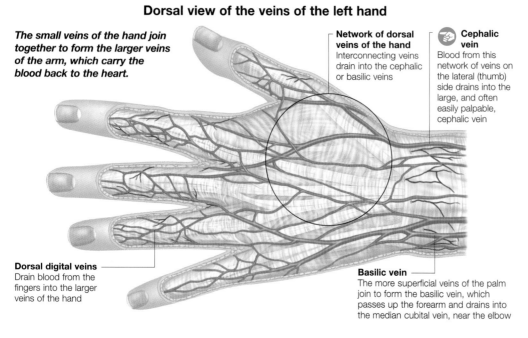

**Network of dorsal veins of the hand**
Interconnecting veins drain into the cephalic or basilic veins

**Cephalic vein**
Blood from this network of veins on the lateral (thumb) side drains into the large, and often easily palpable, cephalic vein

**Dorsal digital veins**
Drain blood from the fingers into the larger veins of the hand

**Basilic vein**
The more superficial veins of the palm join to form the basilic vein, which passes up the forearm and drains into the median cubital vein, near the elbow

The veins of the back of the fingers join to form the prominent dorsal venous arch. Blood from this network of veins on the lateral (thumb) side drains into the large cephalic vein. On the other side of the back of the hand, the network drains into the large basilic vein.

### PALMAR VEINS

The veins of the palm form interconnecting arches which lie deeply alongside the deep palmar arterial arch and, more superficially, accompany the superficial palmar arch. They receive blood from the fingers via small digital veins running down either side of each finger.

The deep veins of the palm run with the radial and ulnar arteries of the forearm. The superficial palmar veins run with their equivalent arteries.

# Nerves of the hand

The structures of the hand receive their nerve supply from terminal branches of the three main nerves of the upper limb: the median, ulnar and radial nerves.

The median nerve enters the hand on the palmar side by passing under the flexor retinaculum (a restraining band of connective tissue) within the carpal tunnel.

In the hand the median nerve supplies:
■ The three muscles of the thenar eminence – abductor pollicis brevis, flexor pollicis brevis and opponens pollicis. If the median nerve is damaged there will be loss of innervation to these muscles with corresponding loss of function of the thumb. This will include the inability to perform the important action of opposition of the thumb.
■ The first and second lumbrical muscles.
■ The skin of the palm and palmar surface of the first three-and-a-half digits as well as the dorsal surface (back) of the tips of those fingers. The branch of the median nerve which supplies the skin of the central palm arises before the median nerve enters the carpal tunnel and passes over, not under, the flexor retinaculum so the skin will continue to receive its nerve supply if the median nerve is damaged there.

**Ulnar nerve**
Passes over the flexor retinaculum and supplies skin on the little finger side of the hand and most of the hand's small 'intrinsic' muscles

**Small recurrent branch of median nerve**
Supplies three thumb muscles

**Common palmar digital branch of ulnar nerve**
Divides from the ulnar nerve and may join a branch of the median nerve

**Fibrous sheath**
Connective tissue which wraps around the outside of the flexor tendons

**Palmar branch of the median nerve**
Supplies the skin of the central palm

**Flexor retinaculum**
Band of strong connective tissue which lies across the front of the wrist to prevent 'bowstringing' of long tendons

**Median nerve**
Runs under the flexor retinaculum; it is vulnerable to damage if there is swelling of the tendons and their sheaths under the flexor retinaculum – this is known as carpal tunnel syndrome

**Palmar digital nerve**
Branch of the median nerve which supplies the fingers

**Digital branches of median nerve**
Branches of the median nerve supply lateral three-and-a-half fingers

*The hand is supplied by three major nerves: the median, ulnar and radial (not shown). Branches of these nerves supply all the muscles and skin of the hand.*

## Nerve supply of the hand

Musculo-cutaneous nerve
Median cutaneous nerve
Radial nerve
Ulnar nerve
Median nerve

Median cutaneous nerve
Musculo-cutaneous nerve
Radial nerve
Ulnar nerve
Median nerve

*These two diagrams show the areas of skin innervated by the nerves of the hand. The ulnar nerve supplies the areas shaded purple. The median nerve supplies the pink areas. The radial nerve supplies the yellow areas. The median cutaneous nerve and the musculocutaneous nerve areas are shaded green and blue respectively.*

### The ulnar nerve
The ulnar nerve enters the medial side of the hand by passing over the flexor retinaculum. In the hand the ulnar nerve supplies:
■ The skin on the medial side of the palm, via its palmar cutaneous branch
■ The skin of the medial half of the back of the hand, little finger and medial half of the ring finger via its dorsal cutaneous branch
■ The skin of the palmar side of the little finger and half the ring finger via its superficial branch
■ The muscles of the hypothenar eminence via its deep branch
■ The adductor pollicis muscle, which acts to pull the thumb back down to the palm
■ The third and fourth lumbrical muscles and all the interosseous muscles.

### The radial nerve
The radial nerve only supplies the skin within the hand. It runs down the back of the forearm to the dorsal surface (back) of the hand to supply the skin of the back of the lateral three-and-a-half digits.

# Overview of the abdomen

The abdomen is the part of the trunk which lies between the thorax (above) and the pelvis (below). The contents of the abdominal cavity are supported by a bony framework and the abdominal wall.

The organs of the upper part of the abdominal cavity – the liver, gall bladder, stomach and spleen – lie under the domes of the diaphragm and are protected by the lower ribs.

The vertebrae and their associated muscles, form the back wall of the abdominal cavity, while the bones of the pelvis support it from beneath.

The abdomen is relatively unprotected by bone. This does, however, allow for mobility of the trunk and enables the abdomen to distend when necessary, such as during pregnancy or after a large meal.

### ABDOMINAL CONTENTS

The contents of the abdominal cavity include:
■ Much of the gastro-intestinal tract
■ Liver
■ Pancreas
■ Spleen
■ Kidneys.

As well as these viscera the abdominal cavity contains all the blood vessels, lymphatics and nerves which supply them, together with a variable amount of fatty tissue.

*The abdominal cavity contains the digestive organs, such as the stomach and intestines, known collectively as viscera.*

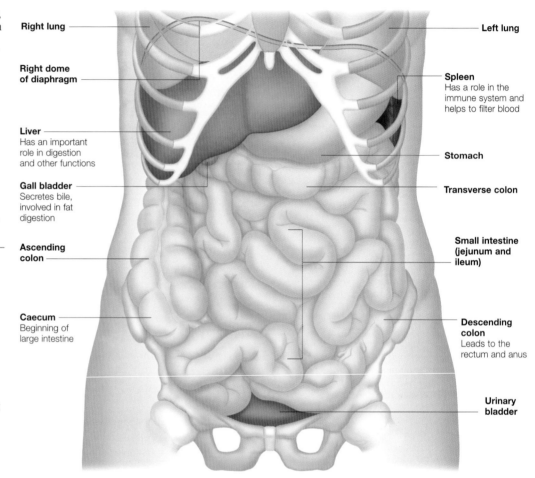

**Right lung**

**Right dome of diaphragm**

**Liver**
Has an important role in digestion and other functions

**Gall bladder**
Secretes bile, involved in fat digestion

**Ascending colon**

**Caecum**
Beginning of large intestine

**Left lung**

**Spleen**
Has a role in the immune system and helps to filter blood

**Stomach**

**Transverse colon**

**Small intestine (jejunum and ileum)**

**Descending colon**
Leads to the rectum and anus

**Urinary bladder**

## The omentum

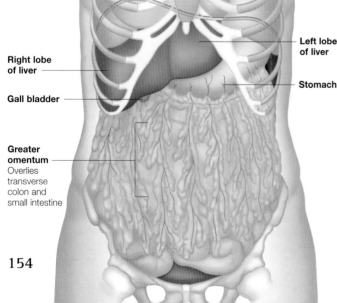

**Right lobe of liver**

**Gall bladder**

**Greater omentum**
Overlies transverse colon and small intestine

**Left lobe of liver**

**Stomach**

The majority of the contents of the abdominal cavity are clothed in a thin, lubricating sheet of tissue, known as the peritoneum. Folds of peritoneum attach the abdominal viscera to the walls of the abdominal cavity, and enable these organs to slide easily over one another.

The most noticeable part of the peritoneum is the greater omentum, which hangs down from the lower border of the

*The greater omentum is a curtain of fatty tissue that hangs in front of the abdominal organs. It acts to protect and insulate the underlying structures.*

stomach and covers the transverse colon and the coils of small bowel like an apron. The greater omentum contains a large amount of fat within it, which gives it a yellowish appearance.

### PROTECTIVE ROLE

The greater omentum has been called the 'abdominal policeman' due to its action in wrapping itself around an inflamed organ to prevent spread of infection to other organs.

It also helps to protect the abdominal organs from injury and to insulate the abdomen against heat loss.

# Planes and regions of the abdomen

In order to describe the position of organs or the site of abdominal pain, doctors find it useful to divide the abdomen into regions defined by imaginary vertical and horizontal planes. These areas help in the making of a clinical diagnosis.

The abdomen may be divided into nine regions for precise descriptions. These regions are delineated by two horizontal (subcostal and transtubercular) planes and two vertical (midclavicular) planes.

The nine regions are:
- Right hypochondrium
- Epigastrium
- Left hypochondrium
- Right flank (lumbar)
- Umbilical
- Left flank (lumbar)
- Right inguinal (groin)
- Suprapubic
- Left inguinal (groin).

### FOUR QUADRANTS
For general clinical purposes it is usually sufficient to divide the abdomen into just four sections delineated by one horizontal (transumbilical) plane and one vertical (median) plane.

The four sections are known simply as the right and left upper quadrants and the right and left lower quadrants.

### CLINICAL IMPORTANCE
It is important to know which of the abdominal contents lie in each of the regions. If an abnormality is found, or if the patient has an abdominal pain, these regions can be used to indicate the site in the patient's notes for future reference.

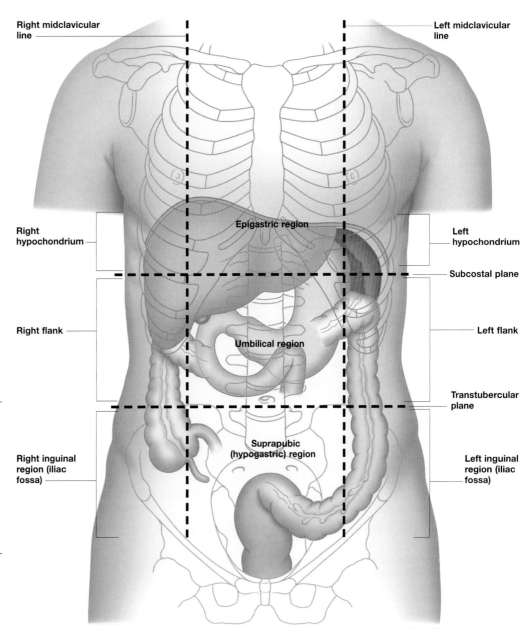

Right midclavicular line

Left midclavicular line

Right hypochondrium

Epigastric region

Left hypochondrium

Subcostal plane

Right flank

Umbilical region

Left flank

Transtubercular plane

Right inguinal region (iliac fossa)

Suprapubic (hypogastric) region

Left inguinal region (iliac fossa)

## Surgical incisions

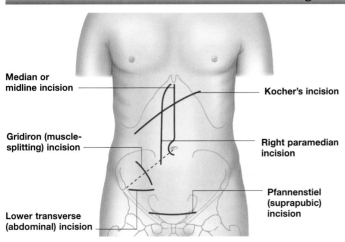

Median or midline incision

Kocher's incision

Gridiron (muscle-splitting) incision

Right paramedian incision

Lower transverse (abdominal) incision

Pfannenstiel (suprapubic) incision

Knowledge of the anatomy of the abdominal wall is important for surgeons performing abdominal operations.

If possible the surgeon will cut along the natural lines of cleavage (Langer's lines) of the skin, which lie parallel to the collagen fibres in the skin and so will close more neatly.

Other anatomical factors will be taken into account such as

*Surgeons employ a number of incisions to gain access to the abdominal cavity. Incisions need to allow adequate exposure during the operation.*

the layout of nerves supplying the abdominal wall, the direction in which the muscle fibres run and the position of connective tissue sheets (aponeuroses) so that the surgeon can minimize the damage he or she does to the healthy structures of the abdominal wall.

### TYPES OF INCISION
These various factors, together with the particular requirements of each clinical case, lead to a variety of incisions being used including the midline (median), the paramedian and the transverse (abdominal) incisions.

155

# Abdominal wall

The abdominal cavity lies between the diaphragm and the pelvis.
The abdominal wall at the front and sides of the body consists of
different muscular layers, surrounding and supporting the cavity.

The posterior (rear) abdominal
wall is formed by the lower ribs,
the spine and accompanying
muscles, while the anterolateral
(front and side) wall consists
entirely of muscle and fibrous
sheets (aponeuroses).

Under the skin and
subcutaneous fat layer there lie
the muscle layers of the
abdominal wall. The muscles
here lie in three broad sheets:
the external oblique, the internal
oblique and the transversus
abdominis, which give the
abdomen support in all
directions. In addition, there is a
wide band of muscle, the rectus
abdominis, which runs vertically
from the front of the ribcage
down to the front of the pelvis.

### EXTERNAL OBLIQUE

The external oblique muscle
forms the most superficial layer
of abdominal muscles. It is in the
form of a broad, thin sheet whose
fibres run down and inwards.

The muscle arises from the
under-surfaces of the lower ribs.
The fibres fan out into the wide
sheet of tough connective tissue
known as the external oblique
aponeurosis. At the lower end
the fibres insert into the top of
the pubic bones.

*The external oblique muscle is
part of the anterior abdominal
wall. It is the longest and most
superficial of the anterolateral
flat abdominal muscles.*

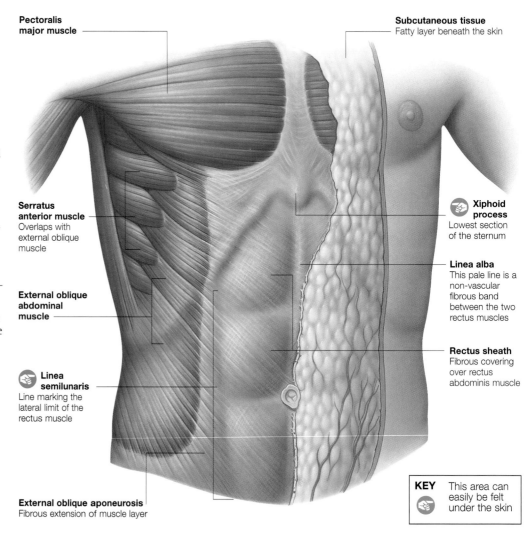

**Pectoralis
major muscle**

**Subcutaneous tissue**
Fatty layer beneath the skin

**Serratus
anterior muscle**
Overlaps with
external oblique
muscle

**External oblique
abdominal
muscle**

**Linea
semilunaris**
Line marking the
lateral limit of the
rectus muscle

**External oblique aponeurosis**
Fibrous extension of muscle layer

**Xiphoid
process**
Lowest section
of the sternum

**Linea alba**
This pale line is a
non-vascular
fibrous band
between the two
rectus muscles

**Rectus sheath**
Fibrous covering
over rectus
abdominis muscle

**KEY** This area can
easily be felt
under the skin

## Layers of the abdominal wall

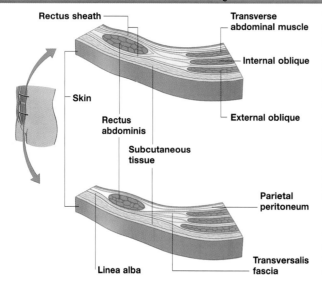

**Rectus sheath**

**Transverse
abdominal muscle**

**Internal oblique**

**Skin**

**Rectus
abdominis**

**External oblique**

**Subcutaneous
tissue**

**Parietal
peritoneum**

**Linea alba**

**Transversalis
fascia**

The layers of the abdominal wall
include:
■ Skin – the natural lines of
cleavage of the skin lie
horizontally over the greater part
of the abdominal wall
■ Superficial fatty layer, or
Camper's fascia – this may be
very thick and, in obese people,
may cause the abdominal wall to
lie in folds
■ Superficial membranous layer,
or Scarpa's fascia – this thin
layer is continuous with the
superficial fascia in adjoining

*These transverse sections of the
abdominal wall show its layered
structure. The fibrous layers
from the muscle interweave
around the rectus abdominis.*

parts of the body
■ Three muscle layers: external
and internal oblique, and
transversus abdominis
■ Deep fascia layers lying
between, and separating, these
muscle layers
■ Transversalis fascia – this
firm, membranous sheet lines
most of the abdominal wall,
merging with the tissues lining
the underside of the diaphragm
above and the pelvis below
■ Fat, lying between the
transversalis fascia and the
peritoneum
■ Peritoneum – this is the
delicate, lubricating membrane
that lines the abdominal cavity
and covers the surfaces of many
abdominal organs.

# Deeper muscles of the abdominal wall

Beneath the large external oblique muscle lie two more layers of sheet-like muscle, the internal oblique and the transversus abdominis. In addition, running vertically down the centre of the abdominal wall is the rectus abdominis.

The internal oblique muscle is a broad, thin sheet which lies deep to the external oblique. Its fibres run upwards and inwards, at approximately 90 degrees to those of the external oblique.

The fibres of the internal oblique originate from the lumbar fascia (a layer of connective tissue on either side of the spine), the iliac crest of the pelvis and the inguinal ligament (formed in the groin).

Like the external oblique, the internal oblique muscle inserts into a tough, broad aponeurosis which splits to enclose the rectus abdominis muscle (rectus sheath).

### TRANSVERSUS ABDOMINIS

This is the innermost of the three sheets of muscle which support the abdominal contents. Its fibres run horizontally to insert into an aponeurosis which lies behind the rectus abdominis muscle for much of its length.

### RECTUS ABDOMINIS

These two strap-like muscles run vertically down the front of the abdominal wall.

The upper part of each muscle is wider and thinner than the lower part. Lying between the muscles is a thin, tendinous band of tough connective tissue, the linea alba.

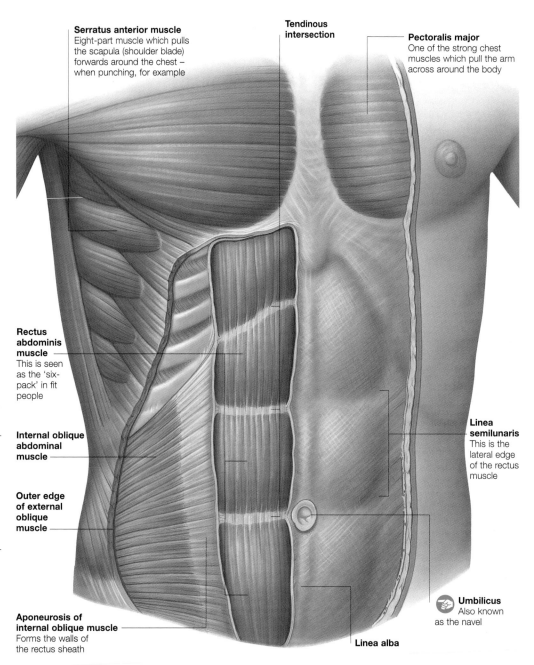

**Serratus anterior muscle**
Eight-part muscle which pulls the scapula (shoulder blade) forwards around the chest – when punching, for example

**Tendinous intersection**

**Pectoralis major**
One of the strong chest muscles which pull the arm across around the body

**Rectus abdominis muscle**
This is seen as the 'six-pack' in fit people

**Internal oblique abdominal muscle**

**Outer edge of external oblique muscle**

**Aponeurosis of internal oblique muscle**
Forms the walls of the rectus sheath

**Linea semilunaris**
This is the lateral edge of the rectus muscle

**Umbilicus**
Also known as the navel

**Linea alba**

## The rectus sheath

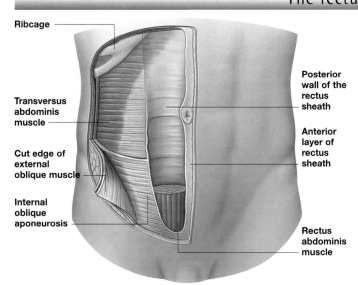

**Ribcage**

**Transversus abdominis muscle**

**Cut edge of external oblique muscle**

**Internal oblique aponeurosis**

**Posterior wall of the rectus sheath**

**Anterior layer of rectus sheath**

**Rectus abdominis muscle**

The rectus abdominis muscle is enclosed within a sheath of connective tissue formed by the coming together of the aponeuroses of the three muscle sheets of the abdominal wall. (An aponeurosis is a thin but strong sheet of fibrous tissue.)

The upper three-quarters of the rectus sheath differ from the lower quarter due to the way in which the three aponeuroses interweave.

*The rectus abdominis muscle extends along the front of the abdomen. It is enclosed by connective tissue known as the rectus sheath.*

■ **The upper rectus sheath**
The anterior wall is formed by the external oblique aponeurosis and half of the internal oblique aponeurosis, while the posterior wall is formed by the remaining half of the internal oblique and the transversus aponeurosis.

■ **The lower rectus sheath**
Three aponeuroses lie in front of the rectus abdominis muscle which lies, therefore, directly on the transversalis fascia beneath.

The three aponeuroses meet in the mid-line to form the tough linea alba. As well as the rectus abdominis muscle, the rectus sheath contains blood vessels which lie deep to the muscle.

157

# Oesophagus

The oesophagus is the tubular connection between the pharynx in the neck and the stomach. It is used solely as a passage for food, and plays no part in digestion and absorption.

The oesophagus is about 25 cm long in adults and is the muscular tube for the passage of food from mouth to stomach.

### SHAPE OF OESOPHAGUS

As it is soft and somewhat flexible, the contour and path of the oesophagus is not straight; rather it curves around, and is indented by, firmer structures such as the arch of the aorta and the left main bronchus.

### PASSAGE OF FOOD

When no food is passing through the oesophagus, its inner lining lies in folds which fill the lumen, or central space. As a bolus (lump) of food is swallowed and passes down, it distends this lining and the oesophageal walls. Food is carried down the oesophagus by waves of contractions in a process known as peristalsis.

### OESOPHAGEAL STRUCTURE

In cross-section, the oesophagus has four layers:
■ Mucosa – the innermost layer lined by stratified squamous epithelium; it is resistant to abrasion by food
■ Submucosa – composed of loose connective tissue; it also contains glands which secrete mucus to aid the passage of food
■ Muscle layer – striated muscle (under voluntary control) lines the upper oesophagus; smooth muscle the lower part; and a combination in the mid-region.
■ Adventitia – a covering layer of fibrous connective tissue.

*The oesophagus in cross-section is a multilayered structure. The layers are similar to those found in the rest of the gastro-intestinal tract.*

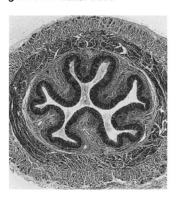

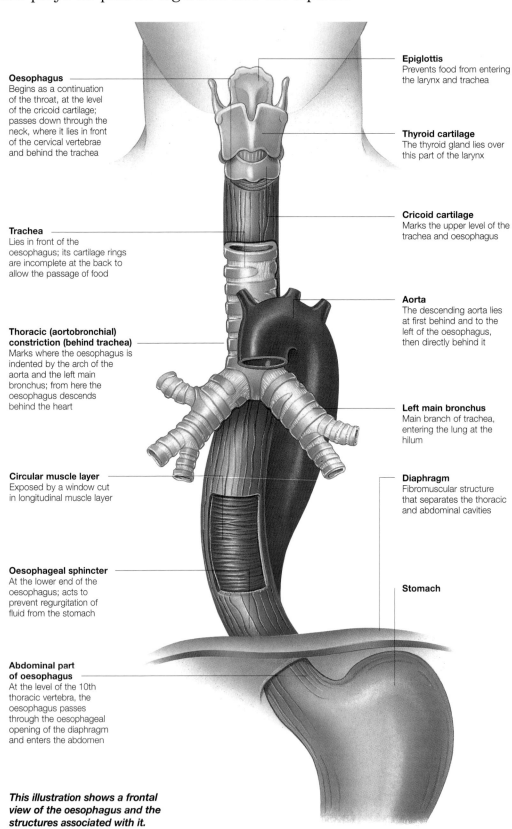

**Oesophagus**
Begins as a continuation of the throat, at the level of the cricoid cartilage; passes down through the neck, where it lies in front of the cervical vertebrae and behind the trachea

**Trachea**
Lies in front of the oesophagus; its cartilage rings are incomplete at the back to allow the passage of food

**Thoracic (aortobronchial) constriction (behind trachea)**
Marks where the oesophagus is indented by the arch of the aorta and the left main bronchus; from here the oesophagus descends behind the heart

**Circular muscle layer**
Exposed by a window cut in longitudinal muscle layer

**Oesophageal sphincter**
At the lower end of the oesophagus; acts to prevent regurgitation of fluid from the stomach

**Abdominal part of oesophagus**
At the level of the 10th thoracic vertebra, the oesophagus passes through the oesophageal opening of the diaphragm and enters the abdomen

**Epiglottis**
Prevents food from entering the larynx and trachea

**Thyroid cartilage**
The thyroid gland lies over this part of the larynx

**Cricoid cartilage**
Marks the upper level of the trachea and oesophagus

**Aorta**
The descending aorta lies at first behind and to the left of the oesophagus, then directly behind it

**Left main bronchus**
Main branch of trachea, entering the lung at the hilum

**Diaphragm**
Fibromuscular structure that separates the thoracic and abdominal cavities

**Stomach**

*This illustration shows a frontal view of the oesophagus and the structures associated with it. The tube forms a link between the mouth and the stomach.*

# Blood vessels and nerves

The arterial supply of the oesophagus derives from branches of the aorta and subclavian artery. As with much of the body, the veins which drain blood from the oesophagus tend to run alongside the arteries.

A network of small veins surrounds and drains blood from the oesophagus.

### UPPER OESOPHAGUS
The veins from the upper third of the oesophagus drain into the inferior thyroid veins. Blood from the middle third of the oesophagus is drained into the azygos venous system.

### LOWER OESOPHAGUS
Blood from the lower third of the oesophagus may enter the left gastric vein – part of the portal venous system which drains blood via the liver. This is clinically important because increased pressure in the portal system, may cause blood to travel back up into the oesophageal veins. As a result, the veins in the lower oesophagus become distended (varices form) and may rupture.

*The oesophagus is surrounded by a network of veins. These drain either into the SVC via its tributaries or the portal vein via the left gastric vein.*

## Veins of the oesophagus

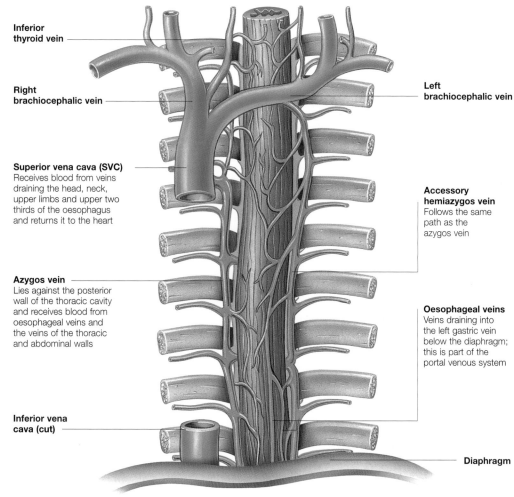

**Inferior thyroid vein**

**Right brachiocephalic vein**

**Superior vena cava (SVC)**
Receives blood from veins draining the head, neck, upper limbs and upper two thirds of the oesophagus and returns it to the heart

**Azygos vein**
Lies against the posterior wall of the thoracic cavity and receives blood from oesophageal veins and the veins of the thoracic and abdominal walls

**Inferior vena cava (cut)**

**Left brachiocephalic vein**

**Accessory hemiazygos vein**
Follows the same path as the azygos vein

**Oesophageal veins**
Veins draining into the left gastric vein below the diaphragm; this is part of the portal venous system

**Diaphragm**

## Nerves of the oesophagus

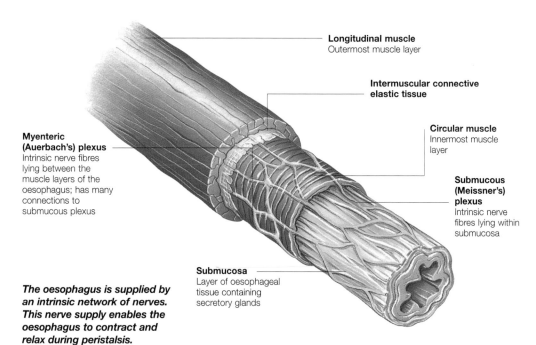

**Longitudinal muscle**
Outermost muscle layer

**Intermuscular connective elastic tissue**

**Circular muscle**
Innermost muscle layer

**Submucous (Meissner's) plexus**
Intrinsic nerve fibres lying within submucosa

**Myenteric (Auerbach's) plexus**
Intrinsic nerve fibres lying between the muscle layers of the oesophagus; has many connections to submucous plexus

**Submucosa**
Layer of oesophageal tissue containing secretory glands

*The oesophagus is supplied by an intrinsic network of nerves. This nerve supply enables the oesophagus to contract and relax during peristalsis.*

In common with the rest of the gastro-intestinal tract, the oesophagus has its own intrinsic nerve supply, which allows it to contract and relax during the process of peristalsis without any external nervous stimulation.

This intrinsic nerve supply derives from two main nerve plexuses within the walls known as the submucous (Meissner's) plexus and the myenteric (Auerbach's) plexus. These connect with each other, and together regulate the glandular secretion and movements of the oesophagus.

### EXTERNAL CONTROL
The functioning of the intrinsic system can be modified by the autonomic nervous system, which regulates the body's internal environment. External nerve fibres come from the sympathetic trunk and from the vagus (10th cranial) nerve.

159

# Stomach

The stomach is the expanded part of the digestive tract that receives
swallowed food from the oesophagus. Food is stored here
before being propelled into the small intestine as digestion continues.

The stomach is a distendable
muscular bag lined by mucous
membrane. It is fixed at two
points: the oesophageal opening
at the top and at the beginning
of the small intestine below.
Between these points it is mobile
and can vary in position.

### STOMACH LINING

When empty, the stomach lining
lies in numerous folds, or rugae,
which run from one opening to
the other.

The walls of the stomach are
similar to other parts of the gut
but with some modifications:

■ The gastric epithelium – this is
the layer of cells which lines the
stomach; it contains many
glands that secrete protective
mucus, and others that produce
enzymes and acid, which begin
the process of digestion.

■ The muscle layer – this has
an inner oblique layer of muscle
as well as the usual longitudinal
and circular fibres. This
arrangement helps the stomach
to churn food thoroughly before
propelling it on towards the
small intestine.

### REGIONS OF
### THE STOMACH

The stomach is said to have four
parts, and two curvatures:

■ The cardia
■ The fundus
■ The body
■ The pyloric region – the
outlet area of the stomach
■ The lesser curvature
■ The greater curvature.

## Location and structure of the stomach

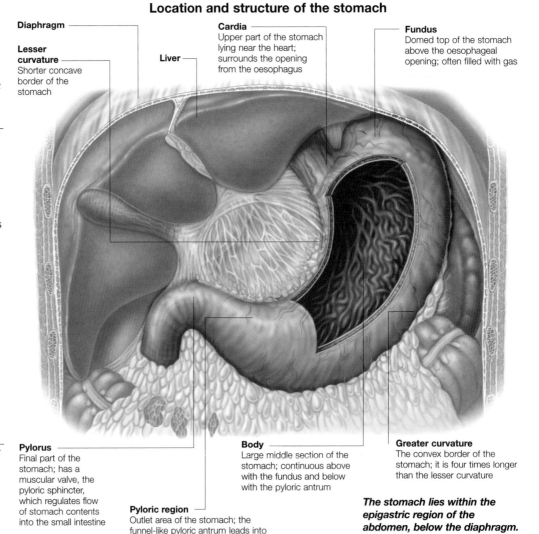

**Diaphragm**

**Lesser curvature**
Shorter concave
border of the
stomach

**Liver**

**Cardia**
Upper part of the stomach
lying near the heart;
surrounds the opening
from the oesophagus

**Fundus**
Domed top of the stomach
above the oesophageal
opening; often filled with gas

**Pylorus**
Final part of the
stomach; has a
muscular valve, the
pyloric sphincter,
which regulates flow
of stomach contents
into the small intestine

**Pyloric region**
Outlet area of the stomach; the
funnel-like pyloric antrum leads into
the narrow pyloric canal; at the end
of the canal lies the pylorus

**Body**
Large middle section of the
stomach; continuous above
with the fundus and below
with the pyloric antrum

**Greater curvature**
The convex border of the
stomach; it is four times longer
than the lesser curvature

*The stomach lies within the
epigastric region of the
abdomen, below the diaphragm.
It lies to the right of the spleen
and partly under the liver.*

## The gastro-oesophageal junction

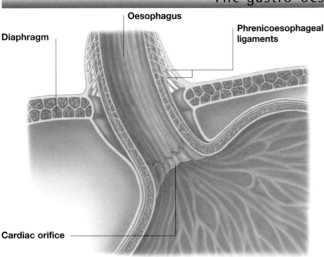

**Diaphragm**

**Oesophagus**

**Phrenicoesophageal ligaments**

**Cardiac orifice**

At the lower end of the
oesophagus the epithelium,
or lining layer of cells, changes
from multilayered, stratified
squamous, to the typical gastric
mucosa in a zig-zag junction.

### CONNECTIVE LIGAMENTS

The oesophagus and upper
part of the stomach are held
to the diaphragm by the
phrenicoesophageal ligaments.

*The muscular tube of the
oesophagus becomes
continuous with the stomach
just below the diaphragm.
This is where the oesophageal
contents enter the stomach.*

These ligaments are extensions
of the fascia, a connective tissue
that covers the diaphragm's
surface.

### PHYSIOLOGICAL
### SPHINCTER

There is no identifiable valve
at the top of the stomach to
control the passage of food.
However, the surrounding
muscle fibres of the diaphragm
act to keep the tube closed
except when a bolus (swallowed
mass) of food passes through.
This is referred to as the
physiological oesophageal
sphincter, through which the
oesophagus passes.

# Blood supply of the stomach

**The stomach has a profuse blood supply, which comes from the various branches of the coeliac trunk.**

The vessels that supply the stomach are:
- Left gastric artery – a branch of the coeliac trunk
- Right gastric artery – usually arises from the hepatic artery (a branch of the coeliac trunk)
- Right gastroepiploic artery – arises from the gastroduodenal branch of the hepatic artery
- Left gastroepiploic artery – arises from the splenic artery
- Short gastric arteries – arise from the splenic artery.

### VEINS AND LYMPHATICS

The gastric veins run alongside the various gastric arteries. Blood from the stomach is drained ultimately into the portal venous system, which takes blood through the liver before returning it to the heart.

Lymph collected from the stomach walls drains through lymphatic vessels into the many lymph nodes which lie in groups along the lesser and greater curvature. It is then transported to the coeliac lymph nodes.

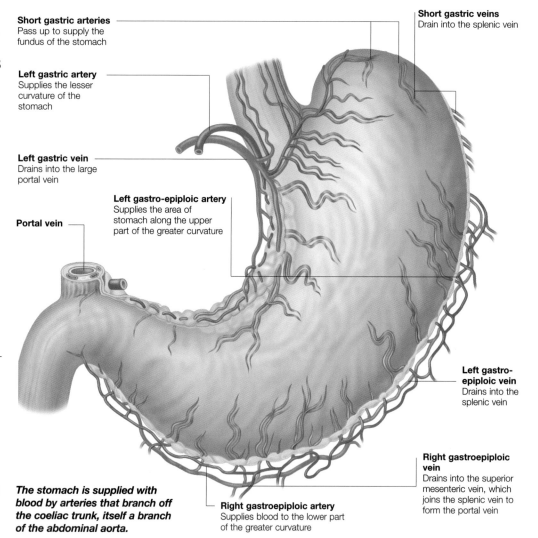

**Short gastric arteries**
Pass up to supply the fundus of the stomach

**Left gastric artery**
Supplies the lesser curvature of the stomach

**Left gastric vein**
Drains into the large portal vein

**Portal vein**

**Left gastro-epiploic artery**
Supplies the area of stomach along the upper part of the greater curvature

**Short gastric veins**
Drain into the splenic vein

**Left gastro-epiploic vein**
Drains into the splenic vein

**Right gastroepiploic vein**
Drains into the superior mesenteric vein, which joins the splenic vein to form the portal vein

**Right gastroepiploic artery**
Supplies blood to the lower part of the greater curvature

*The stomach is supplied with blood by arteries that branch off the coeliac trunk, itself a branch of the abdominal aorta.*

## Shape and position of the stomach

The stomach can expand greatly to accept food. Since it is fixed only at its upper and lower ends, it can vary considerably in its position, size and shape.

### Normal

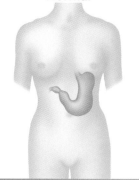

The normal stomach is an elongated pouch whose size and shape will vary with the position of the body and the degree of filling. This can also be affected by other abdominal contents, such as the fetus in pregnancy.

### Active

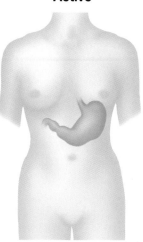

When the stomach is active, and its muscular tone high, it will lie higher and more horizontally. This is common in short, stout people. When there is less muscle activity the stomach may descend into a long 'J' shape.

### Stretched

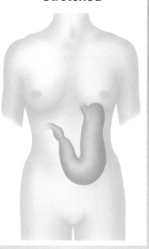

The stomach can hold up to three litres of food and may extend down to below the umbilicus after a particularly large meal. The stomach can become permanently stretched as a result of overeating.

### Pregnant

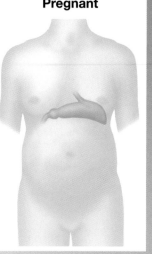

A heavily pregnant uterus will push the stomach up to a more horizontal position and even affect its ability to fill. This explains why pregnant women tend to eat little and often, and are more prone to heartburn.

# Small intestine

The small intestine extends from the stomach to the junction with the large intestine. It is made up of three parts, and is the main site in the body where food is digested and absorbed.

The small intestine is the main site of digestion and absorption of food. It is about seven metres in length in adults and extends from the stomach to the junction with the large intestine. It is divided into three parts: the duodenum, the jejunum and the ileum.

### THE DUODENUM

The duodenum is the first part of the small intestine and the shortest (about 25 cm in length). It receives the contents of the stomach with each wave of contraction of the stomach walls. In the duodenum the contents are mixed with secretions from the duodenal walls, pancreas and gall bladder.

The duodenum cannot move, but it is fixed in place behind the peritoneum, the sheet of connective tissue that lines the abdominal cavity.

### BLOOD SUPPLY OF THE DUODENUM

The duodenum receives arterial blood from various branches off the aorta. These, in turn, give off small branches that provide each part of the duodenum with a rich supply of blood. Venous blood supply mirrors the arterial pattern, returning blood to the hepatic portal venous system.

*The duodenum is the first part of the small intestine. It is roughly C-shaped and is made up of four parts.*

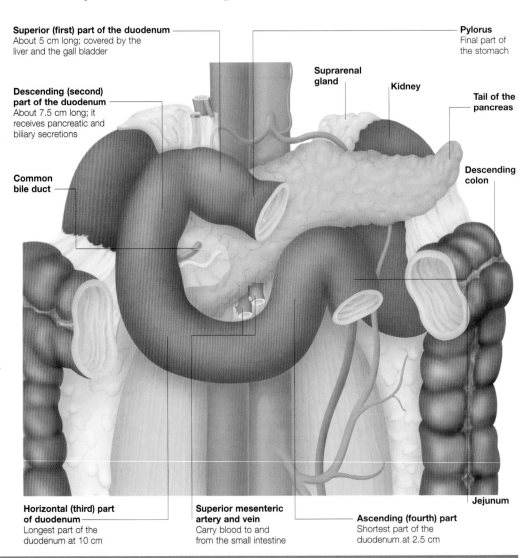

**Superior (first) part of the duodenum**
About 5 cm long; covered by the liver and the gall bladder

**Descending (second) part of the duodenum**
About 7.5 cm long; it receives pancreatic and biliary secretions

**Common bile duct**

**Horizontal (third) part of duodenum**
Longest part of the duodenum at 10 cm

**Superior mesenteric artery and vein**
Carry blood to and from the small intestine

**Pylorus**
Final part of the stomach

**Suprarenal gland**

**Kidney**

**Tail of the pancreas**

**Descending colon**

**Jejunum**

**Ascending (fourth) part**
Shortest part of the duodenum at 2.5 cm

## Structure of the duodenum

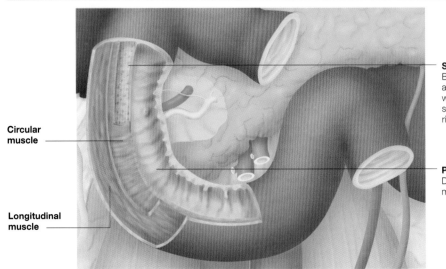

**Circular muscle**

**Longitudinal muscle**

**Submucosa**
Brunner's glands are embedded within, which secrete alkaline-rich mucus

**Plicae**
Deep folds of mucous tissue

The duodenum's walls have two layers of muscle fibres, one circular and one longitudinal. The mucosa, or lining, of the duodenum is particularly thick. It contains numerous glands, (Brunner's glands), which secrete a thick alkaline fluid that helps to counteract the acidic nature of the contents that have reached the duodenum from the stomach.

The mucosa in the first part of the duodenum is smooth, but thereafter it is thrown into deep, permanent folds of tissue, known as plicae.

*There are two layers of muscle fibres in the duodenum. Together, they produce the waves of contraction known as peristalsis.*

# The jejunum and ileum

The jejunum and the ileum together form the longest part of the small intestine. Unlike the duodenum, they can move within the abdomen.

The jejunum and the ileum comprise the longest part of the small intestine. They are surrounded and supported by a fan-shaped fold of the peritoneum – the mesentery – which allows them to move within the abdominal cavity. The mesentery is 15 cm long.

## BLOOD SUPPLY

The jejunum and the ileum receive their arterial blood supply from 15–18 branches of the superior mesenteric artery. These branches anastomose (join) to form arches, called arterial arcades. Straight arteries pass out from the arterial arcades to supply all parts of the small intestine. Venous blood from the jejunum and ileum enters the superior mesenteric vein. This vein lies alongside the superior mesenteric artery and drains into the hepatic portal venous system.

## ROLE OF LYMPH IN DIGESTION

Fat is absorbed from the contents of the small intestine into specialized lymphatic vessels, known as lacteals, which are found within the mucosa. The milky lymphatic fluid produced by this absorption enters lymphatic plexuses (networks of lymphatic vessels) within the walls of the intestine. The fluid is then carried to special nodes called mesenteric lymph nodes.

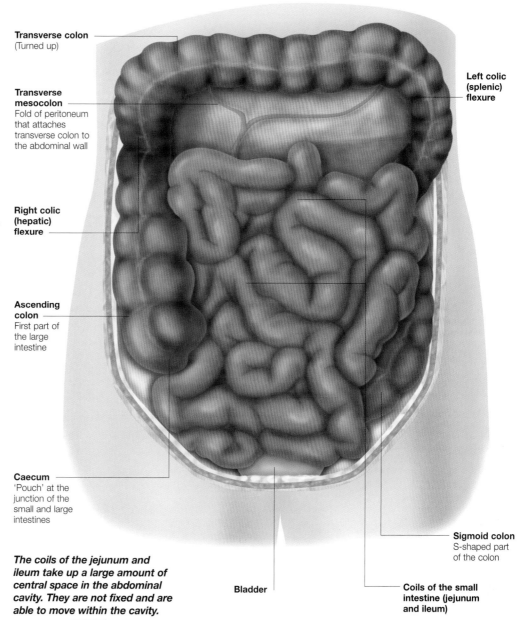

Transverse colon
(Turned up)

Transverse mesocolon
Fold of peritoneum that attaches transverse colon to the abdominal wall

Right colic (hepatic) flexure

Ascending colon
First part of the large intestine

Caecum
'Pouch' at the junction of the small and large intestines

Left colic (splenic) flexure

Sigmoid colon
S-shaped part of the colon

Bladder

Coils of the small intestine (jejunum and ileum)

*The coils of the jejunum and ileum take up a large amount of central space in the abdominal cavity. They are not fixed and are able to move within the cavity.*

---

## Differences between the jejunum and the ileum

### Jejunum

Mesentery

Straight arteries

### Ileum

Anastomotic loops of arteries

Mesentery

Lymphoid nodules (Peyer's patches)

Straight arteries

Anastomotic loop of arteries

There are many structural differences between the jejunum and the ileum. There are differences in:

■ Plicae – the walls of the jejunum are a deeper red and thicker than those of the ileum; the thickness is due to the presence of numerous plicae. These plicae help the lining of the jejunum to absorb nutrients by increasing its surface area and making the jejunum's contents travel more slowly.

*There are a number of structural differences between the jejunum and the ileum. The transition from the jejunum to the ileum occurs gradually.*

■ The mesentery – the arterial arcades of the jejunum are made up by a few large loops, which pass only infrequent straight branches out to the intestinal wall, while those of the ileum have many short loops with numerous straight branches.
■ Fat deposits – the jejunum has less fat lying near the root of the mesentery than the ileum, which has a much greater amount of fat which is distributed throughout the mesentery.
■ Lymphoid tissue – the lower ileum has many areas of lymphoid tissue (called Peyer's patches) at its lower end, while the jejunum has only a few solitary lymphoid nodules.

# Liver and biliary system

The liver is the largest abdominal organ, weighing about 1.5 kg in adult men. It plays an important role in digestion, and also produces bile, which is secreted into the duodenum.

The liver lies under the diaphragm in the abdominal cavity, on the right side, protected largely by the ribcage.

The tissue of the liver is soft and pliable, and reddish brown in colour. It has a rich blood supply from both the portal vein and the hepatic artery and so will bleed profusely if cut or damaged.

### LOBES OF THE LIVER

Although it has four lobes, functionally, the liver is divided into two parts, right and left, each receiving its own separate blood supply. The two smaller lobes, the caudate and the quadrate, can only be seen on the underside of the liver.

### PERITONEAL COVERINGS

The greater part of the liver is covered with the peritoneum, a sheet of connective tissue which lines the walls and structures of the abdomen. Folds of the peritoneum form the various ligaments of the liver.

*As it lies against the diaphragm, the position of the liver may vary during respiration. It is pushed down on inhalation, and rises again as the breath is exhaled.*

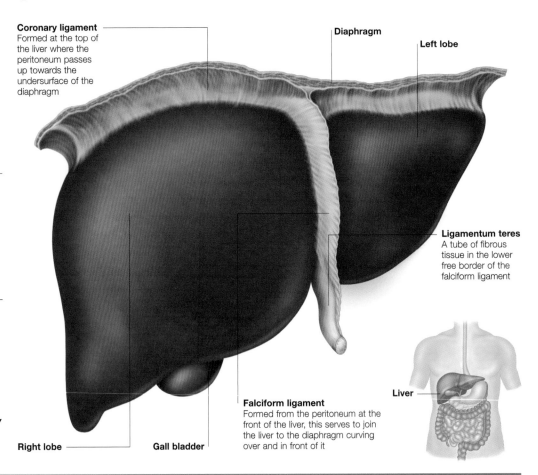

**Coronary ligament**
Formed at the top of the liver where the peritoneum passes up towards the undersurface of the diaphragm

**Diaphragm**

**Left lobe**

**Ligamentum teres**
A tube of fibrous tissue in the lower free border of the falciform ligament

**Falciform ligament**
Formed from the peritoneum at the front of the liver, this serves to join the liver to the diaphragm curving over and in front of it

**Liver**

**Right lobe**

**Gall bladder**

---

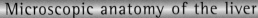

## Microscopic anatomy of the liver

*The sinusoids within each lobule contain tiny specialized cells known as Kupffer cells. These remove debris and worn out blood cells from the blood before it is taken back to the heart.*

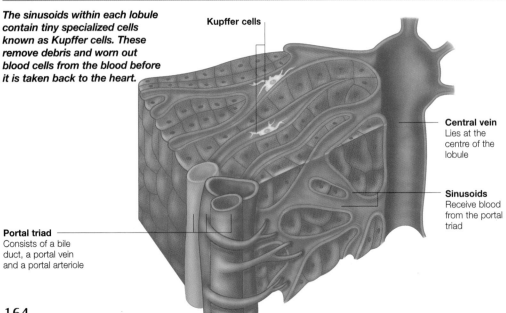

**Kupffer cells**

**Central vein**
Lies at the centre of the lobule

**Sinusoids**
Receive blood from the portal triad

**Portal triad**
Consists of a bile duct, a portal vein and a portal arteriole

The liver is composed of numerous tiny groups of cells called lobules, which are hexagonal in shape. They have a distinctive structure, with hepatocytes (liver cells) arranged like the spokes of a wheel around a central vein, which is a tributary of the hepatic vein. Blood flows past the hepatocytes and into this central vein through tiny vessels known as sinusoids.

The sinusoids receive blood from the vessels of the portal triads, groupings of three vessels which lie at the six points of the lobule. The portal triad is made up of a small branch of the hepatic artery, a small branch of the portal vein and a small biliary duct which collects the bile made by the liver cells.

# Visceral surface of the liver

The underside of the liver is known as the visceral surface as it lies against the abdominal organs, or viscera. The impressions of adjacent organs, the related vessels and the positions of the inferior vena cava and gall bladder can be seen.

The liver lies closely against many other organs in the abdomen. Because the tissue of the liver is soft and pliable, these surrounding structures may leave impressions on its surface. The largest and most obvious impressions are seen on the surfaces of the right and left lobes.

### PORTA HEPATIS
The porta hepatis is an area which is similar to the hilum of the lungs, in that major vessels enter and leave the liver together clothed in a sleeve of connective tissue, in this case peritoneum.

Structures which pass through the porta hepatis include the portal vein, the hepatic artery, the bile ducts, lymphatic vessels and nerves.

### BLOOD SUPPLY
The liver is unusual in that it receives blood from two sources:

■ The hepatic artery. Conveys 30 per cent of the liver's blood supply. It arises from the common hepatic artery

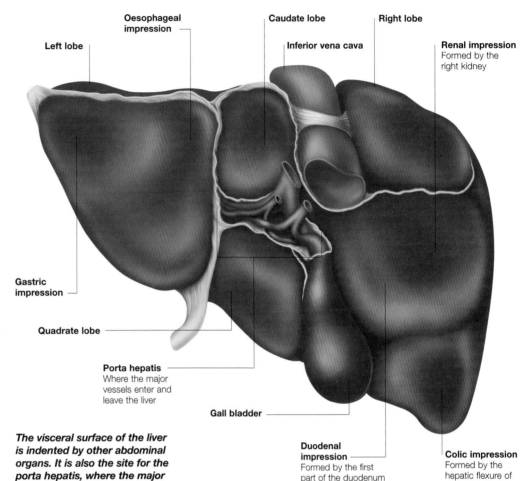

**Left lobe**

**Oesophageal impression**

**Caudate lobe**

**Inferior vena cava**

**Right lobe**

**Renal impression**
Formed by the right kidney

**Gastric impression**

**Quadrate lobe**

**Porta hepatis**
Where the major vessels enter and leave the liver

**Gall bladder**

**Duodenal impression**
Formed by the first part of the duodenum

**Colic impression**
Formed by the hepatic flexure of the colon

*The visceral surface of the liver is indented by other abdominal organs. It is also the site for the porta hepatis, where the major vessels enter and leave the liver.*

and carries fresh oxygenated blood. On entering the liver it divides into right and left branches. The right branch supplies the right lobe and the left branch supplies the caudate, quadrate and left lobes.

■ The hepatic portal vein. Conveys 70 per cent of the liver's blood supply. This large vein drains blood from the gastro-intestinal tract, from the stomach to the rectum. Portal blood is rich in nutrients which

have been absorbed after digestion in the gut. Like the hepatic artery, it divides into right and left branches with similar distributions. Venous blood from the liver is returned to the heart via the hepatic vein.

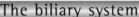

## The biliary system

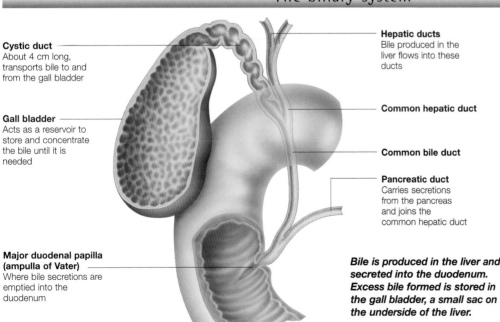

**Cystic duct**
About 4 cm long, transports bile to and from the gall bladder

**Gall bladder**
Acts as a reservoir to store and concentrate the bile until it is needed

**Major duodenal papilla (ampulla of Vater)**
Where bile secretions are emptied into the duodenum

**Hepatic ducts**
Bile produced in the liver flows into these ducts

**Common hepatic duct**

**Common bile duct**

**Pancreatic duct**
Carries secretions from the pancreas and joins the common hepatic duct

*Bile is produced in the liver and secreted into the duodenum. Excess bile formed is stored in the gall bladder, a small sac on the underside of the liver.*

Bile is a greenish fluid which aids the digestion of fats within the small intestine. It is secreted by the cells of the liver.

### PASSAGE OF BILE
Bile is passed into small bile ducts which merge to form the right and left hepatic ducts. These ducts pass out of the liver through the porta hepatis then unite to form the common hepatic duct.

### THE COMMON BILE DUCT
The common hepatic duct is then joined by the cystic duct, forming the common bile duct. This continues down towards the duodenum where, together with the duct carrying secretions of the pancreas, it empties through the major duodenal papilla (or ampulla of Vater).

# Caecum and appendix

The caecum and appendix lie at the junction of the large and small intestine, an area also known as the ileocaecal region. The caecum, from which the appendix arises, receives food from the small intestine.

The caecum is the first part of the large intestine. Food is passed from the terminal ileum, part of the small intestine, into the large intestine through the ileocaecal valve; the caecum lies below this valve. The caecum is a blind-ending pouch, about 7.5 cm in length and breadth, which continues above as the ascending colon, the next part of the large intestine. The appendix, a long, thin pouch of intestine arises from the caecum.

## MUSCLE FIBRES

The muscular 'coat' of the small intestine is continued in the walls of the large intestine, but here it becomes separated into three strips of muscle, the taeniae coli. As food passes through the intestine, the caecum may become distended with faeces or gas. It may then be palpable through the abdominal wall.

## BLOOD SUPPLY

The arterial blood supply to the caecum is from the anterior and posterior caecal arteries, which arise from the ileocolic artery. Venous blood returns through a similar layout of veins, ultimately draining into the superior mesenteric vein.

*The ileocaecal region is the area surrounding the junction where the small intestine meets the large intestine. It consists of the caecum and the appendix.*

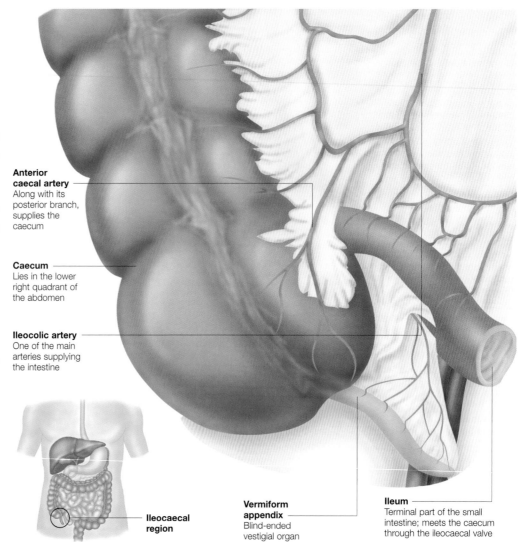

**Anterior caecal artery**
Along with its posterior branch, supplies the caecum

**Caecum**
Lies in the lower right quadrant of the abdomen

**Ileocolic artery**
One of the main arteries supplying the intestine

**Ileocaecal region**

**Vermiform appendix**
Blind-ended vestigial organ

**Ileum**
Terminal part of the small intestine; meets the caecum through the ileocaecal valve

## The ileocaecal valve

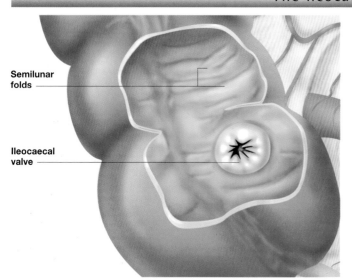

**Semilunar folds**

**Ileocaecal valve**

The ileocaecal valve surrounds the orifice, or opening, through which the liquefied contents of the terminal ileum, the last part of the small intestine, enter the caecum.

### ANATOMICAL STUDIES

Anatomical studies of cadavers (dead bodies) in the past had shown this orifice to be enclosed between folds or ridges in the caecal wall, which were thought to act like a valve.

Now that it is possible to

*The ileocaecal valve surrounds the orifice through which intestinal contents pass into the caecum. This valve is not believed to be very effective.*

study this area in living people, using endoscopes, it is clear that the opening looks quite different in life. The ileocaecal orifice is in fact raised above the caecal wall and is surrounded by a ring of circular muscle fibres, which help to keep it closed.

### BARIUM STUDIES

Although the contents of the caecum do not easily pass back into the ileum when the caecal walls contract, the ileocaecal valve is not very effective. Barium X-ray studies of the large intestine commonly show leakage of contents backwards from the caecum into the terminal ileum through the ileocaecal valve.

# The appendix

The appendix is a narrow, muscular outpouching of the caecum. It is usually between six and 10 cm in length, although it may be much longer or shorter. It arises from the back of the caecum, its lower end being free and mobile.

The vermiform (or 'wormlike') appendix is attached to the caecum at the beginning of the large intestine. The walls of the appendix contain lymphoid tissue. The lymphoid tissue of the appendix and that within the walls of the small intestine, protects the body from micro-organisms within the gut.

### MUSCLE LAYER
Whereas the longitudinal muscle in the walls of the rest of the large intestine is present only in three strips – the taeniae coli – the appendix has a complete muscle layer. This is because the three taeniae coli converge on the base of the appendix and their fibres join to cover its entire surface.

### PERITONEUM
The appendix is enclosed within a covering of peritoneum which forms a fold between the ileum, the caecum and the first part of the appendix. This fold is known as the mesoappendix.

### BASE OF THE APPENDIX
The base of the appendix, where it arises from the caecum, is usually in a fixed position. The corresponding area on the surface of the abdomen is known as McBurney's point.

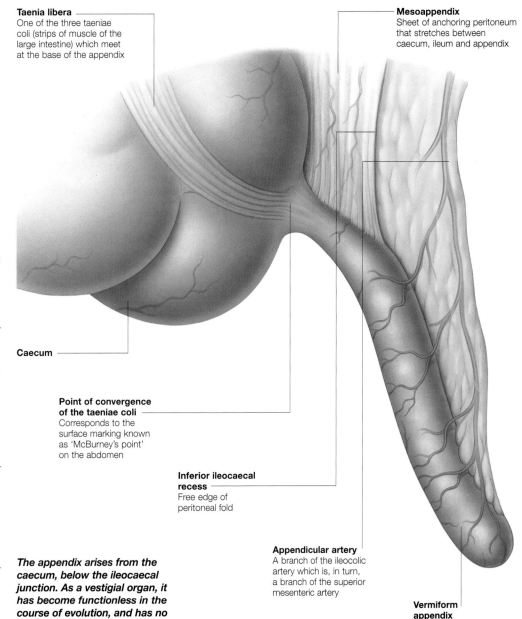

**Taenia libera**
One of the three taeniae coli (strips of muscle of the large intestine) which meet at the base of the appendix

**Mesoappendix**
Sheet of anchoring peritoneum that stretches between caecum, ileum and appendix

**Caecum**

**Point of convergence of the taeniae coli**
Corresponds to the surface marking known as 'McBurney's point' on the abdomen

**Inferior ileocaecal recess**
Free edge of peritoneal fold

**Appendicular artery**
A branch of the ileocolic artery which is, in turn, a branch of the superior mesenteric artery

**Vermiform appendix**

*The appendix arises from the caecum, below the ileocaecal junction. As a vestigial organ, it has become functionless in the course of evolution, and has no role in the process of digestion.*

## Positions of the appendix

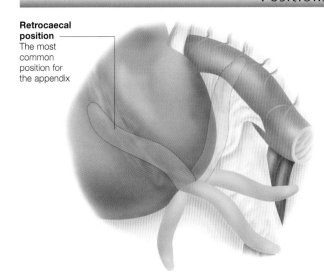

**Retrocaecal position**
The most common position for the appendix

Although the base of the appendix is usually at a fixed point, the far end is free and may lie in a variety of positions.

### COMMON POSITIONS
The most common position is the retrocaecal position, wherein the appendix passes upwards to lie behind the caecum.

In other cases the appendix may lie next to the terminal ileum, or project downwards into the pelvis.

*There are various locations for the appendix. The position will determine where pain and tenderness is felt if it becomes inflamed.*

### UNCOMMON POSITIONS
Uncommonly, the caecum may lie abnormally high or low and therefore the appendix will also be in an unusual position.

### APPENDICITIS
The position of the appendix is important in the diagnosis of appendicitis, when the appendix becomes inflamed and swollen. The pain and tenderness this causes may be felt in different places according to where the appendix lies.

The position of the appendix can cause confusion: when an appendix lies in the pelvis the symptoms may be similar to a urinary tract infection.

# Colon

The colon forms the main part of the large intestine. Although a continuous tube, the colon has four parts: the ascending colon, the transverse colon, the descending colon and the sigmoid colon.

The colon receives the liquefied contents of the small intestine and reabsorbs the water to form semi-solid waste, which is then expelled through the rectum and anal canal as faeces. There are two sharp bends, or flexures, in the colon known as the right colic (or hepatic) flexure and the left colic (or splenic) flexure.

## ASCENDING COLON

The ascending colon runs from the ileocaecal valve up to the right colic flexure, where it becomes the transverse colon. It is about 12 cm long and lies against the posterior (back) abdominal wall, being covered on the front and sides only by the peritoneum, the thin sheet of connective tissue that lines the abdominal organs.

## TRANSVERSE COLON

The transverse colon begins at the right colic flexure, under the right lobe of the liver, and runs across the body towards the left colic flexure next to the spleen.

With a length of about 45 cm, the transverse colon is the longest and the most mobile part of the large intestine, as it hangs down suspended within a fold of peritoneum (or mesentery).

## THE DESCENDING COLON

The descending colon runs from the left colic flexure down to the brim of the pelvis where it becomes the sigmoid colon. As the left colic flexure is higher than the right, the descending colon is consequently longer than the ascending colon.

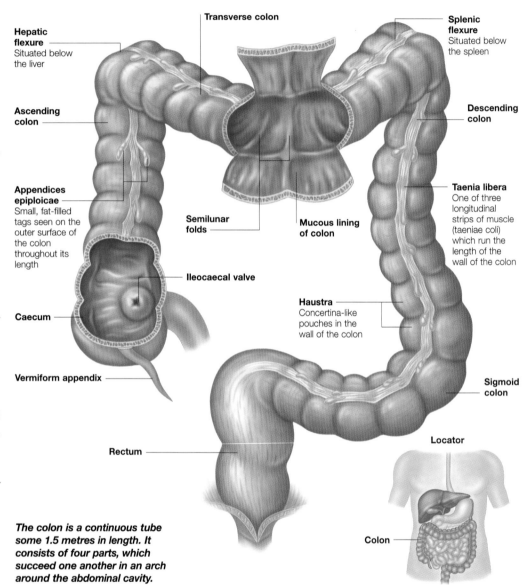

**Transverse colon**

**Hepatic flexure**
Situated below the liver

**Ascending colon**

**Appendices epiploicae**
Small, fat-filled tags seen on the outer surface of the colon throughout its length

**Caecum**

**Vermiform appendix**

**Semilunar folds**

**Ileocaecal valve**

**Rectum**

**Splenic flexure**
Situated below the spleen

**Descending colon**

**Taenia libera**
One of three longitudinal strips of muscle (taeniae coli) which run the length of the wall of the colon

**Mucous lining of colon**

**Haustra**
Concertina-like pouches in the wall of the colon

**Sigmoid colon**

**Locator**

**Colon**

*The colon is a continuous tube some 1.5 metres in length. It consists of four parts, which succeed one another in an arch around the abdominal cavity.*

## Sigmoid colon and the lining of the colon

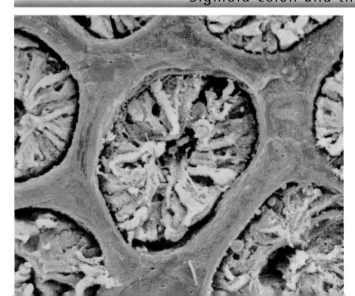

*The lining of the colon – the mucosa (green) – contains glands (yellow). Cells in these glands are involved in water absorption and mucus secretion.*

The sigmoid – 'S-shaped' – colon is the continuation of the descending colon, starting at the pelvic brim.

### CHARACTERISTICS

It is about 40 cm long and, unlike the descending colon, quite mobile as it lies within its mesentery, or fold of peritoneum. At its far end the sigmoid colon leads into the rectum. The function of the sigmoid colon is to store faeces before defecation, and so its size and position vary depending on whether it is full or empty and dietary intake.

### LINING OF THE COLON

The lining of the colon has a simple layer of cells with many deep depressions, or crypts, which contain mucus-secreting cells. The mucus is important for lubricating the passage of faeces and protecting the walls from acids and gases produced by the intestinal bacteria.

# Blood supply and drainage of the colon

Like the rest of the intestine, each of the parts of the colon is readily supplied with blood from a network of arteries.

Venous blood draining from the colon passes through the hepatic portal system, for treatment by the liver, before re-entering the general circulation.

### ARTERIAL SUPPLY OF THE COLON

The arterial supply to the colon comes from the superior and inferior mesenteric branches of the aorta, the large central artery of the abdomen.

The ascending colon and first two thirds of the transverse colon are supplied by the superior mesenteric artery, while the last third of the transverse colon, the descending colon and the sigmoid colon are supplied by the inferior mesenteric.

### PATTERN OF THE ARTERIES

As in other parts of the gastro-intestinal tract, there are anastomoses, or connections, between the branches of these two major arteries.

The superior mesenteric artery gives off the ileocolic, right colic and middle colic arteries which anastomose with each other and with the left colic and sigmoid branches of the inferior mesenteric artery.

In this way an 'arcade' of arteries is formed around the wall of the colon, supplying all parts with arterial blood.

**Arterial system of the colon**

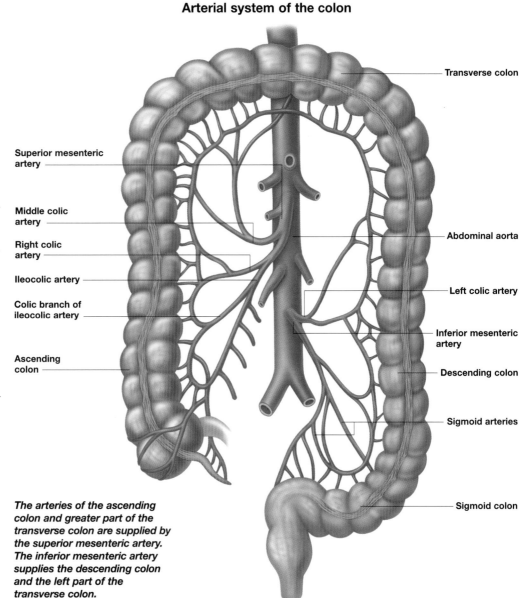

*The arteries of the ascending colon and greater part of the transverse colon are supplied by the superior mesenteric artery. The inferior mesenteric artery supplies the descending colon and the left part of the transverse colon.*

## Venous drainage of the colon

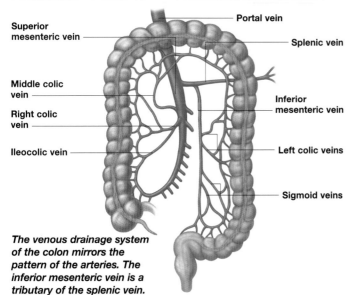

*The venous drainage system of the colon mirrors the pattern of the arteries. The inferior mesenteric vein is a tributary of the splenic vein.*

Venous blood from the colon is collected ultimately into the portal vein. In general, blood from the ascending colon and first two-thirds of the transverse colon runs into the superior mesenteric vein, with blood from the remainder of the colon being drained by the inferior mesenteric vein.

The inferior mesenteric vein drains into the splenic vein, which then joins with the superior mesenteric vein to form the portal vein. The portal vein then carries all the venous blood through the liver on its way back to the heart.

### LYMPHATIC DRAINAGE

Lymph collected from the walls of the colon travels in lymphatic vessels back alongside the arteries towards the main abdominal lymph-collecting vessel, the cysterna chyli. There are many lymph nodes which filter the fluid before it is returned to the venous system.

Lymph passes through the lymph nodes on the wall of the colon, through the nodes adjacent to the small arteries supplying the colon and then through the superior and inferior mesenteric nodes.

### COLON CHARACTERISTICS

Unlike the small intestine, the walls of the colon are puckered into concertina-like pockets, or haustra, which show up quite clearly on direct examination, although this pattern can be absent if there is chronic inflammation such as in colitis.

# Rectum and anal canal

The rectum and anal canal together form the last part of the gastro-intestinal tract. They receive waste matter in the form of faeces and allow it to be passed out of the body.

The rectum continues on from the sigmoid colon, which lies at the level of the third sacral vertebra. Rectum means 'straight' but in fact the rectum follows the curve of the sacrum and coccyx, which form the back of the bony pelvis.

The lower end of the rectum joins to the anal canal with an 80–90 degree change in direction. This anorectal flexure prevents faeces passing into the anal canal until required.

The longitudinal muscle of the rectum is in two broad bands, which run down the front and the back surfaces. There are three horizontal folds in the wall of the rectum, known as the superior (upper), middle and inferior (lower) transverse folds. Below the inferior fold the rectum widens into the ampulla.

## THE ANAL CANAL

The anal canal runs from the anorectal flexure down to the anus. Except during defecation the canal is empty and closed.

The lining of the anal canal changes along its length. The upper part carries longitudinal ridges called anal columns which begin above at the anorectal junction and end below at the pectinate line.

At the lower end of the anal columns are the anal sinuses and anal valves. The anal sinuses produce mucus when faeces are being passed, which acts as a lubricant. The valves help to prevent the passage of mucus out of the anal canal at other times.

### Coronal section through the rectum and anal canal

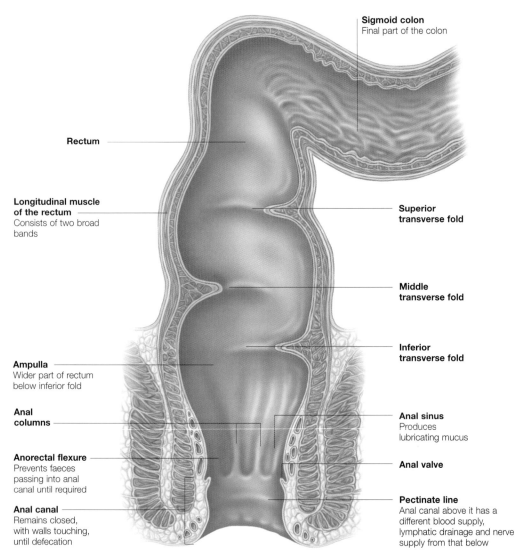

Sigmoid colon
Final part of the colon

Rectum

Longitudinal muscle of the rectum
Consists of two broad bands

Superior transverse fold

Middle transverse fold

Inferior transverse fold

Ampulla
Wider part of rectum below inferior fold

Anal columns

Anal sinus
Produces lubricating mucus

Anorectal flexure
Prevents faeces passing into anal canal until required

Anal valve

Anal canal
Remains closed, with walls touching, until defecation

Pectinate line
Anal canal above it has a different blood supply, lymphatic drainage and nerve supply from that below

## The anal sphincter

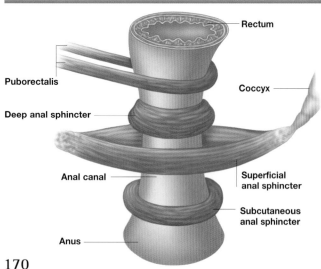

Rectum

Puborectalis

Coccyx

Deep anal sphincter

Anal canal

Superficial anal sphincter

Subcutaneous anal sphincter

Anus

The contents of the intestines are constantly being moved on to the next stage without conscious awareness of it.

However, it is obviously important that there is control of such motions at the final stage. This control is achieved through the function of the anal sphincter, which is made up of several parts:

*The anal sphincter, which consists of several parts, controls the release of faeces from the body. Only the external anal sphincter is under voluntary control.*

■ **The internal anal sphincter** A thickening of the normal circular muscle layer of the bowel in the upper two thirds of the anal canal. It is not under voluntary control.

■ **The puborectalis muscle** A sling of muscle which loops around the anorectal junction forming an angle and preventing passage of the contents of the rectum into the anal canal.

■ **External anal sphincter** In three parts, deep, superficial and subcutaneous, this sphincter is under voluntary control, and so can be relaxed by an act of will when convenient.

# Vessels of the rectum and anus

**The rectum and anal canal have a rich blood supply. A network of veins drains blood from this area.**

Beneath the lining of the rectum and anal canal lies a network of small veins, the rectal venous plexus. This is in two parts:
■ The internal rectal venous plexus – lies just under the lining
■ The external rectal venous plexus – lies outside the muscle layer.

These receive blood from the tissues and carry it to the larger veins that drain the area. These larger veins are the superior, middle and inferior rectal veins which drain the corresponding parts of the rectum.

The internal venous plexus of the anal canal drains blood in two directions on either side of the pectinate line region. Above this level blood drains mainly into the superior rectal vein while from below it drains into the inferior rectal vein.

### ARTERIAL BLOOD SUPPLY

The rectum receives its blood supply from three sources. The upper part is supplied by the superior rectal artery, the lower portion is supplied by the middle rectal arteries while the anorectal junction receives blood from the inferior rectal arteries.

Within the anal canal the superior rectal artery travels down to provide blood above the pectinate line. The two inferior rectal arteries, branches of the pudendal, supply the anal canal below the pectinate line.

**Venous drainage system of the rectum and anus**

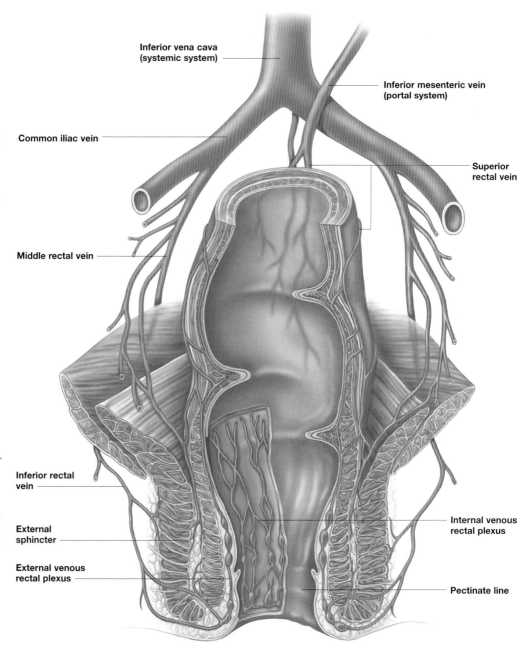

- Inferior vena cava (systemic system)
- Inferior mesenteric vein (portal system)
- Common iliac vein
- Superior rectal vein
- Middle rectal vein
- Inferior rectal vein
- External sphincter
- External venous rectal plexus
- Internal venous rectal plexus
- Pectinate line

## Nerves of the rectum and anal canal

### Nerve supply

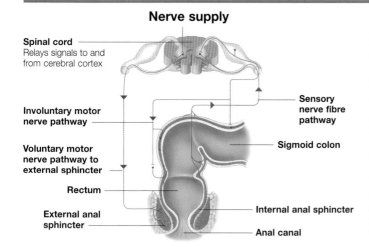

- Spinal cord
  Relays signals to and from cerebral cortex
- Involuntary motor nerve pathway
- Voluntary motor nerve pathway to external sphincter
- Rectum
- External anal sphincter
- Sensory nerve fibre pathway
- Sigmoid colon
- Internal anal sphincter
- Anal canal

Like the rest of the gastro-intestinal tract, the walls of the rectum and anal canal have a nerve supply from the body's autonomic nervous system. This system works 'in the background', usually without us being aware of it, to regulate and control the body's internal functions.

These nerves can sense the filling of the rectum and can

*When the rectum is full, a defecation reflex is triggered in the spinal cord. Signals are sent to the rectal muscles to start contracting.*

then cause the reflex contraction of the rectal walls to push the faeces into the anal canal and the relaxation of the internal anal sphincter.

However, the anal canal, or more specifically the external anal sphincter, also has a nerve supply from the 'voluntary' nervous system.

These nerves, which originate from the second, third and fourth sacral spinal nerves, allow us to contract the sphincter muscle by an act of will and so prevent filling of the anal canal until an appropriate time for defecation.

# Pancreas and spleen

The pancreas is a large gland that produces both enzymes and hormones. It lies in the upper abdomen behind the stomach, one end in the curve of the duodenum and the other end touching the spleen.

The pancreas secretes enzymes into the duodenum, the first part of the small intestine, to aid the digestion of food. It also produces the hormones insulin and glucagon, which regulate the use of glucose by cells.

Lying across the posterior wall of the abdomen, the pancreas is said to have four parts:
■ The head – which lies within the C-shaped curve of the duodenum. It is attached to the inner side of the duodenum; a small, hook-like projection, the uncinate process, projects towards the midline
■ The neck – which is narrower than the head, due to the large hepatic portal vein behind; it lies over the superior mesenteric blood vessels
■ The body – which is triangular in cross-section and lies in front of the aorta; it passes up and to the left to merge with the tail
■ The tail – which comes to a tapering end within the concavity of the spleen.

## BLOOD SUPPLY

The pancreas has a very rich blood supply. The pancreatic head is supplied from two arterial arcades which are formed from the superior and inferior pancreaticoduodenal arteries. The body and tail of the pancreas are supplied with blood by branches of the splenic artery.

Venous blood from the pancreas travels to the liver via the portal venous system, the veins lying in an arrangement which mirrors the arterial supply.

## Location of pancreas

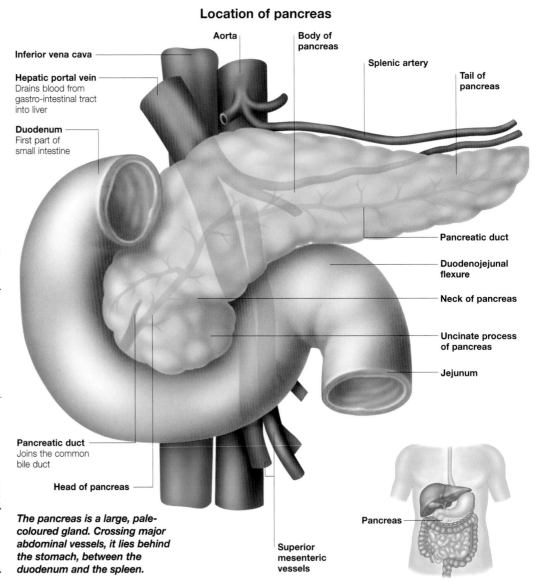

Aorta

Body of pancreas

Inferior vena cava

Splenic artery

Hepatic portal vein
Drains blood from gastro-intestinal tract into liver

Tail of pancreas

Duodenum
First part of small intestine

Pancreatic duct

Duodenojejunal flexure

Neck of pancreas

Uncinate process of pancreas

Jejunum

Pancreatic duct
Joins the common bile duct

Head of pancreas

*The pancreas is a large, pale-coloured gland. Crossing major abdominal vessels, it lies behind the stomach, between the duodenum and the spleen.*

Superior mesenteric vessels

Pancreas

---

## The pancreatic duct and duodenal papilla

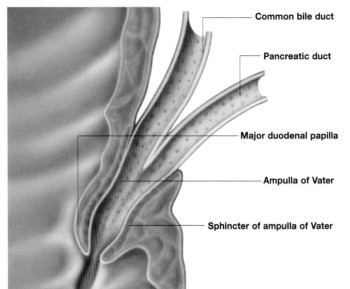

Common bile duct

Pancreatic duct

Major duodenal papilla

Ampulla of Vater

Sphincter of ampulla of Vater

The main pancreatic duct runs the length of the pancreas from tail to head, receiving smaller tributaries as it goes.

At the head of the pancreas it joins with the bile duct to form a short, dilated tube known as the hepatopancreatic ampulla, or ampulla of Vater. This duct opens to discharge its contents into the duodenum at the tip of the major duodenal papilla.

*The pancreatic duct and common bile duct join within the head of the pancreas to form the ampulla of Vater. This empties into the duodenum.*

## MUSCLE FIBRES

Involuntary muscle fibres run around the walls of the two ducts, and around the wall of the combined duct they form, to provide sphincters (specialized rings of muscle that surround an orifice), which regulate the flow of the ducts' contents into the duodenum.

## ACCESSORY DUCT

An accessory pancreatic duct may be present in addition to the main duct, and this may have its own, smaller opening into the duodenum, known as the minor duodenal papilla.

# The spleen

The spleen is the largest of the lymphatic organs. It is dark purple in colour and lies under the lower ribs on the left side of the upper abdomen.

The dimensions of the spleen can vary greatly, but is usually about the size of a clenched fist. In old age, the spleen naturally atrophies and reduces in size.

The hilum of the spleen contains its blood vessels (the splenic artery and vein) and some lymphatic vessels. The hilum also contains lymph nodes and the tail of the pancreas, all enclosed within the lienorenal ligament – a fold of peritoneum.

### SURFACE OF THE SPLEEN

The spleen shows indentations of the organs which surround it. The surface which lies against the diaphragm is curved smoothly, while the visceral surface carries the impressions of the stomach, the left kidney and the splenic flexure of the colon.

### SPLEEN COVERINGS

The spleen is surrounded and protected by a thin capsule, which is composed of irregular fibro-elastic connective tissue. Contained within the tissue of the capsule are muscle fibres that allow the spleen to contract periodically. These contractions expel the blood the spleen has filtered back into the circulation.

Outside the capsule the spleen is completely enclosed by the peritoneum, the thin sheet of connective tissue which lines the abdominal cavity and covers the organs within it.

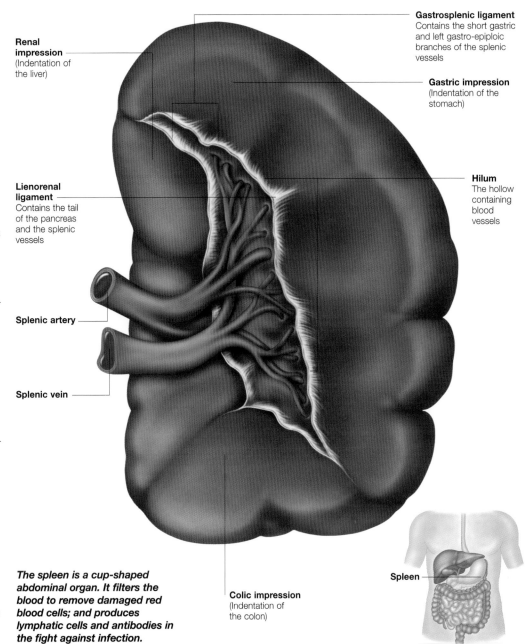

**Renal impression**
(Indentation of the liver)

**Gastrosplenic ligament**
Contains the short gastric and left gastro-epiploic branches of the splenic vessels

**Gastric impression**
(Indentation of the stomach)

**Lienorenal ligament**
Contains the tail of the pancreas and the splenic vessels

**Hilum**
The hollow containing blood vessels

**Splenic artery**

**Splenic vein**

**Colic impression**
(Indentation of the colon)

**Spleen**

*The spleen is a cup-shaped abdominal organ. It filters the blood to remove damaged red blood cells; and produces lymphatic cells and antibodies in the fight against infection.*

## Microanatomy of the spleen

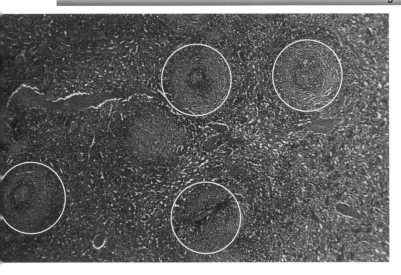

*A micrograph of the spleen shows areas of white pulp (circled) embedded in the matrix of the red pulp. Each area of white pulp has a central artery.*

The spleen is enclosed within a capsule, projections of which (the trabeculae) pass down into its substance. The trabeculae support the soft splenic tissue and also carry numerous blood vessels.

By cutting its surface, the tissue of the spleen itself can be seen to be composed of pale areas lying within a red background, the two types of tissue being known as white pulp and red pulp.

### WHITE PULP

The white pulp is composed mainly of lymphoid cells lying clustered around the small branches of the splenic artery, which bring blood into the spleen.

### RED PULP

The red pulp (within which the islands of white pulp lie) consists of connective tissue. This connective tissue contains red blood cells and macrophages, cells which can engulf and destroy other cells.

The function of this tissue is to filter the blood and remove damaged red cells from the bloodstream.

# Inguinal region

The inguinal region, commonly known as the groin, is the site of inguinal hernias. The abdominal wall has an area of weakness, which may allow the abdominal contents to protrude through it.

The bilateral areas of weakness in the inguinal region are due to the presence of the inguinal canals, tubes through which pass the spermatic cords in males, and the round ligaments in females.

## INGUINAL CANAL

The design of the inguinal canal minimizes the likelihood of herniation (protrusion) of abdominal contents. It passes down towards the midline of the body from its origin, the deep inguinal ring (the entrance to the inguinal canal), to emerge at the superficial inguinal ring (the exit from the canal).

## WALLS OF THE CANAL

The inguinal canal has a roof, a floor and two walls:
■ Roof – formed by the arching fibres of the internal oblique and the transversus abdominis muscle
■ Floor – a shallow gutter, formed by the inguinal ligament
■ Anterior wall – formed mainly by the strong aponeurosis of the external oblique muscle, with a contribution from the internal oblique at the outer edges
■ Posterior wall – formed by the transversalis fascia with the medial part of the wall being reinforced by the conjoint tendon.

*The inguinal canal passes through the layers of the lower abdominal wall. In adults, it is about 4 cm long, although in babies it is much shorter.*

### Inguinal region in a male

**Transversus abdominis muscle**
Deepest of three layers of abdominal muscle

**External oblique**
Forms the outermost muscle layer of the abdominal wall

**Deep inguinal ring**
An oval opening to the inguinal canal through transversalis fascia

**Conjoint tendon**
Insertion of internal oblique and transversus abdominis

**Inguinal ligament**
Rolled-under edge of the external oblique aponeurosis

**Internal oblique muscle (cut and turned back)**

**Linea alba**

**Spermatic cord**

**Superficial inguinal ring**
Exit of the inguinal canal; a triangular slit in the external oblique muscle

## The inguinal ligament

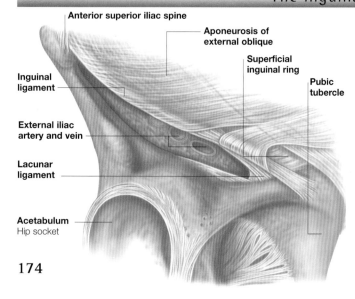

**Anterior superior iliac spine**

**Aponeurosis of external oblique**

**Superficial inguinal ring**

**Pubic tubercle**

**Inguinal ligament**

**External iliac artery and vein**

**Lacunar ligament**

**Acetabulum**
Hip socket

The inguinal ligament is a tough, fibrous band that bridges a gap at the front of the pelvis.

The ligament passes across the groin from the anterior superior iliac spine, a prominence of the pelvis above the hip, to the pubic tubercle, a small prominence of the pelvis near the midline.

*The inguinal ligament is formed by the inferior, underturned fibres of the aponeurosis of the external oblique muscle. The ligament forms the floor of the inguinal canal.*

### FORMATION OF THE INGUINAL LIGAMENT

The inguinal ligament is formed from the lower edge of the aponeurosis of the external oblique muscle as it rolls under and reflects back upon itself. The shallow trough produced by this reflection forms the floor of the inguinal canal.

At the medial (inner) end of the inguinal ligament some of its fibres splay out to form the lacunar ligament, knowledge of which is important for the surgeon performing an operation to correct an inguinal hernia.

# Behind the inguinal ligament

The inguinal ligament encloses behind it a number of vital structures including blood vessels and nerves serving the lower limb and two groups of lymph nodes (deep and superficial).

There are two major blood vessels which pass behind the inguinal ligament:
■ Femoral artery – the main vessel supplying blood to the lower limb
■ Femoral vein – lies medially to the femoral artery (on the inner side).

### FEMORAL NERVE
Lateral to these vessels, on the outer side, lies the femoral nerve which is the largest branch of the lumbar plexus, a network of nerves within the abdomen.

### FEMORAL SHEATH
The femoral blood vessels are enclosed within a thin, funnel-shaped sheet of connective tissue, known as the femoral sheath. This allows the femoral vessels to glide harmlessly against the inguinal ligament during movements of the hip.

### INGUINAL LYMPH NODES
Within the groin lie two groups of lymph nodes:
■ Superficial inguinal nodes – these lie just under the skin in a horizontal and a vertical group, and drain areas which include the buttocks, external genitalia and superficial layers of the lower limb
■ Deep inguinal nodes – these lie around the femoral artery and vein as they pass under the inguinal ligament, and drain lymph from the lower limb.

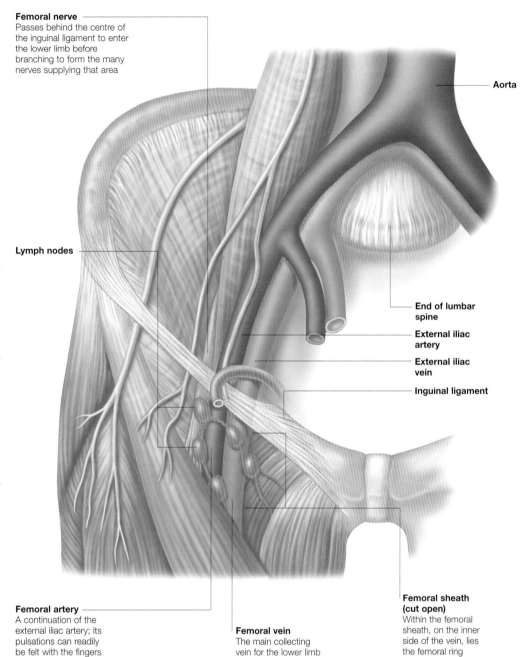

**Femoral nerve**
Passes behind the centre of the inguinal ligament to enter the lower limb before branching to form the many nerves supplying that area

**Lymph nodes**

**Aorta**

**End of lumbar spine**

**External iliac artery**

**External iliac vein**

**Inguinal ligament**

**Femoral artery**
A continuation of the external iliac artery; its pulsations can readily be felt with the fingers

**Femoral vein**
The main collecting vein for the lower limb

**Femoral sheath (cut open)**
Within the femoral sheath, on the inner side of the vein, lies the femoral ring

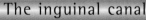

## The inguinal canal

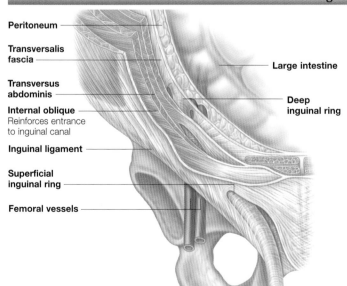

**Peritoneum**

**Transversalis fascia**

**Transversus abdominis**

**Internal oblique**
Reinforces entrance to inguinal canal

**Inguinal ligament**

**Superficial inguinal ring**

**Femoral vessels**

**Large intestine**

**Deep inguinal ring**

The presence of the inguinal canal leaves a potential defect in the otherwise continuous abdominal wall, through which the abdominal contents may herniate (protrude). The risk of this happening is minimized by a number of features:
■ Length – other than in infants, the inguinal canal is a relatively long structure with the entrance and exit some distance apart

*The inguinal canal is supported by numerous structures, such as muscles and tendons. These structures prevent abdominal hernias developing*

■ Deep ring – the entrance; is reinforced in front by the strong internal oblique muscle
■ Superficial ring – the exit; is reinforced behind by the strong conjoint tendon
■ Raised pressure in the abdomen – the muscle fibres arching over the canal automatically contract (when sneezing and coughing) to close it and compress the contents.

During defecation and childbirth, the body naturally assumes a squatting position, so that the fronts of the thighs come up to support the inguinal area.

# Overview of the urinary tract

The urinary tract consists of the kidneys, ureters, urinary bladder and urethra. Together, these organs are responsible for the production of urine and its expulsion from the body.

The paired kidneys filter the blood to remove waste chemicals and excess fluid, which they excrete as urine. Urine passes down through the narrow ureters to the bladder, which stores it temporarily before it is expelled through the urethra.

■ Kidneys
The bean-shaped kidneys lie within the abdomen, against the posterior abdominal wall behind the intestines

■ Ureters
From the hilus, or 'stalk' of each of the two kidneys, emerge the right and left ureters. These are narrow tubes which receive the urine produced continuously by the kidney

■ Bladder
Urine is received and stored temporarily in the urinary bladder, a collapsible, balloon-like structure which lies within the pelvis

■ Urethra
When appropriate, the bladder contracts to expel its contents through the urethra, a thin-walled muscular tube.

*The urinary tract consists of the structures involved in the, production, storage and expulsion of urine. It extends from the abdomen into the pelvis.*

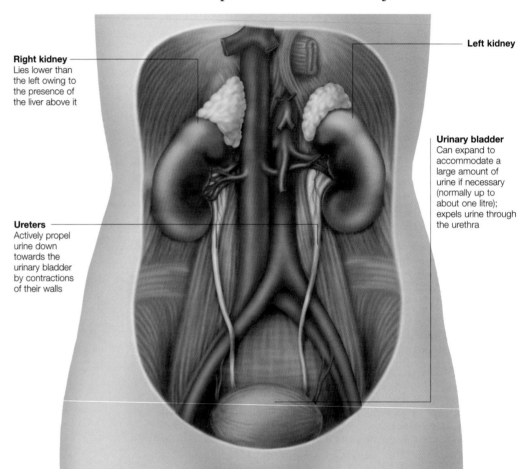

**Right kidney**
Lies lower than the left owing to the presence of the liver above it

**Left kidney**

**Urinary bladder**
Can expand to accommodate a large amount of urine if necessary (normally up to about one litre); expels urine through the urethra

**Ureters**
Actively propel urine down towards the urinary bladder by contractions of their walls

## Rear view of the kidneys

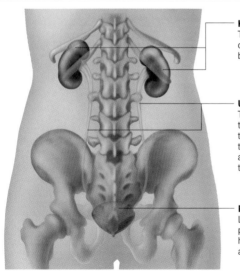

**Kidneys**
These bean-shaped organs are protected by the lower rib-cage

**Ureters**
These lengthy tubes extend from the kidneys down to the lower pelvis, and drain urine into the bladder

**Bladder**
Lies low in the pelvis but rises higher in the abdomen as it fills

The kidneys lie against the posterior (back) wall of the abdomen, their upper poles lying under the 11th and 12th ribs. Because of this posterior position, surgery on the kidneys is usually performed from the back.

### POSITION OF KIDNEYS
The right kidney lies approximately 2.5 cm lower than the left. Both kidneys move up and down during respiration and with changes in posture.

*The urinary tract extends down the length of the abdomen and pelvis. The kidneys lie behind the lower ribs and the bladder is situated on the pelvic floor.*

### PROTECTION
The kidneys are protected by the lower ribs, which form a bony cage around them. In addition they are surrounded by a protective layer of fat. The ureters are also well cushioned as they are buried deep within a dense mass of tissue.

### PALPATION OF KIDNEYS
Palpation of the lower pole of the right kidney is usually possible by using two hands, one behind the flank and one pressing down from the front. The left kidney, being higher, is not usually palpable unless it is abnormally enlarged or contains a large cyst or tumour.

# The adrenal glands

The adrenal glands are situated above the kidneys, but are not part of the urinary tract. Each one consists of two separate parts: a medulla surrounded by a cortex.

Lying on top of the kidneys are the paired adrenal glands, also known as the suprarenal glands. Although they are physically close to the kidneys they play no part in the urinary system: they are endocrine glands which produce hormones vital to the healthy functioning of the body.

### SURROUNDING TISSUES
The yellowish adrenal glands lie above the kidneys and under the diaphragm. They are surrounded by a thick layer of fatty tissue and are enclosed by renal fascia although they are separated from the kidneys themselves by fibrous tissue.

This separation allows a kidney to be surgically removed without damaging these delicate and important glands.

### GLAND DIFFERENCES
Due to the position of the surrounding structures the soft adrenal glands differ in appearance:
■ **The right adrenal gland**
The right adrenal gland is pyramid-shaped and sits on the upper pole of the right kidney. It lies in contact with the diaphragm, the liver and the inferior vena cava, the main vein of the abdomen
■ **The left adrenal gland**
The left adrenal gland has the shape of a half moon and lies along the upper surface of the

Adrenal glands

Ureters

Kidneys

Inferior vena cava

Aorta

*Although the adrenal glands sit on top of the kidneys, they are entirely unrelated to the urinary tract. Instead, they are endocrine glands that secrete hormones into the bloodstream.*

left kidney from the pole down to the hilus. It lies in contact with the spleen, the stomach, the pancreas and the diaphragm.

### BLOOD SUPPLY
As with other endocrine glands, which secrete their hormones directly into the bloodstream,

the adrenal glands have a very rich blood supply. They receive arterial blood from three sources – the superior, middle and inferior adrenal arteries – which arise from the inferior phrenic artery, the aorta and the renal artery respectively.

Near the adrenal glands these

arteries branch repeatedly, numerous tiny arteries thereby entering the glands over their entire surface.

A single vein leaves the adrenal glands on each side to drain blood into the inferior vena cava on the right and the renal vein on the left.

## Structure of the adrenal glands

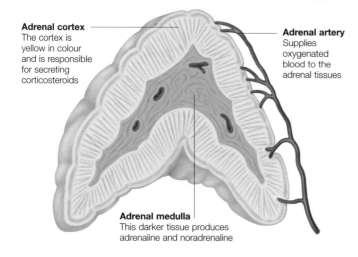

**Adrenal cortex**
The cortex is yellow in colour and is responsible for secreting corticosteroids

**Adrenal artery**
Supplies oxygenated blood to the adrenal tissues

**Adrenal medulla**
This darker tissue produces adrenaline and noradrenaline

Within the protective capsule, each adrenal gland is composed of an outer region, known as a cortex, and an inner region – a medulla. The regions are made up of two separate types of tissue which have differing functions.

### ADRENAL CORTEX
The yellow adrenal cortex makes up the bulk of the gland. It makes and secretes a wide

*Adrenal glands consist of two types of tissue – cortex and medulla. Each area is responsible for producing different types of hormones.*

variety of hormones collectively known as corticosteroids which are vital for control of the metabolism of the body, fluid balance and response to stress. The cortex also produces a very small amount of male sex hormones (androgens).

### ADRENAL MEDULLA
The darker adrenal medulla is made up of a 'knot' of nervous tissue surrounded by numerous small blood vessels, and is the site of formation of the hormones adrenaline and noradrenaline. These hormones prepare the body for the 'fight or flight' response to stress.

# Kidneys

The kidneys are a pair of solid organs situated at the back of the abdomen. They act as filtering units for blood and maintain the balance and composition of fluids within the body.

The paired kidneys lie within the abdominal cavity against the posterior abdominal wall. Each kidney is about 10 cm in length, reddish brown in colour and has the characteristic shape, after which the 'kidney bean' is named. On the medial, or inward facing, surface lies the hilus of the kidney from which the blood vessels enter and leave. The hilus is also the site of exit for the right and left ureters, via which urine leaves the kidney and is transported to the bladder.

### REGIONS OF THE KIDNEY
The kidney has three regions, each of which plays a role in the production or collection of urine:
■ The renal cortex – the most superficial layer; it is quite pale and has a granular appearance
■ The renal medulla – composed of dark reddish tissue, it lies within the cortex in the form of 'pyramids'
■ The renal pelvis – the central, funnel-like area of the kidney which collects the urine and is continuous with the ureters at the hilus.

### OUTER LAYERS
Each kidney is covered by a tough, fibrous capsule. Outside the kidney lies a protective layer of fat which is contained within the renal fascia – a dense connective tissue that anchors the kidneys and adrenal glands, to surrounding structures.

*The kidneys are responsible for the excretion of waste from the blood. Each has three regions: cortex, medulla and renal pelvis.*

## Cross-section through kidney

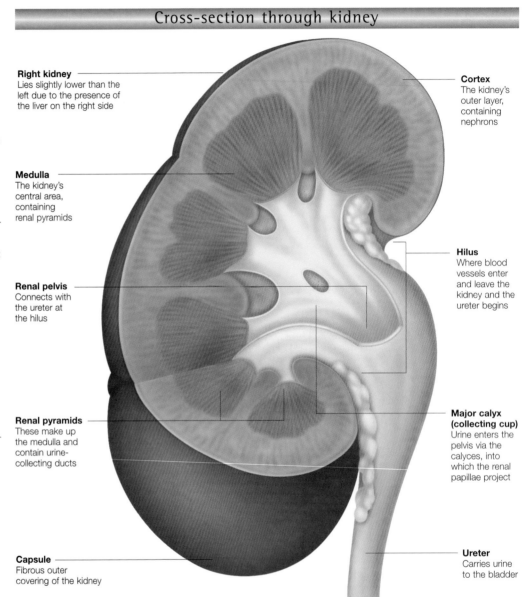

**Right kidney**
Lies slightly lower than the left due to the presence of the liver on the right side

**Medulla**
The kidney's central area, containing renal pyramids

**Renal pelvis**
Connects with the ureter at the hilus

**Renal pyramids**
These make up the medulla and contain urine-collecting ducts

**Capsule**
Fibrous outer covering of the kidney

**Cortex**
The kidney's outer layer, containing nephrons

**Hilus**
Where blood vessels enter and leave the kidney and the ureter begins

**Major calyx (collecting cup)**
Urine enters the pelvis via the calyces, into which the renal papillae project

**Ureter**
Carries urine to the bladder

## Nephrons of the kidney

**Glomerulus**

**Bowman's capsule**

**Urine-collecting tubule**

**Distal tubule**

**Afferent arteriole**

**Efferent arteriole**

**Proximal tubule**

**Loop of Henle**

The work of the kidneys is achieved by the action of over a million tiny nephrons, or blood-processing units. Each nephron contains a renal corpuscle within the medulla, from which projects a long loop of renal tubule:
■ **Renal corpuscle**
The renal corpuscle is composed of a clump of tiny arterioles, the glomerulus, surrounded by an expanded cup of renal tubule, known as the Bowman's capsule. Fluid filters out of the blood to enter the renal tubule here for processing
■ **Renal tubule**
The renal tubule makes a long journey from its origin at the Bowman's capsule into the cortex and back again as Henle's loop. It then ultimately drains its contents, processed urine, into a collecting tubule which carries it away to the renal pelvis.

*Water and solutes from arterial blood pass across a membrane in the glomerulus. This fluid, or urine, passes into the renal tubule where it is processed.*

# Blood supply to the kidneys

The function of the kidneys is to filter blood, for which they receive an exceedingly rich blood supply. As with other parts of the body, the pattern of drainage of venous blood mirrors the pattern of arterial supply.

Arterial blood is carried to the kidneys by the right and left renal arteries, which arise directly from the main artery of the body, the aorta. The right renal artery is longer than the left as the aorta lies slightly to the left of the midline. One in three people have an additional, accessory, renal artery.

### RENAL ARTERIES

The renal artery enters the kidney at the hilus and divides into between three and five segmental arteries, each of which further divides into lobar arteries. There are no connections between branches of neighbouring segmental arteries.

The interlobar arteries pass between the renal pyramids and branch to form the arcuate arteries, which run along the junction of cortex and medulla. Numerous interlobular arteries pass into the tissue of the renal cortex to carry blood to the glomeruli of the nephrons, where it is filtered to remove excess fluid and waste products.

### VENOUS DRAINAGE

Blood enters the interlobular, arcuate and then interlobar veins before being collected by the renal vein and returned to the inferior vena cava, the main collecting vein of the abdomen.

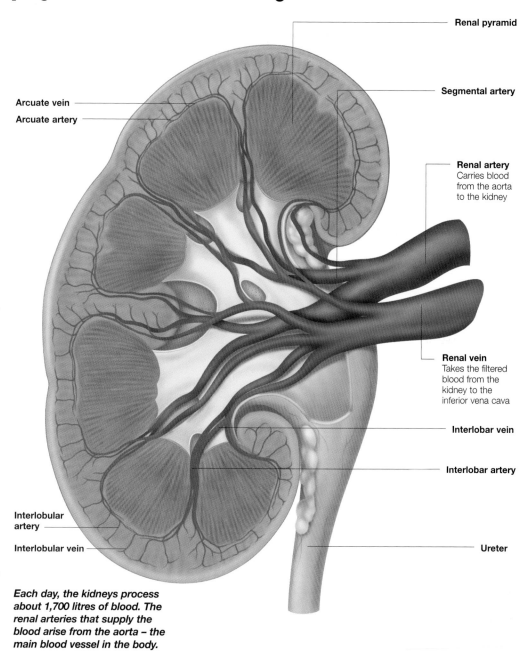

Arcuate vein

Arcuate artery

Renal pyramid

Segmental artery

**Renal artery**
Carries blood from the aorta to the kidney

**Renal vein**
Takes the filtered blood from the kidney to the inferior vena cava

Interlobar vein

Interlobar artery

Interlobular artery

Interlobular vein

Ureter

*Each day, the kidneys process about 1,700 litres of blood. The renal arteries that supply the blood arise from the aorta – the main blood vessel in the body.*

## Congenital abnormalities

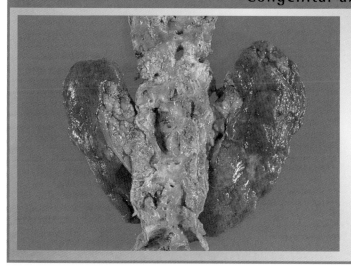

During early fetal life, the kidneys develop close together in the pelvis and then later ascend into their final resting position on the posterior abdominal wall under the diaphragm. Very occasionally, the kidneys and their associated structures do not develop normally, which leads to congenital abnormalities:

■ **Horseshoe kidney**
In about one in 600 children, the

*A horseshoe kidney is an abnormality in which the kidneys become fused together during development. Usually, kidney function is not affected.*

kidneys become fused together at their lower poles during development. The resulting U-shaped kidney usually lies at a lower level than normal kidneys

■ **Renal agenesis**
Occasionally, a baby is born with only one kidney. However, it is possible to live normally with a single kidney, which enlarges to cope with the increased workload

■ **Duplex ureters**
Some children are born with duplicated ureters. This condition, which is not uncommon, can occur on one or both sides, and may be partial or complete.

# Bladder and ureters

The ureters channel urine produced by the kidneys down their length and into the urinary bladder. Urine is stored in the bladder until it is expelled from the body via the urethra.

Urine is continuously produced by the kidneys and is carried down to the urinary bladder by two muscular tubes, the ureters.

## THE BLADDER

The bladder stores urine until it is passed out via the urethra. When the bladder is empty, it is pyramidal in shape, its walls thrown into folds, or rugae, which flatten out on filling. The position of the bladder varies:
■ In adults the empty bladder lies low within the pelvis, rising up into the abdomen as it fills
■ In infants the bladder is higher, being within the abdomen even when empty
■ The walls contain many muscle fibres, collectively known as the detrusor muscle, which allow the bladder to contract and expel its contents.

## TRIGONE

The trigone is a triangular area of the bladder wall at the base of the structure. The wall here contains muscle fibres which act to prevent urine from ascending the ureters when the bladder contracts. A muscular sphincter around the urethral opening keeps it closed until urine is passed out of the body.

*The urinary bladder is flexible enough to expand as it fills. It is made from strong muscle fibres that facilitate the expulsion of urine when necessary.*

### Coronal section of female bladder and urethra

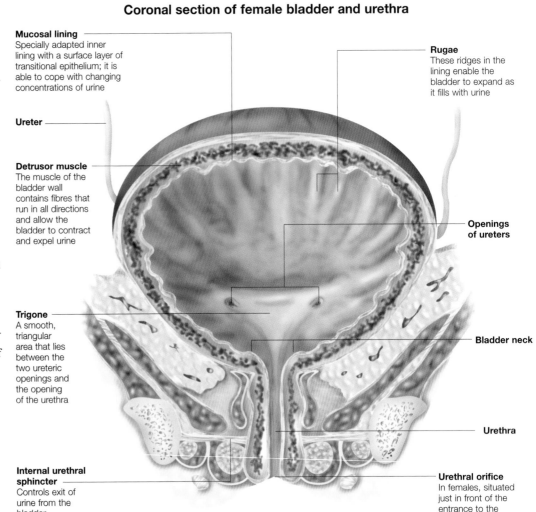

**Mucosal lining**
Specially adapted inner lining with a surface layer of transitional epithelium; it is able to cope with changing concentrations of urine

**Ureter**

**Detrusor muscle**
The muscle of the bladder wall contains fibres that run in all directions and allow the bladder to contract and expel urine

**Trigone**
A smooth, triangular area that lies between the two ureteric openings and the opening of the urethra

**Internal urethral sphincter**
Controls exit of urine from the bladder

**Rugae**
These ridges in the lining enable the bladder to expand as it fills with urine

**Openings of ureters**

**Bladder neck**

**Urethra**

**Urethral orifice**
In females, situated just in front of the entrance to the vagina

## Differences in male and female anatomy

### Female

### Male

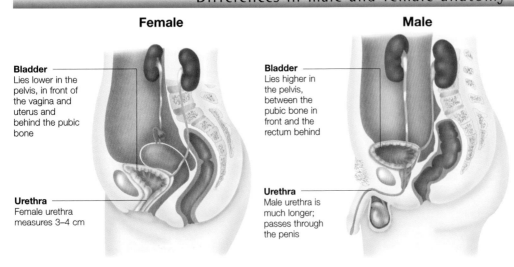

**Bladder**
Lies lower in the pelvis, in front of the vagina and uterus and behind the pubic bone

**Urethra**
Female urethra measures 3–4 cm

**Bladder**
Lies higher in the pelvis, between the pubic bone in front and the rectum behind

**Urethra**
Male urethra is much longer; passes through the penis

Owing to the presence of the reproductive organs the position of the bladder, and size, shape and position of the urethra vary between males and females:
■ In men the urethra is about 20 cm long, passing through the prostate gland and then running along the penis before opening at the external urethral orifice
■ In women the urethra is 3–4 cm in length and opens at the urethral orifice, which lies just in front of the vaginal opening.

*The major difference in male and female urinary tract anatomy is the length of the urethra. An adult male urethra is five times the length of a female one.*

# The ureters

The ureters are tubular and propel the urine towards the bladder. Each ureter squeezes and contracts its muscles to encourage the free flow of urine.

The ureters are narrow, thin-walled muscular tubes which carry urine from the kidneys to the urinary bladder.

Each of the two ureters is 25–30 cm in length and about 3 mm wide. They originate at the kidney and pass down the posterior abdominal wall to cross the bony brim of the pelvis and enter the bladder by piercing its posterior wall.

### PARTS OF THE URETER

Each ureter consists of three anatomically distinct parts:

#### ■ Renal pelvis
This is the first part of the ureter, which lies within the hilum of the kidney. It is funnel-shaped as it receives urine from the major calyces and then tapers to form the narrow ureteric tube. The junction of this part of the ureter with the next is one of the narrowest parts of the whole structure.
#### ■ Abdominal ureter
The ureter passes downwards through the abdomen and then slightly towards the midline until it reaches the pelvic brim and enters the pelvis. During its course through the abdomen the ureter runs behind the peritoneum, the membranous lining of the abdominal cavity.
#### ■ Pelvic ureter
The ureter enters the pelvis just in front of the division of the large common iliac artery. It runs down the back wall of the pelvis before turning to enter the posterior wall of the bladder.

## View of the ureters and bladder from behind

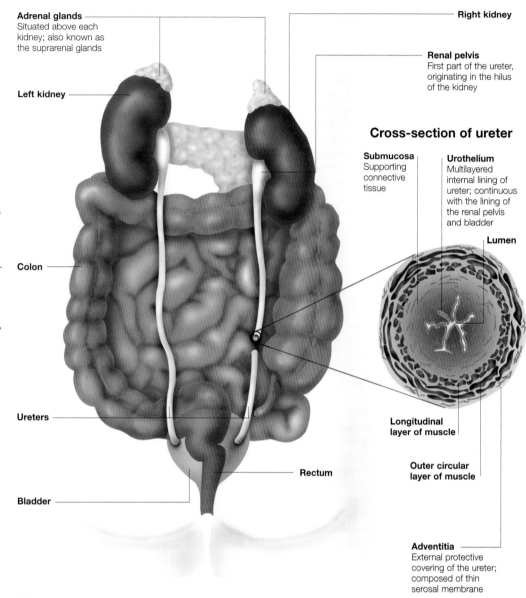

**Adrenal glands**
Situated above each kidney; also known as the suprarenal glands

**Left kidney**

**Colon**

**Ureters**

**Bladder**

**Right kidney**

**Renal pelvis**
First part of the ureter, originating in the hilus of the kidney

**Rectum**

### Cross-section of ureter

**Submucosa**
Supporting connective tissue

**Urothelium**
Multilayered internal lining of ureter; continuous with the lining of the renal pelvis and bladder

**Lumen**

**Longitudinal layer of muscle**

**Outer circular layer of muscle**

**Adventitia**
External protective covering of the ureter; composed of thin serosal membrane

*Urine is actively propelled along the ureters to the bladder by contraction of the muscular walls. This is the action known as 'peristalsis'.*

## Looking at the ureter on X-ray

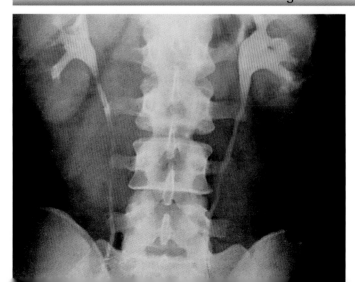

The ureter does not show up on a plain X-ray. However, calcium-rich renal stones may be seen on X-ray at one of the narrower points of the ureter.

### UROGRAPHY
The kidneys, ureters and bladder may be outlined by performing an intravenous urogram.

*This contrast X-ray of the urinary tract clearly shows two normal ureters. These muscular tubes pass down the entire length of the abdomen.*

In this investigation a contrast dye, which shows up on X-ray, is injected intravenously and is then concentrated and excreted by the kidneys. Radiographs taken at intervals show the course of the ureters as they run from the kidneys down through the abdomen to the bladder.

The ureters appear to have constricted and dilated sections. This is due to the presence of waves of peristalsis, the muscular action by which the ureter propels urine towards the urinary bladder.

# Male reproductive system

The male reproductive system includes the penis, scrotum and the two testes (contained within the scrotum). The internal structures of the reproductive system are contained within the pelvis.

The structures constituting the male reproductive tract are responsible for the production of sperm and seminal fluid and their carriage out of the body. Unlike other organs it is not until puberty that they develop and become fully functional.

### CONSTITUENT PARTS

The male reproductive system consists of a number of interrelated parts:

■ Testis – the paired testes lie suspended in the scrotum. Sperm are carried away from the testes through tubes or ducts, the first of which is the epididymis
■ Epididymis – on ejaculation sperm leave the epididymis and enter the vas deferens
■ Vas deferens – sperm are carried along this muscular tube en route to the prostate gland
■ Seminal vesicle – on leaving the vas deferens sperm mix with fluid from the seminal vesicle gland in a combined 'ejaculatory' duct
■ Prostate – the ejaculatory duct empties into the urethra within the prostate gland
■ Penis – on leaving the prostate gland, the urethra then becomes the central core of the penis.

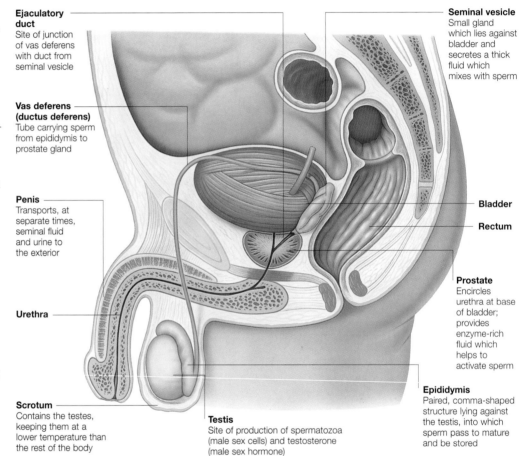

**Ejaculatory duct**
Site of junction of vas deferens with duct from seminal vesicle

**Vas deferens (ductus deferens)**
Tube carrying sperm from epididymis to prostate gland

**Penis**
Transports, at separate times, seminal fluid and urine to the exterior

**Urethra**

**Scrotum**
Contains the testes, keeping them at a lower temperature than the rest of the body

**Testis**
Site of production of spermatozoa (male sex cells) and testosterone (male sex hormone)

**Seminal vesicle**
Small gland which lies against bladder and secretes a thick fluid which mixes with sperm

**Bladder**

**Rectum**

**Prostate**
Encircles urethra at base of bladder; provides enzyme-rich fluid which helps to activate sperm

**Epididymis**
Paired, comma-shaped structure lying against the testis, into which sperm pass to mature and be stored

## External genitalia

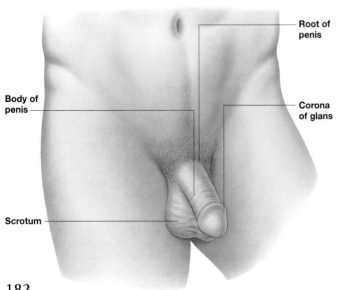

**Root of penis**

**Body of penis**

**Corona of glans**

**Scrotum**

*The external male genitalia consist of the scrotum and the penis, which are situated in the pubic area. In adults, pubic hair surrounds the root of the penis*

The external genitalia are those parts of the reproductive tract which lie visible in the pubic region, while other parts remain hidden within the pelvic cavity.

Male external genitalia consists of:
■ The scrotum
■ The penis.
In adults, these are surrounded by coarse pubic hair.

### SCROTUM

The scrotum is a loose bag of skin and connective tissue which holds the testes suspended within it. There is a midline septum, or partition, which separates each testis from its fellow.

Although it would seem unusual for the testes to be held in such a vulnerable position outside the protection of the body cavity, it is necessary for sperm production for them to be kept cool.

### PENIS

Most of the penis consists of erectile tissue, which becomes engorged with blood during sexual arousal, causing the penis to become erect. The urethra, through which urine and semen pass, runs through the penis.

# Prostate gland

The prostate gland forms a vital part of the male reproductive system, providing enzyme-rich fluid, and produces up to a third of the total volume of the seminal fluid.

About 3 cm in length, the prostate gland lies just under the bladder and encircles the first part of the urethra. Its base lies closely attached to the base of the bladder, its rounded anterior (front) surface lying just behind the pubic bone.

### CAPSULE
The prostate is covered by a tough capsule made up of dense fibrous connective tissue. Outside this true capsule is a further layer of fibrous connective tissue, which is known as the prostatic sheath.

### INTERNAL STRUCTURE
The urethra, the outflow tract from the bladder, runs vertically through the centre of the prostate gland, where it is known as the prostatic urethra. The ejaculatory ducts open into the prostatic urethra on a raised ridge, the seminal colliculus.

The prostate is said to be divided into lobes, although they are not as distinct as they may be in other organs:
■ Anterior lobe – this lies in front of the urethra and contains mainly fibromuscular tissue
■ Posterior lobe – this lies behind the urethra and beneath the ejaculatory ducts
■ Lateral lobes – these two lobes, lying on either side of the urethra, form the main part of the gland
■ Median lobe – this lies between the urethra and the ejaculatory ducts.

## Location of the prostate gland

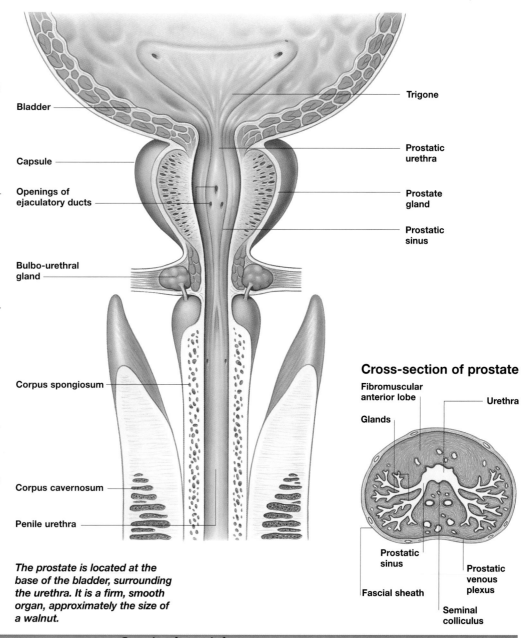

Bladder

Capsule

Openings of ejaculatory ducts

Bulbo-urethral gland

Corpus spongiosum

Corpus cavernosum

Penile urethra

Trigone

Prostatic urethra

Prostate gland

Prostatic sinus

*The prostate is located at the base of the bladder, surrounding the urethra. It is a firm, smooth organ, approximately the size of a walnut.*

## Cross-section of prostate

Fibromuscular anterior lobe

Glands

Urethra

Prostatic sinus

Fascial sheath

Prostatic venous plexus

Seminal colliculus

## Seminal vesicles

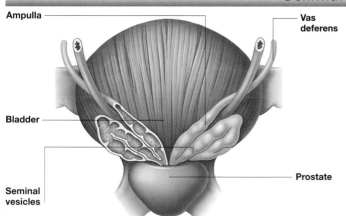

Ampulla

Bladder

Seminal vesicles

Vas deferens

Prostate

The paired seminal vesicles are accessory glands of the male reproductive tract and produce a thick, sugary, alkaline fluid that forms the main part of the seminal fluid.

### STRUCTURE AND SHAPE
Each seminal vesicle is an elongated structure about the

*The seminal vesicles are situated at the back of the bladder. Secretions pass into the vas deferentia, which empty into the prostatic urethra.*

size and shape of a little finger and lies behind the bladder and in front of the rectum, the two forming a V-shape.

### PROSTATE VOLUME
The prostate gland is sac-like, with a volume of approximately 10–15 millilitres. It consists internally of coiled secretory tubules with muscular walls.

The secretions leave the gland in the duct of the seminal vesicle, which joins with the vas deferens just inside the prostate to form the ejaculatory duct.

# Testes, scrotum and epididymis

The testes, which lie suspended within the scrotum, are the sites of sperm production. The scrotum also contains the two epididymides – long, coiled tubes, which connect to the vas deferens.

The paired testes are firm, mobile, oval-shaped structures about 4 cm in length and 2.5 cm in width. The testes lie within the scrotum, a bag formed as an outpouching of the anterior abdominal wall, and are attached above to the spermatic cord, from which they hang.

### TEMPERATURE CONTROL

Normal sperm can only be produced if the temperature of the testes is about three degrees lower than the internal body temperature. Muscle fibres within the spermatic cord and walls of the scrotum help to regulate the scrotal temperature by lifting the testes up towards the body when it is cold, and relaxing when the ambient temperature is higher.

### EPIDIDYMIS

Each epididymis is a firm, comma-shaped structure which lies closely attached to the upper pole of the testis, running down its posterior surface. The epididymis receives the sperm made in the testis and is composed of a highly coiled tube which, if extended, would be six metres in length.

From the tail of the epididymis emerges the vas deferens. This tube will carry the sperm back up the spermatic cord and into the pelvic cavity on the next stage of the journey.

## Sagittal section of the contents of the scrotum

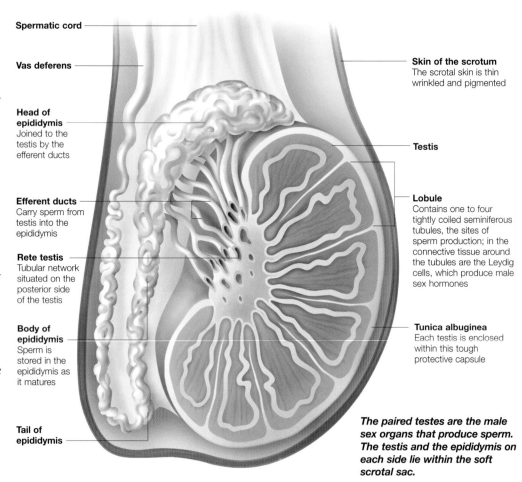

**Spermatic cord**

**Vas deferens**

**Head of epididymis**
Joined to the testis by the efferent ducts

**Efferent ducts**
Carry sperm from testis into the epididymis

**Rete testis**
Tubular network situated on the posterior side of the testis

**Body of epididymis**
Sperm is stored in the epididymis as it matures

**Tail of epididymis**

**Skin of the scrotum**
The scrotal skin is thin wrinkled and pigmented

**Testis**

**Lobule**
Contains one to four tightly coiled seminiferous tubules, the sites of sperm production; in the connective tissue around the tubules are the Leydig cells, which produce male sex hormones

**Tunica albuginea**
Each testis is enclosed within this tough protective capsule

*The paired testes are the male sex organs that produce sperm. The testis and the epididymis on each side lie within the soft scrotal sac.*

## Walls of the scrotum

### Cross-section of the scrotum

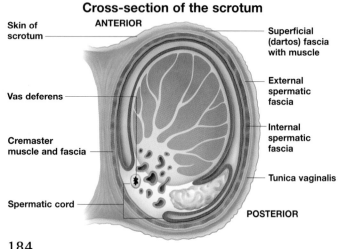

**Skin of scrotum**

ANTERIOR

**Vas deferens**

**Cremaster muscle and fascia**

**Spermatic cord**

**Superficial (dartos) fascia with muscle**

**External spermatic fascia**

**Internal spermatic fascia**

**Tunica vaginalis**

POSTERIOR

*The scrotum contains the testes and hangs outside the body. It consists of an outer covering of skin, which surrounds several protective layers.*

The walls of the scrotum have a number of layers, as would be expected from its origin as an outpouching of the multi-layered anterior abdominal wall.

### LAYERS OF THE SCROTUM

The scrotum consists of:
■ Skin, which is thin, wrinkled and pigmented
■ Dartos fascia, a layer of connective tissue with smooth muscle fibres
■ Three layers of fascia derived from the three muscular layers of the abdominal wall, with further cremasteric muscle fibres
■ Tunica vaginalis, a closed sac of thin, slippery, serous membrane, like the peritoneum in the abdomen, which contains a small amount of fluid to lubricate movement of the testes against surrounding structures.

Unlike the abdominal wall, there is no fat in the coverings around the testes, which is believed to help keep them cool.

# Blood supply of the testes

The arterial blood supply of the testes arises from the abdominal aorta, and descends to the scrotum. Venous drainage follows the same route in reverse.

During embryonic life, the testes develop within the abdomen; it is only at birth that they descend into their final position within the scrotum. Because of this the blood supply of the testes arises from the abdominal aorta, and travels down with the descending testis to the scrotum.

### TESTICULAR ARTERIES

The paired testicular arteries are long and narrow and arise from the abdominal aorta. They then pass down on the posterior abdominal wall, crossing the ureters as they go, until they reach the deep inguinal rings and enter the inguinal canal.

As part of the spermatic cord they leave the inguinal canal and enter the scrotum where they supply the testis, also forming interconnections with the artery to the vas deferens.

### TESTICULAR VEINS

Testicular veins arise from the testis and epididymis on each side. Their course differs from that of the testicular arteries within the spermatic cord where, instead of a single vein, there is a network of veins, known as the pampiniform plexus.

Further up in the abdomen, the right testicular vein drains into the large inferior vena cava, while the left normally drains into the left renal vein.

*The blood supply to the testes originates from high up in the abdominal blood vessels. These resulting long vessels allow for the testes' descent in early life.*

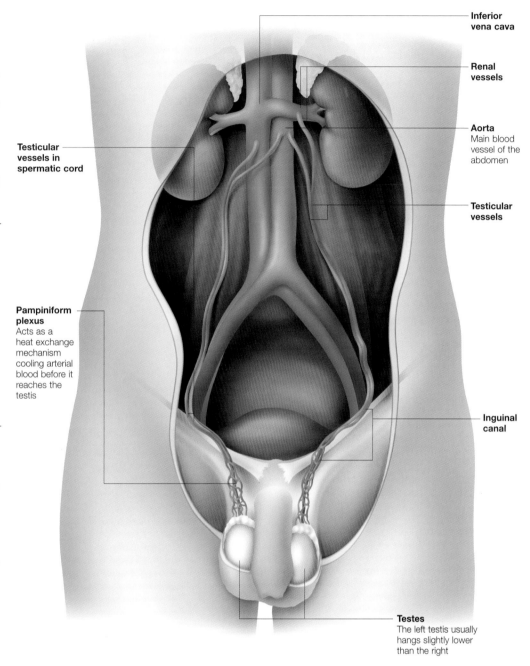

**Inferior vena cava**

**Renal vessels**

**Aorta**
Main blood vessel of the abdomen

**Testicular vessels in spermatic cord**

**Testicular vessels**

**Pampiniform plexus**
Acts as a heat exchange mechanism cooling arterial blood before it reaches the testis

**Inguinal canal**

**Testes**
The left testis usually hangs slightly lower than the right

## Internal structure of the testis

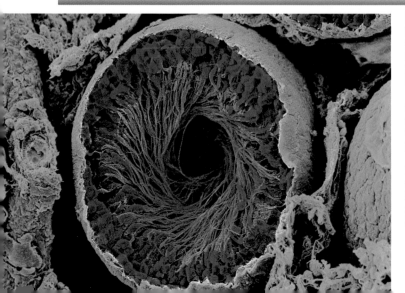

Each testis is enclosed within a tough, protective capsule, the tunica albuginea, from which numerous septa, or partitions, pass down to divide the testis into about 250 tiny lobules.

Each wedge-shaped lobule contains one to four tightly coiled seminiferous tubules, which are the actual sites of production of sperm.

*This micrograph shows a sectioned seminiferous tubule. Developing sperm (red) are inside the tubule, which is surrounded by Leydig cells (green).*

It has been estimated that there is a total of 350 metres of sperm-producing tubules in each testis.

### TUBULES

Sperm are collected from the coiled seminiferous tubules into the straight tubules of the rete testis and from there into the epididymis.

Between the seminiferous tubules lie groups of specialized cells, the interstitial or Leydig cells, which are the site of production of hormones such as testosterone.

185

# Penis

The penis is the male copulatory organ, which, when erect,
conveys sperm into the vagina during sexual intercourse.
To enable this, the penis is largely composed of erectile tissue.

The penis is mostly composed of three columns of sponge-like erectile tissue, the two corpora cavernosa and the corpus spongiosum. These are able to fill and become engorged with blood, causing an erection.

## STRUCTURE OF THE PENIS

There is only a small amount of muscular tissue associated with the penis, and what there is lies in its root. The shaft and glans have no muscle fibres.

The main components of the penis are:

■ Root – this first part of the penis is fixed in position and is made up of the expanded bases of the three columns of erectile tissue covered by muscle fibres

■ Shaft – this hangs down in the flaccid condition and is made up of erectile tissue, connective tissue, and blood and lymphatic vessels

■ Glans – the tip of the penis, this is formed from the expanded end of the corpus spongiosum and carries the outlet of the urethra, the external urethral orifice

■ Skin – this is continuous with that of the scrotum and is thin, dark and hairless. It is attached only loosely to the underlying fascia and lies in wrinkles when the penis is flaccid.

At the tip of the penis the skin extends as a double layer which covers the glans; this is known as the prepuce, or foreskin.

*The penis is anatomically divided into three parts: the root, the shaft and the glans, or head of the penis.*

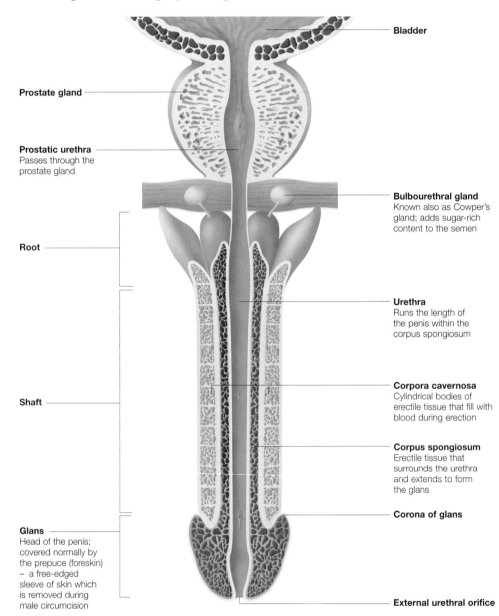

**Bladder**

**Prostate gland**

**Prostatic urethra**
Passes through the prostate gland

**Root**

**Shaft**

**Glans**
Head of the penis; covered normally by the prepuce (foreskin) – a free-edged sleeve of skin which is removed during male circumcision

**Bulbourethral gland**
Known also as Cowper's gland; adds sugar-rich content to the semen

**Urethra**
Runs the length of the penis within the corpus spongiosum

**Corpora cavernosa**
Cylindrical bodies of erectile tissue that fill with blood during erection

**Corpus spongiosum**
Erectile tissue that surrounds the urethra and extends to form the glans

**Corona of glans**

**External urethral orifice**

## Cross-section through the penis

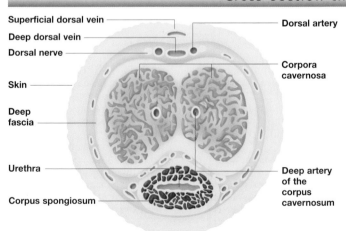

**Superficial dorsal vein**

**Deep dorsal vein**

**Dorsal nerve**

**Skin**

**Deep fascia**

**Urethra**

**Corpus spongiosum**

**Dorsal artery**

**Corpora cavernosa**

**Deep artery of the corpus cavernosum**

In a cross-section of the shaft of the penis, the relationship of erectile tissue, blood vessels and fascia can be seen more easily. The main bulk is made up of the three masses of erectile tissue, the smaller corpus spongiosum containing within its length the urethra. Each corpus cavernosum carries a central deep artery,

*The main body of the penis, the shaft, consists of three bodies of erectile tissue. These fill with blood during sexual stimulation, resulting in an erection.*

which supplies the blood needed for erection.

## CONNECTIVE TISSUE

A sleeve of connective tissue, the deep fascia, encloses the erectile tissue and the deep dorsal vein and dorsal arteries and nerves. Outside the deep fascia is a layer of loose connective tissue which contains the superficial veins. The skin which overlies this loose connective tissue layer is firmly attached to the underlying structures only at the glans.

# Muscles associated with the penis

Several muscles are associated with the penis. Their fibres are confined to the root and structures around the penis, rather than to the shaft or glans.

These muscles are known collectively as the superficial perineal muscles, due to the fact that they lie in the perineum, the area around the anus and external genitalia.

There are three main muscles in this area:

### ■ Superficial transverse perineal muscle

This narrow, paired muscle lies just under the skin in front of the anus. It runs from the ischial tuberosity of the pelvic bone on each side right across to the midline of the body.

### ■ Bulbospongiosus

This muscle acts to compress the base of the corpus spongiosum, and thus the urethra, to help expel its contents. It originates in a central tendon or raphe, which unites the two sides and passes round to encircle the root of the penis.

### ■ Ischiocavernosus

This muscle originates from the ischial tuberosity of the pelvic bone to surround the crura or bases of the corpora cavernosa on each side. Contraction of this muscle helps to maintain erection of the penis.

*The muscles near the penis are known as the superficial perineal muscles. They surround the base of the penis and help to maintain an erection.*

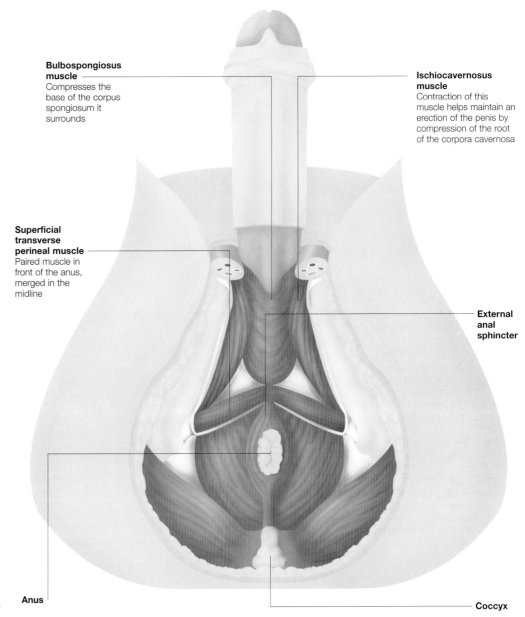

**Bulbospongiosus muscle**
Compresses the base of the corpus spongiosum it surrounds

**Ischiocavernosus muscle**
Contraction of this muscle helps maintain an erection of the penis by compression of the root of the corpora cavernosa

**Superficial transverse perineal muscle**
Paired muscle in front of the anus, merged in the midline

**External anal sphincter**

**Anus**

**Coccyx**

## Blood supply of the penis

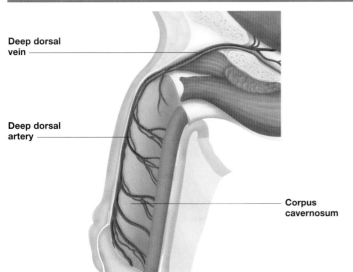

**Deep dorsal vein**

**Deep dorsal artery**

**Corpus cavernosum**

The arterial supply of the penis has two functions. As with any organ, it has to provide the necessary oxygenated blood for the tissues of the penis. It must also, however, provide an additional supply to allow engorgement of the spongy erectile tissues for erection.

### ARTERIES
All the arteries supplying the penis originate from the internal pudendal arteries of the pelvis.

*The blood supply of the penis originates from the internal pudendal arteries. The deep arteries supply the corpora cavernosa during an erection.*

The dorsal arteries lie on each side of the midline deep dorsal vein, and supply connective tissue and skin.

The deep arteries run within the spongy tissue of the corpora cavernosa to supply tissue there and to allow flooding of that tissue during erection.

### VENOUS DRAINAGE
The deep dorsal vein of the penis receives blood from the cavernous spaces while blood from the overlying connective tissue and skin is drained by the superficial dorsal vein.

Venous blood drains ultimately into the pudendal veins within the pelvis.

187

# Female reproductive system

The role of the female reproductive tract is twofold.
The ovaries produce eggs for fertilization, and the uterus nurtures
and protects any resulting fetus for its nine-month gestation.

The female reproductive tract is composed of the internal genitalia – the ovaries, uterine (Fallopian) tubes, uterus and vagina – and the external genitalia (the vulva).

### INTERNAL GENITALIA

The almond-shaped ovaries lie on either side of the uterus, suspended by ligaments. Above the ovaries are the paired uterine tubes, each of which provides a site for fertilization of the oocyte (egg), which then travels down the tube to the uterus.

The uterus lies within the pelvic cavity and rises into the lower abdominal cavity as a pregnancy progresses. The vagina, which connects the cervix to the vulva, can be distended greatly, as occurs during childbirth when it forms much of the birth canal.

### EXTERNAL GENITALIA

The female external genitalia, or vulva, is where the reproductive tract opens to the exterior. The vaginal opening lies behind the opening of the urethra in an area known as the vestibule. This is covered by two folds of skin on each side, the labia minora and labia majora, in front of which lies the raised clitoris.

*The female reproductive system is composed of internal and external organs. The internal genitalia are T-shaped and lie within the pelvic cavity.*

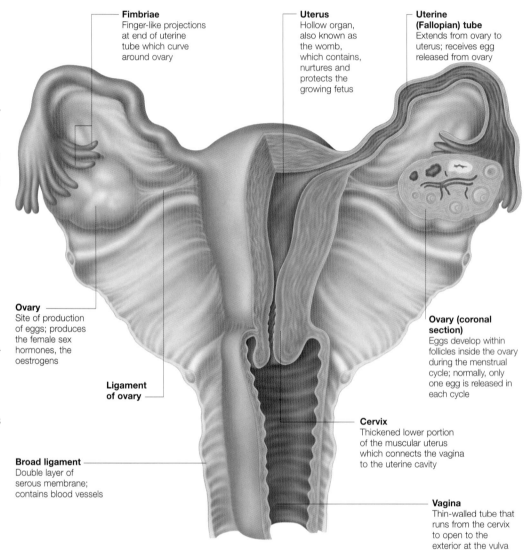

**Fimbriae**
Finger-like projections at end of uterine tube which curve around ovary

**Uterus**
Hollow organ, also known as the womb, which contains, nurtures and protects the growing fetus

**Uterine (Fallopian) tube**
Extends from ovary to uterus; receives egg released from ovary

**Ovary**
Site of production of eggs; produces the female sex hormones, the oestrogens

**Ligament of ovary**

**Broad ligament**
Double layer of serous membrane; contains blood vessels

**Ovary (coronal section)**
Eggs develop within follicles inside the ovary during the menstrual cycle; normally, only one egg is released in each cycle

**Cervix**
Thickened lower portion of the muscular uterus which connects the vagina to the uterine cavity

**Vagina**
Thin-walled tube that runs from the cervix to open to the exterior at the vulva

## Position of the female reproductive tract

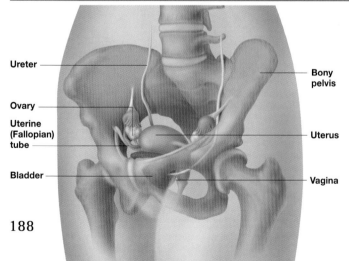

**Ureter**

**Ovary**

**Uterine (Fallopian) tube**

**Bladder**

**Bony pelvis**

**Uterus**

**Vagina**

In adult women the internal genitalia (which, apart from the ovaries, are basically tubular in structure) are located deep within the pelvic cavity. They are thus protected by the presence of the circle of bone which makes up the pelvis.

This is in contrast to the

*The internal reproductive organs in adult women are positioned deep within the pelvic cavity. They are therefore protected by the bony pelvis.*

pelvic cavity of young children, which is relatively shallow. A child's uterus, therefore, like the bladder behind which it sits, is located within the lower abdomen.

### BROAD LIGAMENTS

The upper surface of the uterus and ovaries is draped in a 'tent' of peritoneum, the thin lining of the abdominal and pelvic cavities, forming the broad ligament which helps to keep the uterus in its position.

# Blood supply of the internal genitalia

The female reproductive tract receives a rich blood supply via an interconnecting network of arteries. Venous blood is drained by a network of veins.

The four principal arteries of the female genitalia are:

■ **Ovarian artery** – this runs from the abdominal aorta to the ovary.

Branches from the ovarian artery on each side pass through the mesovarium, the fold of peritoneum in which the ovary lies, to supply the ovary and uterine (Fallopian) tubes. The ovarian artery in the tissue of the mesovarium connects with the uterine artery

■ **Uterine artery** – this is a branch of the large internal iliac artery of the pelvis. The uterine artery approaches the uterus at the level of the cervix, which is anchored in place by cervical ligaments.

The uterine artery connects with the ovarian artery above, while a branch connects with the arteries below to supply the cervix and vagina

■ **Vaginal artery** – this is also a branch of the internal iliac artery. Together with blood from the uterine artery, its branches supply blood to the vaginal walls

■ **Internal pudendal artery** – this contributes to the blood supply of the lower third of the vagina and anus.

## VEINS

A plexus, or network, of small veins lies within the walls of the uterus and vagina. Blood received into these vessels drains into the internal iliac veins via the uterine vein.

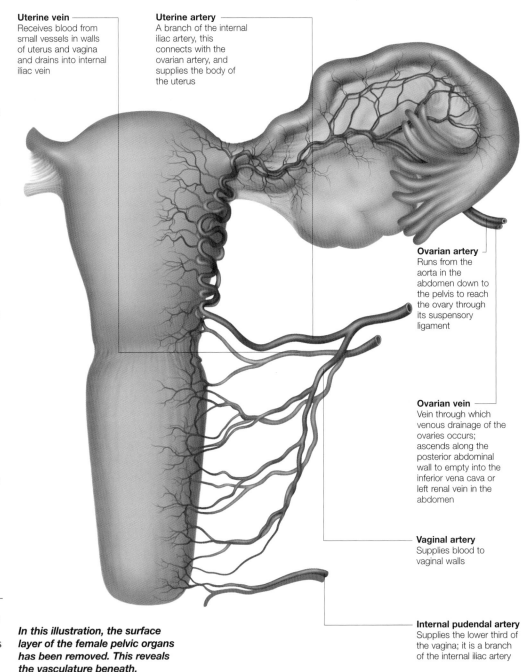

**Uterine vein**
Receives blood from small vessels in walls of uterus and vagina and drains into internal iliac vein

**Uterine artery**
A branch of the internal iliac artery, this connects with the ovarian artery, and supplies the body of the uterus

**Ovarian artery**
Runs from the aorta in the abdomen down to the pelvis to reach the ovary through its suspensory ligament

**Ovarian vein**
Vein through which venous drainage of the ovaries occurs; ascends along the posterior abdominal wall to empty into the inferior vena cava or left renal vein in the abdomen

**Vaginal artery**
Supplies blood to vaginal walls

**Internal pudendal artery**
Supplies the lower third of the vagina; it is a branch of the internal iliac artery

*In this illustration, the surface layer of the female pelvic organs has been removed. This reveals the vasculature beneath.*

## Visualizing the female reproductive tract

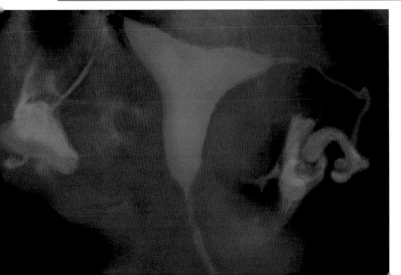

The tubal or hollow parts of the female reproductive tract can be outlined by performing a hysterosalpingogram.

In this procedure a special radio-opaque dye is passed up into the uterus through the cervix, while X-ray pictures of the area are taken. The dye fills the uterine cavity, and enters

*This hysterosalpingogram shows the uterine cavity (centre) filled with dye. Dye is also seen in the uterine tubes and emerging into the peritoneal cavity.*

the uterine tubes. It then runs along their length until it flows into the peritoneal cavity at their far end.

### ASSESSING TUBES

A hysterosalpingogram is sometimes carried out in the investigation of infertility to determine whether the uterine tubes are still patent (unobstructed). If the tubes have been blocked, as may happen after an infection, the dye will not be able to travel along their full length.

189

# Uterus

The uterus, or womb, is the part of the female reproductive
tract that nurtures and protects the fetus during pregnancy. It lies
within the pelvic cavity and is a hollow, muscular organ.

During a woman's reproductive
years, in the non-pregnant state,
the uterus is about 7.5 cm long
and 5 cm across at its widest
point. However, it can expand
enormously to accommodate the
fetus during pregnancy.

### STRUCTURE
The uterus is said to be made up
of two parts:
■ The body, forming the upper
part of the uterus – this is fairly
mobile as it must expand during
pregnancy. The central triangular
space, or cavity, of the body
receives the openings of the
paired uterine (Fallopian) tubes
■ The cervix, the lower part of
the uterus – this is a thick,
muscular canal, which is
anchored to the surrounding
pelvic structures for stability.

### UTERINE WALLS
The main part of the uterus, the
body, has a thick wall which is
composed of three layers:
■ Perimetrium – the thin outer
coat which is continuous with
the pelvic peritoneum
■ Myometrium – forming the
great bulk of the uterine wall
■ Endometrium – the delicate
lining, which is specialized to
allow implantation of an embryo
should fertilization occur.

*The uterus resembles an
inverted pear in shape. It is
suspended in the pelvic cavity
by peritoneal folds or ligaments.*

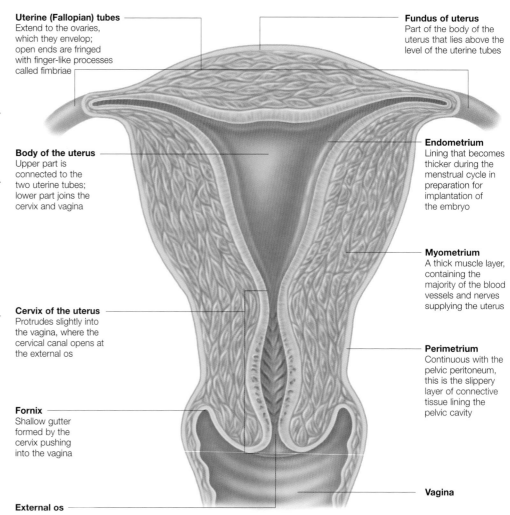

**Uterine (Fallopian) tubes**
Extend to the ovaries,
which they envelop;
open ends are fringed
with finger-like processes
called fimbriae

**Body of the uterus**
Upper part is
connected to the
two uterine tubes;
lower part joins the
cervix and vagina

**Cervix of the uterus**
Protrudes slightly into
the vagina, where the
cervical canal opens at
the external os

**Fornix**
Shallow gutter
formed by the
cervix pushing
into the vagina

**External os**

**Fundus of uterus**
Part of the body of the
uterus that lies above the
level of the uterine tubes

**Endometrium**
Lining that becomes
thicker during the
menstrual cycle in
preparation for
implantation of
the embryo

**Myometrium**
A thick muscle layer,
containing the
majority of the blood
vessels and nerves
supplying the uterus

**Perimetrium**
Continuous with the
pelvic peritoneum,
this is the slippery
layer of connective
tissue lining the
pelvic cavity

**Vagina**

## Position of the uterus

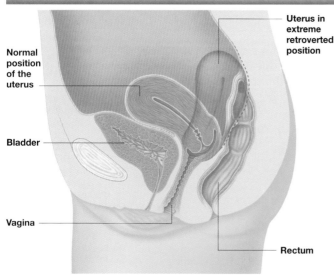

**Normal
position
of the
uterus**

**Bladder**

**Vagina**

**Uterus in
extreme
retroverted
position**

**Rectum**

The uterus lies in the pelvis
between the bladder and the
rectum. However, its position
changes with the stage of filling
of these two structures and with
different postures.

### NORMAL POSITION
Normally the long axis of the
uterus forms an angle of 90
degrees with the long axis of the
vagina, with the uterus lying
forward on top of the bladder.
This usual position is known as
anteversion.

*In most women the uterus lies on
the bladder, moving backwards
as the bladder fills. However, it
may lie in any position between
the two extremes shown.*

### ANTEFLEXION
In some women, the uterus lies
in the normal position, but may
curve forwards slightly between
the cervix and fundus, This is
termed anteflexion.

### RETROFLEXION
In some cases, however, the
uterus bends not forwards but
backwards, the fundus coming
to lie next to the rectum. This is
known as a retroverted uterus.

Regardless of the uterine
position it will normally bend
forwards as it expands in
pregnancy. A pregnant
retroverted uterus, however, may
take longer to reach the pelvic
brim, at which point it becomes
palpable abdominally.

# The uterus in pregnancy

In pregnancy the uterus must enlarge to hold the growing fetus. From being a small pelvic organ, it increases in size to take up much of the space of the abdominal cavity.

Pressure of the enlarged uterus on the abdominal organs pushes them up against the diaphragm, encroaching on the thoracic cavity and causing the ribs to flare out to compensate. Organs such as the stomach and bladder are compressed to such an extent in late pregnancy that their capacity is greatly diminished and they become full sooner.

After pregnancy, the uterus will rapidly decrease in size again although it will always remain slightly larger than one which has never been pregnant.

### HEIGHT OF FUNDUS

During pregnancy the enlarging uterus can be accommodated within the pelvis for the first 12 weeks, at which time the uppermost part, the fundus, can just be palpated in the lower abdomen. By 20 weeks, the fundus will have reached the region of the umbilicus, and by late pregnancy it may have reached the xiphisternum, the lowest part of the breastbone.

### WEIGHT OF UTERUS

In the final stages of pregnancy the uterus will have increased in weight from a pre-pregnant 45 g to around 900 g. The myometrium (muscle layer) grows as the individual fibres increase in size (hypertrophy). In addition, the fibres increase in number (hyperplasia).

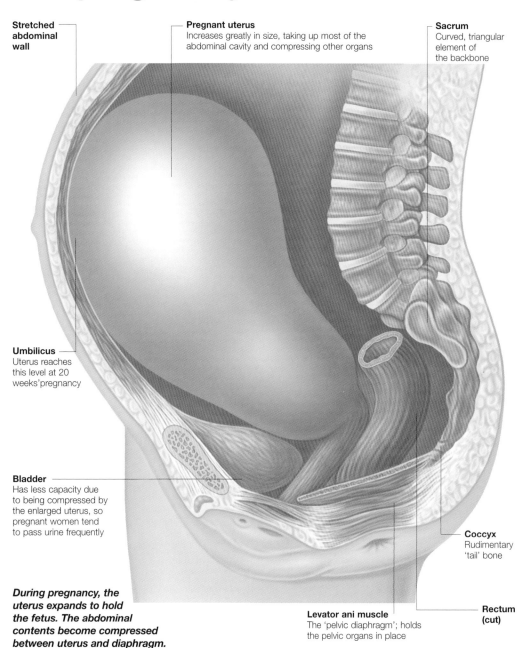

**Stretched abdominal wall**

**Pregnant uterus**
Increases greatly in size, taking up most of the abdominal cavity and compressing other organs

**Sacrum**
Curved, triangular element of the backbone

**Umbilicus**
Uterus reaches this level at 20 weeks' pregnancy

**Bladder**
Has less capacity due to being compressed by the enlarged uterus, so pregnant women tend to pass urine frequently

**Coccyx**
Rudimentary 'tail' bone

**Levator ani muscle**
The 'pelvic diaphragm'; holds the pelvic organs in place

**Rectum (cut)**

*During pregnancy, the uterus expands to hold the fetus. The abdominal contents become compressed between uterus and diaphragm.*

## Lining of the uterus

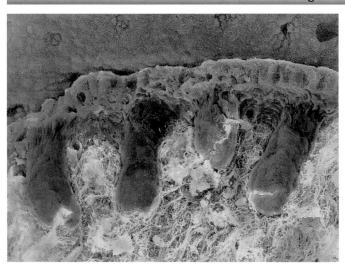

The endometrium is the name given to the lining of the uterus. It consists of a simple surface layer, or epithelium, overlying a thicker layer of highly cellular connective tissue, the lamina propria. Numerous tubular glands are also present within the endometrium.

### MENSTRUAL CYCLE

Under the influence of sex hormones the endometrium undergoes changes during the

*This enlarged section through the endometrium of the uterus shows the layer of epithelial cells (blue). Three tubular glands are also clearly visible.*

monthly menstrual cycle which prepare it for the possible implantation of an embryo. It may vary in thickness from 1 mm to 5 mm before being shed at menstruation.

### BLOOD SUPPLY

Arteries within the myometrium, the underlying muscle layer, send numerous small branches into the endometrium. There are two types: straight arteries, which supply the lower, permanent layer; and tortuous (twisted) spiral arteries, which supply the upper layer shed during menstruation. The tortuosity of the spiral arteries prevents excess bleeding during menstruation.

191

# Vagina and cervix

The vagina is the thin-walled muscular tube that extends from the cervix of the uterus to the external genitalia. The vagina is closed at rest but is designed to stretch during intercourse or childbirth.

The vagina is approximately 8 cm in length and lies between the bladder and the rectum. It forms the main part of the birth canal and receives the penis during sexual intercourse.

## STRUCTURE OF THE VAGINA

The front and back walls of the vagina normally lie in contact with one another, closing the lumen (central space), although the vagina can expand greatly, as occurs in childbirth.

The cervix, the lower end of the uterus, projects down into the lumen of the vagina at its upper end. Where the vagina arches up to meet the cervix, it forms recesses known as the vaginal fornices. These are divided into anterior, posterior, right and left fornices, although they form a complete ring.

The thin wall of the vagina has three layers:
■ Adventitia – outer layer composed of fibroelastic connective tissue which allows distension when necessary
■ Muscularis – the central muscular layer of the vaginal wall
■ Mucosa – the inner layer of the vagina; this is thrown into many rugae (deep folds), and has a layered, stratified squamous (skin-like) epithelium (cell lining), which helps to resist abrasion during intercourse.

*The vagina is a muscular, tubular organ designed to expand during sexual intercourse and childbirth. It is approximately 8 cm in length.*

### Coronal section through the vagina

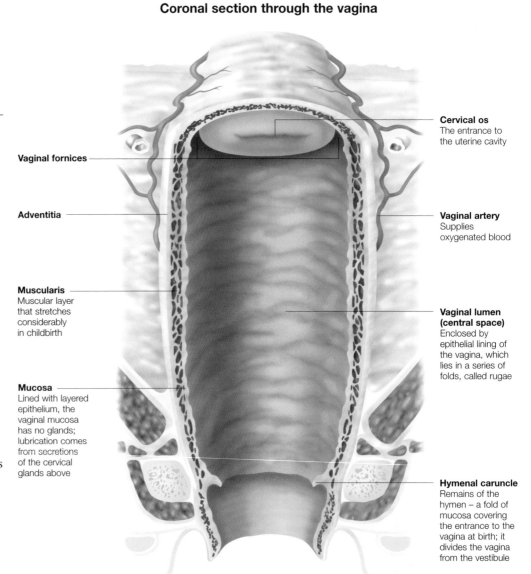

**Vaginal fornices**

**Adventitia**

**Muscularis**
Muscular layer that stretches considerably in childbirth

**Mucosa**
Lined with layered epithelium, the vaginal mucosa has no glands; lubrication comes from secretions of the cervical glands above

**Cervical os**
The entrance to the uterine cavity

**Vaginal artery**
Supplies oxygenated blood

**Vaginal lumen (central space)**
Enclosed by epithelial lining of the vagina, which lies in a series of folds, called rugae

**Hymenal caruncle**
Remains of the hymen – a fold of mucosa covering the entrance to the vagina at birth; it divides the vagina from the vestibule

## External genitalia

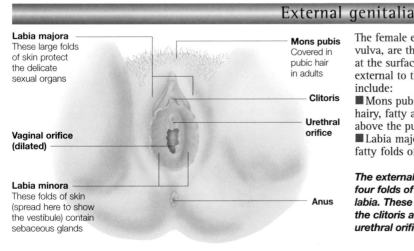

**Labia majora**
These large folds of skin protect the delicate sexual organs

**Vaginal orifice (dilated)**

**Labia minora**
These folds of skin (spread here to show the vestibule) contain sebaceous glands

**Mons pubis**
Covered in pubic hair in adults

**Clitoris**

**Urethral orifice**

**Anus**

The female external genitalia, or vulva, are those parts which lie at the surface of the body, external to the vagina. They include:
■ Mons pubis – the rounded, hairy, fatty area which lies above the pubic bone
■ Labia majora – the two outer fatty folds of skin, which lie

*The external genitalia include four folds of skin, known as the labia. These cover and protect the clitoris and the vaginal and urethral orifices.*

across the vulval opening
■ Labia minora – the two smaller folds of skin which lie inside the cleft of the vulva
■ Vestibule – area into which the urethra and vagina open
■ Clitoris – a structure composed of erectile tissue and containing a rich sensory nerve supply; it is analogous to the penis in males.

The vulval opening is partially closed off by a fold of mucosa, the hymen; this may rupture at first intercourse, with tampon use or during a pelvic examination.

# The cervix

**The cervix, or neck of the uterus, is the narrowed, lower part of the uterus which projects down into the upper vagina.**

The cervix is fixed in position by the cervical ligaments, and so anchors the relatively mobile uterine body above.

### CERVICAL STRUCTURE

The cervix has a narrow canal which is approximately 2.5 cm long in adult women. The walls of the cervix are tough, containing much fibrous tissue as well as muscle, unlike the body of the uterus, which is mainly muscular.

The central canal of the cervix is the downwards continuation of the uterine cavity which opens at its lower end, the external os, into the vagina. The canal is widest at its central point, constricting slightly at the internal os at the upper end and the external os below.

### LINING OF THE CERVIX

The epithelium, or lining, of the cervix is of two types:
■ Endocervix – this is the lining of the cervical canal, inside the cervix. The epithelium is a simple, single layer of columnar cells which overlies a surface thrown into many folds containing glands.
■ Ectocervix – this covers the portion of the cervix which projects down into the vagina; it is composed of squamous epithelium and has many layers.

*The cervix is located at the lower end of the uterus. It contains less muscle tissue than the uterus and is lined with two different types of epithelial cell.*

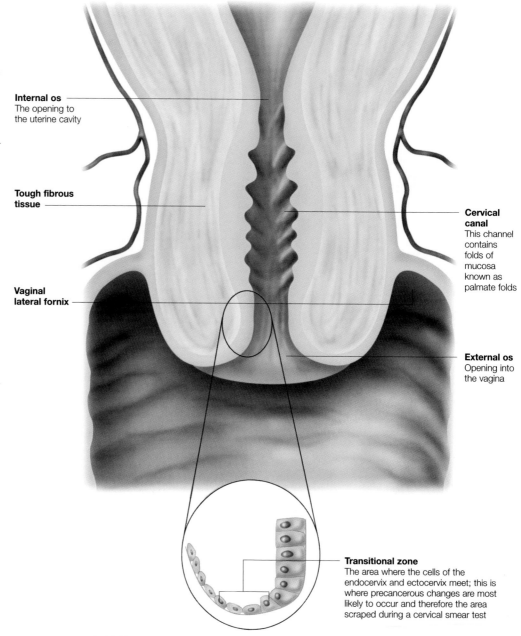

**Internal os**
The opening to the uterine cavity

**Tough fibrous tissue**

**Vaginal lateral fornix**

**Cervical canal**
This channel contains folds of mucosa known as palmate folds

**External os**
Opening into the vagina

**Transitional zone**
The area where the cells of the endocervix and ectocervix meet; this is where precancerous changes are most likely to occur and therefore the area scraped during a cervical smear test

## Cervical os

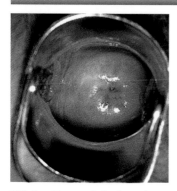

*This healthy cervix is viewed through a metal speculum. The deeper pink lining of the inside of the cervix can be seen at the external cervical os.*

The opening of the cervical canal into the upper vagina is known as the cervical os.

It may be necessary to look more closely at this area if, for example, some abnormal cells have been seen under the microscope during a routine cervical smear test. In this case a colposcope, a type of low-powered microscope, is used.

### COLPOSCOPY

During colposcopy, the cervix is coated with a staining fluid that shows up any abnormal cells. A biopsy may be taken of any suspicious areas; further treatment may then be needed.

### Nulliparous cervix

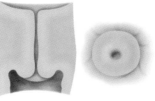

*In a woman who has never given birth (nulliparous), the cervical os appears round in shape. The canal is also more tightly closed before childbirth.*

### Parous cervix

*After childbirth, the os becomes slit-like in appearance. The cervical canal is slightly looser, following the passage of the fetus.*

# Ovaries and uterine tubes

The ovaries are the site of production of oocytes, or eggs, which are fertilized by sperm to produce embryos. The uterine (or Fallopian) tubes conduct the oocytes from the ovaries to the uterus.

The paired ovaries are situated in the lower abdomen and lie on either side of the uterus. Their position may be variable, especially after childbirth, when the supporting ligaments have been stretched.

Each ovary consists of:
■ Tunica albuginea – a protective layer of fibrous tissue
■ Medulla – a central region with blood vessels and nerves
■ Cortex – within which the oocytes develop
■ Surface layer – smooth before puberty but becoming more pitted in the reproductive years.

### BLOOD SUPPLY

The arterial supply to the ovaries comes via the ovarian arteries, which arise from the abdominal aorta. After supplying the uterine tubes also, the ovarian arteries overlap with the uterine arteries.

Blood from the ovaries enters a network of tiny veins, the pampiniform plexus, within the broad ligament, from which it enters the right and left ovarian veins. These ascend into the abdomen to drain ultimately into the large inferior vena cava and the renal vein respectively.

*This cross-section shows the follicles situated in the cortex of the ovary. Each follicle contains an oocyte at a different stage of development.*

## Cross-section of an ovary

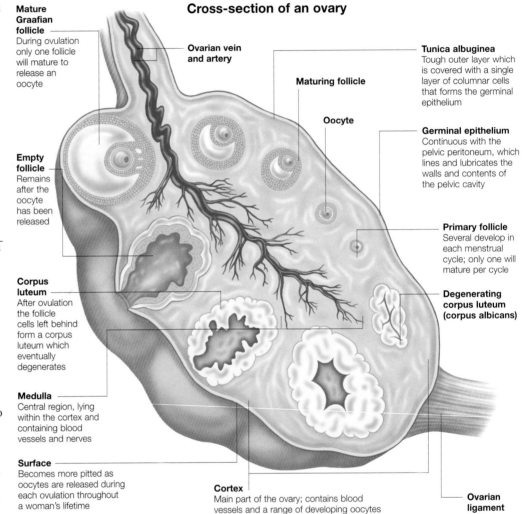

**Mature Graafian follicle**
During ovulation only one follicle will mature to release an oocyte

**Empty follicle**
Remains after the oocyte has been released

**Corpus luteum**
After ovulation the follicle cells left behind form a corpus luteum which eventually degenerates

**Medulla**
Central region, lying within the cortex and containing blood vessels and nerves

**Surface**
Becomes more pitted as oocytes are released during each ovulation throughout a woman's lifetime

**Ovarian vein and artery**

**Maturing follicle**

**Oocyte**

**Cortex**
Main part of the ovary; contains blood vessels and a range of developing oocytes

**Tunica albuginea**
Tough outer layer which is covered with a single layer of columnar cells that forms the germinal epithelium

**Germinal epithelium**
Continuous with the pelvic peritoneum, which lines and lubricates the walls and contents of the pelvic cavity

**Primary follicle**
Several develop in each menstrual cycle; only one will mature per cycle

**Degenerating corpus luteum (corpus albicans)**

**Ovarian ligament**

## Supporting ligaments

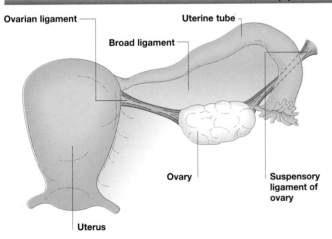

**Ovarian ligament**

**Uterine tube**

**Broad ligament**

**Ovary**

**Suspensory ligament of ovary**

**Uterus**

Each ovary is held in its position relative to the uterus and uterine tubes by several ligaments.

### MAIN LIGAMENTS

These ligaments include the following:
■ Broad ligament – the tent-like fold of pelvic peritoneum which hangs down on either side of the uterus, enclosing the uterine tubes and ovaries

*Each ovary is suspended by several ligaments to hold it in position. However, the position varies, especially if the ligaments have stretched.*

■ Suspensory ligament of the ovary – that part of the broad ligament which anchors the ovary to the side wall of the pelvis and carries the ovarian vessels and lymphatics
■ Mesovarium – the fold of the broad ligament within which the ovary lies.
■ Ovarian ligament – attaches the ovary to the uterus and runs within the broad ligament.

These ligaments may become stretched in women following childbirth, which in many cases means that the position of the ovary may be more variable than before pregnancy.

# The uterine tubes

The uterine, or Fallopian, tubes collect the oocytes released from the ovaries and transport them to the uterus. They also provide a site for fertilization of the oocyte by a sperm to take place.

Each uterine tube is about 10 cm long and extends outwards from the upper part of the body of the uterus towards the lateral wall of the pelvic cavity.

The tubes run within the upper edge of the broad ligament and open into the peritoneal cavity in the region of the ovary.

### STRUCTURE
The tubes are divided anatomically into four parts which, from outer to inner are:

■ Infundibulum – the funnel-shaped outer end of the uterine tubes which opens into the peritoneal cavity
■ Ampulla – the longest and widest part and the most usual site for fertilization of the oocyte
■ Isthmus – a constricted region with thick walls
■ Uterine part – this is the shortest part of the tube.

### BLOOD SUPPLY
The uterine tubes have a very rich blood supply which comes from both the ovarian and the uterine arteries; these overlap to form an arterial arcade.

Venous blood drains from the tubes in a pattern which mirrors the arterial supply.

## Major parts of a uterine tube

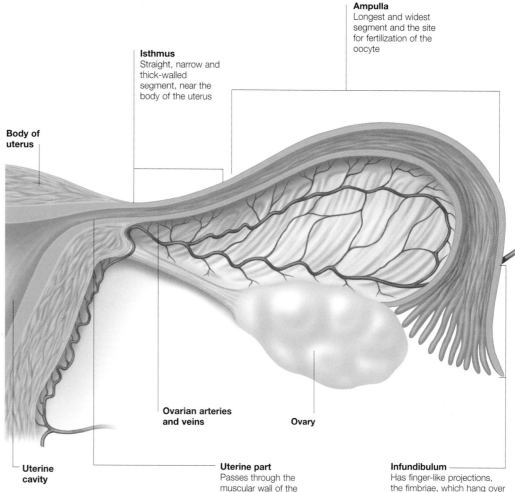

**Isthmus**
Straight, narrow and thick-walled segment, near the body of the uterus

**Ampulla**
Longest and widest segment and the site for fertilization of the oocyte

**Body of uterus**

**Ovarian arteries and veins**

**Ovary**

**Uterine cavity**

**Uterine part**
Passes through the muscular wall of the uterus to open at the uterine ostium (opening)

**Infundibulum**
Has finger-like projections, the fimbriae, which hang over the ovary, ready to scoop up the oocyte at ovulation

*The uterine tubes lie on either side of the body. The outer part of each tube lies near the ovary, its end opening there into the abdominal cavity.*

## Wall of a uterine tube

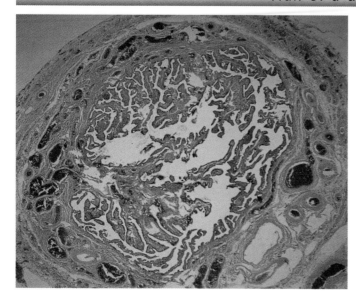

The structure of the wall of a uterine tube shows features which have developed to assist in the task of maintaining the oocyte and carrying it safely to the uterus for implantation:

■ A layer of smooth muscle fibres within the walls allows the uterine tubes to contract rhythmically, the waves of contraction passing towards the uterus.

■ The walls are lined with cells which bear cilia, tiny brush-like

*The uterine tube wall is lined with two types of cell: mucus-secreting and ciliated. These act to nourish and propel the oocyte along the length of the tube.*

projections which beat to 'sweep' the oocyte inwards towards the uterus.

■ Non-ciliated cells in deep crypts in the lining of the uterine tubes produce secretions which keep the oocyte, and any sperm which may be present, nourished during their journey along the tube.

### OVARIAN HORMONES
The lining of the uterine tubes is influenced by ovarian hormones, and so may vary in its activity according to the phase of the menstrual cycle. The hormone progesterone, for instance, increases the amount of mucous secretions that are produced.

# Bones of the pelvis

The basin-like pelvis is formed by the hip bones, sacrum and coccyx.
The pelvic bones provide sites of attachment for many
important muscles, and also help to protect the vital pelvic organs.

The bones of the pelvis form a ring which connects the spine to the lower limbs and protects the pelvic contents, including the reproductive organs and bladder.

The pelvic bones, to which many powerful muscles are attached, allow the weight of the body to be transferred to the legs with great stability.

## STRUCTURE OF THE PELVIS

The basin-like pelvis consists of the innominate (hip) bones, the sacrum and the coccyx. The innominate bones meet at the pubic symphysis anteriorly. Posteriorly, these two bones are joined to the sacrum. Extending down from the sacrum at the back of the pelvis is the coccyx.

## FALSE AND TRUE PELVIS

The pelvis can be said to be divided into two parts by an imaginary plane passing through the sacral promontory and the pubic symphysis:
■ Above the sacral promontory, the false pelvis flares out and supports the lower abdominal contents
■ Below this plane lies the true pelvis lies; in females, it forms the constricted birth canal through which the baby passes.

*The bony structure of the pelvis is formed by the hip bones, sacrum and coccyx. The adult female pelvis, shown here, is adapted for childbirth.*

### Adult female pelvis from the front

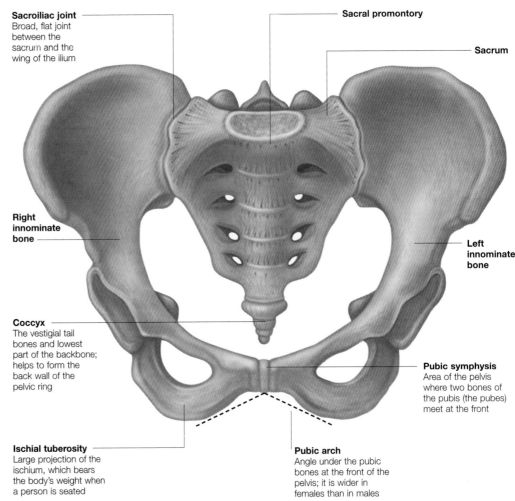

**Sacroiliac joint**
Broad, flat joint between the sacrum and the wing of the ilium

**Sacral promontory**

**Sacrum**

**Right innominate bone**

**Left innominate bone**

**Coccyx**
The vestigial tail bones and lowest part of the backbone; helps to form the back wall of the pelvic ring

**Pubic symphysis**
Area of the pelvis where two bones of the pubis (the pubes) meet at the front

**Ischial tuberosity**
Large projection of the ischium, which bears the body's weight when a person is seated

**Pubic arch**
Angle under the pubic bones at the front of the pelvis; it is wider in females than in males

---

## Differences between male and female pelvis

### Adult male pelvis from the front

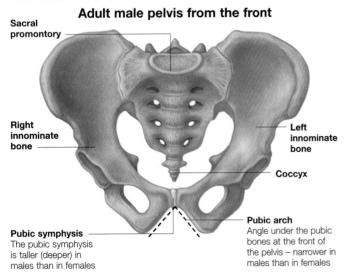

**Sacral promontory**

**Right innominate bone**

**Left innominate bone**

**Coccyx**

**Pubic symphysis**
The pubic symphysis is taller (deeper) in males than in females

**Pubic arch**
Angle under the pubic bones at the front of the pelvis – narrower in males than in females

The skeletons of men and women differ in a number of places, but nowhere is this more marked than in the pelvis.

### PHYSICAL VARIATIONS

The differences between the male and female pelvis can be attributed to two factors: the requirements of childbirth and the fact that, in general, men are heavier and more muscular than women. Some of the more obvious differences are:
■ General structure – the male

*The male pelvis differs from the female pelvis in being heavier, with thicker bones. The pubic arch is narrower and the pubic symphysis deeper in males.*

pelvis is heavier, with thicker bones
■ Pelvic inlet – the 'way into' the true pelvis is a wide oval in females but narrower and heart-shaped in males
■ Pelvic canal – the 'way through' the true pelvis is roughly cylindrical in females, whereas in males it tapers
■ Pubic arch – the angle under the pubic bones at the front of the pelvis is wider in females (100 degrees or more) than in males (90 degrees or less).

These differences, together with other, more subtle, measurements, may be used by forensic pathologists and anthropologists to determine the sex of a skeleton.

# The hip bone

The two hip bones are fused together at the front and join with the sacrum at the back. They each consist of three bones – the ilium, ischium and pubis.

The two innominate (hip) bones constitute the greater part of the pelvis, joining with each other at the front and with the sacrum at the back.

## STRUCTURE

The hip bone is large and strong, due to its function of transmitting the forces between the legs and the spine. As with most bones, it has areas which are raised or roughened by the attachments of muscle or ligaments.

The hip bone is formed by the fusion of three separate bones: the ilium, the ischium and the pubis. In children, these three bones are joined only by cartilage. At puberty, they fuse to form the single innominate, or hip, bone on each side.

## FEATURES

The upper margin of the hip bone is formed by the widened iliac crest. Further down the hip bone is the ischial tuberosity, a projection of the ischium.

The obturator foramen lies below and slightly in front of the acetabulum, the latter receiving the head of the femur (thigh bone).

*This lateral view of the hip bone clearly shows its constituent parts of ilium, ischium and pubis. These three bones fuse together at puberty.*

### Right hip bone, lateral view

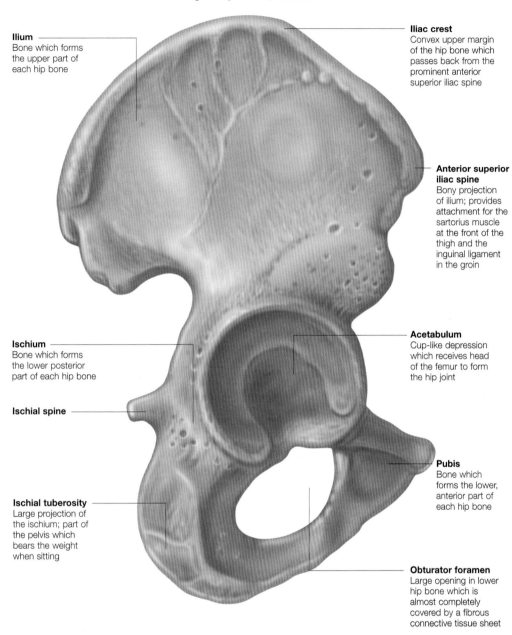

**Ilium**
Bone which forms the upper part of each hip bone

**Iliac crest**
Convex upper margin of the hip bone which passes back from the prominent anterior superior iliac spine

**Anterior superior iliac spine**
Bony projection of ilium; provides attachment for the sartorius muscle at the front of the thigh and the inguinal ligament in the groin

**Ischium**
Bone which forms the lower posterior part of each hip bone

**Ischial spine**

**Acetabulum**
Cup-like depression which receives head of the femur to form the hip joint

**Ischial tuberosity**
Large projection of the ischium; part of the pelvis which bears the weight when sitting

**Pubis**
Bone which forms the lower, anterior part of each hip bone

**Obturator foramen**
Large opening in lower hip bone which is almost completely covered by a fibrous connective tissue sheet

## The female pelvic canal

### Lateral view of right pelvis

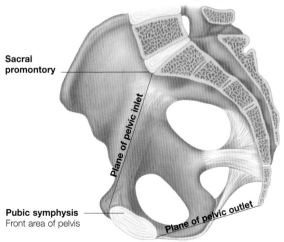

**Sacral promontory**

**Plane of pelvic inlet**

**Plane of pelvic outlet**

**Pubic symphysis**
Front area of pelvis

In childbirth, the baby passes down into the pelvic canal, through the pelvic inlet and out through the pelvic outlet. The dimensions of the pelvic canal in women are therefore vital.

### TRIANGULAR SHAPE

The pelvic canal is almost triangular in section, the short front wall being formed by the pubic symphysis. The much longer back wall is formed by the sacrum and coccyx.

*The pelvic canal is defined by the pubic symphysis at the front, and the sacrum and coccyx at the back. The coccyx moves back out of the way in childbirth.*

From front to back, the pelvic inlet usually has a diameter of about 11 cm, known as the obstetric conjugate. The inlet is slightly wider from side to side owing to its oval shape.

### CHANGES IN CHILDBIRTH

The pelvic outlet is normally slightly larger than the inlet, especially at the end of pregnancy when the ligaments holding the pelvic bones together can stretch under the influence of hormones.

The joint between the coccyx and the sacrum also becomes looser, allowing the coccyx to move back out of the way during childbirth.

# Pelvic floor muscles

The muscles of the pelvic floor play a vital role in supporting the abdominal and pelvic organs. They also help to regulate the processes of defecation and urination.

The pelvic floor muscles play an important role in supporting the abdominal and pelvic organs. In pregnancy, these muscles help to carry the growing weight of the uterus, and in childbirth they support the baby's head as the cervix dilates.

## MUSCLES

The muscles of the pelvic floor are attached to the inside of the ring of bone that makes up the pelvic skeleton, and slope downwards to form a rough funnel shape.

The levator ani is the largest muscle of the pelvic floor. It is a wide, thin sheet made up of three parts:
■ Pubococcygeus – the main part of the levator ani muscle
■ Puborectalis – joins with its counterpart on the other side to form a U-shaped sling around the rectum
■ Iliococcygeus – the posterior fibres of the levator ani.

A second muscle, the coccygeus (or ischiococcygeus), lies behind the levator ani.

## PELVIC WALLS

The pelvic cavity is described as having an anterior, a posterior and two lateral walls.

The anterior wall is formed by the pubic bones and their connection, the pubic symphysis. The posterior wall is formed by the sacrum and coccyx and the neighbouring parts of the iliac bones. The two lateral walls are formed by the obturator internus muscles overlying the hip bones.

Female pelvic diaphragm from above

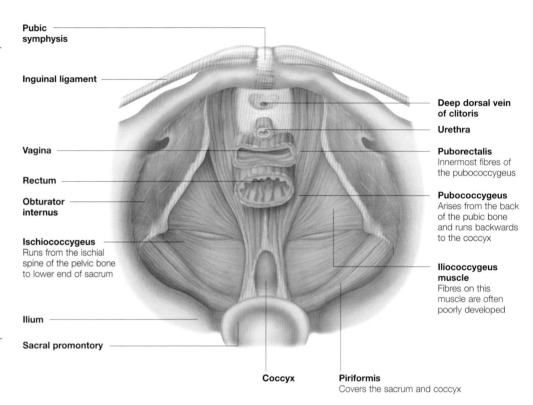

Pubic symphysis

Inguinal ligament

Vagina

Rectum

Obturator internus

Ischiococcygeus
Runs from the ischial spine of the pelvic bone to lower end of sacrum

Ilium

Sacral promontory

Deep dorsal vein of clitoris

Urethra

**Puborectalis**
Innermost fibres of the pubococcygeus

**Pubococcygeus**
Arises from the back of the pubic bone and runs backwards to the coccyx

**Iliococcygeus muscle**
Fibres on this muscle are often poorly developed

Coccyx

Piriformis
Covers the sacrum and coccyx

*The pelvic floor muscles are known as the pelvic diaphragm. The levator ani is the most important muscle and is named for its action in lifting the anus.*

## Perineal body

### Female pelvis

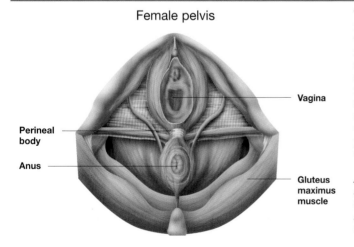

Perineal body

Anus

Vagina

Gluteus maximus muscle

The perineal body is a small mass of fibrous tissue that lies within the pelvic floor, just in front of the anal canal. This structure provides a site for the attachment of many of the pelvic floor and perineal muscles, so allowing paired muscles to pull against each other, normally one of the functions of bone. It also provides support for the internal organs of the pelvis.

*Although the perineal body is small and tucked away, it is a very important structure. It supports the organs of the pelvis which lie above it.*

### EPISIOTOMY

The perineal body may become damaged during childbirth, either by stretching or tearing as the baby's head passes through the pelvic floor. Loss of the perineal body's support of the posterior vaginal wall may eventually lead to vaginal prolapse.

To prevent damage to the perineal body during childbirth, an obstetrician may perform an episiotomy. This deliberate incision into the muscle behind the vaginal opening enlarges this opening and avoids damage to the perineal body.

# Openings of the pelvic floor

The pelvic floor resembles the diaphragm in the chest in that it forms a nearly continuous sheet, but does have openings to allow important structures to pass through it. There are two important openings situated in the pelvic floor region.

From below, the pelvic floor can be seen to assume a funnel shape. The muscles of the pelvic floor are so arranged that there are two main openings:
■ Anorectal hiatus – this opening, or hiatus, allows the rectum and anal canal to pass through the sheet of pelvic floor muscles to reach the anus beneath. The U-shaped fibres of the puborectalis muscle form the posterior edge of this hiatus
■ Urogenital hiatus – lying in front of the anorectal hiatus there is an opening in the pelvic floor for the urethra, which carries urine from the bladder out of the body. In females, the vagina also passes through the pelvic diaphragm within this opening, just behind the urethra.

### FUNCTIONS OF THE PELVIC FLOOR MUSCLES

The functions of the pelvic floor include:
■ Supporting the internal organs of the abdomen and pelvis
■ Helping to resist rises in pressure within the abdomen, such as during coughing and sneezing, which would otherwise cause the bladder/bowel to empty
■ Assisting in the control of defecation and urination
■ Helping to fix and brace the trunk during forceful movements of the upper limbs, such as weight-lifting.

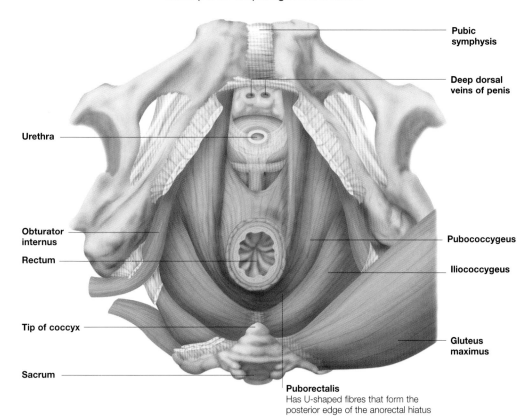

Male pelvic diaphragm from below

Pubic symphysis

Deep dorsal veins of penis

Urethra

Obturator internus

Rectum

Pubococcygeus

Iliococcygeus

Tip of coccyx

Gluteus maximus

Sacrum

**Puborectalis**
Has U-shaped fibres that form the posterior edge of the anorectal hiatus

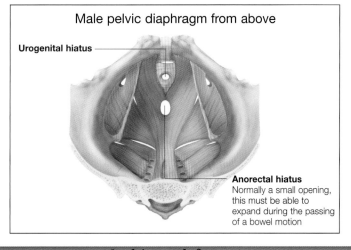

Male pelvic diaphragm from above

**Urogenital hiatus**

**Anorectal hiatus**
Normally a small opening, this must be able to expand during the passing of a bowel motion

*The pelvic floor muscles play a vital supporting role. Without them, the internal organs of the abdomen and pelvis would sink through the bony pelvic ring.*

## Ischioanal fossae

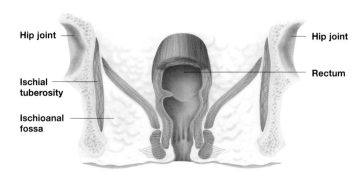

Coronal section through pelvis

Hip joint

Hip joint

Ischial tuberosity

Rectum

Ischioanal fossa

The ischioanal, or ischiorectal, fossae are spaces formed between the outside of the pelvic diaphragm and the skin around the anus.

The ischioanal fossae are filled with fat. This fat is divided into sections and supported by bands of connective tissue. The fat in the ischioanal fossae acts as a

*The ischioanal fossae are wedge-shaped, being narrowest at the top and widest at the bottom. The fossae are filled with sections of fat.*

soft packing material which accommodates changes in the size and position of the anus during a bowel movement.

### INFECTION

Ischioanal fossae can become infected (ischioanal/ischiorectal abscess). Any area of the body with a poor blood supply is susceptible to infection and this is certainly the case with the fat within the ischioanal fossae. Infection may spread to the other side and infected areas may need to be surgically drained.

# Muscles of the gluteal region

The gluteus maximus is the largest and heaviest of all the gluteal muscles and is situated in the buttock region. This strong, thick muscle plays an important part in enabling humans to stand.

The gluteal, or buttock, region lies behind the pelvis. The shape is formed by a number of large muscles which help to stabilize and move the hip joint. A layer of fat covers these muscles.

## GLUTEUS MAXIMUS

This is one of the largest muscles in the body. It covers the other gluteal muscles with the exception of about one-third of the smaller gluteus medius. The gluteus maximus arises from the ilium (a part of the bony pelvis), the back of the sacrum and the coccyx. Its fibres run down and outwards at a 45 degree angle towards the femur. Most of the fibres then insert into a band (the iliotibial tract).

## ACTIONS

The main function of the gluteus maximus is to extend (straighten) the leg as in standing from a sitting position. When the leg is extended, as in standing, the gluteus maximus covers the bony ischial tuberosity. This bears the weight of the body when sitting. However, we never sit on the gluteus maximus muscle itself as it moves up and away from the ischial tuberosity when the leg is flexed (bent forward).

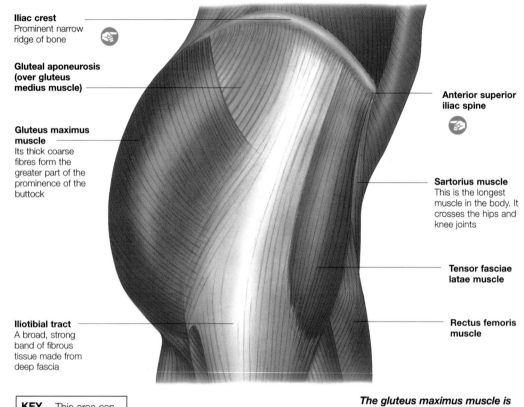

**Iliac crest**
Prominent narrow ridge of bone

**Gluteal aponeurosis (over gluteus medius muscle)**

**Gluteus maximus muscle**
Its thick coarse fibres form the greater part of the prominence of the buttock

**Iliotibial tract**
A broad, strong band of fibrous tissue made from deep fascia

**Anterior superior iliac spine**

**Sartorius muscle**
This is the longest muscle in the body. It crosses the hips and knee joints

**Tensor fasciae latae muscle**

**Rectus femoris muscle**

**KEY** This area can easily be felt under the skin

*The gluteus maximus muscle is not very active during normal walking but comes into play during forceful actions such as running or walking upstairs.*

## Surface anatomy of the gluteal region

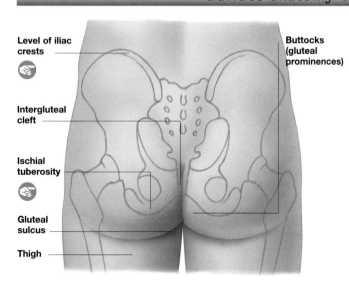

**Level of iliac crests**

**Intergluteal cleft**

**Ischial tuberosity**

**Gluteal sulcus**

**Thigh**

**Buttocks (gluteal prominences)**

The gluteal region overlies the back of the bony pelvis between the level of the iliac crests and the lower edge of the gluteus maximus muscle. Its shape is formed mainly by the mass of that muscle and by some fat.

### FEATURES

There are a number of obvious features of the gluteal region:
■ The intergluteal or natal cleft which separates the buttocks
■ The gluteal fold is formed by the lower edge of the gluteus

*Muscle and fat form the familiar shape of the gluteal region. The gluteal sulcus is the dividing line between the lower end of the buttock and the top of the thigh.*

maximus muscle, which is usually covered by a layer of fat
■ The gluteal sulcus is the crease which lies beneath the gluteal fold. It is the line that separates the buttock and thigh.

### BONY LANDMARKS

Except in very overweight people, some of the underlying bony protuberances of the gluteal region can be felt through the skin:
■ The iliac crests are usually palpable along their lengths
■ The ischial tuberosity can be felt in the lower part of the buttock, covered by the gluteus maximus when standing
■ The tip of the coccyx can be felt in the upper natal cleft.

# Deeper muscles of the gluteal region

The muscles that lie deep to the gluteus maximus region play an important part in walking. They keep the pelvis level as each foot is lifted off the ground.

Beneath the gluteus maximus lie a number of other muscles which act to stabilise the hip joint and move the lower limb.

### GLUTEUS MEDIUS AND MINIMUS

The gluteus medius and gluteus minimus muscles lie deep to the gluteus maximus. They are both fan-shaped muscles with fibres that run in the same direction.

Gluteus medius lies directly beneath gluteus maximus, with only about one-third of it not covered by this larger muscle. Its fibres originate from the external surface of the ilium (part of the pelvis) and insert into the greater trochanter, a protuberance of the femur.

Gluteus minimus lies directly beneath gluteus medius and is of a similar fan-like shape. Its fibres also originate from the ilium and insert into the greater trochanter.

### ESSENTIAL ROLE

The gluteus medius and gluteus minimus together have an essential role in the action of walking. These muscles act to hold the pelvis level when one foot is lifted from the ground, rather than letting it sag to that side. This allows the non-weight-bearing foot to clear the ground before being swung further forward.

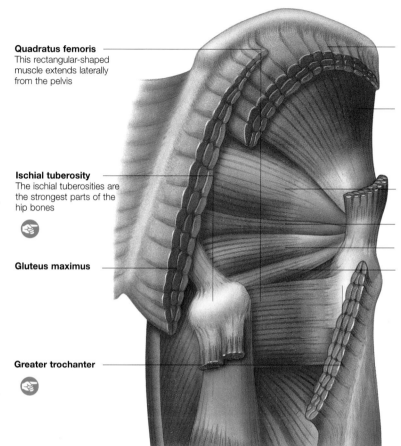

**Quadratus femoris**
This rectangular-shaped muscle extends laterally from the pelvis

**Ischial tuberosity**
The ischial tuberosities are the strongest parts of the hip bones

**Gluteus maximus**

**Greater trochanter**

**Gluteus medius muscle**
This is a thick muscle largely covered by the gluteus maximus

**Gluteus minimus muscle**
The smallest and deepest of the gluteal muscles

**Piriformis muscle**

**Superior gemellus muscle**

**Obturator internus**

**Inferior gemellus muscle**

**KEY** This area can easily be felt under the skin

A number of other muscles lie within this region, acting mainly to help certain movements of the lower limb at the hip. These include:
■ Piriformis – this muscle, which is named for its pear shape, lies below gluteus minimus. It acts to rotate the thigh laterally, a movement which results in the foot turning outwards
■ Obturator internus, superior and inferior gemelli – these three muscles together form a composite three-headed muscle which lies below the piriformis muscle. These muscles rotate the thigh laterally and stabilize the hip joint

*The deep muscles of this group rotate the thigh laterally and stabilize the hip joint. The main muscles are the gluteus medius and gluteus minimus.*

■ Quadratus femoris – this short, thick muscle rotates the thigh laterally and helps to stabilize the hip joint.

## Bursae of the gluteal region

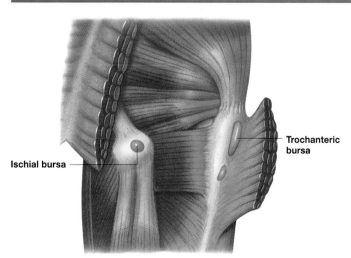

**Ischial bursa**

**Trochanteric bursa**

A bursa is a small fluid-filled sac rather like an underfilled water bottle. In many places in the body a bursa will be found where two structures, usually bone and tendon, regularly move against each other.

### PROTECTION

The bursa lies between these structures, protecting them from wear and tear.

There are three main groups of bursae in the gluteal region:

*The gluteal region contains three main groups of bursae. The bursae help to ease the movement of the bones and tendons upon each other.*

■ The trochanteric bursae
These large bursae lie between the thick, upper fibres of the gluteus maximus muscle and the greater trochanter of the upper femur (thigh bone)

■ The ischial bursa
This bursa, if present, lies between the lower fibres of the gluteus maximus muscle and the ischial tuberosity, the part of the pelvis which bears our weight during sitting

■ The gluteofemoral bursa
This bursa lies on the outer side of the leg, between the gluteus maximus and vastus lateralis muscles.

201

# Hip joint

The hip joint is the strong ball-and-socket joint that connects the lower limb to the pelvis. Of all the body's joints, the hip is second only to the shoulder in the variety of movements it allows.

In the hip joint, the head of the femur (thigh bone) is the 'ball' that fits tightly into the 'socket' formed by the cup-like acetabulum of the hip bone of the pelvis.

The articular surfaces – the parts of the bone which come into contact with each other – are covered by a protective layer of hyaline cartilage, which is very smooth and slippery. The hip joint is a synovial joint, which means that movement is further lubricated by a thin layer of synovial fluid, which lies between these articular surfaces within the synovial cavity. The fluid is secreted by the synovial membrane.

## ACETABULAR LABRUM

The depth of the socket formed by the acetabulum is increased by the presence of the acetabular labrum. This structure brings greater stability to the joint, allowing the almost spherical femoral head to rest deep within the joint.

The cartilage-covered articular surface of the acetabulum is not a continuous cup, or even a ring, but is horseshoe-shaped. There is a gap, the acetabular notch, at the lowest point, which is bridged by the complete ring of the acetabular labrum. The open centre of the 'horseshoe' is filled with a cushioning pad of fat.

*The hip joint is the ball-and-socket joint between the head of the femur and the hip bone. The joint is capable of a wide range of movement.*

### Cross-section of the right hip joint

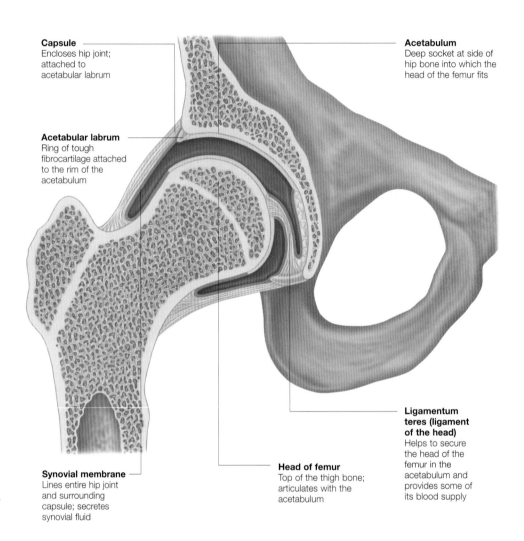

**Capsule**
Encloses hip joint; attached to acetabular labrum

**Acetabular labrum**
Ring of tough fibrocartilage attached to the rim of the acetabulum

**Synovial membrane**
Lines entire hip joint and surrounding capsule; secretes synovial fluid

**Acetabulum**
Deep socket at side of hip bone into which the head of the femur fits

**Ligamentum teres (ligament of the head)**
Helps to secure the head of the femur in the acetabulum and provides some of its blood supply

**Head of femur**
Top of the thigh bone; articulates with the acetabulum

## Blood supply of the hip joint

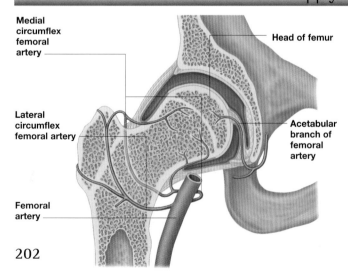

**Medial circumflex femoral artery**

**Lateral circumflex femoral artery**

**Femoral artery**

**Head of femur**

**Acetabular branch of femoral artery**

The hip joint receives its blood supply from two main sources:
■ The medial and lateral circumflex femoral arteries, – approach the femoral head from the femoral neck
■ The artery to the head of the femur – approaches the femoral head from the acetabulum, passing through the ligamentum teres (ligament of the head).

*Blood is supplied to the hip joint from two main sources. These are the medial/lateral circumflex femoral arteries and the artery to the femoral head.*

### AVASCULAR NECROSIS
The origin of the blood supply of the hip is important clinically. In children especially a significant amount of the blood supplying the femoral head comes via the artery passing through the ligamentum teres.

If this artery is damaged then the femoral head may undergo avascular necrosis, (tissue death due to lack of an adequate blood supply). This damage may occur particularly in children aged three to nine years and may result in pain in the hip and knee.

# Ligaments of the hip joint

The hip joint is enclosed and protected by a thick, fibrous capsule. The capsule is flexible enough to allow the joint a wide range of movements but is strengthened by a number of tough ligaments.

The ligaments of the hip joint are thickened parts of the joint capsule, which extends from the rim of the acetabulum down to the neck of the femur. These ligaments, which generally follow a spiral path from the hip bone to the femur, are named according to the parts of the bone to which they attach:
■ Iliofemoral ligament
■ Pubofemoral ligament
■ Ischiofemoral ligament.

## MOVEMENT AND STABILITY
The ball-and-socket nature of the hip joint allows it great mobility, second only to the shoulder joint in its range of movement. Unlike the shoulder, however, it needs to be very stable as it is a major weight-bearing joint. It is capable of the following movements:

■ Flexion (bending forward, the knee coming up)
■ Extension (bending the leg back behind the body)
■ Abduction (moving the leg out to the side)
■ Adduction (bringing the leg back to the midline)
■ Rotation, which is greatest when the leg is flexed.

*A fibrous capsule encloses the hip joint. This capsule is reinforced by a number of ligaments which spiral down from the hip bone to the femur.*

**Anterior view of right hip**

**Posterior view of right hip**

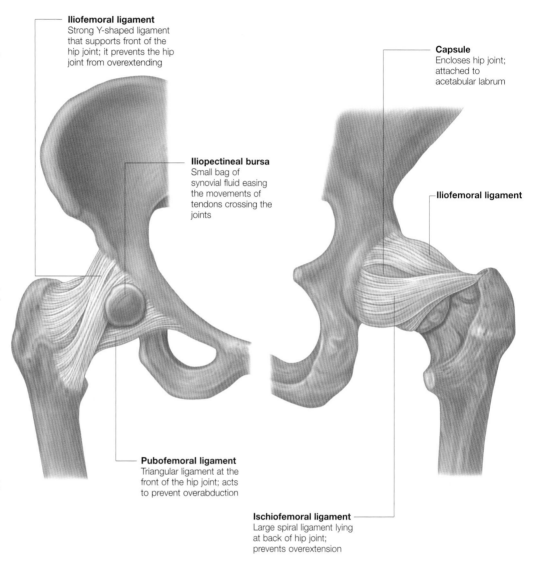

**Iliofemoral ligament**
Strong Y-shaped ligament that supports front of the hip joint; it prevents the hip joint from overextending

**Iliopectineal bursa**
Small bag of synovial fluid easing the movements of tendons crossing the joints

**Pubofemoral ligament**
Triangular ligament at the front of the hip joint; acts to prevent overabduction

**Capsule**
Encloses hip joint; attached to acetabular labrum

**Iliofemoral ligament**

**Ischiofemoral ligament**
Large spiral ligament lying at back of hip joint; prevents overextension

---

## Artificial hip joints

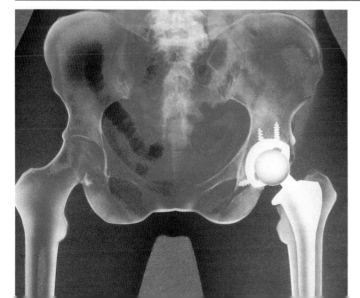

The hip was the first joint for which a successful prosthesis (artificial replacement) was developed, the first total hip replacement being carried out by Sir John Charnley in 1963.

Although the hip joint is generally very stable, it is susceptible to damage due to trauma, or to arthritis, which can be very disabling. Great improvements in mobility and a

*This composite X-ray shows a left hip prosthesis. It consists of a plastic socket inserted into the pelvis, and a metal prosthesis cemented into the femur.*

decrease in pain can be achieved by hip replacement surgery.

During surgery, the damaged femoral head and neck are replaced by a metal prosthesis, which is anchored into the femur with special bone cement. The acetabulum of the hip bone is replaced by a plastic socket which is cemented to the pelvis.

Currently, artificial hips have an expected lifespan of about 10 years and so are not really suitable for young, active people. It is hoped that, with research, the techniques and materials used will improve and more people will benefit from them.

# Femur

The femur, or thigh bone, is the longest and heaviest bone in the body. Measuring approximately 45 cm in length in adult males, the femur makes up about one quarter of a person's total height.

The femur has a long, thick shaft with two expanded ends. The upper end articulates with the pelvis to form the hip joint while the lower end articulates with the tibia and patella to form the knee joint.

## UPPER END

The femur upper end includes:
■ Head – this is the near-spherical projection which forms the 'ball' of the ball and socket hip joint
■ Neck – this is the narrowed area which connects the head to the body of the femur
■ Greater and lesser trochanters – projections of bone allowing the attachment of muscles.

## SHAFT

The long central shaft of the femur is slightly bowed, being concave on its posterior surface. For much of its length the femur appears cylindrical, with a circular cross-section.

## LOWER END

The lower end of the femur is made up of two enlarged bony processes, the medial and lateral femoral condyles. These carry the smooth, curved surfaces which articulate with the tibia and patella to form the knee joint. The shape of the femoral condyles is outlined when the leg is viewed with the knee bent.

*The femur is the thigh bone, running from the hip joint to the knee. It is the longest bone in the body and is very strong.*

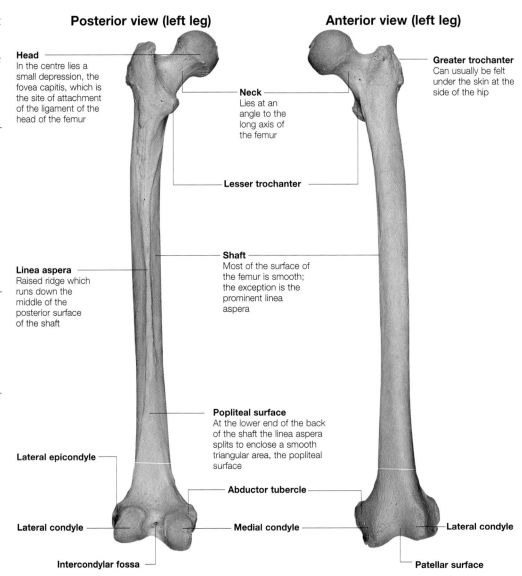

**Posterior view (left leg)**

**Head**
In the centre lies a small depression, the fovea capitis, which is the site of attachment of the ligament of the head of the femur

**Neck**
Lies at an angle to the long axis of the femur

**Lesser trochanter**

**Linea aspera**
Raised ridge which runs down the middle of the posterior surface of the shaft

**Shaft**
Most of the surface of the femur is smooth; the exception is the prominent linea aspera

**Popliteal surface**
At the lower end of the back of the shaft the linea aspera splits to enclose a smooth triangular area, the popliteal surface

**Lateral epicondyle**

**Abductor tubercle**

**Lateral condyle**

**Medial condyle**

**Intercondylar fossa**

**Anterior view (left leg)**

**Greater trochanter**
Can usually be felt under the skin at the side of the hip

**Lateral condyle**

**Patellar surface**

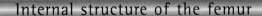

## Internal structure of the femur

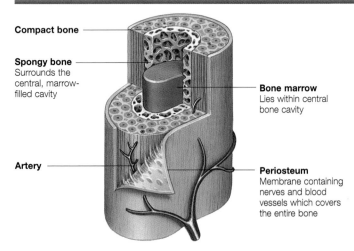

**Compact bone**

**Spongy bone**
Surrounds the central, marrow-filled cavity

**Artery**

**Bone marrow**
Lies within central bone cavity

**Periosteum**
Membrane containing nerves and blood vessels which covers the entire bone

The femur is one of the bones of the body classed as a long bone. Bones of this type have a relatively long shaft, or diaphysis, and two expanded ends, or epiphyses.

### PERIOSTEUM

All the bone is covered with a protective membrane, the periosteum, nourished by tiny nutrient arteries in the bone.

*The shaft of long bones is composed of layers of spongy and compact bone around a central cavity. The periosteum surrounds the outer layer.*

### DIAPHYSIS

The diaphysis of the femur is a tube composed of compact bone, which is strong and dense. This layer of compact bone encloses a core of yellow bone marrow which, in adults, is made up of fat cells.

### EPIPHYSES

The expanded ends of the femur are made up of a surface layer of compact bone which surrounds a central area of spongy bone. This central area is much looser in structure and there is no marrow in the epiphyses.

# Muscle attachments of the femur

The femur is a very strong bone which provides sites of attachment for many of the muscles of locomotion in the hip joint and legs.

### MUSCLE ORIGINS

Some muscles, such as the powerful gluteus muscles, have their origins on the pelvic bones and so cross the hip joint to insert into the femur. When these muscles contract they cause the hip joint to move, allowing the leg to bend, straighten or move sideways.

Other muscles originate on the femur itself and pass down across the knee joint to insert on the tibia or the fibula, the two bones of the lower leg. These muscles allow the knee to bend or straighten.

Together these muscles bring about movements of the legs such as in climbing, or rising from a sitting position.

### BONY PROCESSES

Where muscle is attached to bone it causes a projection, or bony process, to arise. If the muscle is powerful, or if a number of muscles attach at the same site, the bony process can be pronounced. This is the case in the femur. The surface of the bone at the site of muscle attachment can also become quite roughened, unlike the smooth bone surface in between.

*The surface of the femur is roughened by projections to which muscles are attached. These muscles bring about movements in the legs and hips.*

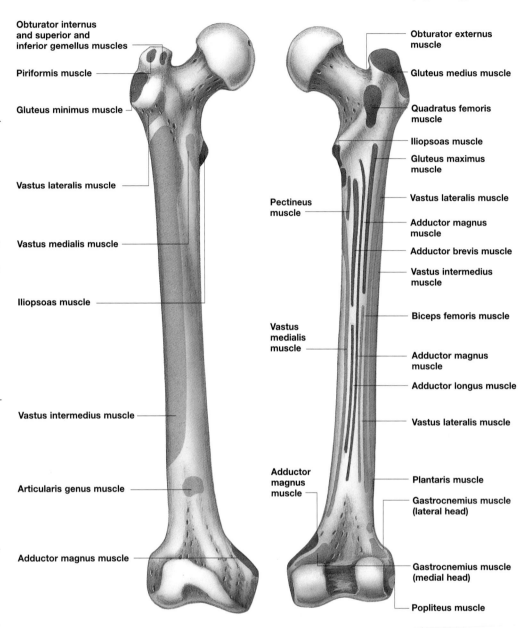

**Anterior view (right leg)**

- Obturator internus and superior and inferior gemellus muscles
- Piriformis muscle
- Gluteus minimus muscle
- Vastus lateralis muscle
- Vastus medialis muscle
- Iliopsoas muscle
- Vastus intermedius muscle
- Articularis genus muscle
- Adductor magnus muscle

**Posterior view (right leg)**

- Obturator externus muscle
- Gluteus medius muscle
- Quadratus femoris muscle
- Iliopsoas muscle
- Gluteus maximus muscle
- Vastus lateralis muscle
- Adductor magnus muscle
- Adductor brevis muscle
- Vastus intermedius muscle
- Biceps femoris muscle
- Adductor magnus muscle
- Adductor longus muscle
- Vastus lateralis muscle
- Plantaris muscle
- Gastrocnemius muscle (lateral head)
- Gastrocnemius muscle (medial head)
- Popliteus muscle
- Pectineus muscle
- Vastus medialis muscle
- Adductor magnus muscle

## Fractures of the femur

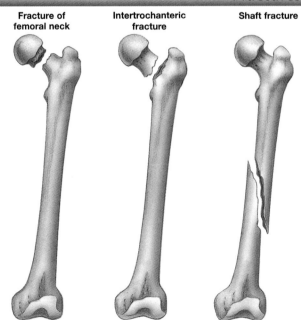

**Fracture of femoral neck**

**Intertrochanteric fracture**

**Shaft fracture**

Fracture of the neck of the femur, the narrowed segment which attaches the head to the body, is a fairly common event.

### 'BROKEN HIP'

Often referred to as a 'broken hip', a femoral neck fracture usually occurs in older people, especially over the age of 60 years and often as the result of a minor fall. It is more common in women due to the effects of osteoporosis, or thinning of the

*Intertrochanteric and femoral neck fractures are common in elderly people who fall. However, a shaft fracture is usually caused by a violent direct injury.*

bones, which can occur after the menopause.

### INTERTROCHANTERIC FRACTURES

Intertrochanteric fractures, where the fracture line runs between the greater and lesser trochanters, are also fairly common in elderly women.

### SHAFT FRACTURES

Fracture of the shaft of the femur is a much less common injury due to the great strength of the bone. Fractures here are usually the result of major trauma such as a road traffic accident, and may take many months to heal.

# Tibia and fibula

The tibia and fibula together form the skeleton of the lower leg. The tibia is much larger and stronger than the fibula as it must bear the weight of the body.

Second only to the femur (thigh bone) in size, the tibia (shin bone) has the shape of a typical long bone, with an elongated shaft and two expanded ends. The tibia lies alongside the fibula, on the medial (inner) side, and articulates with the fibula at its upper and lower ends.

### TIBIAL CONDYLES
The upper end of the tibia is expanded to form the medial and lateral tibial condyles, which articulate with the femoral condyles at the knee joint. The lower end of the tibia is less pronounced than the upper end. It articulates with both the talus (ankle bone) and the lower end of the fibula.

### FIBULA
The fibula is a long, narrow bone which has none of the strength of the tibia. It lies next to the tibia, on its lateral (outer) side, and articulates with that bone. The fibula plays no part in the knee joint, but is an important support for the ankle.

The shaft of the fibula is narrow and bears the grooves and ridges associated with its major role as a site of attachment for leg muscles.

*The tibia (shin bone) articulates with the thigh bone above, the ankle below and the fibula to the side. The thinner fibula helps to form the ankle joint.*

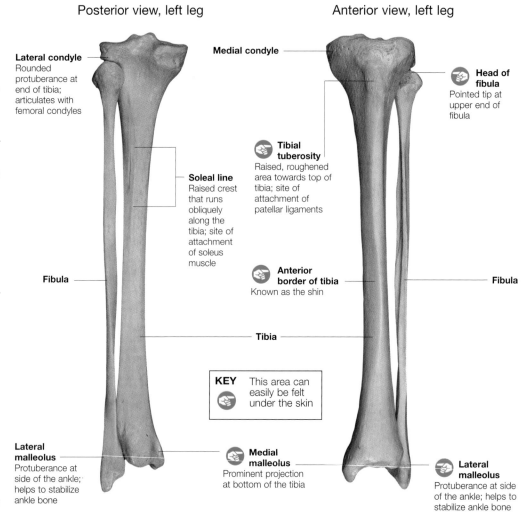

Posterior view, left leg

**Lateral condyle**
Rounded protuberance at end of tibia; articulates with femoral condyles

**Fibula**

**Lateral malleolus**
Protuberance at side of the ankle; helps to stabilize ankle bone

**Soleal line**
Raised crest that runs obliquely along the tibia; site of attachment of soleus muscle

**Medial malleolus**
Prominent projection at bottom of the tibia

Anterior view, left leg

**Medial condyle**

**Head of fibula**
Pointed tip at upper end of fibula

**Tibial tuberosity**
Raised, roughened area towards top of tibia; site of attachment of patellar ligaments

**Anterior border of tibia**
Known as the shin

**Tibia**

**Fibula**

**Lateral malleolus**
Protuberance at side of the ankle; helps to stabilize ankle bone

**KEY** This area can easily be felt under the skin

## Cross-section of tibia and fibula

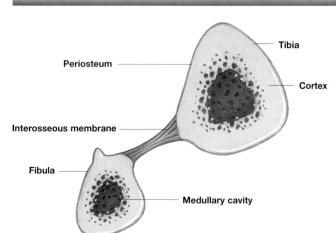

**Tibia**

**Periosteum**

**Cortex**

**Interosseous membrane**

**Fibula**

**Medullary cavity**

The shafts of the tibia and fibula are roughly triangular in cross section. The tibial shaft is much greater in diameter than that of the fibula as it is the main weight-bearing element of the lower leg. The fibula acts as a strut, increasing the stability of the lower leg under load.

### LONG BONES
The tibia and fibula have a typical long bone structure, with a thick, tubular outer cortex surrounding a spongy medullary

*In cross-section, the tibial and fibular shafts are triangular in shape. The two bones are anchored together by the interosseous membrane.*

cavity. Their hollow structure provides maximal mechanical strength with minimal support material, namely dense, cortical bone.

The shape of the bones is genetically determined, but is modified by the pull of developing muscles during childhood and into adulthood. In this way the bony ridges, such as the soleal line and tuberosities, form.

The tibia and fibula are enveloped in the periosteum (a tough connective tissue layer). The periosteum from the lateral border of the tibia and the medial border of the fibula blends into the interosseous membrane.

# Ligaments of the tibia and fibula

The ligaments which surround the tibia and fibula bind the two bones to each other and to the other leg bones with which they articulate.

Ligaments are the strong fibrous bands which bind bones together. There are a number of ligaments which surround the tibia and the fibula; they bind the two bones to each other and to other bones of the leg.

### PROXIMAL (UPPER) END
Just under the knee is the upper joint between the head of the fibula and the underside of the lateral tibial condyle. The joint is surrounded and protected by a fibrous joint capsule, which is strengthened by the anterior and posterior tibiofibular ligaments.

The anterior ligament of the head of the fibula runs from the front of the fibular head across to the front of the lateral tibial condyle. The posterior ligament of the head of the fibula runs in a similar fashion behind the fibular head.

Other ligaments bind the bones of the lower leg to the femur. The strongest of these are the medial and lateral collateral ligaments of the knee joint, which run vertically down from the femur to the corresponding bone (tibia or fibula) beneath.

### DISTAL (LOWER) END
The joint between the lower ends of the tibia and fibula allows no movement of one bone upon the other. Rather, the fibula is bound tightly to the tibia by fibrous ligaments in order to maintain the stability of

Anterior view of left leg with ligament attachments

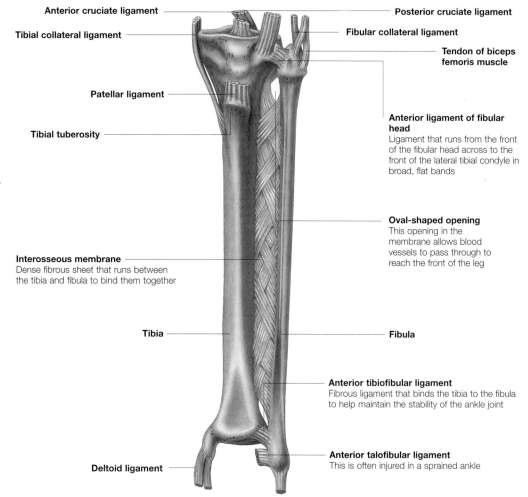

Anterior cruciate ligament
Tibial collateral ligament
Patellar ligament
Tibial tuberosity
Interosseous membrane
Dense fibrous sheet that runs between the tibia and fibula to bind them together
Tibia
Deltoid ligament

Posterior cruciate ligament
Fibular collateral ligament
Tendon of biceps femoris muscle
Anterior ligament of fibular head
Ligament that runs from the front of the fibular head across to the front of the lateral tibial condyle in broad, flat bands
Oval-shaped opening
This opening in the membrane allows blood vessels to pass through to reach the front of the leg
Fibula
Anterior tibiofibular ligament
Fibrous ligament that binds the tibia to the fibula to help maintain the stability of the ankle joint
Anterior talofibular ligament
This is often injured in a sprained ankle

the ankle joint. The main ligaments concerned are the anterior and posterior inferior (lower) tibiofibular ligaments. Other ligaments around the ankle bind the tibia and fibula to the bones of the foot.

### INTEROSSEOUS MEMBRANE
The fibres of the dense interosseous membrane run obliquely from the sharp interosseous border of the tibia across to the front of the fibula, binding the two bones together.

*The tibia and fibula of the lower leg are surrounded by a number of ligaments. Ligaments are tough fibrous bands of connective tissue that bind bones together where they articulate at a joint.*

---

## Fractures of the tibia and fibula

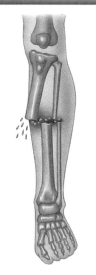

The tibia lies close to the skin surface throughout its length and is therefore the bone that is most susceptible to compound fractures. These are fractures in which the skin is torn and blood vessels are damaged as well as bone being broken.

### SPORTS INJURIES
The weakest part of the tibia is at the junction of its middle and inferior thirds. Fractures may occur in this area during contact

*The tibia and fibula can be fractured in a number of different places. Fractures usually occur as a result of sports or road traffic injuries.*

sports or skiing, or as a result of road accidents.

The cortex (outer surface) of the tibia may also be the site of stress (or march) fractures which can occur after long walks, especially if a person is unfit.

### FIBULAR FRACTURES
Fractures of the fibula may be associated with tibial fractures if the trauma is severe.

The most usual site for a fracture of the fibula is about 2 to 6 cm above the lateral malleolus at the lower end. Fractures of the fibula are frequently associated with fracture-dislocations of the ankle joint.

# Knee joint and patella

The knee is the joint between the end of the thigh bone and the top of the tibia. In front of the knee is the patella (kneecap), the convex surface of which can readily be felt under the skin.

The knee is the joint between the lower end of the femur (thigh bone) and the upper end of the tibia (the largest bone of the lower leg). The fibula (the smaller of the two lower leg bones) plays no part in the joint.

## STRUCTURE

The knee is a synovial joint – one in which movement is lubricated by synovial fluid which is secreted by a membrane lining the joint cavity.

Although the knee tends to be thought of as a single joint it is, in fact, the most complex joint in the body, being made up of three joints which share a common joint cavity. These three joints are:

■ The joint between the patella (kneecap) and the lower end of the femur. Classified as a plane joint, this allows one bone to slide upon the other

■ A joint on either side between the femoral condyles (the large bulbous ends of the femur) and the corresponding part of the upper tibia. These are said to be hinge joints as the movement they allow is akin to the movement of a door on its hinges.

## STABILITY OF THE KNEE

Considering that there is not a very good 'fit' between the femoral condyles and the upper end of the tibia, the knee is actually a reasonably stable joint. It relies heavily on the surrounding muscles and ligaments for its stability.

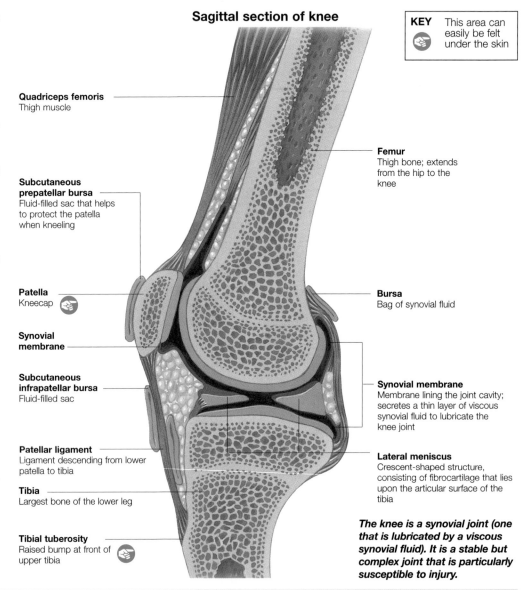

**Sagittal section of knee**

**KEY** This area can easily be felt under the skin

**Quadriceps femoris**
Thigh muscle

**Subcutaneous prepatellar bursa**
Fluid-filled sac that helps to protect the patella when kneeling

**Patella**
Kneecap

**Synovial membrane**

**Subcutaneous infrapatellar bursa**
Fluid-filled sac

**Patellar ligament**
Ligament descending from lower patella to tibia

**Tibia**
Largest bone of the lower leg

**Tibial tuberosity**
Raised bump at front of upper tibia

**Femur**
Thigh bone; extends from the hip to the knee

**Bursa**
Bag of synovial fluid

**Synovial membrane**
Membrane lining the joint cavity; secretes a thin layer of viscous synovial fluid to lubricate the knee joint

**Lateral meniscus**
Crescent-shaped structure, consisting of fibrocartilage that lies upon the articular surface of the tibia

*The knee is a synovial joint (one that is lubricated by a viscous synovial fluid). It is a stable but complex joint that is particularly susceptible to injury.*

## Surface anatomy of the knee

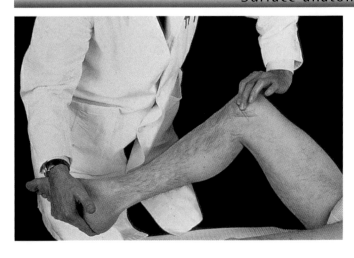

Many of the structures of the knee can be discerned by gently feeling the overlying skin, especially when the knee is flexed (bent).

### PATELLAR LIGAMENT

The outline of the patella can be seen and its surface readily felt. Underneath the patella is the patellar ligament, the strong fibrous band which descends

*A physical examination of the knee can reveal many of its components. The bony areas are particularly easy to feel as they lie just beneath the skin.*

from the patella to the front of the tibia.

On either side of the patella, and just behind it, are the medial and lateral femoral condyles (the rounded ends of the femur). Below the patella the tibial tuberosity (a raised area at the front of the upper tibia) can easily be felt.

### ARTERY

At the back of the knee lies a depression known as the popliteal fossa. Gentle pressure over this area, when the knee is flexed, reveals the pulsations of the large popliteal artery.

# Inside the knee – the menisci

The menisci are crescent-shaped plates of tough fibrocartilage lying on the articular surface of the tibia. They act as 'shock absorbers' within the knee and prevent sideways movement of the femur.

Looking down on the upper surface of the tibia within the opened knee, the two c-shaped menisci can clearly be seen.

Named after the Greek word for 'crescent', the menisci are plates of tough fibrocartilage which lie upon the articular surface of the tibia, deepening the depression into which the femoral condyles fit.

### SHOCK ABSORBERS
The menisci also have the function of acting as 'shock absorbers' within the knee and help to prevent the side-to-side rocking of the joint.

### STRUCTURE OF THE MENISCI
The two menisci are wedge-shaped in cross-section, their external margins being widest. Centrally, they taper to a thin, unattached edge. Anteriorly, the two menisci are attached to each other by the transverse ligament of the knee, while the outer edges of the menisci are firmly attached to the joint capsule.

### ATTACHMENT
Attachment of the medial meniscus to the tibial collateral ligament is of great clinical significance as the meniscus can be damaged when this ligament is injured during contact sports.

### Superior view of knee (tibial plateau)

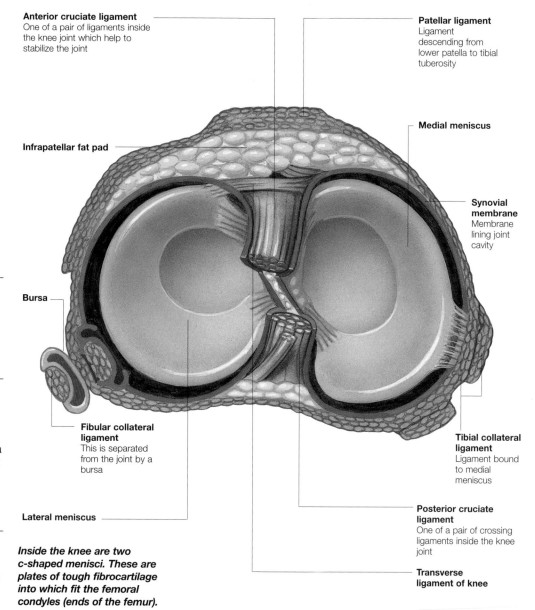

**Anterior cruciate ligament**
One of a pair of ligaments inside the knee joint which help to stabilize the joint

**Infrapatellar fat pad**

**Bursa**

**Fibular collateral ligament**
This is separated from the joint by a bursa

**Lateral meniscus**

**Patellar ligament**
Ligament descending from lower patella to tibial tuberosity

**Medial meniscus**

**Synovial membrane**
Membrane lining joint cavity

**Tibial collateral ligament**
Ligament bound to medial meniscus

**Posterior cruciate ligament**
One of a pair of crossing ligaments inside the knee joint

**Transverse ligament of knee**

*Inside the knee are two c-shaped menisci. These are plates of tough fibrocartilage into which fit the femoral condyles (ends of the femur).*

---

## The patella

### Anterior view

### Posterior view

Lying within the tendon of the powerful quadriceps femoris thigh muscle, the patella is the largest sesamoid bone in the body. A sesamoid bone is one which develops within the tendon of a muscle to protect that tendon from wear and tear where it passes over the end of a long bone.

### STRUCTURE
The patella is flattened with a convex surface at the front

*The patella (kneecap) is situated over the front of the knee. It has a flattened shape, and its convex outer surface can easily be felt beneath the skin.*

which can readily be felt under the skin. Between the patella and the skin lies a bursa (fluid-filled sac), which helps to reduce friction and protect the bone when kneeling.

### CARTILAGE
The posterior, or back, surface of the patella is covered with smooth cartilage and articulates with the lower end of the femur in a synovial joint.

Fibres from the strong quadriceps thigh muscle insert into the upper border of the patella, while the patellar ligament passes from the lower border of the patella down to the tibial tuberosity.

# Ligaments and bursae of the knee

The knee joint is only partially enclosed in a capsule and relies on ligaments for its stability. Bursae are situated around the knee and allow smooth movement to take place.

Unlike the bones of the hip joint, the bones of the knee do not fit together in a particularly stable fashion. For this reason the stability of the knee joint depends to a great extent upon the ligaments and muscles that surround it.

The joint cavity of the knee is enclosed within a fibrous capsule. The ligaments that support the knee can be divided into two groups, depending on their relationship to this capsule.

### EXTRACAPSULAR LIGAMENTS

The extracapsular ligaments lie outside the capsule and act to prevent the lower leg bending forward at the knee, or hyperextending. They include:

■ Quadriceps tendon – extends from tendon of the quadriceps femoris muscle. This supports the front of the knee (not shown)

■ Fibular (or lateral) collateral ligament – a strong cord which binds the lower end of the outer femur to the head of the fibula

■ Tibial (or medial) collateral ligament – a strong flat band, which runs from the lower end of the inner femur down to the tibia. It is weaker than the fibular collateral ligament and is more easily damaged

■ Oblique popliteal ligament – this strengthens the capsule at the back (not shown)

■ Arcuate popliteal ligament – also adds strength to the back of the knee (not shown).

**Anterior view of flexed left knee**

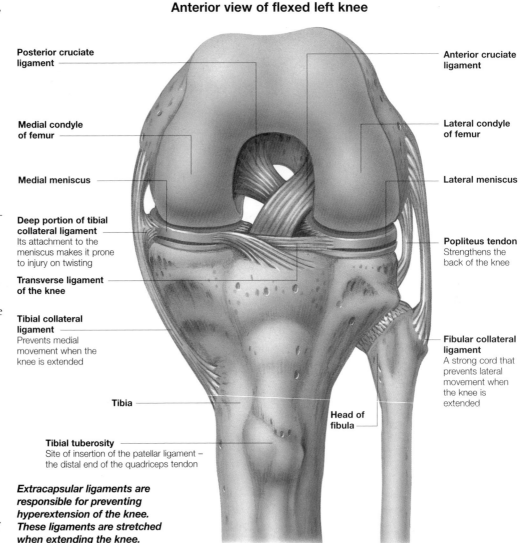

Posterior cruciate ligament

Medial condyle of femur

Medial meniscus

Deep portion of tibial collateral ligament
Its attachment to the meniscus makes it prone to injury on twisting

Transverse ligament of the knee

Tibial collateral ligament
Prevents medial movement when the knee is extended

Tibia

Tibial tuberosity
Site of insertion of the patellar ligament – the distal end of the quadriceps tendon

Anterior cruciate ligament

Lateral condyle of femur

Lateral meniscus

Popliteus tendon
Strengthens the back of the knee

Fibular collateral ligament
A strong cord that prevents lateral movement when the knee is extended

Head of fibula

*Extracapsular ligaments are responsible for preventing hyperextension of the knee. These ligaments are stretched when extending the knee.*

## Intracapsular ligaments

### Lateral view of intracapsular ligaments

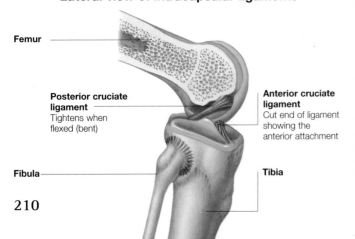

Femur

Posterior cruciate ligament
Tightens when flexed (bent)

Fibula

Anterior cruciate ligament
Cut end of ligament showing the anterior attachment

Tibia

*The intracapsular, or cruciate, ligaments form a cross. They act to prevent anterior–posterior displacement and to stabilize articulating bones.*

Intracapsular ligaments connect the tibia to the femur within the centre of the knee joint and prevent forward and backward displacement of the knee.

### CRUCIATES

The two main intracapsular ligaments are known as the cruciate ligaments, as they form the shape of a cross.

■ The anterior cruciate ligament – this is the weaker of the two cruciates, and is slack when the knee is flexed, taut when the knee is extended (straightened)

■ The posterior cruciate ligament – this ligament tightens during flexion (bending) and is very important for the stability of the knee when bearing weight in a flexed position (for example, when walking downhill).

210

# Bursae of the knee

The bursae of the knee are small sacs filled with synovial fluid. They act to protect the structures inside the knee, reducing friction, as they slide over each other when the joint is moving.

Bursae are small fluid-filled sacs found between two structures, usually bone and tendon, that regularly move against each other. The bursae protect the structures from wear and tear.

There are a number of bursae around the knee that protect the tendons during movement or allow easy movement of the skin across the patella.

### SUPRAPATELLAR BURSA
Some of the bursae around the knee joint are continuous with the joint cavity, the fluid-filled space between the articular surfaces. The suprapatellar bursa lies above the joint cavity between the lower end of the femur and the powerful quadriceps femoris muscle.

### PREPATELLAR AND INFRAPATELLAR BURSAE
These bursae surround the patella and the patellar ligament. The prepatellar bursa allows the skin to move freely over the patella during movement. The superficial and deep infrapatellar bursae lie around the lower end of the patellar ligament where it attaches to the tibial tuberosity.

*There are about a dozen bursae located around the knee joint. They allow the structures of the knee to move freely over one another, reducing friction.*

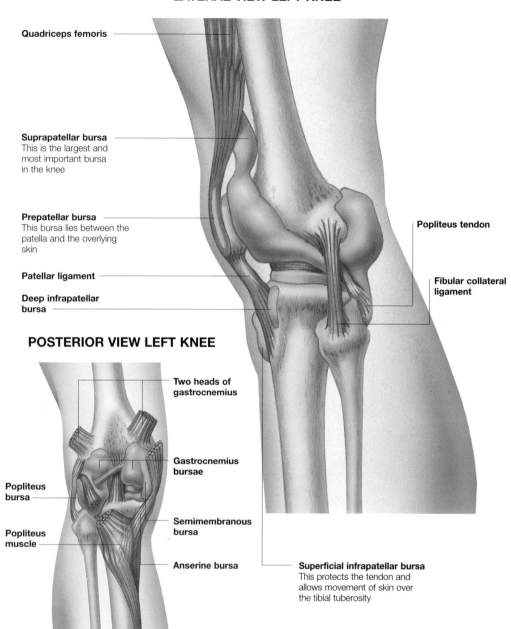

**LATERAL VIEW LEFT KNEE**

- Quadriceps femoris
- **Suprapatellar bursa** This is the largest and most important bursa in the knee
- **Prepatellar bursa** This bursa lies between the patella and the overlying skin
- Patellar ligament
- **Deep infrapatellar bursa**
- Popliteus tendon
- Fibular collateral ligament

**POSTERIOR VIEW LEFT KNEE**

- Two heads of gastrocnemius
- Gastrocnemius bursae
- Popliteus bursa
- Semimembranous bursa
- Popliteus muscle
- Anserine bursa
- **Superficial infrapatellar bursa** This protects the tendon and allows movement of skin over the tibial tuberosity

## Investigating the knee joint

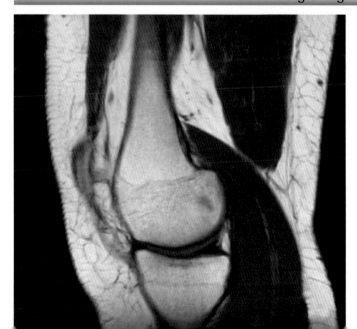

The knee joint is very susceptible to damage from trauma or osteoarthritis. To determine the extent of such damage involves clinical examination and often some further investigation.

### X-RAYS
X-rays of the knee in different positions, perhaps with the injection of a dye into the joint space (arthrography), may be useful to show up abnormalities of the bones and menisci.

*MRI is an effective technique for visualizing the complex anatomy of joints. In this scan, the bones of the knee joint and the tissues around them are clearly visible.*

### MRI INVESTIGATIONS
Magnetic resonance imaging (MRI) has greatly helped in the investigation of knee disorders. This type of non-invasive scanning can show up problems within the soft tissues around the knee as well as within the bone and so has largely taken over from arthrography.

### ARTHROSCOPY
Another way of looking inside the knee is to use a tiny camera in an endoscope (arthroscopy). During this procedure, which is carried out under a general anaesthetic, the surgeon can often remove damaged tissue, thus avoiding further surgery.

# Muscles of the thigh

The thigh is composed mainly of groups of large muscles which act to move the hip and the knee joint. Muscles that effect the movements of the thigh are among the strongest in the body.

The muscles of the thigh are divided into three basic groups; the anterior muscles lie in front of the femur, the posterior muscles lie behind, and the medial muscles (adductors) run between the inner femur (thigh) and the pelvis.

### ANTERIOR MUSCLES

The muscles of the anterior compartment of the thigh flex or bend the hip, and extend or straighten the knee. These are the actions associated with lifting the leg up and bringing it forward during walking.

The muscles of this group include:

■ Iliopsoas. This large muscle arises partly from the inside of the pelvis and partly from the lumbar (lower) vertebrae. Its fibres insert into the projection of the upper femur known as the lesser trochanter. The iliopsoas is the most powerful of the muscles that flex the thigh, bringing the knee up and forwards

■ Tensor fasciae latae. This muscle inserts into the strong band of connective tissue that runs down the outside of the leg to the tibia below the knee

■ Sartorius. The longest muscle in the body, the sartorius runs as a flat strap across the thigh from the anterior superior iliac spine of the pelvis. It crosses both the hip and the knee joint before it inserts into the inner side of the top of the tibia.

■ Quadriceps femoris. A large four-headed muscle.

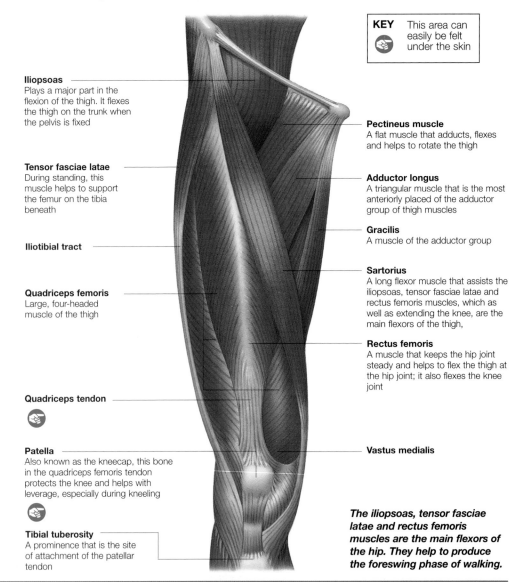

**KEY** This area can easily be felt under the skin

**Iliopsoas**
Plays a major part in the flexion of the thigh. It flexes the thigh on the trunk when the pelvis is fixed

**Tensor fasciae latae**
During standing, this muscle helps to support the femur on the tibia beneath

**Iliotibial tract**

**Quadriceps femoris**
Large, four-headed muscle of the thigh

**Quadriceps tendon**

**Patella**
Also known as the kneecap, this bone in the quadriceps femoris tendon protects the knee and helps with leverage, especially during kneeling

**Tibial tuberosity**
A prominence that is the site of attachment of the patellar tendon

**Pectineus muscle**
A flat muscle that adducts, flexes and helps to rotate the thigh

**Adductor longus**
A triangular muscle that is the most anteriorly placed of the adductor group of thigh muscles

**Gracilis**
A muscle of the adductor group

**Sartorius**
A long flexor muscle that assists the iliopsoas, tensor fasciae latae and rectus femoris muscles, which as well as extending the knee, are the main flexors of the thigh,

**Rectus femoris**
A muscle that keeps the hip joint steady and helps to flex the thigh at the hip joint; it also flexes the knee joint

**Vastus medialis**

*The iliopsoas, tensor fasciae latae and rectus femoris muscles are the main flexors of the hip. They help to produce the foreswing phase of walking.*

## Quadriceps femoris

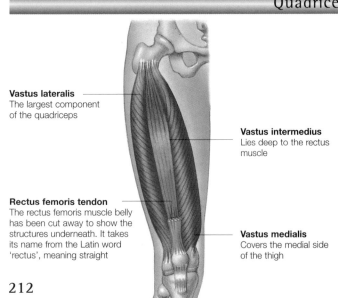

**Vastus lateralis**
The largest component of the quadriceps

**Vastus intermedius**
Lies deep to the rectus muscle

**Rectus femoris tendon**
The rectus femoris muscle belly has been cut away to show the structures underneath. It takes its name from the Latin word 'rectus', meaning straight

**Vastus medialis**
Covers the medial side of the thigh

This large, four-headed muscle makes up the bulk of the thigh and is one of the most powerful muscles in the body. It consists of four major parts whose tendons combine to form the strong quadriceps tendon. This inserts into the top of the patella and then continues down, as the patella tendon, to the front of the top of the tibia. The quadriceps femoris acts to straighten the knee.

*The quadriceps femoris is an extensor that is used in running, jumping and climbing. It helps to straighten the knee when standing from a sitting position.*

The four parts of the quadriceps femoris are:

■ Rectus femoris – a straight muscle, overlying the other parts. It helps to flex the hip joint and straighten the knee

■ Vastus lateralis – the largest part of the quadriceps muscle

■ Vastus medialis – lies on the inner side of the thigh

■ Vastus intermedius – lies centrally, underneath the rectus femoris muscle.

A few small slips of the vastus intermedius pass down to the joint capsule of the knee. They ensure that folds of the capsule do not become trapped when the knee is straightened.

# Posterior thigh muscles

The three large muscles of the posterior thigh are commonly known as the hamstrings. These three muscles are the biceps femoris, semitendinosus and semimembranosus.

The hamstring muscles can both extend the hip and flex the knee. However, they cannot do both fully at the same time.

### BICEPS FEMORIS
The biceps femoris has two heads. The long head arises from the ischial tuberosity of the pelvis and the short head arises from the back of the femur. The rounded tendon of the biceps femoris can easily be felt and seen behind the outer side of the knee, especially if the knee is flexed against resistance.

### SEMITENDINOSUS
Like the biceps femoris muscle, the semitendinosus arises from the ischial tuberosity of the pelvis. It is named for its long tendon, which begins about two-thirds of the way down its course. This tendon attaches to the inner side of the upper tibia.

### SEMIMEMBRANOSUS
This muscle arises from a flattened, membranous attachment to the ischial tuberosity of the pelvis. The muscle runs down the back of the thigh, deep to the semitendinosus. It inserts into the inner side of the upper tibia.

**KEY** This area can easily be felt under the skin

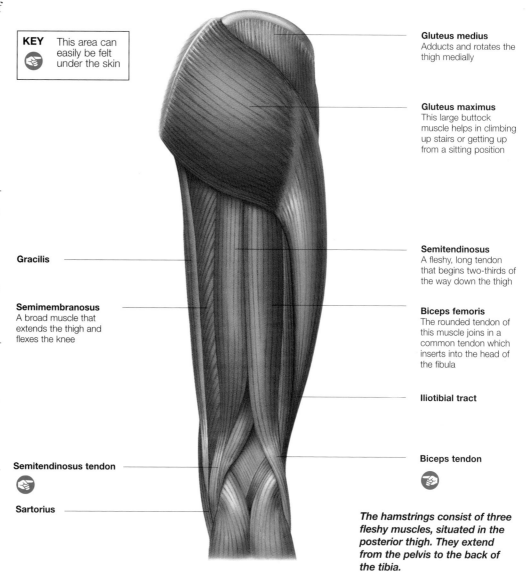

**Gluteus medius**
Adducts and rotates the thigh medially

**Gluteus maximus**
This large buttock muscle helps in climbing up stairs or getting up from a sitting position

**Gracilis**

**Semimembranosus**
A broad muscle that extends the thigh and flexes the knee

**Semitendinosus**
A fleshy, long tendon that begins two-thirds of the way down the thigh

**Biceps femoris**
The rounded tendon of this muscle joins in a common tendon which inserts into the head of the fibula

**Iliotibial tract**

**Semitendinosus tendon**

**Sartorius**

**Biceps tendon**

*The hamstrings consist of three fleshy muscles, situated in the posterior thigh. They extend from the pelvis to the back of the tibia.*

## The adductors

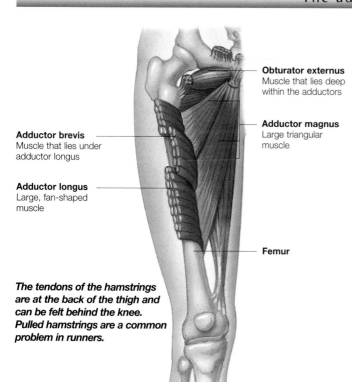

**Adductor brevis**
Muscle that lies under adductor longus

**Adductor longus**
Large, fan-shaped muscle

**Obturator externus**
Muscle that lies deep within the adductors

**Adductor magnus**
Large triangular muscle

**Femur**

*The tendons of the hamstrings are at the back of the thigh and can be felt behind the knee. Pulled hamstrings are a common problem in runners.*

The muscles of the inner thigh are known as adductors because they allow adduction of the thigh, which means moving the lower limb in towards the midline as when gripping the sides of a horse when riding. These muscles arise from the lower part of the pelvis and insert into the femur at various levels. The muscles of this group include:
■ **Adductor longus** – a large, fan-shaped muscle which lies in front of the other adductors and has a palpable tendon in the groin
■ **Adductor brevis** – a shorter muscle which lies under the adductor longus
■ **Adductor magnus** – a large triangular muscle which fulfils the function of both an adductor and a hamstring muscle
■ **Gracilis** – a strap-like muscle that runs vertically down the inner thigh (not shown)

■ **Obturator externus** – a small muscle which lies deeply within this group of adductors.

It is this adductor group of muscles which are active when gripping the horse during horse-riding and may become strained during sporting activities, leading to a groin injury.

*Footballers are at risk of groin injuries (pulled adductor muscles). This is due to the kicking action that moves the leg across the midline.*

213

# Muscles of the lower leg

There are three groups of muscles in the lower leg.
Depending where they lie, they support and flex the ankle and foot,
extend the toes and assist in lifting the body weight at the heel.

The muscles of the lower leg can be divided into three groups: the anterior group which lie in front of the tibia, the lateral group which lie on the outer side of the lower leg and the posterior group.

### ANTERIOR MUSCLES

The anterior muscles of the lower leg include:

■ Tibialis anterior – this muscle can be felt under the skin alongside the edge of the tibia
■ Extensor digitorum longus – this muscle lies under the tibialis anterior and attaches to the outer four toes
■ Peroneus (fibularis) tertius – this muscle is not always present but, when it is, it may join the extensor digitorum longus muscle. It inserts into the fifth metatarsal bone near the little toe
■ Extensor hallucis longus – this thin muscle runs down to insert into the end of the hallux (big toe).

### ACTION OF THE ANTERIOR MUSCLES

These muscles all have a similar action in that they are dorsiflexors of the foot. This means that when they contract they bend the ankle, bringing the toes up and the heel down.

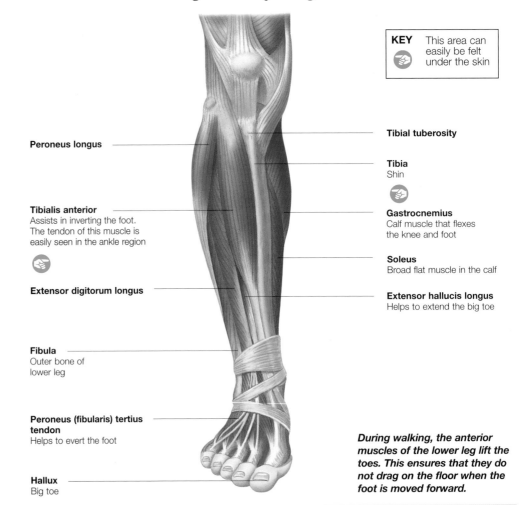

**KEY** This area can easily be felt under the skin

Peroneus longus

Tibialis anterior
Assists in inverting the foot. The tendon of this muscle is easily seen in the ankle region

Extensor digitorum longus

Fibula
Outer bone of lower leg

Peroneus (fibularis) tertius tendon
Helps to evert the foot

Hallux
Big toe

Tibial tuberosity

Tibia
Shin

Gastrocnemius
Calf muscle that flexes the knee and foot

Soleus
Broad flat muscle in the calf

Extensor hallucis longus
Helps to extend the big toe

*During walking, the anterior muscles of the lower leg lift the toes. This ensures that they do not drag on the floor when the foot is moved forward.*

## Lateral muscles of the lower leg

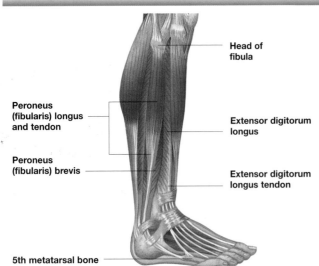

Head of fibula

Peroneus (fibularis) longus and tendon

Peroneus (fibularis) brevis

Extensor digitorum longus

Extensor digitorum longus tendon

5th metatarsal bone

The muscles of the lateral (outer) compartment lie alongside the smaller of the two lower leg bones, the fibula. There are two muscles in this group:
■ Peroneus (fibularis) longus
This muscle is the longer of the two and lies more superficially. It arises from the head and the upper portion of the narrow fibula and runs down to the sole of the foot
■ Peroneus (fibularis) brevis
As its name suggests, this is a

short muscle, which lies underneath the peroneus longus muscle. It arises from the lower portion of the fibula and has a broad tendon that runs down to insert into the base of the fifth metatarsal bone of the foot.

### ACTION OF THE LATERAL MUSCLES

These two muscles together cause the foot to plantar flex, when the toes point down, and to evert, which means bending so that the sole faces outwards. In practice, these muscles help to support the ankle by resisting the movement of inversion (the sole facing inwards), which is when the joint is weakest.

*The lateral muscles protect the ankle by resisting inversion of the foot. When the foot is inverted, the ankle is in a very weak position.*

# Posterior muscles of the lower leg

The posterior group of muscles of the lower leg form the mound of the calf. Together, these muscles are strong and heavy, enabling them to work together to flex the foot and to support the weight of the body.

The muscles that lie within the posterior compartment form the largest group of the lower leg. Also known as the 'calf muscles', this group can be further divided into superficial and deep layers.

### SUPERFICIAL CALF MUSCLES

The superficial group of posterior muscles forms the bulk of the rounded calf, a feature peculiar to humans and which is due to our upright posture. These muscles include:

■ **Gastrocnemius** – this large fleshy muscle is the most superficial. It has a distinctive shape with two heads which arise from the medial and lateral condyles of the femur. Its fibres run mainly vertically, which allows for the rapid and strong contractions needed in running and jumping

■ **Soleus** – this is a large and powerful muscle which lies under the gastrocnemius. It takes its name from its shape, being flat like a sole (a type of flatfish). Contraction of the soleus muscle is important for maintaining balance when standing

■ **Plantaris** – this muscle is sometimes absent, and when it is present it is rather small and thin. Due to its relative unimportance in the lower leg, it

**Plantaris muscle**
This muscle is not always present

**Gastrocnemius**
A two-headed muscle, used in running and jumping

**Soleus**

**Flexor hallucis longus**

**Flexor retinaculum**

**Soleus**
Can be felt deep to the gastrocnemius when a person is standing on tiptoe

**Calcaneal (Achilles) tendon**
The largest tendon in the body; it is located at the back of the ankle and attached to the heel bone (calcaneus)

**Calcaneal tuberosity**

is sometimes used by surgeons to replace damaged tendons in the hand.

### ACTIONS OF THE SUPERFICIAL MUSCLES

These muscles have the job of plantar flexing the foot, which means lifting the heel and

pointing the toes downwards. Strong muscles are needed for this job because, during walking, running and jumping, the heel needs to be lifted against the whole body weight.

Gastrocnemius and soleus have a single, common tendon that is known as the large and

*Together, the gastrocnemius, soleus and plantaris muscles help to flex the foot at the ankle joint. The tiny plantaris is the weakest of the three muscles.*

powerful Achilles tendon, which runs down from the lower edge of the calf to the heel.

## Deep calf muscles

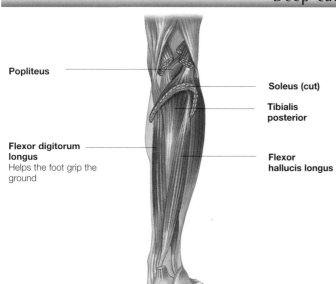

**Popliteus**

**Flexor digitorum longus**
Helps the foot grip the ground

**Soleus (cut)**

**Tibialis posterior**

**Flexor hallucis longus**

There are four muscles which together make up the deep group of calf muscles:

■ **Popliteus** – this is a thin, triangular muscle that lies at the back of the knee in the popliteal fossa. Popliteus has the particular role of 'unlocking' the knee joint by rotating it slightly to allow the straightened leg to be bent

■ **Flexor digitorum longus** – this muscle has long tendons

*The actions of the deep muscles vary. The popliteus helps to unlock the knee joint, whereas the other muscles act on the ankle and foot joints.*

which pass down to the outer four toes to allow them to curl under, or to flex

■ **Flexor hallucis longus** – although this muscle only runs to one toe, the big toe or hallux, it is a very powerful muscle. Its long tendon runs between the sesamoid bones located at the base of the big toe and it acts to give a 'push off' or 'spring' to the step during walking and running

■ **Tibialis posterior** – this is the deepest muscle in this group. It is the main provider of the action of inversion, in which the foot moves so that the sole faces inwards.

215

# Arteries of the leg

The lower limb is supplied by a series of arteries which arise from the external iliac artery of the pelvis. These arteries pass down the leg, branching to reach muscles, bones, joints and skin.

A network of arteries supply the tissues of the lower limb with nutrients. The main arteries give off important and smaller branches to provide nourishment to various joints and muscles.

### THE ARTERIES

■ **The femoral artery** – the main artery of the leg. Its main branch is the profunda femoris (deep femoral) artery. Small branches supply nearby muscles before the artery enters a gap in the adductor magnus muscle, the 'adductor hiatus', to enter the popliteal fossa (behind the knee)

■ **Profunda femoris (deep femoral artery)** – the main artery of the thigh. It gives off several branches including the medial and lateral circumflex femoral arteries and the four perforating arteries

■ **Popliteal artery** – a continuation of the femoral artery. It runs down the back of the knee, giving off small branches to nourish that joint, before dividing into the anterior and posterior tibial arteries

■ **Anterior tibial artery** – this supplies the structures within the anterior (front) compartment of the lower leg. It runs downwards to the foot and becomes the dorsalis pedis artery

■ **Posterior tibial artery** – this artery remains at the back of the lower leg and, together with the peroneal (fibular) artery, it supplies the structures of the back and outer compartments.

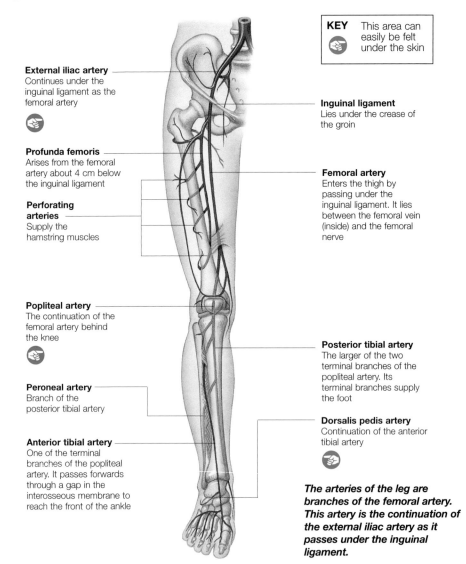

**KEY** This area can easily be felt under the skin

**External iliac artery**
Continues under the inguinal ligament as the femoral artery

**Profunda femoris**
Arises from the femoral artery about 4 cm below the inguinal ligament

**Perforating arteries**
Supply the hamstring muscles

**Popliteal artery**
The continuation of the femoral artery behind the knee

**Peroneal artery**
Branch of the posterior tibial artery

**Anterior tibial artery**
One of the terminal branches of the popliteal artery. It passes forwards through a gap in the interosseous membrane to reach the front of the ankle

**Inguinal ligament**
Lies under the crease of the groin

**Femoral artery**
Enters the thigh by passing under the inguinal ligament. It lies between the femoral vein (inside) and the femoral nerve

**Posterior tibial artery**
The larger of the two terminal branches of the popliteal artery. Its terminal branches supply the foot

**Dorsalis pedis artery**
Continuation of the anterior tibial artery

*The arteries of the leg are branches of the femoral artery. This artery is the continuation of the external iliac artery as it passes under the inguinal ligament.*

## Arteries around the knee

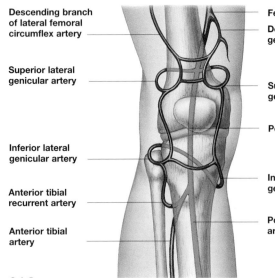

**Descending branch of lateral femoral circumflex artery**

**Superior lateral genicular artery**

**Inferior lateral genicular artery**

**Anterior tibial recurrent artery**

**Anterior tibial artery**

**Femoral artery**

**Descending genicular artery**

**Superior medial genicular artery**

**Popliteal artery**

**Inferior medial genicular artery**

**Posterior tibial artery**

Behind the knee, the popliteal artery gives off a number of small branches which surround the knee joint and form connections, or anastomoses, with other small branches of the femoral and the anterior and posterior tibial arteries. Together they form an arterial network through which blood can bypass the normal route via the main popliteal artery. This may be of importance when the knee is held bent for a considerable time

*The arterial supply around the knee forms a network of vessels that connect the femoral artery to the terminal branches of the popliteal artery.*

or if the main artery is narrowed or blocked.

### POPLITEAL PULSE

Just like the pulsations of the femoral artery, which can be felt in the groin, those of the popliteal artery can be felt behind the knee. However, since the popliteal artery lies so deeply within the tissues behind the knee, it may be difficult to feel. It is often necessary to examine the leg when flexed (bent) to loosen the fascia and muscle in the popliteal fossa so making the pulse easier to feel. If the pulse is weak or absent this means that the femoral artery is narrowed or blocked.

# Arteries of the foot

In a pattern similar to that in the hand, the small arteries of the foot form arches which interconnect, giving off branches to each side of the toes. Branches of the arteries give the sole of the foot a particularly rich blood supply.

The arterial supply of the foot is provided by the terminal branches of the anterior and posterior tibial arteries.

### TOP OF THE FOOT

As the anterior tibial artery passes down in front of the ankle it becomes the 'dorsalis pedis' artery. This then runs down across the top of the foot towards the space between the first and second toes, where it gives off a deep branch that joins the arteries on the sole of the foot. Branches of the dorsalis pedis on the top of the foot join to form an arch which gives off branches to the toes.

The dorsalis pedis pulse can be felt by an examining doctor on the top of the foot next to the tendon of tibialis anterior. As the artery lies just under the skin the pulse should be fairly easy to feel if the blood vessels are healthy.

### SOLE OF THE FOOT

The sole of the foot has a rich blood supply which is provided by branches of the posterior tibial artery. As the artery enters the sole, it divides into two parts to form the medial and lateral plantar arteries.

**Plantar aspect of foot (sole)**

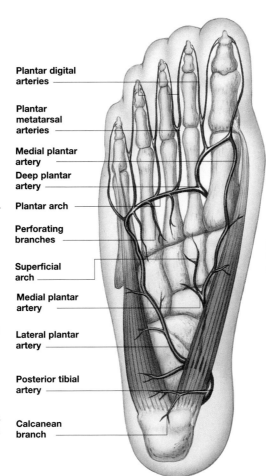

Plantar digital arteries

Plantar metatarsal arteries

Medial plantar artery

Deep plantar artery

Plantar arch

Perforating branches

Superficial arch

Medial plantar artery

Lateral plantar artery

Posterior tibial artery

Calcanean branch

**Dorsum of foot (top)**

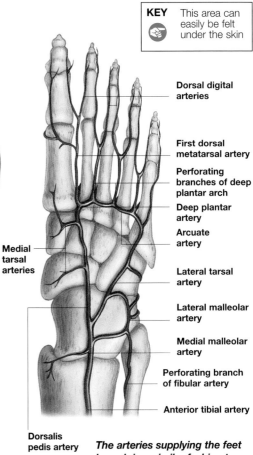

**KEY** This area can easily be felt under the skin

Dorsal digital arteries

First dorsal metatarsal artery

Perforating branches of deep plantar arch

Deep plantar artery

Arcuate artery

Lateral tarsal artery

Lateral malleolar artery

Medial malleolar artery

Perforating branch of fibular artery

Anterior tibial artery

Medial tarsal arteries

Dorsalis pedis artery

*The arteries supplying the feet branch in a similar fashion to those of the hands. The sole of the foot has a particularly rich blood supply.*

■ **The medial plantar artery** – this is the smaller of the two branches of the posterior tibial artery. It provides blood for the muscles of the big toe and sends tiny branches to the other toes.

■ **The lateral plantar artery** – this artery is much larger than the medial plantar artery and curves around under the metatarsal bones to form the deep plantar arch.

The deep branch of the dorsalis pedis artery joins the inner end of this arch so making a connection between the arterial supply of the top of the foot and the sole.

## Arteriograms

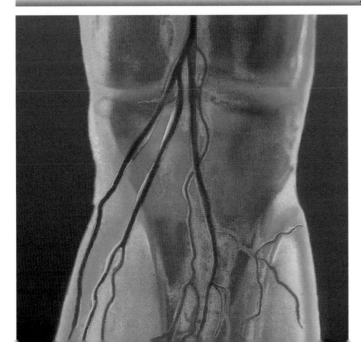

*Arteriography is used to identify the exact location of a blockage in the artery. Radio-opaque dye is injected into the bloodstream, making vessels visible on X-ray.*

It is possible to examine an artery by using arteriography. This involves the injection of a dye into an artery followed by a series of X-ray pictures which show how the dye travels onward through the arterial system. If dye is injected into the femoral artery high in the thigh a study can be made of the arterial system of the leg. This can show up areas of blockage or narrowing, or the bulging outline of a popliteal aneurysm.

Arteriography may be used if surgery is being contemplated but there are less invasive ways to investigate blood flow in the leg. These include Doppler ultrasound scanning and MRI, which provide information with less discomfort and risk.

### ATHEROSCLEROSIS

One of the more common conditions that affects the blood flow in the leg is atherosclerosis, or hardening of the arteries, which is often due to smoking. This may cause cramping pain in the calf muscles during exercise, which settles down after a few minutes rest. Such pain is due to decreased blood supply to the muscles caused by narrowed arteries.

217

# Veins of the leg

The lower limb is drained by a series of veins which can be divided into two groups, superficial and deep. The perforating veins connect the two groups of veins.

Lying within the subcutaneous (beneath the skin) tissue, there are two main superficial veins of the leg, the great and small saphenous veins.

### GREAT SAPHENOUS VEIN

The great saphenous vein is the longest vein in the body and is sometimes used during surgical procedures to replace damaged or diseased arteries in areas such as the heart. It arises from the medial (inner) end of the dorsal venous arch of the foot and runs up the leg towards the groin.

On its journey, the great saphenous vein passes in front of the medial malleolus (inner ankle bone), tucks behind the medial condyle of the femur at the knee and passes through the saphenous opening in the groin to drain into the large femoral vein.

### SMALL SAPHENOUS VEIN

This smaller superficial vein arises from the lateral (outer) end of the dorsal venous arch and passes behind the lateral malleolus (outer ankle bone) and up the centre of the back of the calf. As it approaches the knee, the small saphenous vein empties into the deep popliteal vein.

### TRIBUTARIES

The great and small saphenous veins receive blood along the way from many smaller veins and also intercommunicate freely, or 'anastomose', with each other.

**Superficial veins of leg, anterior view**

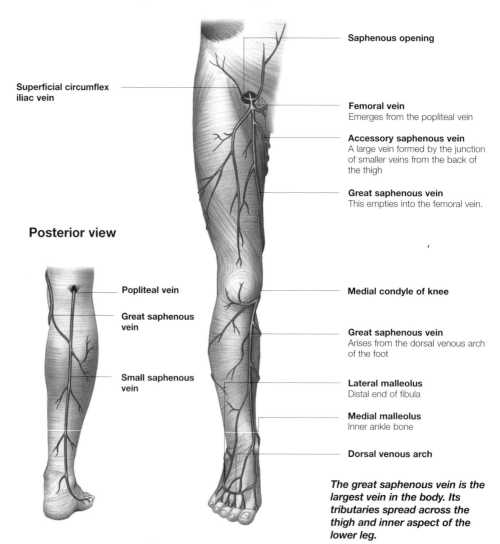

Saphenous opening

Superficial circumflex iliac vein

**Femoral vein**
Emerges from the popliteal vein

**Accessory saphenous vein**
A large vein formed by the junction of smaller veins from the back of the thigh

**Great saphenous vein**
This empties into the femoral vein.

**Posterior view**

Popliteal vein

Great saphenous vein

Small saphenous vein

**Medial condyle of knee**

**Great saphenous vein**
Arises from the dorsal venous arch of the foot

**Lateral malleolus**
Distal end of fibula

**Medial malleolus**
Inner ankle bone

**Dorsal venous arch**

*The great saphenous vein is the largest vein in the body. Its tributaries spread across the thigh and inner aspect of the lower leg.*

## Valves and venous pump

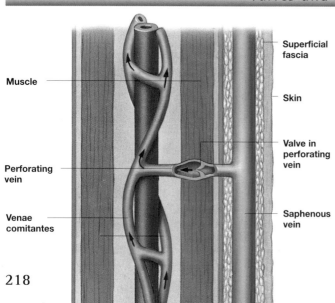

Muscle

Perforating vein

Venae comitantes

Superficial fascia

Skin

Valve in perforating vein

Saphenous vein

The arrangement of blood vessels in the leg means that blood flows from the superficial veins through the perforating veins to the deep veins. Venous blood is then pumped back up to the body mainly by the calf muscles which surround these deep veins (the venous pump).

Unlike arteries, veins contain tiny valves which prevent the backflow of blood within them. These valves are of great importance in the veins of the leg as they ensure that, when the calf muscles contract, the blood is pushed up the vein towards the heart rather than back out into the superficial veins.

### VARICOSE VEINS

If the valves in the perforating veins become damaged, then there can be backflow into the relatively low pressure superficial veins, which then become distended and tortuous. Causes of these varicose veins include hereditary factors, pregnancy, obesity and thrombosis (abnormal clotting) of the deep leg veins.

*The valved perforating veins play a key role in helping the venous pump to function. The valves enable the blood to make its way towards the heart.*

# Deep veins of the leg

The deep veins of the leg follow the pattern of the arteries, which they accompany along their length. As well as draining venous blood from the tissues of the leg, the deep veins receive blood from the superficial veins via the perforating veins.

Although the deep leg veins are referred to and illustrated as single veins they are usually, in fact, paired veins which lie either side of the artery. These veins are known as venae comitantes and they are common throughout the body.

### DEEP VEINS

The main deep veins comprise:

■ **The posterior tibial vein** – this is formed by the joining together of the small medial and lateral plantar veins of the sole of the foot. As it approaches the knee it is joined from its lateral side by the fibular (peroneal) vein before joining with the anterior tibial vein to form the large popliteal vein

■ **The anterior tibial vein** – this is the continuation of the dorsalis pedis vein on the top of the foot. It passes up the front of the lower leg

■ **The popliteal vein** – this lies behind the knee and receives blood from the small veins which surround the knee joint

■ **The femoral vein** – this is the continuation of the popliteal vein as it passes up the thigh. The large femoral vein receives blood from the superficial veins and continues up into the groin to become the external iliac vein of the pelvis.

## Deep veins of leg, anterior view

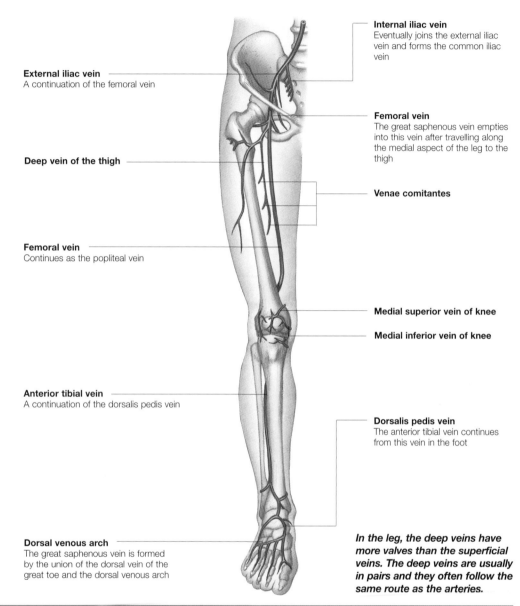

**External iliac vein**
A continuation of the femoral vein

**Deep vein of the thigh**

**Femoral vein**
Continues as the popliteal vein

**Anterior tibial vein**
A continuation of the dorsalis pedis vein

**Dorsal venous arch**
The great saphenous vein is formed by the union of the dorsal vein of the great toe and the dorsal venous arch

**Internal iliac vein**
Eventually joins the external iliac vein and forms the common iliac vein

**Femoral vein**
The great saphenous vein empties into this vein after travelling along the medial aspect of the leg to the thigh

**Venae comitantes**

**Medial superior vein of knee**

**Medial inferior vein of knee**

**Dorsalis pedis vein**
The anterior tibial vein continues from this vein in the foot

*In the leg, the deep veins have more valves than the superficial veins. The deep veins are usually in pairs and they often follow the same route as the arteries.*

## Deep vein thrombosis

*Sitting in cramped conditions on a long-haul flight is believed to contribute to DVT formation. Passengers are encouraged to carry out in-flight leg exercises.*

Thrombosis of the blood within the deep veins of the leg is a relatively common disorder. It is usually associated with sluggish blood flow in these vessels, which may have a number of causes, including:

■ Prolonged bed rest – this increases the risk of developing a deep vein thrombosis (DVT). It is for this reason that post-operative patients and women who have just given birth are encouraged to be up and about as soon as possible

■ Inactivity for long periods (for example, on long-haul air flights) – this is known to predispose to DVT formation

■ Fractures of the leg bones – this increases the likelihood of developing a DVT

■ Pregnancy, or the presence of abnormal abdominal masses – this can impede the return of blood from the leg and cause sluggish flow in the deep veins.

The main clinical importance of DVTs is that they may lead to a pulmonary embolus, in which a piece of the blood clot breaks off and is carried to the lungs. In some cases, a pulmonary embolism is fatal.

# Nerves of the leg

The main nerve of the leg – the sciatic nerve – is the largest nerve in the body. Its branches supply the muscles of the hip, many of the thigh and all of the muscles of the lower leg and foot.

The sciatic nerve is made up of two nerves, the tibial nerve and the common peroneal (or fibular) nerve. These are bound together by connective tissue to form a wide band that runs the full length of the back of the thigh.

### ORIGIN AND COURSE

The sciatic nerve arises from a network of nerves at the base of the spine, called the sacral plexus. From here, it passes out through the greater sciatic foramen and then curves downwards through the gluteal region under the gluteus maximus muscle (midway between the bony landmarks of the greater trochanter of the femur and the ischial tuberosity of the pelvis).

The sciatic nerve leaves the gluteal region by passing under the long head of the biceps femoris muscle to enter the thigh and runs down the centre of the back of the thigh, branching off into the hamstring muscles (a collective name for the biceps femoris, semitendinosus and semimembranosus muscles). It then divides to form two branches, the tibial nerve and the common peroneal nerve just above the knee.

### HIGHER DIVISION

In a few cases the sciatic nerve divides into two at a much higher level. In this situation the common peroneal nerve may pass above or even through the piriformis muscle.

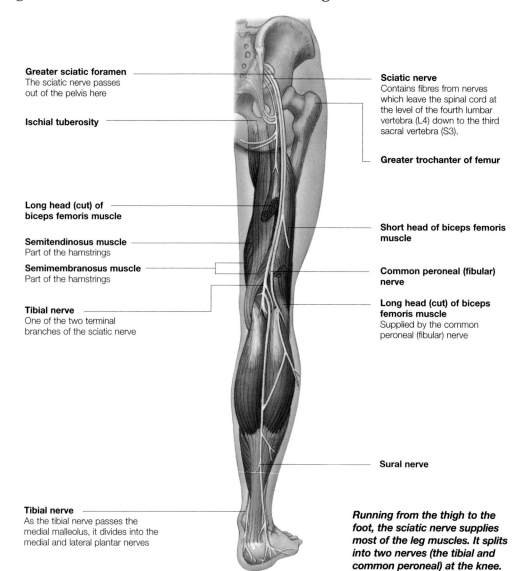

**Greater sciatic foramen**
The sciatic nerve passes out of the pelvis here

**Ischial tuberosity**

**Long head (cut) of biceps femoris muscle**

**Semitendinosus muscle**
Part of the hamstrings

**Semimembranosus muscle**
Part of the hamstrings

**Tibial nerve**
One of the two terminal branches of the sciatic nerve

**Tibial nerve**
As the tibial nerve passes the medial malleolus, it divides into the medial and lateral plantar nerves

**Sciatic nerve**
Contains fibres from nerves which leave the spinal cord at the level of the fourth lumbar vertebra (L4) down to the third sacral vertebra (S3).

**Greater trochanter of femur**

**Short head of biceps femoris muscle**

**Common peroneal (fibular) nerve**

**Long head (cut) of biceps femoris muscle**
Supplied by the common peroneal (fibular) nerve

**Sural nerve**

*Running from the thigh to the foot, the sciatic nerve supplies most of the leg muscles. It splits into two nerves (the tibial and common peroneal) at the knee.*

## The sciatic nerve and intramuscular injections

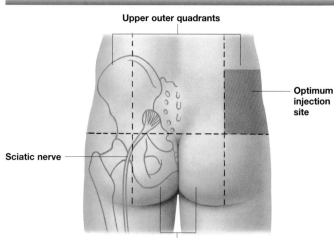

**Upper outer quadrants**

**Optimum injection site**

**Sciatic nerve**

**Inner lower quadrants**

The buttock is often chosen as a site for intramuscular injections as it has a large muscle mass.

It is vitally important to have an accurate knowledge of the position and course of the sciatic nerve when administering intramuscular injections in this area. If the injection site impinges on the sciatic nerve there is a high risk of damaging it, with severe consequences for the future function of the leg.

*Intramuscular injections are often given in the gluteal area. The sciatic nerve can be safely avoided if injections are given in the upper outer quadrant.*

If each gluteal (buttock) region is divided into four quadrants it can be seen that the sciatic nerve lies within the lower quadrants. The only safe place for an intramuscular injection in the buttock, therefore, is in the upper outer quadrant.

### ALTERNATIVE SITE

Anyone responsible for giving injections will have been taught the importance of injecting only in the upper outer quadrant. In many cases people choose to inject the outer side of the thigh in preference to the buttock as there is much less risk of damage to important structures.

# Terminal branches of the sciatic nerve

The sciatic nerve divides into two terminal branches: the common peroneal (fibular) nerve and the tibial nerve. The common peroneal nerve supplies the front of the leg, while the tibial nerve supplies the muscles and skin at the back.

The common peroneal nerve leaves the sciatic nerve in the lower third of the thigh and runs down around the outer side of the lower leg before dividing into two just below the knee.

### NERVE BRANCHES

The two branches of the peroneal nerve comprise:
■ The superficial branch of the peroneal nerve – supplies the lateral (outer) compartment of the lower leg in which it lies. It sub-divides into smaller branches to supply the muscles around it
■ The deep peroneal nerve – runs in front of the interosseous membrane between the tibia and the fibula, and then passes over the ankle into the foot.

These two branches also supply the knee joint and the skin over the outer side of the calf and the top of the foot.

### DAMAGE

As the common peroneal nerve passes around the outer side of the lower leg, it lies just under the skin and very close to the head of the fibula. It is very vulnerable to damage, especially if the fibula suffers a fracture, and is the most commonly damaged nerve in the leg.

**Common peroneal (fibular) nerve**
Branches off the sciatic nerve and runs around the outer side of the lower leg before dividing into deep and superficial branches

**Common peroneal nerve**
Point of maximum vulnerability

**Peroneus longus muscle (cut)**
Supplied by the superficial branch of the peroneal nerve

**Superficial peroneal nerve**
Supplies the fibularis longus and fibularis brevis muscles

**Peroneus longus muscle**
Supplied by the superficial branch of the peroneal nerve

**Peroneus brevis muscle**
Supplied by the superficial branch of the peroneal nerve

**Extensor digitorum brevis muscle**
Supplied by the lateral branch of the deep peroneal nerve

**Medial branch of deep peroneal (fibular) nerve**
Supplying the skin between the first and second toes

**Articular branch of common peroneal nerve**

**Head of the fibula**
Lies underneath the peroneal muscles

**Tibia**
Larger inner bone of the lower leg

**Deep peroneal nerve**
Supplies the tibialis anterior and extensor digitorum longus muscles

**Tibialis anterior muscle**
Supplied by the deep peroneal nerve

**Extensor digitorum longus muscle**
Supplied by the deep peroneal nerve

**Extensor hallucis longus muscle**
Supplied by the deep peroneal nerve

**Extensor hallucis brevis muscle**
Supplied by the lateral branch of the deep peroneal nerve

*The common peroneal nerve splits into two branches to supply the inner and outer lower leg. Close to the skin at points, it is vulnerable to damage.*

## The tibial nerve

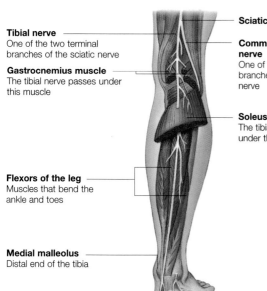

**Tibial nerve**
One of the two terminal branches of the sciatic nerve

**Gastrocnemius muscle**
The tibial nerve passes under this muscle

**Flexors of the leg**
Muscles that bend the ankle and toes

**Medial malleolus**
Distal end of the tibia

**Sciatic nerve**

**Common peroneal (fibular) nerve**
One of the two terminal branches of the sciatic nerve

**Soleus muscle**
The tibial nerve passes under this muscle

The tibial nerve is the larger of the two terminal branches of the sciatic nerve. It supplies the flexors of the leg: those muscles which bend, rather than straighten, the joints.

### PATH DOWN THE LEG

The tibial nerve arises in the lower third of the thigh, where it supplies the hamstring muscles. It then separates from the common peroneal nerve before following a course down the back of the leg:

*The tibial nerve splits off from the sciatic nerve to course down the back of the lower leg. Branches supply the muscles and skin with sensation.*

■ It passes through the popliteal fossa (a space behind the knee) alongside the popliteal artery
■ It then descends under the large gastrocnemius and soleus muscles
■ It reaches the posterior compartment of the lower leg where it gives off branches to the flexor muscles found there
■ At the ankle it passes behind the medial malleolus, before dividing into the medial and lateral plantar nerves of the foot.

### BRANCHES

The tibial nerve has two cutaneous branches which supply areas of skin: the sural nerve (in the calf) and the medial calcaneal nerve (heel).

221

# Ankle

The ankle is the joint between the lower ends of
the tibia and fibula, and the upper surface of the large foot
bone, the talus. It is an example of a hinge joint.

At the ankle, a deep socket is formed by the lower ends of the tibia and fibula, the bones of the lower leg. Into this socket fits the pulley-shaped upper surface of the talus. The shape of the bones and the presence of strong supporting ligaments mean that the ankle is very stable. This is an important feature for such a major weight-bearing joint.

### THE JOINT

The articular surfaces of the ankle joint – those parts of the bone which move against each other – are covered with a layer of smooth hyaline cartilage. This cartilage is surrounded by a thin synovial membrane that secretes a viscous fluid and helps to lubricate the joint.

The articular surfaces of the ankle joint consist of the:
■ Inside of the lateral malleolus, the expanded lower end of the fibula. This carries a facet (depression) that articulates with the outer side of the upper surface of the talus
■ Undersurface of the lower end of the tibia. This forms the roof of the socket, which articulates with the talus
■ Inside of the medial malleolus, the projection at the lower end of the tibia. This moves against the inner side of the upper surface of the talus
■ Trochlea of the talus. Named for its pulley shape, this upper part of the talus fits into the ankle joint, and articulates with the lower ends of the tibia and fibula.

Anterior view, left ankle

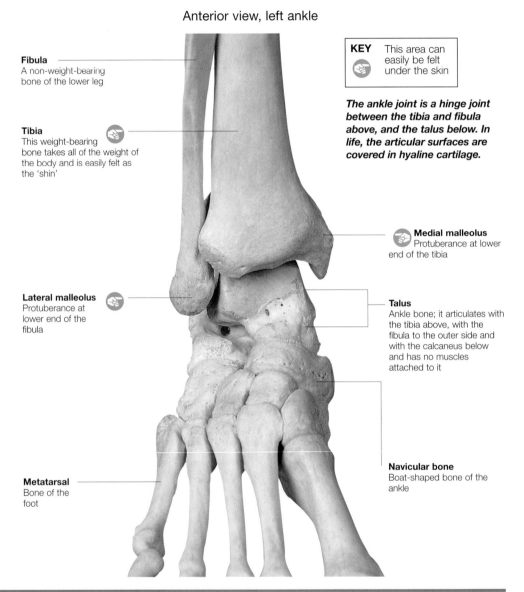

**Fibula**
A non-weight-bearing bone of the lower leg

**Tibia**
This weight-bearing bone takes all of the weight of the body and is easily felt as the 'shin'

**Lateral malleolus**
Protuberance at lower end of the fibula

**Metatarsal**
Bone of the foot

**KEY** This area can easily be felt under the skin

*The ankle joint is a hinge joint between the tibia and fibula above, and the talus below. In life, the articular surfaces are covered in hyaline cartilage.*

**Medial malleolus**
Protuberance at lower end of the tibia

**Talus**
Ankle bone; it articulates with the tibia above, with the fibula to the outer side and with the calcaneus below and has no muscles attached to it

**Navicular bone**
Boat-shaped bone of the ankle

## Movements of the ankle joint

### Plantarflexion

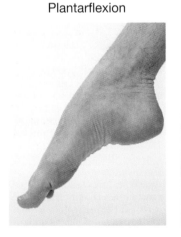

### Dorsiflexion

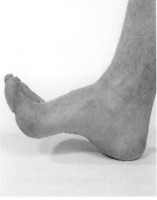

Although the foot is capable of a variety of movements, much of this flexibility is due to the presence of other joints within the foot and below the ankle. The ankle joint itself acts only as a hinge joint, allowing the talus to rotate in one plane only. In this respect, it is rather like the elbow joint.

Movement of the foot at the ankle is thus limited to:

*As a hinge joint, the ankle allows movement in one plane only. In dorsiflexion, the toes are pulled upwards and in plantarflexion, they are pushed downwards.*

■ Dorsiflexion. This is the term that describes the movement of the foot upwards, the heel pointing down and the toes up. The action of dorsiflexion is partly limited by the pull of the calcaneal (or Achilles) tendon at the back of the ankle
■ Plantarflexion. This is the opposite movement to dorsiflexion; the toes point down. This action is limited by the pull of muscles and ligaments at the front of the ankle.

Due to the shape of the bones and ligaments of the ankle, the joint is much more stable in dorsiflexion than plantarflexion.

# Ligaments of the ankle

The ankle is supported by strong ligaments which help to stabilize this important weight-bearing joint.

The ankle joint needs to be stable as it bears the weight of the body. The presence of a variety of strong ligaments around the ankle helps to maintain this stability, while still allowing the necessary freedom of movement.

Like most joints, the ankle is enclosed within a tough fibrous capsule. Although the capsule is quite thin in front and behind, it is reinforced on each side by the strong medial (inner) and lateral (outer) ankle ligaments.

## MEDIAL LIGAMENT

Also known as the deltoid ligament, the medial ligament is a very strong structure which fans out from the tip of the medial malleolus of the tibia. It is usually described in three parts, each named for the bones that they connect:
■ Anterior and posterior tibiotalar ligaments. Lying close against the bones, these parts of the medial ligament connect the tibia to the medial sides of the talus beneath
■ Tibionavicular ligament. More superficially, this part of the ligament runs between the tibia and the navicular, one of the bones of the foot
■ Tibiocalcaneal ligament. This strong ligament runs just under the skin from the tibia to the sustentaculum tali, a projection of the calcaneus (large heel bone).

Together, these parts of the medial ligament support the

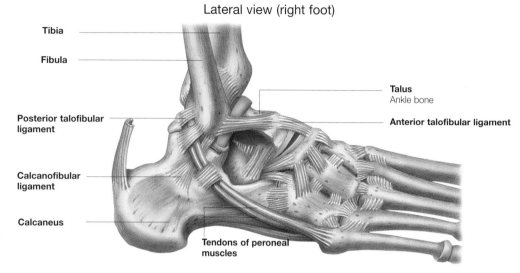

Lateral view (right foot)

Tibia

Fibula

Posterior talofibular ligament

Calcanofibular ligament

Calcaneus

Talus
Ankle bone

Anterior talofibular ligament

Tendons of peroneal muscles

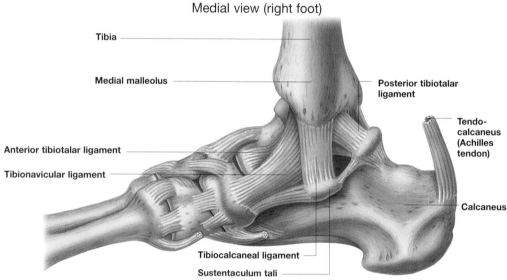

Medial view (right foot)

Tibia

Medial malleolus

Anterior tibiotalar ligament

Tibionavicular ligament

Posterior tibiotalar ligament

Tendo-calcaneus (Achilles tendon)

Calcaneus

Tibiocalcaneal ligament

Sustentaculum tali

ankle joint during the movement of eversion (where the foot is turned out to the side).

## LATERAL LIGAMENT

The lateral ligament is weaker than the medial ligament, and is made up of three distinct bands:
■ Anterior talofibular ligament. This runs forward from the lateral malleolus of the fibula to the talus
■ Calcanofibular ligament. This passes down from the tip of the lateral malleolus to the side of the talus
■ Posterior talofibular ligament. This is a thick, stronger band which passes back from the lateral malleolus to the talus behind.

## Injuries to the ankle

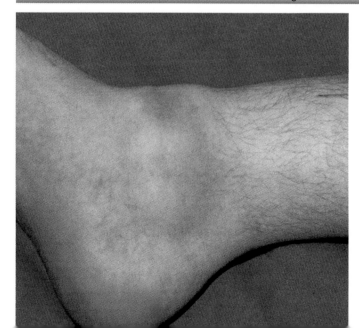

Injuries to the ankle are not uncommon; of all the major joints, it is the most likely to be damaged.

Most injuries to the ankle joint are sprains, in which one or more of the ligaments are stretched to such a degree that some of their fibres tear. A sprained ankle is a common occurrence in the sporting world. It is usually the result of sudden and unexpected twisting of the weight-bearing foot, in which

*If the foot is twisted outwards, a Pott's fracture can occur. This causes the talus to be twisted, the fibula to fracture and the medial ligament to tear.*

the foot becomes inverted (foot facing inwards). Ankle sprains most commonly affect the lateral ligament on the outer side of the joint, as it is by far the weakest ligament.

### POTT'S FRACTURE

A Pott's fracture may occur when the foot is suddenly and forcibly twisted outwards. In this injury, the twisting of the talus causes the fibula to fracture, and the strong medial ligament is stretched until it tears away from the medial malleolus of the tibia. In extreme cases, the damage may be so great that the end of the tibia itself may be sheared off.

# Bones of the foot

The human foot has 26 bones in total: seven larger, irregular tarsal bones; five metatarsals running the length of the foot; and 14 phalanges forming the skeleton of the toes.

The tarsal bones in the foot are equivalent to the carpal bones in the wrist, but there are seven tarsals as opposed to eight wrist bones. The tarsal bones differ somewhat from the wrist in terms of their arrangement, reflecting the different functions of the hand and the foot.

### TARSAL BONES

The tarsal bones consist of:
■ The talus – articulates with the tibia and fibula at the ankle joint. It bears the full weight of the body, transferred down from the tibia. Its shape is such that it can then spread this weight by passing this force backwards and downwards, and forwards to the front of the foot
■ The calcaneus – the large heel bone
■ The navicular – a relatively small bone, named for its boat-like appearance. It has a projection, the navicular tuberosity which, if too large, may cause foot pain as it rubs against the shoe
■ The cuboid – a bone roughly the shape of a cube. It lies on the outer side of the foot, and has a groove on its under surface to allow passage of a muscle tendon
■ The three cuneiforms – bones named according to their positions: medial, intermediate and lateral. The medial cuneiform is the largest of these three wedge-shaped bones.

## Tarsal bones

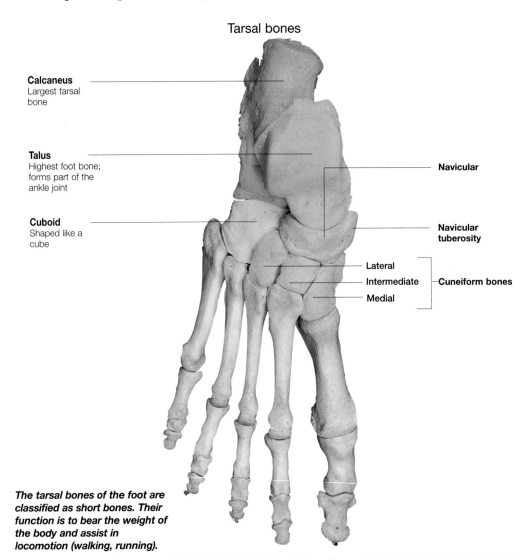

**Calcaneus**
Largest tarsal bone

**Talus**
Highest foot bone; forms part of the ankle joint

**Cuboid**
Shaped like a cube

**Navicular**

**Navicular tuberosity**

Lateral
Intermediate — **Cuneiform bones**
Medial

*The tarsal bones of the foot are classified as short bones. Their function is to bear the weight of the body and assist in locomotion (walking, running).*

---

## Calcaneus (heel bone)

### View from above the calcaneus bone

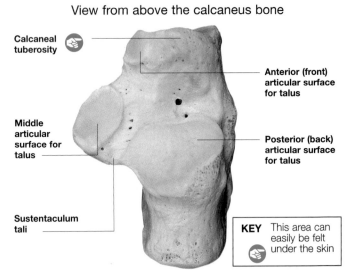

**Calcaneal tuberosity**

**Anterior (front) articular surface for talus**

**Middle articular surface for talus**

**Posterior (back) articular surface for talus**

**Sustentaculum tali**

**KEY** This area can easily be felt under the skin

The calcaneus is the largest bone in the foot and it can easily be felt under the skin as the prominence of the heel. It needs to be a large bone with great strength, as it has the important role of transmitting the weight of the body from the talus to the ground.

### ARTICULAR SURFACES

This large, irregular bone has several articular surfaces where it forms joints with the talus above, and the cuboid in front.

*The calcaneus bone has several articulating surfaces. These surfaces are where the calcaneus moves against the talus and cuboid bones.*

The inner surface of the calcaneus bears a projection, the sustentaculum tali, which supports the head of the talus. On the underside of this projection is a groove for the passage of a long muscle tendon.

### POSTERIOR SURFACE

The back of the calcaneus has a roughened prominence, the calcaneal tuberosity, the medial process of which comes into contact with the ground when standing.

Halfway up the posterior surface of the calcaneus is a ridge which indicates the site of attachment of the powerful Achilles tendon.

# Metatarsals and phalanges

The metatarsals and phalanges in the foot are miniature long bones, consisting of a base, shaft and head.

Like the metacarpals in the hand, there are five metatarsals in the foot. While the individual bones tend to resemble the metacarpals in structure, their arrangement is slightly different. This is mainly due to the fact that the big toe lies in the same plane as the other toes and is not opposable like the thumb.

### METATARSALS
Each metatarsal has a long shaft with two expanded ends, the base and the head. The bases of the metatarsals articulate with the tarsal bones in the middle of the foot. The heads articulate with the phalanges of the corresponding toes.

The metatarsals are numbered from 1 to 5 starting with the most medial, which lies behind the big toe. The first metatarsal is shorter and more sturdy than the rest. It articulates with the first phalanx of the big toe.

### PHALANGES
The phalanges of the toe resemble the phalanges of the fingers. There are 14 phalanges in the foot, the big toe (hallux) having just two while the other four toes have three each.

The base of the first phalanx of each toe articulates with the head of the corresponding metatarsal. The phalanges of the big toe are thicker than those of the other toes.

Lateral view of the foot

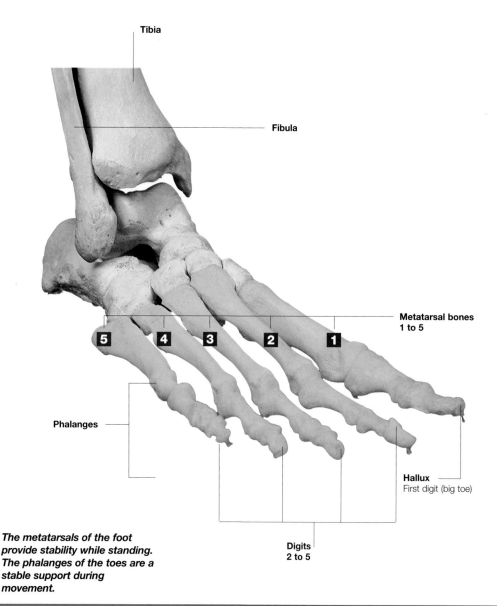

Tibia

Fibula

Metatarsal bones 1 to 5

Phalanges

Hallux
First digit (big toe)

Digits
2 to 5

*The metatarsals of the foot provide stability while standing. The phalanges of the toes are a stable support during movement.*

## Sesamoid bones of the foot

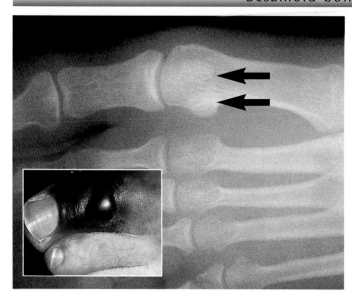

The foot is one of the sites in the body that has sesamoid bones.

### PROTECTIVE ROLE
A sesamoid bone is one which develops within the tendon of a muscle to protect that tendon from wear and tear where it passes over the end of a long bone.

### POSITION OF BONES
The two sesamoid bones in the foot lie under the head of the first metatarsal within the two heads of the flexor hallucis

*The sesamoid bones of the foot can be seen in this X-ray (arrows). These tiny bones are often injured when objects are dropped on to the big toe (inset).*

brevis muscle and bear the weight of the body, especially as the toe pushes off in walking.

Additional sesamoid bones may also be found elsewhere in the foot within other flexor tendons of the digits.

### BONE DEVELOPMENT
The sesamoid bones develop before birth and gradually begin to ossify (become bony) during late childhood. Once ossified these bones can be seen clearly on an X-ray of the foot – the sesamoid bones are seen to overlap with the head of the first metatarsal bone.

These small bones may be damaged by a crushing injury to the foot, such as when a heavy weight falls on the big toe.

# Ligaments and arches of the foot

## The bones of the foot are arranged in such a way that they form bridge-like arches. These bones are supported by the presence of a number of strong ligaments.

The main supportive ligaments of the foot lie on the plantar (under) surface of the bones. The three most prominent ligaments are:

■ The plantar calcaneonavicular, or spring ligament – stretches forward from the sustentaculum tali, a projection of the calcaneus (heel bone), to the back of the navicular (boat-shaped) bone. This ligament is important in helping to maintain the longitudinal arch of the foot

■ The long plantar ligament – runs forward from the underside of the calcaneus to the cuboid (outer) bone and to the bases of the metatarsals (foot bones). It helps to maintain the arches of the foot

■ The plantar calcaneocuboid, or short plantar, ligament – lies under the long plantar ligament and runs from the front of the undersurface of the calcaneus forward to the cuboid.

### OTHER LIGAMENTS

Many other ligaments support and bind together the long metatarsals and the phalanges (toe bones). The metatarsals are bound to the tarsals and to each other by ligaments running across the foot on both their dorsal and plantar surfaces.

### Ligaments of foot (plantar view)

**First phalanx (toe bone)**

**Interphalangeal joints**
Each surrounded by a fibrous capsule, strengthened on either side by tough collateral ligaments

**Fifth metatarsal bone**

**Cuboid bone**
Outer bone of the foot

**Plantar calcaneocuboid ligament**
Stretches forward from front of the undersurface of the calcaneus to the cuboid

**Long plantar ligament**
Stretches forward from the underside of the calcaneus to the cuboid bone and metatarsals

**Plantar calcaneonavicular (spring) ligament**
Stretches from the sustentaculum tali to the back of the navicular bone

**Sustentaculum tali**
Projection of the calcaneus (heel bone)

**Calcaneus**
Heel bone

*Strengthening ligaments ensure that the foot provides a firm but flexible base to bear the weight of the body. The ligaments also facilitate locomotion.*

## Joints of the foot

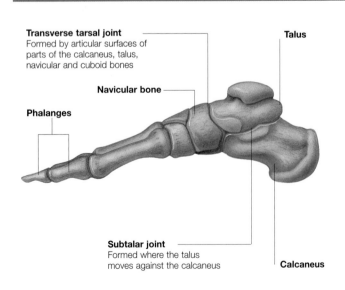

**Transverse tarsal joint**
Formed by articular surfaces of parts of the calcaneus, talus, navicular and cuboid bones

**Talus**

**Navicular bone**

**Phalanges**

**Subtalar joint**
Formed where the talus moves against the calcaneus

**Calcaneus**

The ankle joint allows the foot to move up and down only. Other movements of the foot, such as eversion, where it faces outwards, or inversion, where it faces inwards, take place further down the foot at two joints: the transverse tarsal and the subtalar joint:

■ Transverse tarsal joint. This complicated joint is formed by the adjoining articular surfaces of parts of the calcaneus, talus (ankle bone), navicular and cuboid. It is across this joint that

*Joints between the bones of the foot allow movement between the hind- and forefoot. Such movements are necessary when walking on rough ground.*

amputation of the foot is performed, when necessary
■ Subtalar joint. This is formed where the talus moves against the calcaneus.

### OTHER JOINTS OF THE MID-FOOT

There are many other small synovial (fluid-filled) joints located within the foot where bone meets bone. However, these joints are generally held tightly together by tough ligaments and so little movement is possible.

The joints between the phalanges allow movement of the toes, although the range of movement is less than that for the fingers.

# Arches of the foot

A distinctive feature of the human foot is that the bones within it are arranged in bridge-like arches. This allows the foot to be flexible enough to cope with uneven ground, while still being able to bear the weight of the body.

The arched shape of the foot can be illustrated by looking at a footprint. Only the heel, the outer edge of the foot, the pads under the metatarsal heads and the tips of the toes leave an impression. The rest of the foot is lifted away from the ground.

### THREE ARCHES

The foot has two longitudinal arches (medial and lateral) running along its length, and a transverse arch lying across it:
■ Medial longitudinal arch. This is the higher and more important of the two longitudinal arches. The bones involved are the calcaneus, the talus, the navicular bone, the three cuneiform bones and the first three metatarsals. The head of the talus supports this arch
■ Lateral longitudinal arch. This arch is much lower and flatter, the bones resting on the ground when standing. The lateral arch is formed by the calcaneus, the cuboid and the fourth and fifth metatarsal bones
■ Transverse arch. This arch runs across the foot, supported on either side by the longitudinal arches, and is made up of the bases of the metatarsal bones, the cuboid and the three cuneiform bones.

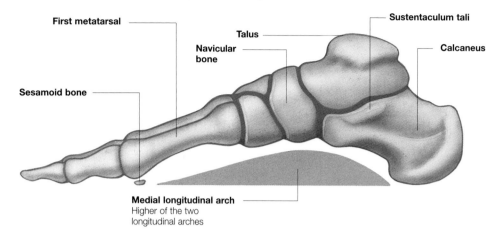

Bones forming medial longitudinal arch of foot

First metatarsal

Talus

Sustentaculum tali

Navicular bone

Calcaneus

Sesamoid bone

**Medial longitudinal arch**
Higher of the two longitudinal arches

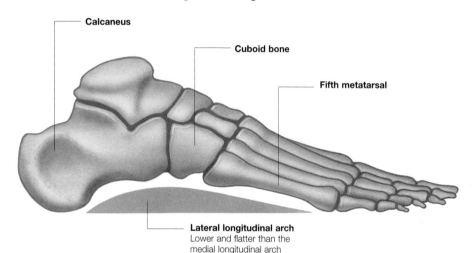

Bones forming lateral longitudinal arch of foot

Calcaneus

Cuboid bone

Fifth metatarsal

**Lateral longitudinal arch**
Lower and flatter than the medial longitudinal arch

*The bones of the foot form bridge-like arches. These are maintained by the shape of the bones and the strength of the ligaments and muscle tendons.*

## Weight bearing in the foot

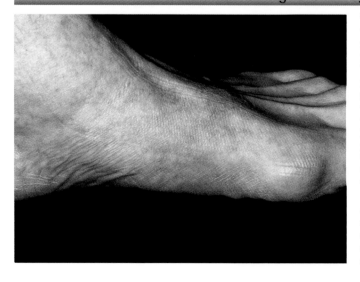

The weight of the body is transmitted down to the talus from the tibia (shin bone). The force is then passed down and backwards to the calcaneus and forwards to the heads of the second to fifth metatarsals and the tiny sesamoid bones underlying the first metatarsal. Between these points the weight is absorbed by the stretching of the 'elastic' longitudinal and transverse arches of the foot, which act as shock absorbers.

*A person with flat feet has collapsed medial longitudinal arches, so that the sole lies flat upon the ground. Treatment is only required if pain is caused.*

### METATARSAL HEADS

It used to be thought that the body's weight was supported on a 'tripod' formed by the heel and the heads of the first and fifth metatarsals. It is now known that all the metatarsal heads are involved in weight bearing and, indeed, long marches may cause a 'stress' fracture of the head of the second metatarsal.

In the condition known as pes planus (flat feet), the medial longitudinal arches collapse until the head of the talus comes down between the navicular and calcaneus. The footprint of an affected person shows the whole foot to be in contact with the ground.

# Muscles of the upper foot

Many of the muscles which move the foot lie in the lower leg, rather than in the foot itself. This allows them to be more powerful than if they were contained within the small space of the foot.

To have an effect upon the bones and joints of the foot, the leg muscles have long tendons. To reach the bones of the foot these tendons must first cross the ankle joint, where they are held in place by a series of retaining bands, or retinacula. If these bands were not present, the tendons would run straight to their attachments like a bow-string rather than following the contours of the ankle joint.

## RETINACULA OF THE FOOT

There are four main retinacula in this area:

■ **Superior extensor retinaculum**. Lies just above the ankle joint and retains the long tendons of the extensor muscles

■ **Inferior extensor retinaculum.** Lies beneath the ankle joint. It also retains extensor muscles

■ **Peroneal retinaculum.** Lies on the outer side of the ankle. It is in two parts, upper and lower, and retains the long peroneal muscle tendons

■ **Flexor retinaculum.** Lies on the inner side of the ankle and retains the long flexor tendons as they pass under the medial malleolus to reach the sole of the foot.

*The leg muscles have long tendons which connect to the foot bones like puppet strings. Retinacula are fibrous bands that hold tendons in place.*

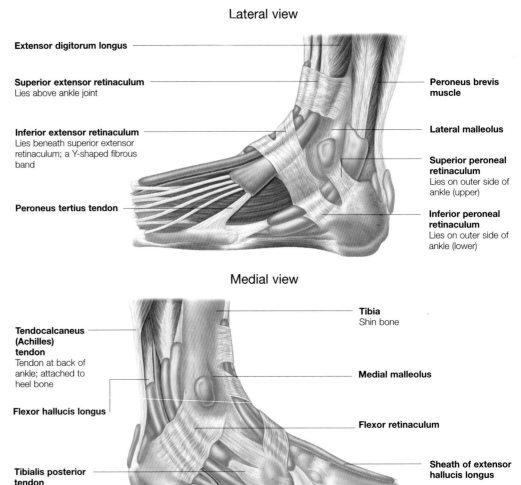

Lateral view

Extensor digitorum longus

Superior extensor retinaculum
Lies above ankle joint

Inferior extensor retinaculum
Lies beneath superior extensor retinaculum; a Y-shaped fibrous band

Peroneus tertius tendon

Peroneus brevis muscle

Lateral malleolus

Superior peroneal retinaculum
Lies on outer side of ankle (upper)

Inferior peroneal retinaculum
Lies on outer side of ankle (lower)

Medial view

Tendocalcaneus (Achilles) tendon
Tendon at back of ankle; attached to heel bone

Flexor hallucis longus

Tibialis posterior tendon

Posterior tibial artery and nerve

Tibia
Shin bone

Medial malleolus

Flexor retinaculum

Sheath of extensor hallucis longus

Tibialis anterior tendon

## Long tendons around the ankle joint

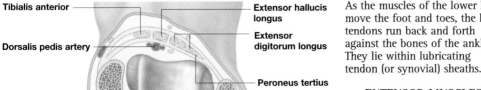

Tibialis anterior

Dorsalis pedis artery

Tibialis posterior

Flexor digitorum longus

Flexor hallucis longus

Plantaris tendon

Extensor hallucis longus

Extensor digitorum longus

Peroneus tertius

Peroneus brevis

Peroneus longus

Tendocalcaneus (Achilles) tendon

As the muscles of the lower leg move the foot and toes, the long tendons run back and forth against the bones of the ankle. They lie within lubricating tendon (or synovial) sheaths.

### EXTENSOR MUSCLES

In front of the ankle lie the long extensor muscles. Extensor digitorum longus and peroneus

*Lubricating tendon sheaths protect the tendons from wear and tear and help them run smoothly. The tendons are situated under the retinacula.*

tertius share a common synovial sheath. The long flexor tendons, which bend the foot down or the toes under, lie behind the bony medial malleolus. Behind the lateral malleolus lie the long tendons of the peroneal muscles, while the tendocalcaneus tendon inserts into the heel bone.

Blood vessels and nerves must also cross the ankle joint. It is important for a doctor to know where these structures lie in relation to the ankle because it is a common site for fractures, sprains and dislocations, which may cause surrounding damage.

# Muscles of the top of the foot

Although they are not particularly powerful, the muscles that lie over the top of the foot play an important part in helping to extend the toes. The extensor digitorum brevis muscle tends to be used when the foot is already pointing upwards.

Most of the muscles which lie within the foot, the intrinsic muscles, are in the sole. The top, or dorsal surface, of the foot has just two muscles: the extensor digitorum brevis and the extensor hallucis brevis.

### MUSCLES OF THE DORSAL SURFACE

■ **Extensor digitorum brevis.** As its name suggests, this is a short muscle which extends (straightens or pulls upwards) the toes. It arises from the upper surface of the calcaneus, or heel bone, and the inferior extensor retinaculum. This muscle divides into three parts, each with a tendon that joins the corresponding long extensor tendon to insert into the second, third and fourth toes

■ **Extensor hallucis brevis.** This short muscle is really part of the extensor digitorum brevis. It runs down to insert into the big toe, or 'hallux', from which its name derives

### ACTION OF THE MUSCLES

Together these two muscles assist the long extensor tendons in

extending the first four toes. Although they do not have a particularly powerful action, they are useful in extending the toes when the foot itself is already pointing up, or dorsiflexed, as in this position the long extensors are unable to act further.

**Extensor digitorum longus muscle** — **Superior extensor retinaculum**

**Inferior extensor retinaculum**

**Peroneus tertius tendon**
This lies over the extensor digitorum brevis

**Extensor hallucis brevis**

**Extensor digitorum brevis** — **Extensor hallucis longus tendon**

### CLINICAL RELEVANCE

The top of the foot is one of the sites in the body where excess tissue fluid (oedema) may accumulate and be visible to an examining doctor. The position of the muscle bellies of these two short extensor muscles must

*The muscles that lie at the top of the foot help to extend the toes. They assist the long extensors when the foot is dorsiflexed.*

be known to prevent them being mistaken for such oedema.

---

## Surface anatomy of the foot

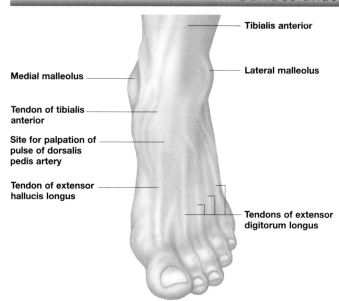

**Tibialis anterior**

**Lateral malleolus**

**Medial malleolus**

**Tendon of tibialis anterior**

**Site for palpation of pulse of dorsalis pedis artery**

**Tendon of extensor hallucis longus**

**Tendons of extensor digitorum longus**

Surface, or living, anatomy is the study of the live, intact body at rest and during movement. The foot is a good example as the relative lack of subcutaneous fat, together with the presence of numerous bony landmarks and prominent tendons, means there are many points of interest.

### BONY LANDMARKS

The most obvious bony landmarks in the area are the medial (inner) and lateral (outer) malleoli, projections on either side of the ankle joint. In the foot itself, the most prominent

*The skin is thinner on the top of the foot than on the sole of the foot. This means that the bony landmarks are easy to locate and to study.*

landmark is the tuberosity of the navicular bone which can be felt on the inner aspect of the foot.

### TENDONS

Many of the long tendons can be seen and felt as they pass across the ankle joint and along the foot. The most obvious are the extensor tendons on the top of the foot, which are prominent when the foot is dorsiflexed.

### PULSES

An important landmark on top of the foot is the site where the pulse of the dorsalis pedis artery can be felt. This is usually midway between the two malleoli at the front of the ankle. A doctor might feel for a pulse here to check the circulation to the foot.

# Muscles of the sole of the foot

Many of the movements of the bones and joints of the feet are brought about by muscles in the lower leg. However, there are also many small 'intrinsic' muscles which lie entirely within the foot.

The sole of the foot has four layers of intrinsic muscles, which work with the extrinsic muscles to meet the varying demands placed upon the foot during standing, walking, running and jumping. They also help to support the bony arches of the foot and to allow us to stand on sloping or uneven ground.

### FIRST MUSCLE LAYER

The first layer of sole muscles is the most superficial, lying just under the thick plantar aponeurosis. The muscles of this layer include:

■ **Abductor hallucis** – this muscle lies along the medial (inner) border of the sole. It acts to abduct the big toe, or 'hallux', which means moving it away from the mid-line. It also flexes, or bends down, the big toe

■ **Flexor digitorum brevis** - this fleshy muscle lies down the centre of the sole and inserts into each of the lateral four toes. Contraction of this muscle causes those toes to flex

■ **Abductor digiti minimi** - lying along the lateral (outer) border of the sole within this first layer, this muscle acts to abduct and flex the little toe.

These muscles are similar to the corresponding muscles in the hand, but their individual function is less important because the toes do not have such a wide range of movement as the fingers.

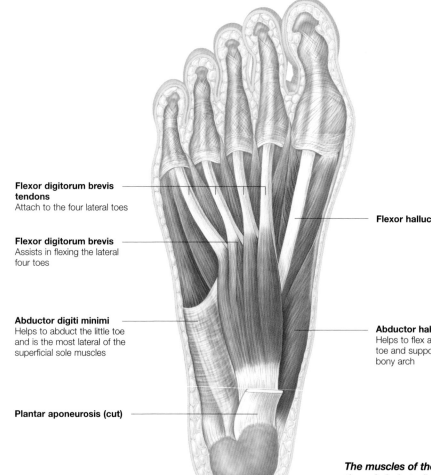

**Flexor digitorum brevis tendons**
Attach to the four lateral toes

**Flexor digitorum brevis**
Assists in flexing the lateral four toes

**Abductor digiti minimi**
Helps to abduct the little toe and is the most lateral of the superficial sole muscles

**Plantar aponeurosis (cut)**

**Flexor hallucis longus tendon**

**Abductor hallucis**
Helps to flex and abduct the big toe and supports the medial bony arch

*The muscles of the first layer of the sole help to flex, abduct and adduct the toes. The muscles of the sole lie in four layers ranging from superficial to deep.*

## Plantar aponeurosis

**Plantar aponeurosis**
A triangular-shaped area of fibrous connective tissue

**Lateral band of plantar aponeurosis (calcaneometatarsal ligament)**

**Digital slips of plantar aponeurosis**

The skin of the sole is thick and overlies a layer of shock-absorbing fat pads. Under this layer lies a sheet of tough connective tissue called the plantar aponeurosis.

The plantar aponeurosis is the thickened central portion of the plantar fascia, the connective tissue which surrounds and

*The plantar aponeurosis is a strong sheet of connective tissue. 'Plantar' refers to the sole of the foot just as 'palmar' refers to the palm of the hand.*

encloses the muscles of the sole. The plantar aponeurosis consists of bands of strong fibrous tissue that run the length of the sole and insert into each of the toes. It also attaches to the skin above it and to the deeper tissues that lie below.

### ACTION

The plantar aponeurosis acts to hold together the parts of the foot and helps to protect the sole of the foot from injury. It also helps to support the bony arches of the foot.

# Deeper muscle layers of the sole

The muscles of the sole of the foot are made up of four different layers; three of these layers lie under the top layer of the sole of the foot. All of these muscles act together, to help to keep the bony arches of the feet stable.

Beneath the superficial layer of intrinsic muscles of the sole lie three further layers. These all have a contribution to make to the stability and flexibility of the foot, both at rest and in motion.

Although the deep muscles each have individual actions, their main role is to act together to maintain the stability of the bony arches of the feet.

### SECOND MUSCLE LAYER OF THE SOLE

The second muscle layer of the sole of the foot includes some tendons from the extrinsic muscles, as well as some smaller intrinsic muscles.

Muscles and tendons that are included within this second layer of the sole are:

■ Quadratus plantae (or flexor accessorius) muscle –
this wide, rectangular muscle arises from two heads on either side of the heel.

It inserts into the edge of the tendon of flexor digitorum longus where it acts by pulling backwards on this tendon and so stabilizing it while it flexes the toes
■ Tendons of flexor hallucis

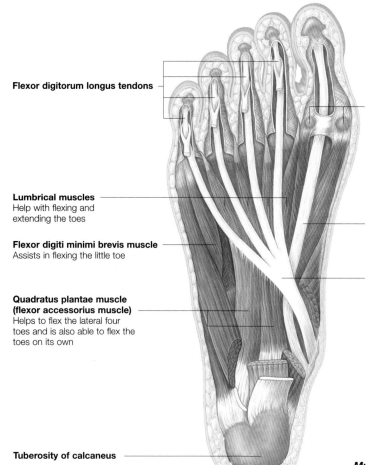

**Flexor digitorum longus tendons**

**Sesamoid bones**

**Lumbrical muscles**
Help with flexing and extending the toes

**Flexor hallucis longus tendon**
Used to 'push off' in walking or jumping

**Flexor digiti minimi brevis muscle**
Assists in flexing the little toe

**Flexor digitorum longus tendon**
Branches to each of the four lateral toes

**Quadratus plantae muscle (flexor accessorius muscle)**
Helps to flex the lateral four toes and is also able to flex the toes on its own

**Tuberosity of calcaneus**

*Muscles from the second layer of the sole of the foot help to extend and flex the toes. They also help to stabilize the tendons during flexion of the toes.*

longus and flexor digitorum longus – these tendons enter the second muscular layer of the sole after winding around the medial malleolus (inner 'ankle bone')

■ The four lumbrical muscles – named for their worm-like appearance, these four muscles arise from the tendons of flexor digitorum longus. They are similar to the lumbrical muscles

in the hand. These muscles act to extend (straighten) the toes while the long tendons are flexing them, which helps to prevent the toes 'buckling under' when walking or running.

## Third and fourth muscle layers

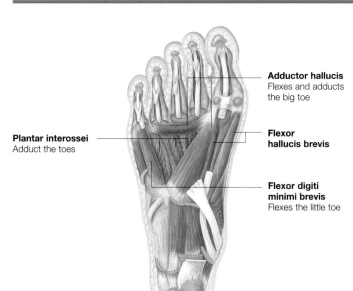

**Plantar interossei**
Adduct the toes

**Adductor hallucis**
Flexes and adducts the big toe

**Flexor hallucis brevis**

**Flexor digiti minimi brevis**
Flexes the little toe

Lying deep to the long flexor tendons, the third muscle layer of the sole is made up of three small muscles:

■ Flexor hallucis brevis. This is a short muscle, which flexes the big toe. It arises from the cuboid and lateral cuneiform bones and then splits into two parts. Each of these two parts has a tendon that inserts into the base of the big toe. The two sesamoid bones of the foot lie within these tendons
■ Adductor hallucis. This

*The three small muscles in the deep muscle layer of the sole help to flex the toes. Even deeper, between the bones, lie the seven interossei muscles.*

muscle arises from two heads; an oblique head and a transverse head. They join to insert into the base of the big toe
■ Flexor digiti minimi brevis. This small muscle runs along the outer border of the foot to the little toe, which it helps to flex.

### FOURTH MUSCLE LAYER OF THE SOLE

The muscles of the fourth, and deepest layer of the sole are called the 'interossei' muscles which literally means 'between the bones'. Unlike the hand, which has eight, there are only seven interossei in the foot. The four dorsal interossei muscles (not shown) abduct the toes, whereas the three plantar interossei adduct them.

# The skeleton

The skeleton is made up of bone and cartilage, and it accounts for one-fifth of the body's weight. Over 200 bones form a living structure, superbly designed to support and protect the body.

The human skeleton provides a stable yet flexible framework for the other tissues of the body. Cartilage is more flexible than bone and is found in the places where movement occurs.

### FUNCTIONS OF BONE

The bones of the skeleton have a number of vital functions:
■ Support – bones support the body when standing, and hold soft internal organs in place
■ Protection – the brain and spinal cord are protected by the skull and vertebral column, while the rib cage protects the heart and lungs
■ Movement – throughout the body, muscles attach to bones to give them the leverage to bring about movement
■ Storage of minerals – calcium and phosphate ions are stored in bone to be drawn upon when necessary
■ Blood cell formation – the marrow cavity of some bones, such as the sternum, is a site of production of red blood cells.

## Formation

The bony skeleton is formed in fetal life, but grows throughout childhood. A fetus of six weeks has a skeleton made of fibrous membranes and hyaline cartilage, which converts into bone during pregnancy. After birth, and until the end of adolescence, the skeleton grows in weight and length as well as being remodelled.

*This image of a fetus shows early bone development. The dark ends of the bone are primary ossification centres, which produce new bone cells.*

Anterior view of the human skeleton

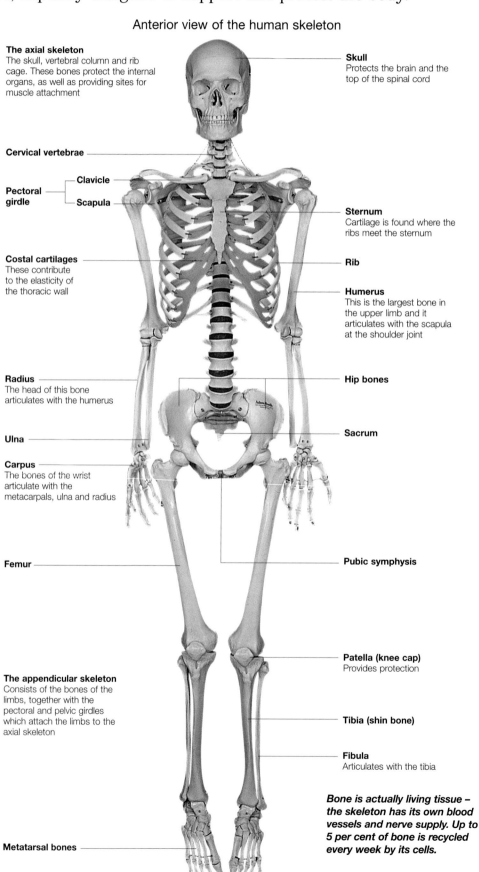

**The axial skeleton**
The skull, vertebral column and rib cage. These bones protect the internal organs, as well as providing sites for muscle attachment

**Skull**
Protects the brain and the top of the spinal cord

**Cervical vertebrae**

**Pectoral girdle**
**Clavicle**
**Scapula**

**Sternum**
Cartilage is found where the ribs meet the sternum

**Costal cartilages**
These contribute to the elasticity of the thoracic wall

**Rib**

**Humerus**
This is the largest bone in the upper limb and it articulates with the scapula at the shoulder joint

**Radius**
The head of this bone articulates with the humerus

**Hip bones**

**Ulna**

**Sacrum**

**Carpus**
The bones of the wrist articulate with the metacarpals, ulna and radius

**Femur**

**Pubic symphysis**

**The appendicular skeleton**
Consists of the bones of the limbs, together with the pectoral and pelvic girdles which attach the limbs to the axial skeleton

**Patella (knee cap)**
Provides protection

**Tibia (shin bone)**

**Fibula**
Articulates with the tibia

**Metatarsal bones**

*Bone is actually living tissue – the skeleton has its own blood vessels and nerve supply. Up to 5 per cent of bone is recycled every week by its cells.*

# Bone markings and features

Each bone of the skeleton is shaped to fulfil its own functions. Bones bear marks, ridges and notches which relate to other structures with which they come into contact.

Over the years, anatomists have given names to the various types of feature which can be found on bones. Using these names, a bone can be described quite clearly and accurately, something which can be of importance clinically.

## PROJECTIONS

Projections on the surface of a bone often occur where muscles, tendons or ligaments are attached or where a joint is formed. Examples include:
■ Condyle – rounded projection at a joint (such as the femoral condyle at the knee)
■ Epicondyle – the raised area above a condyle (such as on the lower humerus, at the elbow)
■ Crest – prominent ridge of bone (such as the iliac crest of the pelvic bone)
■ Tubercle – small raised area (such as the greater tubercle at the top of the humerus)
■ Line – long, narrow raised ridge (such as the soleal line at the back of the tibia).

## Depressions and grooves

Depressions, holes and grooves are usually found where blood vessels and nerves must pass through or around bones.

## FEATURES

Examples include:
■ Fossa – shallow, bowl-like depression (such as the infraspinous fossa of the shoulder blade or the iliac fossa, which is a depression found on the ilium)
■ Foramen – a hole in a bone to allow the passage of a particular vessel or nerve, (such as the jugular foramen in the skull which allows the internal jugular vein to leave)
■ Notch – indentation that is found at the edge of a bone (such as the greater sciatic notch, which is partly formed by the ilium)
■ Groove – a furrow or elongated depression that marks the route of a vessel or nerve along a bone (such as the oblique radial groove at the back of the humerus).

Posterior view of the human skeleton

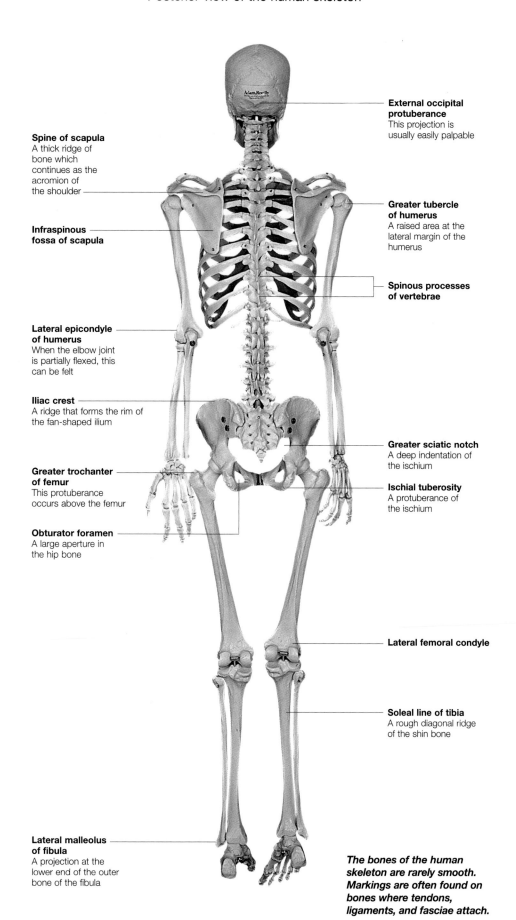

**Spine of scapula**
A thick ridge of bone which continues as the acromion of the shoulder

**Infraspinous fossa of scapula**

**Lateral epicondyle of humerus**
When the elbow joint is partially flexed, this can be felt

**Iliac crest**
A ridge that forms the rim of the fan-shaped ilium

**Greater trochanter of femur**
This protuberance occurs above the femur

**Obturator foramen**
A large aperture in the hip bone

**Lateral malleolus of fibula**
A projection at the lower end of the outer bone of the fibula

**External occipital protuberance**
This projection is usually easily palpable

**Greater tubercle of humerus**
A raised area at the lateral margin of the humerus

**Spinous processes of vertebrae**

**Greater sciatic notch**
A deep indentation of the ischium

**Ischial tuberosity**
A protuberance of the ischium

**Lateral femoral condyle**

**Soleal line of tibia**
A rough diagonal ridge of the shin bone

*The bones of the human skeleton are rarely smooth. Markings are often found on bones where tendons, ligaments, and fasciae attach.*

233

# Types of joints

A joint is formed where two or more bones meet. Some allow movement and so give mobility to the body while others protect and support the body by holding the bones rigid against each another.

The joints of the body can be divided into three main structural groups, according to the tissues that lie between the bones. These groups are fibrous, cartilaginous and synovial.

### FIBROUS JOINTS

Where two bones are connected by a fibrous joint, they are held together with collagen (a protein). Collagen fibres allow little, if any, movement. Fibrous joints are located in the body where the movement of one bone upon the other should be prevented, such as in the skull.

### CARTILAGINOUS JOINTS

The ends of the bones in a cartilaginous joint are covered with a thin layer of hyaline (glass-like) cartilage, with the bones being connected by tough fibrocartilage. The whole joint is covered by a fibrous capsule.

Cartilaginous joints do not allow much movement but they can 'relax' under pressure, so giving flexibility to structures such as the spinal column.

### SYNOVIAL JOINTS

Most joints of the body are synovial, and allow easy movement between the bones. In a synovial joint, the bones are covered by hyaline cartilage and separated by fluid. The joint cavity is lined by a synovial membrane and the whole joint is enclosed by a fibrous capsule.

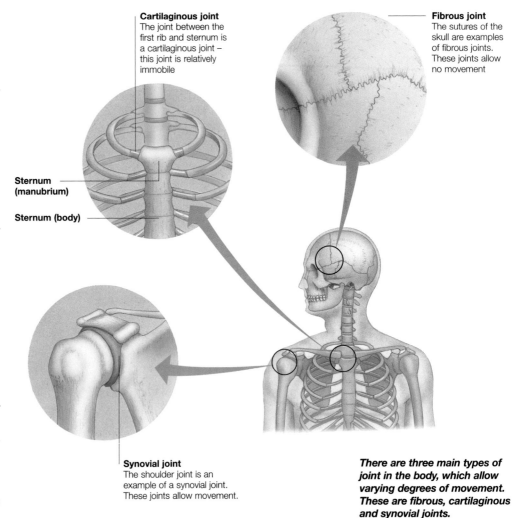

**Cartilaginous joint**
The joint between the first rib and sternum is a cartilaginous joint – this joint is relatively immobile

**Sternum (manubrium)**

**Sternum (body)**

**Fibrous joint**
The sutures of the skull are examples of fibrous joints. These joints allow no movement

**Synovial joint**
The shoulder joint is an example of a synovial joint. These joints allow movement.

*There are three main types of joint in the body, which allow varying degrees of movement. These are fibrous, cartilaginous and synovial joints.*

## Functional groups of joints

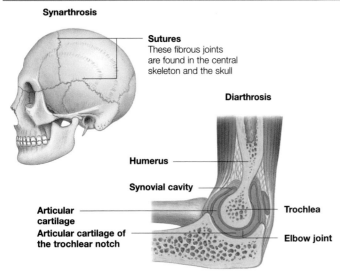

**Synarthrosis**

**Sutures**
These fibrous joints are found in the central skeleton and the skull

**Diarthrosis**

**Humerus**

**Synovial cavity**

**Articular cartilage**

**Articular cartilage of the trochlear notch**

**Trochlea**

**Elbow joint**

*The elbow is a diarthrotic joint, which allows flexibility. The articular capsule allows plenty of freedom for extending the elbow joint.*

The classification of joints shown above is based on the structure of the tissues which make up the joint.

Joints can also be grouped according to their function. Perhaps the most important function of a joint is to allow or prevent movement. On this basis, there are three groups:
■ Synarthroses – joints which allow no movement. These joints lie predominantly within the axial skeleton (the central skeleton, excluding the limbs), where bones are more likely to fulfil the functions of support and protection than mobility. An example is the fibrous joints (sutures) of the skull
■ Amphiarthroses – joints that allow slight movement. These are found in areas where some flexibility is needed but greater degrees of movement would be unsuitable. Examples include the vertebral joints or the fibrous interosseous membrane in the forearm
■ Diarthroses – joints which allow free movement. These predominate in the limbs, where mobility and movement are the prime functions. Some examples are the hip, shoulder and elbow joints.

# Fibrous and cartilaginous joints

Fibrous and cartilaginous joints have an important role to play in the human skeleton. Unlike the more widespread synovial joints, which are designed to allow mobility, fibrous and cartilaginous joints help to maintain stability of the body's frame.

The bones of a fibrous joint are connected solely by long collagen fibres; there is no cartilage, and no fluid-filled joint cavity. Because of its structure, a fibrous joint does not allow much real movement of the bones against each other. What little movement there is, is determined by the length of the collagen fibres.

## GROUPS OF FIBROUS JOINTS

Fibrous joints can be further subdivided into three groups:
■ Sutures – literally meaning 'seams', sutures are the tough fibrous joints between the interlocking bones of the skull. Short collagen fibres allow no side-to-side movement of these bones upon each other although there may be some slight 'springing' of the bones if pressure is applied. The presence of fixed fibrous joints in the skull gives great protection to the vulnerable brain tissue that lies beneath
■ Syndesmoses – here, the bones are connected by a sheet of fibrous connective tissue, and the length of the fibres varies from joint to joint. These may also be known as interosseous membranes and are a feature of the forearm and the lower leg,

**Cranial bone**

**Suture**
Skull sutures consist of dense, fibrous connective tissue. The fixed nature of these joints gives greater protection

*When a person becomes an adult, the fibrous tissue hardens and the skull bones become a single unit. The sutures are then known as synostoses.*

where two bones lie side by side, acting as a unit. Syndesmoses tend to have longer fibres than sutures and so allow a little more movement
■ Gomphoses – this is a very

specialized type of fibrous joint with only one example in the human body, the tooth socket. In a gomphosis, a peg-like process sits in a depression, or socket, and is held in place by fibrous

tissue, in this case the periodontal ligament. Movement is generally abnormal but micromovement is essential to eating to allow adjustment of the pressure of the bite.

## Cartilaginous joints

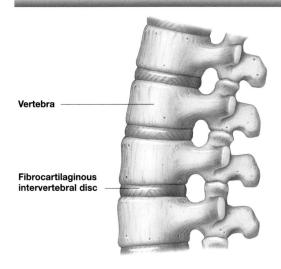

**Vertebra**

**Fibrocartilaginous intervertebral disc**

*The fibrocartilaginous discs are in the joints in the vertebrae and act as shock absorbers. These tough joints allow a small amount of movement.*

In a cartilaginous joint, the bone ends are covered by hyaline cartilage. In some cases, there is a plate of tough fibrocartilage between the bones. The joint is usually enclosed within a fibrous capsule.

There are said to be two types of cartilaginous joints:
■ Primary cartilaginous joints – those where two ends of bone are connected by a plate of hyaline cartilage. They are found

in the growing long bones of children and, in the adult, between the first rib and the top of the sternum (breastbone)
■ Secondary cartilaginous joints or 'symphyses' – joints where a plate of tough fibrocartilage lies between the bones. These are strong, slightly movable joints that often perform the function of shock absorbers. An example of this type of cartilaginous joint is found in the vertebral column, in which the individual vertebrae are covered with hyaline cartilage and are connected to each other by resilient fibrocartilaginous intervertebral discs.

235

# Types of muscle

There are three main types of muscle in the body – skeletal muscle is used for voluntary movement, smooth muscle controls internal organs and cardiac muscle keeps the heart beating.

The most familiar muscles in the body are the skeletal muscles, (also known as striated, or voluntary, muscles), many of which are visible under the skin. Voluntary muscles can be under conscious control, and can also contract in a reflex action such as when the knee straightens when the patellar tendon is tapped (the knee jerk reflex).

## STRUCTURE

The muscle fibres of each skeletal muscle are bound together by connective tissue (epimysium), and divided into groups or fascicles by a sheath (perimysium). Within these fascicles, each muscle fibre is surrounded by an endomysium. The whole muscle is attached to bone by a tough fibrous band, the muscle tendon.

## FUNCTION

Skeletal muscle can be very adaptable. These muscles can contract powerfully, exerting a great deal of force, such as in lifting a heavy object. Alternatively, they can exert a small force to perform a delicate action such as picking up a feather. Another feature of skeletal muscle, which becomes obvious after performing exercise, is that it tires easily. Whereas the heart can beat all day, every day, without ceasing, skeletal muscle needs a period of rest after a contraction.

### Connective tissue sheaths of skeletal muscle

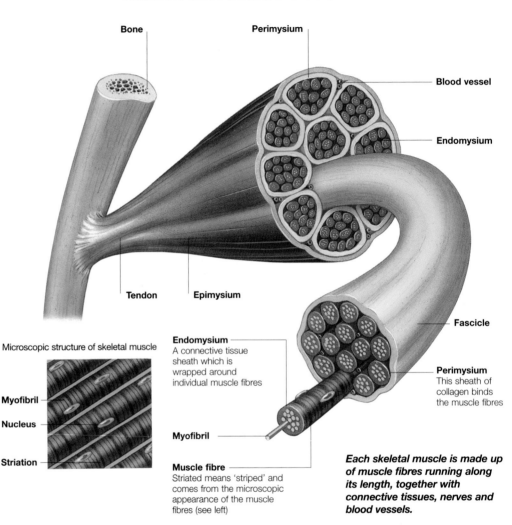

**Bone**

**Perimysium**

**Blood vessel**

**Endomysium**

**Tendon**

**Epimysium**

**Fascicle**

**Perimysium**
This sheath of collagen binds the muscle fibres

**Microscopic structure of skeletal muscle**

**Myofibril**

**Nucleus**

**Striation**

**Endomysium**
A connective tissue sheath which is wrapped around individual muscle fibres

**Myofibril**

**Muscle fibre**
Striated means 'striped' and comes from the microscopic appearance of the muscle fibres (see left)

*Each skeletal muscle is made up of muscle fibres running along its length, together with connective tissues, nerves and blood vessels.*

## Smooth (involuntary) muscle

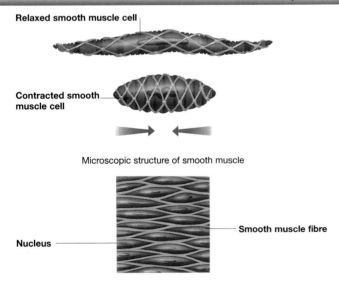

**Relaxed smooth muscle cell**

**Contracted smooth muscle cell**

**Microscopic structure of smooth muscle**

**Nucleus**

**Smooth muscle fibre**

Smooth muscle is named for the lack of striations, or stripes, when viewed under the microscope. It is also known as involuntary muscle as its actions do not come under a person's conscious control.

### LOCATION OF SMOOTH MUSCLE

Smooth muscle is found in the walls of hollow structures within the body, such as the gut, blood vessels and the bladder. Here, it acts to regulate the size of the

*Smooth muscle cells contract in a gradual, synchronized manner. These contractions are much slower than those of the skeletal muscles.*

lumen (central space) as well as causing wave-like peristalsis in some organs (such as the gut and ureters). Smooth muscle is also found in the skin, where it acts upon hairs, and in the eyeball, where it determines the thickness of the lens and size of the pupil.

### NERVOUS SYSTEM

Smooth muscle is controlled by the autonomic nervous system, the part of the nervous system that is concerned with regulation of the internal environment of the body as well as the response to stress. Unlike skeletal muscle, smooth muscle can keep up a steady contraction for a long period of time.

# Shapes of skeletal muscle

Although all skeletal muscles are made up of fascicles, or groups of muscle fibres, the arrangement of these fascicles may vary. This variation leads to a number of different muscle shapes throughout the body.

There are several ways of describing the various shapes of muscle, including:

■ Flat – muscles, such as the external oblique in the abdominal wall, may be flat, yet fairly broad. They may cover a wide area and sometimes insert into an aponeurosis (a broad sheet of connective tissue)

■ Fusiform – many muscles are of this 'spindle-shaped' form, where the rounded belly tapers at each end. Examples include the biceps and triceps muscles of the upper arm which have more than one head

■ Pennate – these muscles are named for their similarity to a feather (the word 'penna' means feather). They may be described as being unipennate (for example, extensor digitorum longus), bipennate (such as rectus femoris) or multipennate (for example, the deltoid). Multipennate muscles resemble a number of feathers placed next to one another

■ Circular – these muscles, also known as sphincteral muscles, surround body openings. Contraction of these muscles, where the fibres are arranged in concentric rings, closes the opening. Circular muscles within

the face include the orbicularis oculi, which closes the eye

■ Convergent – these muscles are fan-shaped and the muscle fibres arise from a wide origin and converge on a narrow tendon. In some cases, these muscles take on a triangular shape. Examples include the large pectoral muscles.

## Fascicle arrangement in relation to muscle structure

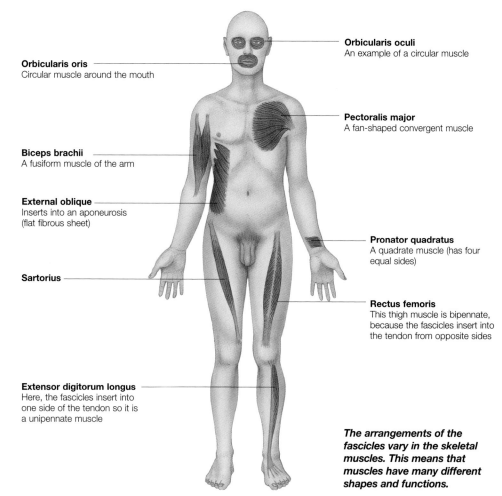

**Orbicularis oris**
Circular muscle around the mouth

**Biceps brachii**
A fusiform muscle of the arm

**External oblique**
Inserts into an aponeurosis (flat fibrous sheet)

**Sartorius**

**Extensor digitorum longus**
Here, the fascicles insert into one side of the tendon so it is a unipennate muscle

**Orbicularis oculi**
An example of a circular muscle

**Pectoralis major**
A fan-shaped convergent muscle

**Pronator quadratus**
A quadrate muscle (has four equal sides)

**Rectus femoris**
This thigh muscle is bipennate, because the fascicles insert into the tendon from opposite sides

*The arrangements of the fascicles vary in the skeletal muscles. This means that muscles have many different shapes and functions.*

## FUNCTION

The arrangement of the fascicles within a muscle influences that muscle's action and power. When muscle fibres contract, they shorten to about 70 per cent of their relaxed length. If the muscle is long with parallel fibres, such as the sartorius muscle in the leg, it can shorten a great deal but has

little strength.

If the degree of shortening is not as important as the power it can produce, the muscle may have numerous fibres packed tightly together and converging on a single point. This is the arrangement in multipennate muscles such as the deltoid in the shoulder.

---

## Cardiac muscle

### Microscopic structure of cardiac muscle

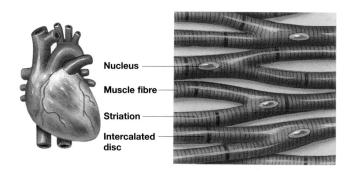

**Nucleus**

**Muscle fibre**

**Striation**

**Intercalated disc**

Cardiac muscle is a specialized form of striated muscle which is found only in the heart and walls of the great vessels adjoining it, such as the aorta and superior vena cava.

This type of muscle makes up almost all the mass of the thick heart walls, the myocardium. Here, the fibres are arranged in a distinctive spiral pattern which causes the blood to be squeezed through the heart as a wave of contraction spreads.

*The function of the cardiac muscle is to pump blood from the heart. This involuntary muscle contracts rhythmically and spontaneously.*

Although cardiac muscle is striated, it is not under conscious control like skeletal muscle, but is controlled by the autonomic nervous system. The fibres in cardiac muscle are unusual in that they branch and have specialized junctions called intercalated discs.

### RATE OF CONTRACTION

Cardiac muscle has the ability to contract spontaneously, without an external signal from a nerve although, in a healthy heart, the rate of contraction is controlled by the heart's nerve supply. Even when removed from the body, the heart will continue to contract for a short time.

# Overview of blood circulation

There are two blood vessel networks in the body. The pulmonary circulation transports blood between the heart and lungs; the systemic circulation supplies blood to all parts except the lungs.

The blood circulatory system can be divided into two parts:
■ Systemic circulation – those vessels that carry blood to and from all the tissues of the body
■ Pulmonary circulation – the vessels that carry blood through the lungs to take up oxygen and release carbon dioxide.

## SYSTEMIC ARTERIAL SYSTEM

The systemic arterial system carries blood away from the heart to nourish the tissues. Oxygenated blood from the lungs is first pumped into the aorta via the heart. Branches from the aorta pass to the upper limbs, head, trunk and the lower limbs in turn. These large branches give off smaller branches, which then divide again and again. The tiniest arteries (arterioles) feed blood into capillaries.

## PULMONARY CIRCULATION

With each beat of the heart, blood is pumped from the right ventricle into the lungs through the pulmonary artery (this carries deoxygenated blood). After many arterial divisions, the blood flows through the capillaries of the alveoli (air sacs) of the lung to be reoxygenated. The blood eventually enters one of the four pulmonary veins. These pass to the left atrium, from where the blood is pumped through the heart to the systemic circulation.

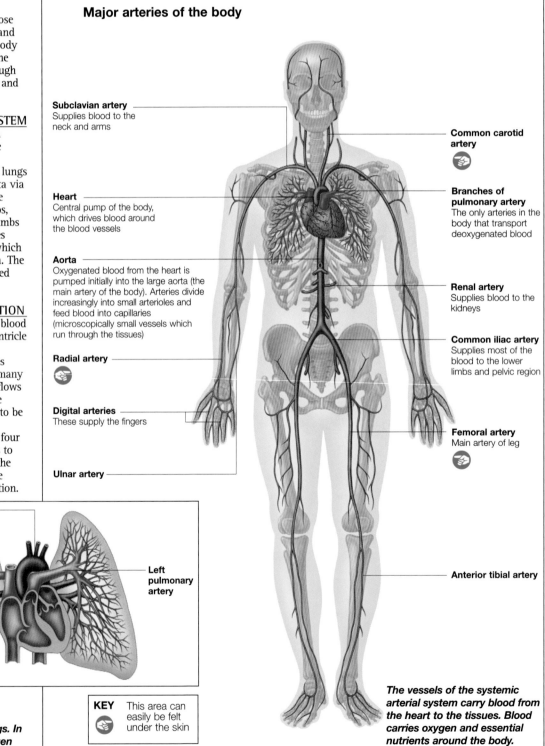

**Major arteries of the body**

**Subclavian artery**
Supplies blood to the neck and arms

**Heart**
Central pump of the body, which drives blood around the blood vessels

**Aorta**
Oxygenated blood from the heart is pumped initially into the large aorta (the main artery of the body). Arteries divide increasingly into small arterioles and feed blood into capillaries (microscopically small vessels which run through the tissues)

**Radial artery**

**Digital arteries**
These supply the fingers

**Ulnar artery**

**Common carotid artery**

**Branches of pulmonary artery**
The only arteries in the body that transport deoxygenated blood

**Renal artery**
Supplies blood to the kidneys

**Common iliac artery**
Supplies most of the blood to the lower limbs and pelvic region

**Femoral artery**
Main artery of leg

**Anterior tibial artery**

*The vessels of the systemic arterial system carry blood from the heart to the tissues. Blood carries oxygen and essential nutrients around the body.*

**Aortic arch**

**Right pulmonary artery**

**Left pulmonary artery**

*The pulmonary circulation involves the flow of blood between the heart and lungs. In the lungs, blood gains oxygen and loses waste carbon dioxide.*

**KEY** This area can easily be felt under the skin

# The venous system

The systemic venous system carries blood back to the heart from the tissues. This blood is then pumped through the pulmonary circulation to be reoxygenated before entering the systemic circulation again.

Veins originate in tiny venules that receive blood from the capillaries. The veins converge upon one another, forming increasingly large vessels until the two main collecting veins of the body, the superior and inferior vena cavae, are formed. These then drain into the heart. At any one time, about 65 per cent of the total blood volume is contained in the venous system.

### DIFFERENCES
The systemic venous system is similar in many ways to the arterial system. However, there are some important differences:
■ Vessel walls – arteries tend to have thicker walls than veins to cope with the greater pressure exerted by arterial blood.
■ Depth – most arteries lie deep within the body to protect them from injury, but many veins lie superficially, just under the skin.
■ Portal venous system – the blood that leaves the gut in the veins of the stomach and intestine does not pass directly back to the heart. It first passes into the hepatic portal venous system, which carries the blood through the liver tissues before it can return to the systemic circulation.
■ Variations – while the pattern of systemic arteries tends to be the same from person to person, there is far greater variability in the layout of the systemic veins.

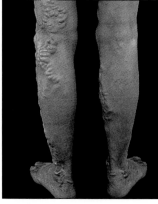

*Varicose veins are enlarged or twisted superficial veins, those of the leg being most commonly affected. They are caused by defective valves in the veins.*

## Major veins of the body

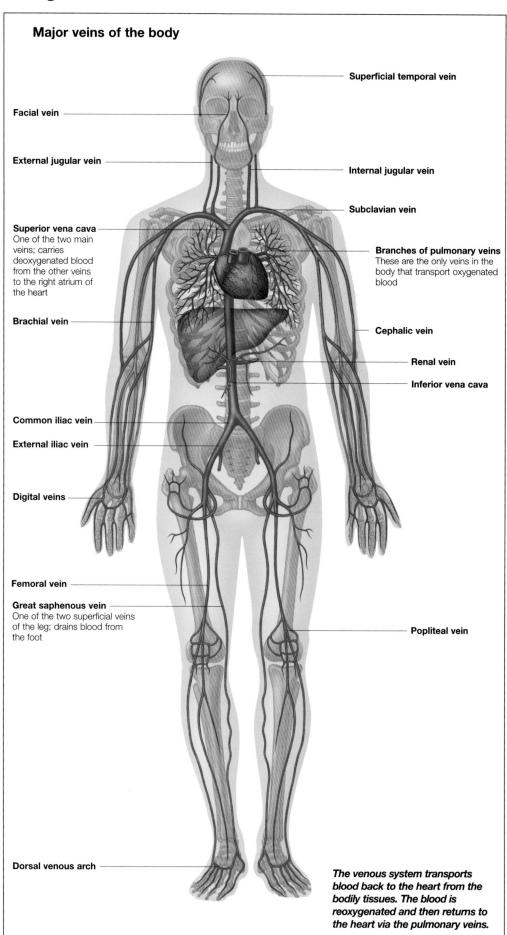

Superficial temporal vein

Facial vein

External jugular vein

Internal jugular vein

Subclavian vein

**Superior vena cava**
One of the two main veins; carries deoxygenated blood from the other veins to the right atrium of the heart

**Branches of pulmonary veins**
These are the only veins in the body that transport oxygenated blood

Brachial vein

Cephalic vein

Renal vein

Inferior vena cava

Common iliac vein

External iliac vein

Digital veins

Femoral vein

**Great saphenous vein**
One of the two superficial veins of the leg; drains blood from the foot

Popliteal vein

Dorsal venous arch

*The venous system transports blood back to the heart from the bodily tissues. The blood is reoxygenated and then returns to the heart via the pulmonary veins.*

# Peripheral nervous system

The peripheral nervous system includes all the body's nerve tissue that is not in the brain and spinal cord. Its principal anatomical components are the cranial and spinal nerves.

The nervous system of the human body is divided into two parts: the central nervous system (CNS) and the peripheral nervous system (PNS).

The major components of the PNS are:
■ Sensory receptors – specialized nerve endings which receive information about temperature, touch, pain, muscle stretching, and taste
■ Peripheral nerves – bundles of nerve fibres which carry information to and from the CNS
■ Motor nerve endings – specialized nerve endings which cause the muscle on which they lie to contract in response to a signal from the CNS.

## ARRANGEMENT

Peripheral nerves are of two types:
■ Cranial nerves
These emerge from the brain and are concerned with receiving information from, and allowing control of, the head and neck. There are 12 pairs of cranial nerves
■ Spinal nerves
These arise from the spinal cord, each containing thousands of nerve fibres, to supply the rest of the body. Many of the 31 pairs of spinal nerves enter one of the complex networks, such as the brachial plexus which serves the upper limb, before becoming part of a large peripheral nerve.

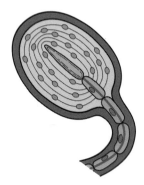

*Sensory nerve endings are either free endings or encapsulated. This 'Pacinian corpuscle' is an example of an encapsulated nerve ending.*

**Major nerves of the peripheral nervous system**

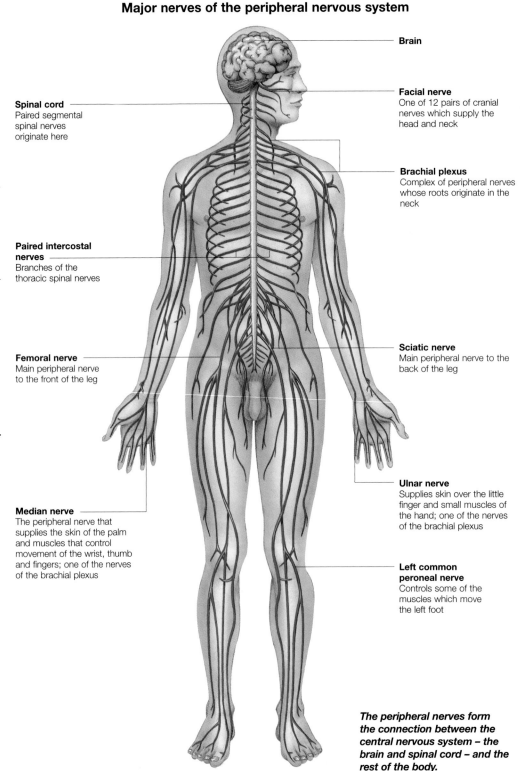

**Brain**

**Facial nerve**
One of 12 pairs of cranial nerves which supply the head and neck

**Brachial plexus**
Complex of peripheral nerves whose roots originate in the neck

**Spinal cord**
Paired segmental spinal nerves originate here

**Paired intercostal nerves**
Branches of the thoracic spinal nerves

**Femoral nerve**
Main peripheral nerve to the front of the leg

**Sciatic nerve**
Main peripheral nerve to the back of the leg

**Ulnar nerve**
Supplies skin over the little finger and small muscles of the hand; one of the nerves of the brachial plexus

**Median nerve**
The peripheral nerve that supplies the skin of the palm and muscles that control movement of the wrist, thumb and fingers; one of the nerves of the brachial plexus

**Left common peroneal nerve**
Controls some of the muscles which move the left foot

*The peripheral nerves form the connection between the central nervous system – the brain and spinal cord – and the rest of the body.*

# Structure of a peripheral nerve

Each peripheral nerve consists of separate nerve fibres, some with an insulating layer of myelin, enclosed within connective tissue.

The greater part of the final bulk of a peripheral nerve is made up of three protective connective tissue coverings, without which the fragile nerve fibres would be vulnerable to injury.

### ■ Endoneurium

The endoneurium is a layer of delicate connective tissue that surrounds the smallest unit of the peripheral nerve, the axon. This layer may also enclose an axon's myelin sheath.

### ■ Perineurium

The perineurium is a layer of connective tissue that encloses a group of protected nerve fibres, called fascicles, that are tied together in bundles.

### ■ Epineurium

Nerve fascicles are bound together by a tough connective tissue coat, the epineurium, into a peripheral nerve. The epineurium also encloses blood vessels which help to nourish the nerve fibres and their connective tissue coverings.

### NERVE FUNCTION

Most peripheral nerves carry information to and from the central nervous system (sensory and motor functions respectively), and thus are known as 'mixed' nerves.

Nerves that are either purely sensory or purely motor are very rare within the body.

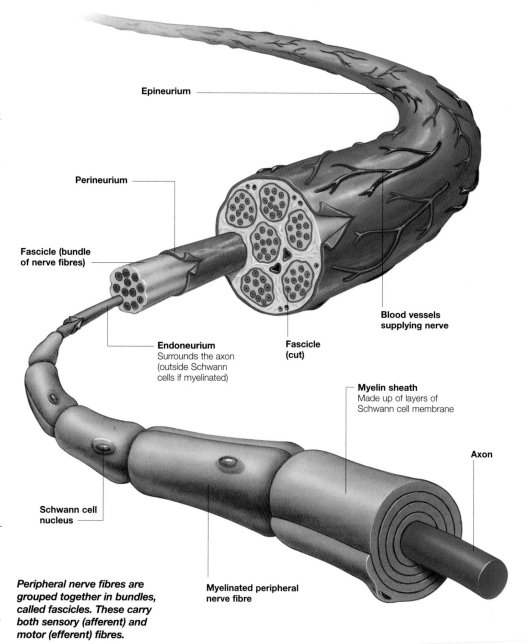

Epineurium

Perineurium

Fascicle (bundle of nerve fibres)

**Endoneurium**
Surrounds the axon (outside Schwann cells if myelinated)

**Fascicle (cut)**

**Blood vessels supplying nerve**

**Myelin sheath**
Made up of layers of Schwann cell membrane

**Axon**

Schwann cell nucleus

**Myelinated peripheral nerve fibre**

*Peripheral nerve fibres are grouped together in bundles, called fascicles. These carry both sensory (afferent) and motor (efferent) fibres.*

## Motor nerve endings

Motor nerve endings are specialized nerve fibres that lie on muscle fibres and secretory cells. They receive signals from the central nervous system via peripheral nerves and pass them on to cause muscles to contract or cells to secrete their products. In this way the CNS is able to control each part of the body.

### JUNCTION

The neuromuscular junction is where a motor nerve ending of a

*A neuromuscular junction is shown on this micrograph. The connections between the nerve fibre and voluntary muscle can be seen at the top of the image.*

peripheral nerve fibre connects with the voluntary muscle (also known as striated or skeletal muscle) which it supplies.

At the junction, the axon of a motor nerve fibre divides and branches several times, like a tree, to produce many tiny endings, which lie against a small muscle fibre.

### TRANSMITTING A SIGNAL

When an electrical signal is sent down the nerve fibre to the neuromuscular junction it is transmitted to the muscle fibre by chemicals (neurotransmitters) released by the motor nerve endings. The muscle then contracts in response.

# Autonomic nervous system

The autonomic nervous system provides the nerve supply to those parts of the body which are not consciously directed. It can be subdivided into the sympathetic and parasympathetic systems.

The autonomic nervous system is divided into two parts: the sympathetic system and the parasympathetic system. Both systems generally supply the same organs, but with opposing effects. In each system two neurones (nerve cells) make up the pathway from the central nervous system (CNS) to the organ which is being supplied.

## SYMPATHETIC NERVOUS SYSTEM

The effects upon the body of stimulation by the sympathetic nervous system are often referred to as the 'fight or flight' response. In exciting or dangerous situations, the sympathetic nervous system becomes more active, causing the heart rate to increase and the skin to become pale and sweaty as blood is diverted to muscle.

## STRUCTURE

The cell bodies of the neurones of the sympathetic nervous system lie within a section of the spinal cord. Fibres from these cell bodies exit the spinal column at the ventral root and pass through the white rami communicantes to reach the paravertebral sympathetic chain.

Some of the fibres which enter the sympathetic chain connect there with the second cell of their pathway. Fibres then exit through the grey rami communicantes to join the ventral spinal nerve.

**Anatomy of a sympathetic trunk**

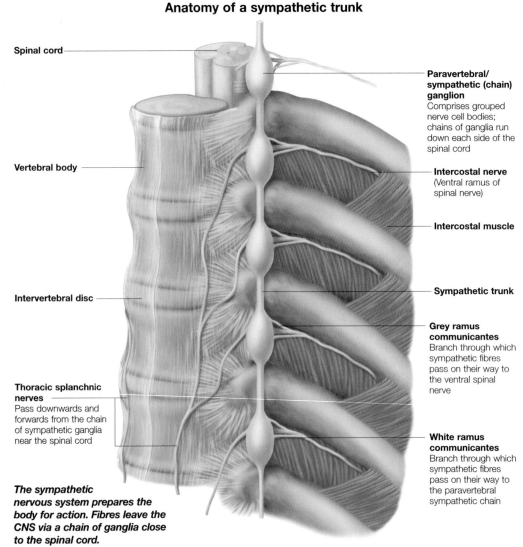

Spinal cord

Vertebral body

Intervertebral disc

**Thoracic splanchnic nerves**
Pass downwards and forwards from the chain of sympathetic ganglia near the spinal cord

**Paravertebral/ sympathetic (chain) ganglion**
Comprises grouped nerve cell bodies; chains of ganglia run down each side of the spinal cord

**Intercostal nerve**
(Ventral ramus of spinal nerve)

**Intercostal muscle**

**Sympathetic trunk**

**Grey ramus communicantes**
Branch through which sympathetic fibres pass on their way to the ventral spinal nerve

**White ramus communicantes**
Branch through which sympathetic fibres pass on their way to the paravertebral sympathetic chain

*The sympathetic nervous system prepares the body for action. Fibres leave the CNS via a chain of ganglia close to the spinal cord.*

## Adrenal medulla

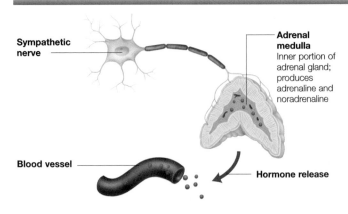

Sympathetic nerve

Blood vessel

**Adrenal medulla**
Inner portion of adrenal gland; produces adrenaline and noradrenaline

Hormone release

In its role as the mediator of the 'fight or flight' response, the sympathetic nervous system also stimulates the adrenal medulla, the inner portion of the adrenal gland.

The adrenal medulla, in turn, releases the hormones adrenaline and noradrenaline into the blood

*As a reaction to stress, the adrenal medulla is stimulated to release hormones into the bloodstream. These hormones prepare the body for action.*

stream. These hormones act upon many parts of the body to amplify the effects of the sympathetic nervous system.

The innervation of the adrenal medulla by the sympathetic nervous system is unique in the body in that there is only one neurone in the pathway from the CNS to the gland, rather than two. The adrenal medulla itself seems to act as a sympathetic ganglion, and indeed is derived embryologically from the same tissue.

# Parasympathetic nervous system

The parasympathetic system is the part of the autonomic nervous system which is most active during periods of rest.

The structure of the parasympathetic nervous system is simpler than that of the sympathetic nervous system.

## LOCATION OF CELL BODIES
The cell bodies of the first of the two neurones in the pathway are located in only two places:
■ The brainstem – fibres from the parasympathetic cell bodies in the grey matter of the brainstem leave the skull as part of a number of cranial nerves. Together, these fibres make up what is known as the cranial parasympathetic outflow
■ The sacral region of the spinal cord – the sacral outflow arises from parasympathetic cell bodies which lie within part of the spinal cord. Fibres leave through the ventral root.

Because of the locations of the origins of parasympathetic fibres, the parasympathetic system is sometimes known as the craniosacral division of the autonomic nervous system; the sympathetic system is known as the thoracolumbar division.

## DISTRIBUTION
The cranial outflow provides parasympathetic innervation for the head, and the sacral outflow supplies the pelvis. The area between (the majority of the abdominal and thoracic internal organs) is supplied by part of the cranial outflow which is carried within the vagus (tenth cranial nerve).

### Organs controlled by the parasympathetic nervous system

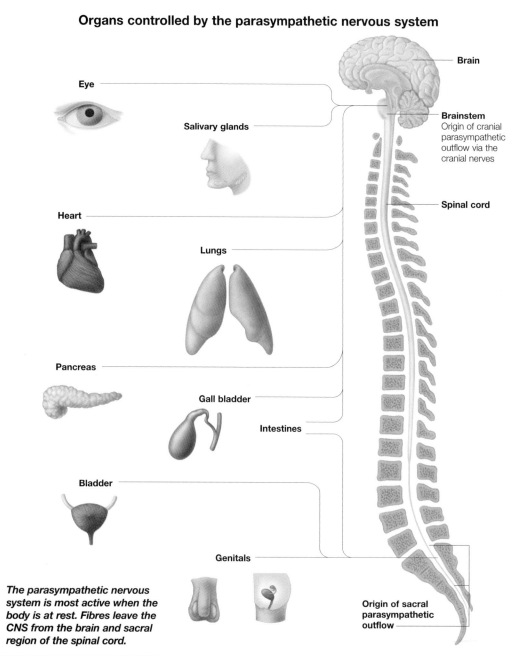

Eye

Salivary glands

Heart

Lungs

Pancreas

Gall bladder

Intestines

Bladder

Genitals

Brain

**Brainstem**
Origin of cranial parasympathetic outflow via the cranial nerves

**Spinal cord**

**Origin of sacral parasympathetic outflow**

*The parasympathetic nervous system is most active when the body is at rest. Fibres leave the CNS from the brain and sacral region of the spinal cord.*

---

## Opposing effects

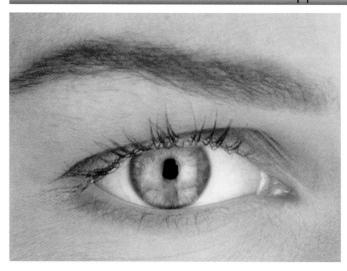

The sympathetic nervous system prepares the body in times of stress or danger, while the parasympathetic system helps the body to rest, digest food and conserve energy. As these tasks are in many ways mutually exclusive, the two systems often have opposite effects upon the body, some of which are:
■ Heart – the sympathetic system increases the rate and the strength of the heartbeat; the parasympathetic system

*The sympathetic and parasympathetic nervous systems have opposing effects on the eye. The former dilates the pupil; the latter constricts it.*

decreases them
■ Digestive tract – the sympathetic system inhibits digestion and reduces the blood supply; the parasympathetic system stimulates them
■ Liver – the sympathetic system encourages the breakdown of glycogen (a carbohydrate) in the liver to provide energy; the parasympathetic system encourages its formation
■ Salivary glands – the sympathetic system reduces the production of saliva, which also becomes thicker; the parasympathetic system promotes a free flow of watery saliva.

# Lymphatic system

The lymphatic system consists of a network of lymph vessels and organs and specialized cells throughout the body. It is an essential part of the body's defence against invading micro-organisms.

The lymphatic system is the lesser known part of the circulatory system, working together with the cardiovascular system to transport a fluid called lymph around the body. The lymphatic system plays a vital role in the defence of the body against disease.

### LYMPH FLUID

Lymph is a clear, watery fluid containing electrolytes and proteins which is derived from blood and bathes the body's tissues. Lymphocytes – specialized white blood cells involved in the body's immune system – are found in lymph. They attack and destroy foreign micro-organisms, thereby maintaining the body's health. This is known as an immune response.

Although the vessels of the lymphatic system carry lymph, the fluid is not pumped around the body as blood is; instead, contractions of muscles surrounding the lymph vessels move the fluid along.

### CONSTITUENT PARTS OF THE LYMPHATIC SYSTEM

The lymphatic system is made up of a number of interrelated parts:
■ Lymph nodes – lie along the routes of the lymphatic vessels and filter lymph
■ Lymphatic vessels – small capillaries leading to larger vessels that eventually drain lymph into the veins
■ Lymphoid cells (lymphocytes) – cells through which the body's immune response is mounted
■ Lymphoid tissues and organs – scattered throughout the body, these act as reservoirs for lymphoid cells and play an important role in immunity.

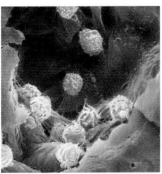

*Lymphocytes, white blood cells involved in the body's immune response, appear blue on this false-colour electron micrograph.*

**Lymphatic system**

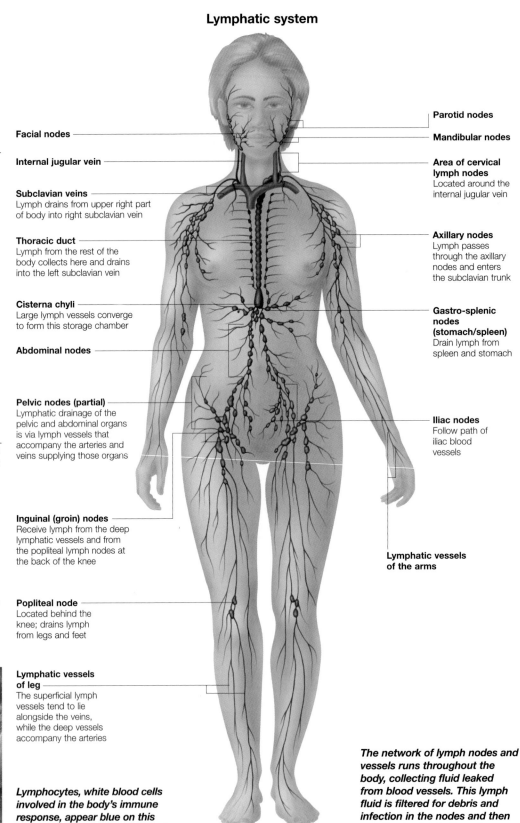

**Facial nodes**

**Internal jugular vein**

**Subclavian veins**
Lymph drains from upper right part of body into right subclavian vein

**Thoracic duct**
Lymph from the rest of the body collects here and drains into the left subclavian vein

**Cisterna chyli**
Large lymph vessels converge to form this storage chamber

**Abdominal nodes**

**Pelvic nodes (partial)**
Lymphatic drainage of the pelvic and abdominal organs is via lymph vessels that accompany the arteries and veins supplying those organs

**Inguinal (groin) nodes**
Receive lymph from the deep lymphatic vessels and from the popliteal lymph nodes at the back of the knee

**Popliteal node**
Located behind the knee; drains lymph from legs and feet

**Lymphatic vessels of leg**
The superficial lymph vessels tend to lie alongside the veins, while the deep vessels accompany the arteries

**Parotid nodes**

**Mandibular nodes**

**Area of cervical lymph nodes**
Located around the internal jugular vein

**Axillary nodes**
Lymph passes through the axillary nodes and enters the subclavian trunk

**Gastro-splenic nodes (stomach/spleen)**
Drain lymph from spleen and stomach

**Iliac nodes**
Follow path of iliac blood vessels

**Lymphatic vessels of the arms**

*The network of lymph nodes and vessels runs throughout the body, collecting fluid leaked from blood vessels. This lymph fluid is filtered for debris and infection in the nodes and then empties back into the veins.*

# Lymph nodes

Lymph nodes lie along the route of the lymphatic vessels. They filter the lymph for invading micro-organisms, infected cells and other foreign particles.

Lymph nodes are small, rounded organs that lie along the course of the lymphatic vessels and act as filters of the lymph. Lymph nodes vary in size, but they are mostly bean-shaped, 1–25 mm in length, surrounded by a fibrous capsule and usually embedded in connective tissue.

## LYMPH NODE FUNCTION

As well as fluid, the tiny lymphatic vessels in the tissues may pick up other items, such as parts of broken cells, bacteria and viruses. Within the lymph node, fluid slows and comes into contact with lymphoid cells which ingest any solid particles and recognize foreign micro-organisms. To prevent these particles from entering the bloodstream – and to allow the body to mount a defence against invading organisms – lymph is filtered through a number of lymph nodes before draining into the veins.

Some lymph nodes are grouped together in regions and given names according to their position, the region in which they are found (for example, the axillary nodes in the axilla, or armpit), the blood vessels they surround (such as the aortic nodes around the large central artery of the body, the aorta), or the organ they receive lymph from (pulmonary nodes in the lungs).

## Structure of a lymph node

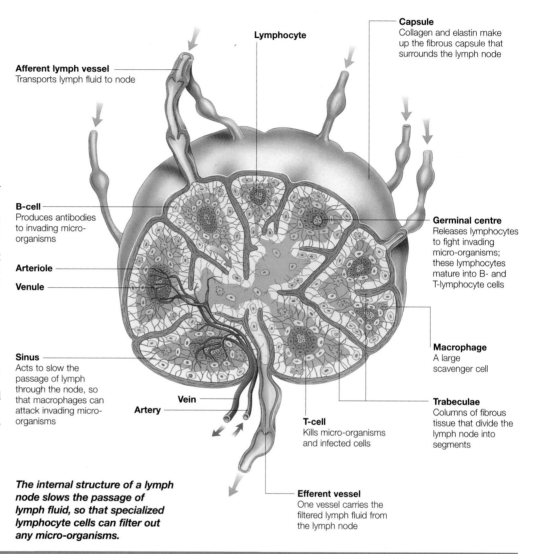

**Lymphocyte**

**Afferent lymph vessel**
Transports lymph fluid to node

**Capsule**
Collagen and elastin make up the fibrous capsule that surrounds the lymph node

**B-cell**
Produces antibodies to invading micro-organisms

**Arteriole**

**Venule**

**Sinus**
Acts to slow the passage of lymph through the node, so that macrophages can attack invading micro-organisms

**Germinal centre**
Releases lymphocytes to fight invading micro-organisms; these lymphocytes mature into B- and T-lymphocyte cells

**Macrophage**
A large scavenger cell

**Trabeculae**
Columns of fibrous tissue that divide the lymph node into segments

**Vein**

**Artery**

**T-cell**
Kills micro-organisms and infected cells

**Efferent vessel**
One vessel carries the filtered lymph fluid from the lymph node

*The internal structure of a lymph node slows the passage of lymph fluid, so that specialized lymphocyte cells can filter out any micro-organisms.*

## Lymph vessels

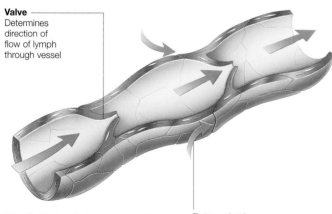

**Valve**
Determines direction of flow of lymph through vessel

*The fluid circulating around the cells in tissues drains into lymph capillaries. From here, it flows through valves in these vessels to the lymph nodes.*

**Entry point for interstitial fluid**
Lymph fluid is called interstitial fluid before it has drained into the lymph capillaries

Arteries supply blood to the body's tissues under pressure. This has the effect of causing fluid and proteins to leak out of the tiny capillaries and into the spaces around the cells of those tissues.

Much of this leaked fluid will pass back into the capillaries, which gradually converge to form veins that carry blood back to the heart for further circulation. However, some of the fluid – and the proteins – remain behind and would accumulate in the tissues were it not for the network of tiny lymphatic vessels in the tissue spaces.

The lymph fluid travels up the converging lymphatic vessels, which eventually join to form the main lymphatic trunks. These unite to form the two large lymphatic ducts – the thoracic duct and the right lymphatic duct. These drain into the large veins above the heart, returning the retrieved fluid and proteins to the bloodstream.

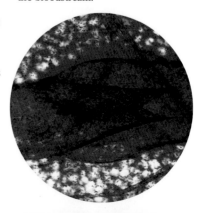

*A valve within a lymph vessel is seen in this light micrograph. The valve allows lymph fluid to pass in one direction only.*

# Skin and nails

The skin, together with the hair and nails, makes up
the integumentary system. Functions of the skin include heat
regulation and defence against microbial attack.

The skin covers the entire
human body and has a surface
area of about 1.5–2 m². It
accounts for about 7 per cent of
the weight of the body and
weighs around 4 kg.

## TWO LAYERS

Skin is composed of two layers –
the epidermis and dermis.

■ Epidermis – this is the thinner
of the two layers of skin and
serves as a tough protective
covering for the underlying
dermis. It is made up of
numerous layers of cells, the
innermost of which consist of
living cube-shaped cells that
divide rapidly, providing cells for
the outer layers.

By the time these cells reach
the outer layers, they have died
and become flattened, before
being 'sloughed off' by abrasion.
The epidermis has no blood
supply of its own, and depends
upon diffusion of nutrients from
the plentiful supply of blood to
the dermis below

■ Dermis – this is the thicker
layer of skin, which lies
protected under the epidermis. It
is composed of connective tissue
which has elastic fibres to keep
it stretchy, and collagen fibres
for strength. The dermis contains
a rich supply of blood vessels as
well as numerous sensory nerve
endings. Lying within this layer
are the other important
structures of the integumentary
system, including hair follicles
and oil (sebaceous) and sweat
glands.

## Cross section of skin

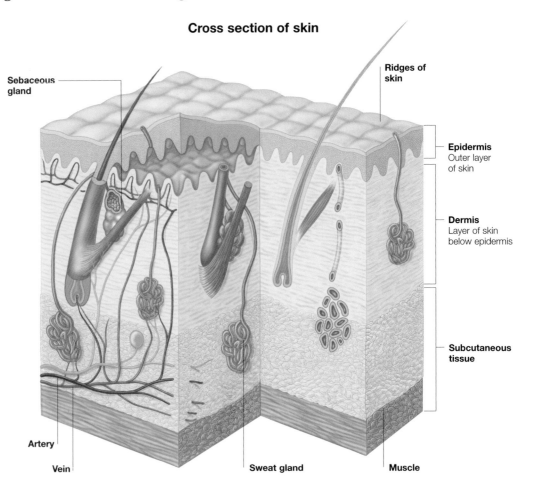

Sebaceous
gland

Ridges of
skin

**Epidermis**
Outer layer
of skin

**Dermis**
Layer of skin
below epidermis

**Subcutaneous
tissue**

Artery

Vein

Sweat gland

Muscle

*The skin has been described as
the largest organ in the body. It
helps to regulate temperature
through narrowing and widening
of blood vessels in the dermis.*

## Skin colour

The colour of skin varies greatly,
not just between different races,
but also between individuals of
the same race.

### THREE PIGMENTS

Skin colour is determined by
three pigments: melanin,
carotene and haemoglobin.
Melanin, which ranges in colour
from red to brown to black, is
made in specialized cells called
melanocytes that lie within the

*Skin colour varies greatly
between individuals, especially
between those of different racial
groups. This is due to varying
levels of the three skin pigments.*

lower layers of the epidermis. All
humans of all racial groups have
the same number of melanocytes
even though skin colour varies
so widely. The melanocytes of
dark-skinned people produce
more and darker melanin than
those of light-skinned people.

Carotene is an orange
pigment, absorbed from
vegetables such as carrots. It
accumulates in the outermost
layer of the epidermis and is
most noticeable on the palms
and soles. Haemoglobin within
the blood vessels of the dermis
gives the skin a pinkish hue,
especially if there is little
melanin present in the skin.

# Nails

Human nails are the equivalent of the hooves or claws of other animals. They form a hard protective covering for the vulnerable fingers and toes, and they provide a useful tool for scratching or scraping when this is required.

Nails lie on the dorsal (back) surfaces of the ends of the fingers and toes, overlying the terminal phalanx, or final bone, of each.

## CONSTITUENT PARTS

The parts of the nail include:
■ Nail plate – each nail is composed of a plate of hard keratin (the same substance as is found in hair) which is continuously produced at its root
■ Nail folds – except for the free edge of the nail, at its furthermost end, the nail is surrounded and overlapped by folds of skin (nail folds)
■ Free edge – the nail separates from the underlying surface at its furthermost point to form a free edge. The extent of this nail at the free edge depends upon personal preference and wear and tear
■ Root, or matrix – this lies at the base of the nail beneath the nail itself and the nailfold. This part of the nail is closest to the skin, and it is here that the hard keratin of the nail is produced by cell division. If the root of the nail is destroyed the nail cannot grow back
■ Lunula – the paler, crescent-shaped area located at the base

of the nail where the matrix is visible through the nail
■ Cuticle (eponychium). This covers the proximal (near) end of the nail and extends over the nail plate to help protect the matrix from infection by invading micro-organisms.

**Cross section of nail**

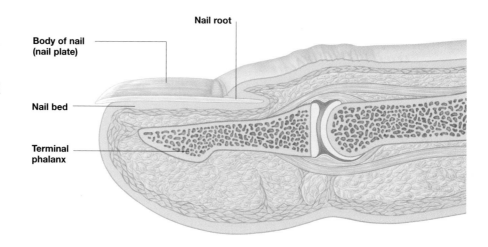

Nail root
Body of nail (nail plate)
Nail bed
Terminal phalanx

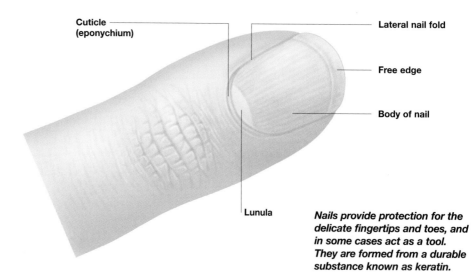

Cuticle (eponychium)
Lateral nail fold
Free edge
Body of nail
Lunula

*Nails provide protection for the delicate fingertips and toes, and in some cases act as a tool. They are formed from a durable substance known as keratin.*

## GROWTH

Fingernails grow much more quickly than toenails. A mark made over the lunula of a fingernail will take three months to reach the free edge, whereas the corresponding time for a toenail may be up to two years. For a normal rate of growth, and

to produce normal, pink, healthy nails, there needs to be a good blood supply to the root of the nail; nails look pink because of the large number of blood vessels in the dermis. Nails grow at a rate of about 0.1mm a day, but when there is injury to a nail, the growth speeds up.

## Psoriasis

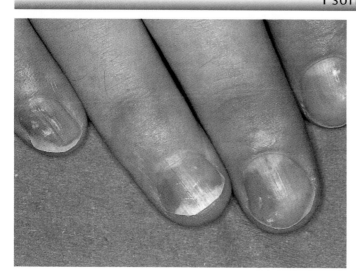

Psoriasis is a troublesome skin condition that occurs in about 2 per cent of the population. Its cause is unknown, although there seems to be an inherited factor in some cases. The onset tends to occur in adolescence and further attacks may be triggered by stress or infection.

### CELL BUILD-UP

The main feature of psoriasis is a very rapid proliferation of the cells at the base of the

*Psoriasis causes certain characteristic changes to the nails. The nails may be pitted, thick and ridged, and may be loosened from the nail bed.*

epidermis, the outermost layer of the skin. This causes a build up of cells in the epidermis which then form red, scaly plaques.

For many people, psoriasis is no more than a nuisance which recurs from time to time. For some, however, it is a severe debilitating disease that can affect other parts of the body as well, such as the joints.

### ABNORMAL NAILS

The nails are often affected in psoriasis. Separation of the nail plate from the nail bed at its distal end (onycholysis) can occur as well as general thickening and ridging of the nails (dystrophy).

# Index

## A

abdomen 154
  contents 154
  planes/regions 155
  surgical incisions 155
abdominal ureter 181
abdominal viscera 154
abdominal wall 156
  deep muscles 157
  layers 156
abducens nerve (CN VI) 43
  role in eye movements 43
abduction
  arm 127
  wrist 147
abductor digiti minimi 150, 151, 230
abductor hallucis 230
abductor pollicis brevis 150, 151
abscesses
  palatine tonsils 78
  retropharyngeal 67
accessory cephalic vein 142
accessory coronary arteries 121
accessory hemiazygos vein 159
accessory lacrimal gland 45
accessory muscles, respiration 103
accessory nerve (CN XI), pharyngeal muscle innervation 79
accessory parotid glands 56
accessory saphenous vein 218
accommodation 41
acetabular labrum 202
acetabulum 197
Achilles tendon (calcaneal) 215, 228
achondroplasia 12
acromioclavicular joint 96
acromion process 96, 97, 124, 125
Adamkiewicz, artery of 93
Adam's apple 72, 79, 80, 82
adduction, shoulder 126
adductor brevis muscle 205, 213
adductor hallucis muscle 231
adductor longus muscle 205, 212, 213
adductor magnus muscle 205, 213
adductor pollicis muscle 151
adrenal artery 177
adrenal cortex 177
adrenal glands 177
  blood supply 177
  differences between left/right 177
  structure 177
adrenal medulla 177, 242
adrenaline 242
adventitia 158, 181, 192
ageing, effect on loss of smell and taste 33
alar cartilage 46
alveolar capillary plexus 112
alveolar ducts 111
  opening 111
alveolar nerve
  anterior superior 61
  inferior 58, 59
    block 59
  posterior superior 61
alveolar pulmonary plexus 112
alveolar sacs 110, 111
  capillary plexus 112
alveoli 111, 238
  lymphatic vessel 112
amphiarthroses 234
ampulla(e)
  inner ear 65
  rectum 170
  uterine tubes 195

ampulla of Vater 165, 172
  sphincter 172
amygdala 26
amylase, salvia component 56
anaesthesia 128
  dental 59
anal canal 170
  nerves 171
anal sinuses 170
anal sphincter 88, 170
  external 170
  internal 170
anal valves 170
anastomoses
  elbow 140
  forearm 141
anatomical snuffbox 145
anconeus muscle 137
angiography 19
  aorta 36
  carotid 36
  veins of brain 19
ankle joint 222
  injuries 223
    fracture-dislocations 207
    sprains 223
  ligaments 223
  movements 222
  tendons 228
ankylosing spondylitis 89
annular ligament 135
annulus fibrosis 68, 87
anorectal flexure 170
anorectal hiatus 199
anosmia 8, 33, 47
  due to head injuries 33
  effect of ageing 33
  loss of taste sensation 33
anserine bursa 211
anterior cerebral arteries 18
anterior chamber of eye 40
anterior corticospinal tract 91
anterior median fissure 92
anterior pituitary gland 17, 25
anterior scalene muscle 102
anterior spinal arteries 93
anterior spinal nerve roots 92, 93
anterior spinocerebellar tract 91
anterior spinothalamic tract 91
anterior superior alveolar nerve 61
anterior superior iliac spine 88, 174, 197, 200
anterior tibial arteries 216
anterior tibial veins 219
anterior tibiofibular ligaments 207
anterior tibiotalar ligaments 223
anvil 62, 64
aorta 120, 238
  angiography 36
  arch 114, 120
  descending 158
  diaphragmatic passage 107
  pancreas relationship 172
aortic aperture 107
aortic sinuses 119
aortic valve 116, 119
aortobronchial constriction 158
apex of heart 114, 116
aphthous ulcers 55
  treatment 55
appendices epiploicae 168
appendicitis 167
appendicular artery 167
appendix 166, 167
  muscle layer 167
  positions 167
  retrocaecal position 167
aqueous humour 40
arachnoid granulations 21
arachnoid mater 14, 21, 93
arches, foot see foot arches
arcuate artery 179, 217
arcuate ligaments 106
arcuate popliteal ligament 210
arcuate vein 179
areola 104
arm
  blood vessels 140
    deep veins 141

superficial veins 141
  cross-section 137
  lymphatic vessels 244
  movements 132
  muscles
    anterior (front) 136
    forearm see forearm muscles
    posterior (back) 137
    upper arm 136–137
  nerves 142
  rotation 127
armpit see axilla
arteries 238
  vs veins 239
arteriograms 217
arteriovenous malformations 19
artery of Adamkiewicz 93
arthritis 203
arthroscopy 211
articular cartilage (hyaline) 131, 202, 235
  ankle joint 222
  shoulder 124
articular cavity 101
articular disc 145
articularis genus muscle 205
aryepiglottic folds 80, 81
aryepiglottic muscles 81
arytenoid cartilages 80, 81
  muscular control of movement 81
ascending tracts (spinal cord) 91
  see also individual paths
astigmatism 41
atherosclerosis, leg 217
atlas 68, 70, 71
atria 116, 117
  contraction 123
  openings 117
  valves 117
atrial septal defects 117
atrioventricular bundle 122, 123
atrioventricular node 122
atrioventricular valves 117, 118
auditory cortex
  association area 23
  primary see primary auditory cortex
auditory meatus
  external 62, 63
  internal 62
auditory tube see Eustachian tube
Auerbach's plexus (myenteric) 159
auricle see pinna (earlobe)
auricle (heart), right 117
auriculotemporal nerve 59
auriscope 62
autonomic nervous system 242
  anal canal 171
  digestive tract 171
  heart 122, 243
  hypothalamic control 25
  liver 243
  rectum 171
  salivary glands 243
  smooth muscle 236
  structure 242
avascular necrosis, hip joint 202
axilla (armpit) 128
  borders 129
  lymphatics 128
  vessels and nerves 128
axillary artery 105, 128, 140
axillary lymph nodes 105, 128
axillary nerve 142
axillary nodes 244
axillary sheath 128
axillary tail of breast 104
axillary vein 105, 128, 141
axis 68, 70, 71
azygos vein 159
  diaphragmatic passage 107

## B

back
  bending forwards 94
  straightening 94
back muscles 94–95

deep 95, 99
  attachments 95
  layers 95
  support of head and neck 95
  superficial 94, 99
backbone see vertebral column
ball and socket joints 124, 202
barium studies, ileocaecal valve 166
basal ganglia 17, 28–29
  components 28
  disorders 29
  locations 28
  role 29
  shape 28, 29
  structure and connections 29
  terminology/grouping of nuclei 28
basilar artery 18
basilic vein 141, 152
'bat' ears 63
B-cell 245
Bell's palsy 38
bending forwards, vertebral column 94
biceps brachii muscle 126, 136, 237
  long head 136
  short head 126
biceps brachii tendon 135, 136
biceps femoris muscle 205, 213
biceps tendon 136, 213
  rupture 136
bicipital aponeurosis 136
bicipital groove 136
bicuspid teeth (premolar) 52
bicuspid (mitral) valve 116, 118
bile 165
bile duct, common 165
biliary system 164, 165
  ducts 165
  passage of bile 165
bladder 176, 180
  female anatomy 180
  male anatomy 180
  position 180
  pregnancy 191
blood, oxygenated 112
blood circulation 238
  pulmonary 112, 238
  systemic arterial 238
  venous system 239
  see also individual systems
blood supply
  adrenal glands 177
  breast 104
  caecum 166
  colon 169
  duodenum 162
  forearm 140, 141
  hand 140, 152
  heart 121
  hip joint 202
  ileum 163
  jejunum 163
  kidneys 179
  legs 218, 219
  liver 165
  lungs 112–113
  mouth (oral cavity) 50
  oesophagus 159
  ovaries 194
  penis 187
  reproductive system (female) 189
  respiratory airways 112
  scalp 15
  spinal nerves 93
  stomach 161
  testis 185
  thyroid glands 83
  uterine (fallopian) tube 195
  see also individual arteries, veins and anatomical regions
blood test, site 141
body temperature, hypothalamic control 25
bone(s)
  cancellous 131
  cancers 85

cortical 131, 206
decalcification 83
formation 232
functions 232
tissue 131
see also individual bones
bone marrow 131, 204
Bowman's capsule 178
brachial artery 140
brachial fascia 137
brachial plexus 76, 128, 240
  branches and divisions 76
  cords 76
  injuries 76
  nerve block 128
  roots 76
  trunks 76
brachial vein 141, 239
brachiocephalic veins 113, 159
brachioradialis muscle 126, 139
brachycephaly 12
brain 16–31
  arterial network 18
    consequences of stopping blood supply 18
  blood vessels 18–19
  coronal section 28
  cross section 17
  development 22
  evolution 27
  grey matter 16, 22
  gyri see gyri
  inferior view (from below) 18
  lobes 16, 22
    see also individual lobes
  membranes 14, 21
  motor body map 23
  sagittal section 74
  sensory body map 23
  sinuses (blood channels) 19
    functions 19
  sub-cortical nuclei 16
  sulci see sulci
  veins 19
    visualization 19
  ventricles see ventricles (brain)
  white matter 16, 22
  see also cerebral hemispheres
brainstem 17, 27, 74–75
  arterial supply 18
  cerebellum connection 30
  decussation of pyramids 74
  divisions 74
  limbic system connections 27
  relationships 74
  structure and cross sections 75
  testing of function 75
brainstem death 75
breast (female) 104–105
  axillary tail 104
  blood vessels 104
  lymphatic drainage 105
  structure 104
breast cancer 105
  lymph node metastasis 105
breastbone see sternum (breastbone)
broad ligament 188, 194
Broca's area 16, 23
'broken hip' 205
bronchi 110, 112
  structure 111
bronchial arteries 112
bronchial tree 111
bronchioles 111, 112
bronchomediastinal lymph nodes 113
bronchopulmonary lymph nodes 113
bronchopulmonary segments 108
  bronchial supply 111, 112
  clinical significance 108
Brunner's gland 162
buccal nerves 38, 58, 59
buccinator 34, 35

functions 35
bulbar conjunctiva 44
bulbospongiosus 187
bursae 124
    gluteal region 201
    knee joint 208, 210, 211
    subacromial 124
    subscapular 124

C
caecal artery, anterior 166
caecum 154, 163, 166
    blood supply 166
calcaneal tendon (Achilles)
    215, 228
calcaneal tuberosity 224
calcanean branch, tibial artery
    217
calcaneofibular ligament 223
calcaneus bone (heel) 224, 227
    articular surfaces 224
    posterior surfaces 224
calcarine sulcus 16, 17
calcitonin, secretion 82
calculi (calcified stones),
    blockage of salivary ducts
    57
calculus 53
calf muscles see leg muscles
calvaria 8, 12
Camper's fascia 156
cancellous bone 131
canines 52
capillaries 238
capitate (wrist bone) 144, 145,
    146
capitulum 130
cardia 160
cardiac cycle 123
cardiac muscle 237
    fibres 115
    rate of contraction 237
cardiac notch, of lung 108
cardiac tamponade 115
cardiac veins 121
carina 110
carinal lymph nodes 113
carotene 246
carotid angiography 36
carotid artery 58
carotid canal 13
carotid endarterectomy 36
carotid sheath 36, 37, 67
carpal tunnel 143, 146
carpal tunnel syndrome 143,
    146
carpometacarpal joints 149
carpus 232
cartilage 232
cartilaginous joints 234
    primary 235
    secondary 235
cataract 40
cauda equina 90, 92
caudate nucleus 28
    shape 29
cauliflower ears 63
caval aperture 107
cavernous sinus 19
    thrombosis 37
central sulcus 16, 17, 22
central venous pressure,
    measurement 37
cephalic vein 129, 137, 141,
    152, 239
    accessory 142
cerebellar arteries 18
cerebellar cortex 31
    layers 31
cerebellar peduncles 17, 30, 31
    inferior 30
    middle 30
    superior 30, 31
cerebellum 17, 30–31
    arterial supply 18
    brainstem connection 30
    functions 17, 30
    nuclei 31
    structure 30, 31
        folia 30
        lobes 30
        vermis 30, 31

cerebral aqueduct 20, 21, 75
    blockage 21
cerebral arteries 18
cerebral cortex 27
    cerebellar connections 31
    limbic system connections
        27
cerebral hemispheres 16,
    22–23
    arterial supply 18
    association areas 23
    divisions 23
    functions 23
    lobes 16, 22
        see also individual lobes
    right 17
    see also brain
cerebral peduncles 75
cerebral veins
    great 19
        cistern of 21
    visualization 19
cerebromedullary cisterna 21
cerebrospinal fluid (CSF) 20
    analysis 21, 92
    circulation 21
    colour changes 20
    drainage 21
    functions 93
    obstruction of flow 20
        in hydrocephalus 21
    production 20, 93
cerumen (earwax), secretion 63
cervical canal 193
cervical curvature of spine 68,
    69
cervical nerves 38
    sensory nerve supply
        to skin 38
cervical os 193
cervical pleura 109
cervical ribs 71
cervical vertebrae 69, 70–71,
    232
    abnormalities 71
    dens see odontoid process
        (dens)
    dislocations 70
    fractures 70
    in neck 67
    thoracic vertebrae
        comparison 85
    transverse process 70
    typical 70
    vertebral arch 70
cervix 188, 190, 193
    lining 193
    structure 193
chest wall
    expansion 103
    internal view 102
chewing 58
childbirth, pelvic canal changes
    197
choana 47, 78
chorda tympani 58
    role in taste sensations 58
chordae tendineae 116, 119
    action 118
choroid 40, 41
choroid plexus 20, 21
    CSF production 20, 93
    villous processes 21
ciliary body 40, 41
ciliary glands 44
ciliary muscle 40
    fibres 41
ciliary process 41
cingulate gyrus 26
circle of Willis 18
circular muscle 158, 159, 237
circumduction, shoulder 126
circumflex arteries 140
circumflex femoral arteries 202
circumvallate papillae 54
cisterna chyli 244
claustrum 28
clavicle (collar bone) 96, 124,
    125, 232
    fracture 98
    functions 96
    joints 96

clavipectoral fascia 129
cleft palate 13, 50
    harelip 50
clitoris 188, 192
coccydynia 89
    causes and treatment 89
coccygeal nerve 89
coccyx (coccygeal) 69, 88,
    191, 196, 200
    clinical aspects 89
    transverse process 88
cochlea 62, 64, 65
    hair cells 65
cochlear implants 65
colic arteries 169
colic veins 169
colitis 169
collagen fibres 235
collar bone see clavicle (collar
    bone)
collateral ligaments
    medial 134
    radial 147
    tibial 207, 209, 210
    ulnar 135, 147
Colles' fracture 133
colon 168
    ascending 154, 168
    blood supply 169
    descending 154, 168
    lining 168
    mucosa 168
    transverse 168
    venous drainage 169
colposcopy 193
common bile duct 165
common carotid arteries 36,
    67, 82, 238
    bifurcation 36
    origins 36
common facial vein 37
common hepatic duct 165
common iliac arteries 238
common iliac veins 171, 239
compound fracture 207
computerized tomography (CT)
    scan, dead tissue following
    cerebral artery blockage 18
concha 63
conductive deafness 65
    hearing aids 65
condylar region 131
condyles 204
    definition 233
cone cells 41
congenital abnormalities,
    kidney 179
conjoint tendon 174
conjunctiva 35, 40, 41, 44
    bulbar 44
    infection/irritation 44
    palpebral 44
conjunctival fornices 44
conus arteriosus 116
conus medullaris 90
coraco-acromial ligaments 125
coracobrachialis muscle 126,
    127, 136
coracohumeral ligaments 125
coracoid process 96, 97, 124,
    125, 126
cornea 40, 41
    increased opacity 40
    irritation 43
    ulceration 45
corona of glans 182
coronal suture 9, 10, 11, 12
coronary arteries 121
    accessory 121
    variations 121
coronary ligament 164
coronary sinus 117, 121
coronoid process 132, 135
corpora cavernosa 186
corpus callosum 16, 17
corpus cavernosum 187
corpus luteum 194
corpus spongiosum 186
corpus striatum 28
Corti, organ of 65
cortical bone 131, 206
corticospinal tracts 91

costal cartilages 100, 101, 232
    attachments 101
    movement during
        respiration 101
costal pleura 109
costochondral joint 101
costoclavicular ligament 96
costocoracoid membrane 129
costodiaphragmatic recess 109
costomediastinal recess 109
cranial nerves 32, 240
    autonomic nerve fibres 32
    in brainstem 74
    functions 32
    motor fibres 32
    sensory nerve fibres 32
    see also individual nerves
craniostenosis 12
cranium 8
    bones 11
    divisions 8
    growth 10
crest, definition 233
cribriform plate 47
cricoid cartilage 80, 81, 110,
    158
cricopharyngeus 79
cricothyroid membrane 80
cricothyroidostomy 80
crista galli 9
crista terminalis 117
Crohn's disease, sacro-iliitis 89
cruciate ligaments 209, 210
    anterior 207, 210
    posterior 207, 210
cubital artery 140
cuboid 224, 227
cuneate nucleus 75
cuneiform bones 224
cuticle (eponychium), nail 247
cysterna chyli 169
cystic duct 165

D
dartos fascia 184
deafness 65
    management 65
death, brainstem 75
death certification 75
deciduous teeth 52
deep back muscles see back
    muscles
deep dorsal arteries 187
deep dorsal veins 187
deep flexor forearm muscles
    138
deep inguinal rings 174
deep palmar arch 152
deep peroneal nerve 221
deep petrosal nerve 61
deep plantar arteries 217
deep vein(s), leg 219
deep vein thrombosis (DVT) 219
    causes 219
deltoid ligament 223
deltoid muscle 94, 98, 127, 142
    shoulder joint 124, 125, 126
dens see odontoid process
    (dens)
dental anaesthetics 59
dental arch 50
dental caries 53
dentate nuclei 31
denticulate ligaments 93
dentine 52
depressor anguli oris 34
dermatomes 77
    arrangement 77
    clinical importance 77
dermis 246
detrusor muscle 180
diabetes mellitus, retinal
    damage 40
diaphragm 106–107, 154, 158,
    164
    abdominal surface
        (underside) 106
    apertures 107
    central tendon 106
    contraction 107
    costal part 106
    function 107

lumbar (vertebral) part 106
    muscle 106
    nerve supply 106
    perforations 106, 107
    pleura 107, 109
    position 107
    sternal part 106
    thoracic surface (from
        above) 107
diaphragmatic pleura 107, 109
diaphysis 131, 204
diarthroses 234
diencephalon 17
    hypothalamus 25
        see also hypothalamus
    thalamus 24
        see also thalamus
digastric muscle 72, 79
    actions 73
    anterior belly 55, 72
    posterior belly 72
digestive tract, autonomic
    nervous system 171
digital arteries 140, 152, 217,
    238
digital veins 141, 152, 239
dilator muscles 34
diplöe (cancellous bone) 11, 14
diploic veins 14, 37
dislocations
    ankle joint 207
    cervical vertebrae 70
    elbow joint 135
    fingers 149
    jaw 39
    shoulder joint 125
dorsal arteries, deep 187
dorsal columns 91
dorsal digital arteries 217
dorsal interosseous muscles 150
dorsal metacarpal ligaments 147
dorsal metatarsal arteries 217
dorsal radiocarpal ligaments
    147
dorsal ramus 92
dorsal root ganglion (DRG) 92
dorsal spinal nerve roots 92, 93
dorsal vagal nucleus 75
dorsal veins, deep 187
dorsal venous arch 219, 239
dorsalis pedis artery 216, 217,
    229
dorsalis pedis vein 219
dorsiflexion 222
dry eye 45
dry mouth (xerostomia) 56
ductus arteriosus 120
duodenal papilla 172
    major 165
    minor 172
duodenojejunal flexure 172
duodenum 162, 172
    blood supply 162
    structure 162
    submucosa 162
duplex ureters 179
dura mater 14, 21, 93
dysphagia, due to thyroid
    gland disorders 82, 83
dyspnoea, due to thyroid gland
    disorders 82, 83

E
ear 62–65
    deformities 63
    external see external ear
    inner see inner ear
    middle see middle ear
    protection
    vibration transmission 64
ear drum see tympanic
    membrane (ear drum)
earlobe see pinna (earlobe)
earwax 63
eating and drinking,
    hypothalamic control 25
ectocervix 193
efferent vessel 245
ejaculatory duct 182
elbow joint 132, 134, 234
    carrying angle 135
    cross-section 135

dislocation 135
ligaments 135
movement 134
emboliform nuclei 31
emissary foramina 13
emissary veins 13, 37
emmetropia 41
emotional behaviour
hypothalamic control 25
enamel 52
endocardium 115
endocervix 193
endolymph 65
endolymphatic sac 62, 64, 65
endometrium 190, 191
endomysium 236
endoneurium 241
epicardium 115
epicondyles
definition 233
humerus 130
medial 135
epidermis 246
epididymis 182, 184
epidural space 93
epigastric region 155
epiglottis 78, 80, 81, 158
inflammation of cartilage 78
protection from inhaled
objects 79
epilepsy, temporal lobe 27
epineurium 241
epiphysis 131, 204
episiotomy 198
epistaxis 46
epithalamus 17
erector spinae muscle 94
ethmoid air cells 49
ethmoidal sinuses 8, 9, 48
location 49
Eustachian tube 62, 64
blockage 78
infection route 64, 78
muscular control of opening
50
pharyngeal opening 78
exophthalmos 42
expiration, diaphragmatic
movements 107
extension, elbow joint 134
extensor carpi radialis brevis
139
extensor carpi radialis longus
139
extensor carpi ulnaris 139
extensor digitorum 139
extensor digitorum brevis 221,
229
extensor digitorum longus
214, 228, 229, 237
extensor digitorum tendons 150
extensor hallucis brevis 221,
229
extensor hallucis longus 214,
221, 229
extensor indicis 139
extensor pollicis brevis 139
extensor retinaculum,
inferior/superior 228
external acoustic meatus 10, 60
external anal sphincter 170
external auditory meatus 62, 63
external carotid arteries 36
branches 36
external ear 62, 63
lobule 63
nerve supply 63
external iliac arteries 216
external iliac veins 219, 239
external intercostal muscles
95, 102
external jugular vein 37, 66,
239
external medullary lamina 24
external oblique 156, 157,
174, 237
aponeurosis 174
external oblique aponeurosis
156
external occipital crest 13
external occipital protuberance
13, 233

external rectal venous plexus
171
extradural space 93
extra-ocular muscles 42
defects 42
innervation 43
extrapyramidal tracts (spinal
cord) 91
eye(s) 40–45
accommodation 41
blood vessels 43
bulging 42
chambers 40
damage 40
defects 41, 42
dry 45
layers 41
light convergence, normal
versus myopic eye 41
muscles 42
muscular control of
movements 43
opening and closing 35
nerves 43
vitreous body 40
watery 45
see also eyelids
eyelashes 44
eyelids 44
cilia 44
muscular control of
movements 35, 44
structure 44
eyesight, impaired 41

F
face
arteries 36
changes over time 9
cheeks 51
muscular control 35
veins 37
interconnections 37
route for spread of
infections 37
thrombosis 37
facial artery 36
facial expression
platysma role 34
role of scalp 14
facial muscles 34–35
attachments 34
functions 34
innervation 38
paralysis 38, 56
facial nerve (CN VII) 38, 240
branches 38
disorders 38
parotid gland tumour 56
functions 38, 43
innervation targets 38
secretomotor fibres 61
facial vein 43
falciform ligaments 164
fallopian tube see uterine
(fallopian) tube
false ribs 100
fascia, abdominal 156
fasciculi proprii 91
feet see foot
female anatomy
bladder 180
breast see breast (female)
pelvic canal 197
changes in childbirth 197
pelvis 196, 198
reproductive system see
reproductive system
(female)
urethra 180
female pelvis 196, 198
femoral artery 175, 216, 238
femoral condyles 208
femoral nerve 175, 240
femoral sheath 175
femoral vein 175, 218, 219,
239
femur 204, 232
bony process 205
fracture 205
shaft 205

hip joint 202
internal structure 204
knee joint 208
see also knee joint
lower end 204
muscle attachments 205
muscle origins 205
shaft 204
fractures 205
upper end 204
fenestra cochleae (round
window) 64, 65
fenestra vestibuli (oval
window) 62, 64, 65
fetus
heart 117, 120
spinal curvature 68
fibrous joints 234
groups 235
fibrous pericardium 115
attachments 115
functions 115
fibrous sheath 152, 153
fibula 206, 222, 232
fracture 207
ligaments 207
fibular artery, perforating
branch 216
fibular collateral ligaments
207, 209, 210
'fight or flight' response 177,
242
filiform papillae 54
filum terminale 90, 92
fimbriae 188
finger joints 149
dislocation 149
movement 151
fingers
blood vessels 152
muscles 150, 151
nerves 153
flat feet (pes planus) 227
flexion
ankle joint 222
elbow joint 134
shoulder 126
vertebral column 94
wrist 147
flexor carpi radialis (muscle)
138, 139, 146
flexor carpi ulnaris (muscle)
138, 139
flexor digiti minimi (muscle)
151
flexor digiti minimi brevis 231
flexor digitorum brevis 230
flexor digitorum longus 215,
231
flexor digitorum profundus
(muscle) 138, 139, 146
flexor digitorum profundus
tendon 150
flexor digitorum superficialis
(muscle) 138, 139, 146
flexor digitorum superficialis
tendon 150
flexor hallucis brevis 231
flexor hallucis longus 215, 231
flexor pollicis brevis 151
flexor pollicis longus 138,
139, 146
flexor retinaculum
foot 228
wrist 146, 152, 153
flexor tendon 152
floating ribs 85, 100
flocculonodular lobe 30
fontanelles 9
food
absorption 162
passage 158
foot
arteries 217
bones 224, 225
bony landmarks 229
joints 226
ligaments 226
muscles
action 229
sole of foot 230, 231
top of foot 229

upper foot 228
plantar aponeurosis 230
pulses 229
retinacula see retinacula,
foot
sesamoid bones 225
see also sesamoid bones,
foot
superficial arch 217
surface anatomy 229
tendons 228, 229
foot arches 227
lateral longitudinal arch
227
medial longitudinal arch
227
transverse arch 227
foramen
definition 233
infra-orbital 8
interventricular 20, 21
jugular 13
mandibular 51
mastoid 13
mental 8, 10
obturator 197, 233
sphenopalatine 60
stylomastoid 13, 38
supra-orbital 35
vertebral 70, 84
foramen lacerum 13
foramen magnum 13
foramen of Luschka 20, 21
foramen of Magendie 20, 21
foramen ovale 13, 117
foramen spinosum 13
forearm
blood vessels 140, 141
cross-section 139
nerves 142
tendons 139
tissue compression 139
forearm muscles 137
deep flexor 138
superior flexor 138
foreskin 186
fornix 190
fossa(e)
definition 233
glenoid 136
iliac see inguinal region
(iliac fossa)
incisive 13
infraspinous 97, 233
infratemporal see
infratemporal fossa
ischioanal 199
olecranon 134, 137
piriform 78, 79, 81
pituitary 11
popliteal 208
pterygopalatine see
pterygopalatine fossa
scaphoid 63
sublingual 57
subscapular 97, 124
supraspinous 97
triangular 63
vallecular 54
fossa ovalis 117
fracture-dislocations, ankle
joint 207
frontal bone 8, 12, 46
frontal crest 12
frontal lobes 16, 17, 22
frontal sinuses 8, 9, 11, 47, 48
frontalis 15
fundus 160
fungiform papillae 54

G
gagging reflex, stimulation of
79
Galen, vein of 19, 21
gall bladder 154, 164
biliary system 165
gastric artery
left 161
short 161
gastric epithelium 160
gastric veins
left 161

short 161
gastrocnemius bursae 211
gastrocnemius muscle 205,
215, 221
lateral head 205
medial head 205
gastro-epiploic artery
left 161
right 161
gastro-epiploic vein
left 161
right 161
gastro-oesophageal junction
160
connective ligaments 160
physiological sphincter 160
gastro-splenic nodes 244
gemellus muscles
inferior 201
superior 201
genicular arteries 216
genioglossus 51, 55
geniohyoid 55, 72
action 73
gingivitis 53, 56
glabella 8
glans, penis 186
glaucoma 40
glenohumeral ligaments 125
glenoid cavity 97
scapula (shoulder blade)
124
glenoid fossa 136
glenoid labrum 124
globose nuclei 31
globus pallidus 28
glomeruli (nephrons) 178, 179
glossopharyngeal nerve (CN
IX), pharynx innervation
79
glottis 80, 81
obstruction 80
glucagon 172
glue ear 78
gluteal aponeurosis 200
gluteal nerves 89
gluteal prominences 200
gluteal region 200
bony landmarks 200
bursae 201
deeper muscles 201
surface anatomy 200
gluteofemoral bursa 201
gluteus maximus 200, 205,
213
gluteus medius 201, 205, 213
gluteus minimus 201, 205
goblet cells, in trachea 110
goitre 82
gomphoses 235
goose pimples 14
Graafian follicle, mature 194
gracilis 213
granule cells, cerebellar 31
great cerebral veins 19
great saphenous vein 218, 239
greater sciatic notch 233
greater superficial petrosal
nerve 61
greater trochanter of femur
233
greater tubercle of humerus
233
greater wing, sphenoid bone 9
grey ramus communicantes
242
gridiron incision 155
groin see inguinal region (iliac
fossa)
groin strain 213
groove, definition 233
gum disease 53
gyri 16, 22
development 22

H
haemoglobin 246
hair 14
loss 14
hallux (big toe) 225
hamate 144, 145, 146
hammer 62, 64

hamstrings *see* thigh muscles
hand
    blood vessels 140, 152
    bones 148
        *see also* individual bones
    cross-section 151
    flexing 139
    muscles 150
    nerve supply 153
hard palate 13, 46, 48, 49
    mucous membrane 50
harelip 13, 50
haustra 168
Haversian canal 131
'hay fever' ganglion 61
head
    bones 9
    support from back muscles 95
head injuries/trauma
    effect on smell 33
    nasal cavity fractures 47
hearing aids 65
heart 114–115, 243
    apex 114, 116
    blood supply 121
    borders 114
    cardiac cycle 123
    chambers 116–117
        atria 116, 117
        ventricles 116
        *see also* individual chambers
    compression 115
    conducting system 122
    diaphragm relation to 106
    fetal 117, 120
    fibrous skeleton 123
    hole in 117
    layers of wall 115
    nerve supply 122
    position in thorax 114
    structure 114
    surfaces 114
    valves 118
    vessels 120
heartbeat 118
heartburn 161
heel bone *see* calcaneus bone (heel)
hemispherical capitulum 134
Henle's loop 178
hepatic artery 165
hepatic ducts 165
    common 165
hepatic flexure 168
hepatic portal vein 165, 172
hepatocytes 164
hepatopancreatic ampulla *see* ampulla of Vater
herniated intervertebral disc 68, 87
herpetic ulcers 55
hilum, of spleen 173
hilus 178
hinge joint 149
hip, 'broken' 205
hip bone 197, 232
    features 197
    structure 197
hip joint 202
    artificial 203
    blood supply 202
    'broken' 205
    capsule 202
    ligaments 203
    movement/stability 203
hippocampus 16, 26
hole in the heart 117
horizontal fissure, of lung 108
hormones 172
horseshoe kidney 179
human dentition 52
    *see also* teeth
humerus 95, 99, 124, 130, 142, 232
    elbow 134
    fractures 130
    interior (inside) 131
    lateral epicondyle 233
    ridges 130
    structure 130

tissue 131
Huntington's chorea 29
hyaline cartilage *see* articular cartilage (hyaline)
hydrocephalus 12
    obstruction of CSF flow 21
hydroxyapatite 11
hymen 192
hymenal caruncle 192
hyoglossus 51, 55
hyoid bone 39, 72, 73, 80
    fixation by infrahyoid muscles 73
    muscular control of movement 72–73
    points of attachments of neck muscles 73
hyperacusis 64
hypermetropia (long-sightedness) 41
hyperparathyroidism 83
hyperthyroid goitre 82
hyperthyroidism, bulging eyes (exophthalmos) 42
hypochondrium
    left 155
    right 155
hypogastric region 155
hypoglossal nerve (CN XII) 58
    removal 57
hypoglossal nucleus 75
hypothalamic sulcus 25
hypothalamus 17, 25, 26
    functions 17, 25
    nuclei 25
        *see also* individual nuclei structures 25
hypothenar eminence 150, 151
hypothyroid goitre 82
hysterosalpingogram 189

I
ileocaecal region 166
ileocaecal valve 166
    anatomical studies 166
ileocolic artery 169
    colic branch 169
ileocolic vein 169
ileum 166
    blood supply 163
    jejunum differences 163
iliac arteries 174, 216, 238
iliac bone 88
iliac crest 88, 197, 233
    gluteal region 200
iliac fossa *see* inguinal region (iliac fossa)
iliac nodes 244
iliac spine, anterior superior 88, 174, 197, 200
iliac veins 171, 174, 219, 239
iliococcygeus 198
iliofemoral ligaments 203
iliopectineal bursa 203
iliopsoas muscle 205, 212
ilium 197
immune response 244
incisive fossa 13
incisors 52
incus (anvil) 62, 64
infants, sutures, large gaps between 9
inferior alveolar nerve 58, 59
    block 59
inferior cerebellar peduncles 30
inferior constrictor muscle 79
inferior gemellus muscles 201
inferior ileocaecal recess 167
inferior mesenteric artery 169
inferior mesenteric vein 171
inferior oblique muscle 42
inferior olivary nucleus 75
inferior parathyroid glands 83
inferior petrosal sinus 19
inferior rectus muscles 42
inferior sagittal sinus 19
inferior serratus posterior 94, 102
inferior tarsi 35
inferior vena cava (IVC) 116, 120, 239

anus 171
    diaphragmatic passage 107
    pancreas 172
    rectum 171
infrahyoid muscles 66, 72–73
    actions 73
    testing 73
infra-orbital artery 60
infra-orbital foramen 8
infra-orbital nerve 61
    branches 61
infrapatellar bursa 208, 211
infraspinatus 94, 99, 127
infraspinous fossa 97, 233
infratemporal fossa 58
    anatomy/skeletal boundaries 58
    contents 58
    tumours 59
infundibulum 25, 195
inguinal canal 174, 175
    walls 174
inguinal hernias 174
inguinal ligament 174, 216
    structures behind 175
inguinal lymph nodes 244
    deep 175
    superficial 175
inguinal region (iliac fossa) 173
    left 155
    right 155
inguinal rings 174
    deep 174
    superficial 174
inhaled objects 79
inner ear 62, 65
    labyrinth 65
    orientation 65
inspiration
    diaphragmatic movements 107
    lung expansion 109
    ribcage movements 103
insulin 172
intercarpal joint 145
interchondral joints 101
interclavicular ligament 101
intercostal arteries 93
intercostal muscles 102
    innermost 102
intercostal nerves 106, 240, 242
    diaphragm innervation 106
interfasicular tract 91
interlobar arteries 179
interlobar fissures 108, 113
intermuscular septum (upper arm)
    lateral 137
    medial 137
internal acoustic meatus 11
internal anal sphincter 170
internal auditory meatus 62
internal capsule 24, 28
internal carotid arteries 18, 36
    branches 18
internal iliac veins 219
internal intercostal muscles 102
internal jugular veins 37, 67, 72, 82, 239
    venous drainage of brain 19
internal medullary lamina 24
internal oblique muscle 157
    aponeurosis 157
internal pudendal artery 189 187
internal rectal venous plexus 171
internal thoracic artery 104
    blood supply to breast 104
internal thoracic vein 104
    venous drainage of breast 104
'interossei' muscles 231
interosseous artery, common 140
interosseous border 133
interosseous membrane 132, 138, 146, 147, 206

elbow 135
    tibia/fibula 207
interosseous muscles 150
    dorsal (hand) 150
    foot 231
    palmar 150
interpectoral nodes 105
interphalangeal joints
    foot 226
    hand 149
interspinous ligament 87
interthalamic adhesion 24
intertrochanteric fractures 205
    blockage 21
interventricular septum 116
intervertebral discs 68, 87
    degeneration 87
    displacement (prolapsed) 68
        MRI scan 87
    functions 87
    slipped 68
intervertebral foramina 69, 84
    spinal nerve formation 92
intracranial pressure, raised 21
intramuscular injections, sciatic nerve 220
intraocular pressure, raised 40
intrapulmonary lymph nodes 113
iris 40, 41
ischial bursa 201
ischial spine 88
ischial tuberosity 196, 197, 233
    gluteal region 200
ischioanal fossae 199
ischiocavernosus muscle 187
ischiococcygeus 198
ischiofemoral ligaments 203
ischium 88, 197
isthmus
    thyroid gland 82
    uterine tube 195

J
jaw
    alveolus 52
    dislocation 39
    muscular control of movement 39
jejunum 162, 163, 172
    blood supply 163
    differences to ileum 163
joints 234
    ball and socket 124, 202
    cartilaginous 234, 235
    fibrous 234, 235
    functional groups 234
    synovial 234
    *see also* individual joints
jugular foramen 13
jugular vein 239
    external 37, 66, 239
    internal *see* internal jugular veins

K
keratin, tongue 'tufts' 54
kidneys 176, 178
    blood supply 179
    congenital abnormalities 179
    nephrons 178
    palpation 176
    protection 176
    rear view 176
    *see also* entries beginning renal
knee joint 208
    arteries 216
    bursae 208, 210, 211
    investigations 211
    ligaments 210
        intracapsular 210
        *see also* cruciate ligaments
    lymphatic vessels 244
    menisci 209
    structure 208
Kocher's incision 155
Kupffer cells 164
kyphosis (curvature of spine) 84

L
labia majora 188, 192
labia minora 188, 192
labyrinth 65
    bony 65
    membranous 65
lacrimal apparatus 45
    canaliculi 45
    lake 45
    papilla 45
    punctum 45
lacrimal ducts 45
lacrimal gland 45
    accessory 45
    disorders 45
    secretions 43, 45
        excessive 45
lacrimal nerve 43
lacrimal sac 35, 45
    infection 45
lactiferous duct 104
lacunar ligament 174
    formation 174
lambdoid suture 10, 11
Langer's lines 155
laryngeal prominence 72, 79, 80, 82
laryngopharynx 78
laryngostomy 80
larynx 67, 80–81
    cartilages 80
    function 80
    location 80
    mucous glands 81
    muscles 81
        innervation 83
    muscular control of movement 72–73
    opening 78
    sphincters 80
lateral corticospinal tract 91
lateral epicondyle, humerus 233
lateral femoral condyle 233
lateral geniculate body 24
lateral malleolar arteries 217
lateral malleolus 206, 221, 229, 233
lateral meniscus 208
lateral plantar arteries 217
lateral pterygoid muscles 39, 58
lateral rectus muscles 42
lateral spinothalamic tract 91
lateral sulcus 22
lateral tarsal arteries 217
lateral thoracic artery 104, 128
    blood supply to breast 104
lateral thoracic veins 104
    venous drainage of breast 104
latissimus dorsi 94, 98, 99, 126, 127
    functions 99
    origin and attachments 99
left atria 116, 117
left brachiocephalic veins 159
left common peroneal nerve 240
left coronary artery 121
left gastric artery 161
left gastric veins 161
left gastro-epiploic artery 161
left gastro-epiploic vein 161
left hypochondrium 155
left inguinal region (iliac fossa) 155
left lateral recess 20, 21
left phrenic nerve 107
left pulmonary arteries 238
left recurrent laryngeal nerves 83
left ventricle 114, 116
leg(s)
    arteries 216
    deep veins 219
    knee joint *see* knee joint
    lymphatic vessels 244
    nerve supply 89, 220, 221
    valves/venous pump 218
    veins 218
leg muscles

lower leg 214
　actions 214, 215
　anterior 214
　deep calf muscles 215
　lateral 214
　posterior 215
　superficial calf muscles 215
　see also individual muscles
　thigh see thigh muscles
lens 40, 41
　increased opacity 40
lentiform nucleus 28
levator ani muscle 191
levator labii superioris 34
levator palati 50, 55
levator palpebrae superioris 35, 42
　muscular control of eye 35, 44
　overstimulation in hyperthyroidism 42
levator scapulae 94
　function 99
levatores costarum muscles 95
Leydig cells 185
lienorenal ligament 173
ligamenta flava 87
ligaments
　ankle 223
　elbow 147
　fibula 207
　foot 226
　hip joint 203
　inguinal 175
　knee 210
　lumbar vertebrae 87
　shoulder joint 125
　supporting ovaries 194
　tibia 207
　wrist 147
　see also individual ligaments
ligamentum arteriosum 120
ligamentum teres 164, 202
limbic system 26–27
　connections 26, 27
　disorders 27
　medial view 26
　role 27
　smell, connections to 26
　structures 26
linea alba 156
linea aspera 204
linea semilunaris 156, 157
lingual artery 36
lingual nerve 51, 58, 59
lingual tonsil 54
lingual vein 37
lips 51
　free red margin 51
　muscular control 34, 35
　nerve supply 59
　translucent membrane 51
liver 154, 164, 243
　blood supply 165
　lobes 164
　lobules 164
　microscopic anatomy 164
　peritoneal coverings 164
　visceral surface 165
　see also entries beginning hepatic
lobar arteries 112
lobar bronchi 111
lobe(s), lung 108
lobule (testis) 184
longitudinal fissure 16, 22
longitudinal muscle 159
long-sightedness 41
Louis, sternal angle of 101, 109
lumbar arteries 93
lumbar curvature of spine 68, 69
lumbar fascia 157
lumbar puncture 20, 21, 92
　site of entry (safe zone) 87, 92
lumbar vertebrae 69, 86–87
　articular facets 86

cylindrical body 86
　disorders 87
　ligaments 87
　spinal nerve 87
　spinous process 86
　strength and stability 87
　synovial joints 87
　transverse processes 86
　typical 86
　vertebral arch 86
lumbosacral nerve roots 92
lumbrical muscles 231, 1450
lunate 144, 145
lungs 108–109
　changes with age 108
　deep plexus 113
　effect of smoking 113
　gaseous exchange 111, 112
　hilum 112
　lobes and fissures 108
　lymphatics 113
　mediastinal surface 108
　mottled 113
　pleural sacs 108
　respiratory epithelium 110, 111
　structure 108
　superficial plexus 113
　vessels 112–113
lunula 247
lymph 105, 113, 161, 244
　cell circulation 105
　role in digestion 163
lymph nodes 66, 113, 244, 245
　axillary (armpit) 105, 128
　function 66, 245
　metastasis 105
　position 244
　structure 245
　superficial 66
　see also individual nodes
lymphangitis 66
lymphatic drainage, colon 169
lymphatic system 105, 161, 244
　constituent parts 244
　disorders of 66
lymphatic vessels 244, 245
　alveoli 112
　arm 244
　leg 244
lymphocytes 244, 245
　circulation 66
lymphoedema 66
lymphoid tissue 163, 173, 244
　appendix 167
lysozyme, lacrimal fluid component 45

M
macrophages 111, 245
magnetic resonance imaging (MRI)
　intervertebral disc protrusion 87
　investigations of knee joint 211
　stress fracture in sacrum 89
　ventricle arrangement in brain 20
major calyx 178
male anatomy
　bladder 180
　reproductive system see reproductive system (male)
　urethra 180
male pelvis 196, 199
malleolar arteries 217
malleolus
　lateral 206, 221, 229, 233
　medial 206, 229
malleus (hammer) 62, 64
mammary glands 104
mammillary bodies 25
mammography 105
mandible 8
　angle 11, 57
　body 8, 10
　condylar process 10, 51, 57
　coronoid process 51, 57
　dislocation 39

muscular control of movement 39
　platysma role 34
　pterygoid muscle roles 58
　ramus 9, 11
mandibular foramen 51
mandibular nerves 38, 59
　branches 59
　innervation targets 51, 59
manubriosternal joint 101
manubrium sterni 98, 100, 101
march fracture (stress) 207
massa intermedia 24
masseter 34, 39, 56
mastication muscles 39
　innervation 59
mastoid foramen 13
mastoid notch 13
mastoid process 13
maxilla 8, 10, 13
　frontal process 46
　palatine process 13
maxillary artery 36, 58, 60
　divisions 60
　supply areas 60
maxillary nerve 61
　branches 61
　innervation targets 61
maxillary sinuses 8, 9, 48
　infections 8, 49
　opening 48, 49
maxillary vein 37
McBurney's point 167
meatus 47
　lower/middle/upper 47, 48
medial collateral ligaments 134
medial epicondyles 135
medial ligament 223
medial longitudinal arch, foot 227
medial malleolar arteries 217
medial malleolus 206, 222, 229
medial plantar arteries 217
medial pterygoid muscles 39
medial pterygoid plate 11
medial rectus muscles 43
medial tarsal arteries 217
median aperture 20, 21
median cubital vein 141
median eminence 25
median incision, abdominal 155
median mammary artery 104
median mammary vein 104
median nerve 126, 128, 143, 153, 240
　damage 143
　digital branches 153
　palmar branch 153
　palmar digital 153
　wrist 146
median palatine suture 13
mediastinal pleura 109
medulla oblongata 17, 74
　cross section 75
　relationships 74
medullary canal 131
medullary lamina 24
medullary reticulospinal tract 91
Meibomian glands 44
Meissner's (submucous) plexus 159
melanin 246
melanocytes 246
memory
　hypothalamic control 25
　smell associations 26
meningitis (meninges infection) 49, 64
mental foramen 8, 10
mental nerve 59
　desensitization (local anaesthetic) 59
mentalis muscle 34
mesenteric arteries 162, 169
mesenteric lymph nodes 163

mesenteric veins 162, 163, 169, 171
mesentery 163
mesoappendix 167
mesovarium 194
metacarpal bone 146, 148, 149
　wrist joint 145
metacarpal ligaments, dorsal 147
metacarpophalangeal joints 149
metaphysis 131
metastasis, lymph node, breast cancer 105
metatarsal arteries 217
metatarsal heads 227
metatarsals 222, 225, 227 232
midbrain 17, 74
　cross section 75
　relationships 74
midclavicular line 155
middle cerebral arteries 18
　damage and symptoms 18
middle constrictor muscle 79
middle ear 62, 64
　infections 78
　protection 63
middle meningeal artery 11, 36
　damage 11
　grooves on exterior surface of skull 11
　grooves on interior surface of skull 11
middle thyroid vein 82
milk, production 104
milk teeth 52
Milroy's disease 66
mitral cells 33
mitral valve (bicuspid) 116, 118
modiolus 65
molars 52
mons pubis 192
motor areas 23
　primary see primary motor cortex
motor body map 23
motor nerve endings 240, 241
　junction 241
　signaling 241
mottled lungs 113
mouth (oral cavity) 50–55
　dry (xerostomia) 56
　floor 51
　muscular control 34, 35, 39
　roof 50
　ulcers 55
　veins and arteries 50
movement
　disorders 29
　finely controlled 23
　neurological control 17, 23
　see also individual joints
MRI see magnetic resonance imaging (MRI)
mucous cells, salivary glands 56, 57
multifidus muscle 95
muscles
　cardiac 237
　fibre 236
　function 236, 237
　shapes 237
　skeletal see skeletal muscle
　smooth (involuntary) 236
　structure 236
　types 236
　see also individual muscles
muscularis layer, vagina 192
musculocutaneous nerve 142, 143
myelin sheath 241
myenteric (Auerbach's) plexus 159
mylohyoid muscle 39, 51, 55, 72
　action 73
myocardium 115
myometrium 190
myopia (short-sightedness) 41

N
nail(s) 246, 247
　constituent parts 247
　dystrophy 247
　growth 247
　psoriasis 247
　structure 247
nasal bones 8, 10, 46
nasal cavity 46–49
　cross section 47
　fibre-optic endoscope 47
　lateral and inferior views (side and from below) 46
　lateral (side) walls 47
　mucous membrane 46
　roof 47
　see also nose
nasal concha (turbinates) 9, 47, 48
nasal nerves 61
nasal septum 8, 10, 47, 48
　cartilage 46
　ethmoid bone, perpendicular plate 11
　vomer 11
nasalis muscle 34
nasion 8
naso-endoscope 79
nasolacrimal duct 45, 47
　infection 45
nasopharynx 78
　adenoid (lymphoid) tissue 78
　tubal elevation 78
navel 157
navicular 222, 224, 227
neck 66–67
　abnormalities 71
　arteries 36
　cervical fasia 66, 67
　cross section 67
　interior view (inside) 66
　investing fasia 67
　muscles 72–73
　natural stress lines 66
　pretracheal fascia 67
　prevertebral fascia 67
　skin 66
　superficial fascia 66, 67
　support from back muscles 95
　veins 37
nephrons 178
nerve supply
　arm 142
　diaphragm 106
　external ear 63
　forearm 142
　hand 153
　heart 122
　legs 89, 220, 221
　lips 59
　oesophagus 159
　pelvis 89
　skin 77
　teeth 51, 59, 61
　wrist 146
　see also individual nerves, anatomical regions
neuromuscular junction 241
neurotransmitters 241
neurovascular bundle 128, 137
newborn, hydrocephalus 20
nipple 104
noradrenaline 242
nose 46–49
　external structure 46
　see also entries beginning with nasal
nosebleeds (epistaxis) 46
nostrils 46
　see also nasal cavity; nose
notch, definition 233
nucleus pulposus 68, 87
nulliparous cervix 193

O
oblique aponeurosis 156, 157
oblique cord 135
oblique fissure, of lung 108
oblique muscles 42, 157
oblique popliteal ligament 210

obturator externus muscle 205, 213
obturator foramen 197, 233
obturator internus 201
occipital artery 36
occipital bone 10, 12
occipital lobe 16, 17, 22
   arterial supply 18
occipital vein 37
occipitalis 15
occipitofrontalis muscle 15, 34
oculomotor nerve (CN III) 43
   role in eye movements 43
oculomotor nuclei 75
odontoid process (dens) 70, 71
   fracture 70
   subluxation 70
oesophageal aperture 107
oesophageal sphincter 158
oesophageal veins 159
oesophagus 66, 67, 158
   blood vessels 159
   diaphragmatic passage 107
   nerves 159
   passage of food 158
   structure 158
olecranon, ulna 132, 134
olecranon fossa 134, 137
olecranon process 132
olfactory bulbs 18, 33
olfactory cortex, primary see
   primary olfactory cortex
olfactory epithelium 33, 46
   location 33
olfactory nerve (CN I) 33
   passage through nasal
      cavity 47
   pathway 33
olfactory receptors 33
olfactory system 26
olfactory tracts 33
olives 74
omentum 154
omohyoid 72
   action 73
   inferior belly 72
   superior belly 72
ophthalmic artery 43
ophthalmic nerve 43
ophthalmic vein, superior 37
ophthalmoscope 41
opponens digiti minimi 151
opponens pollicis 151
optic chiasm 25
optic disc 40
optic nerve (CN II) 43
oral cavity see mouth (oral
   cavity)
orbicularis oculi 34, 237
   functions 35
   innervation 43
   muscular control of eye 35,
      44
   orbital part 35, 44
   palpebral part 35, 44
orbicularis oris 15, 237
   functions 35
orbit 8, 40
   infra-orbital margin 8
   venous drainage 43
orbital fissure, superior 9
organ of Corti 65
oropharynx 78
orthopantomograph 52
ossicles 62, 64
   movement modulation 64
osteopetrosis 10
osteophytes 71, 87
   nerve compression 71
osteoporosis 84, 133, 205
ostium 48
otitis media 78
oval window (fenestra
   vestibuli) 62, 64, 65
ovarian artery 189
ovarian hormones 195
ovarian ligaments 194
ovarian vein 189
ovaries 188, 194
   blood supply 194
   supporting ligaments 194
oxycephaly 12

P
pacemaker (sino-atrial node)
   122
Pacinian corpuscle 240
Paget's disease 10
palate 13, 50
   cleft see cleft palate
   defects 13, 50
   see also hard palate; soft
      palate
palatine arteries 60
palatine maxilla 11
palatine nerves 61
palatine tonsils 54, 78
   infections and abscesses 78
palatoglossal fold 78
palatoglossus 50, 55
   role in swallowing 55
palatopharyngeal fold 78
palatopharyngeus 50, 79
palmar arch
   deep 140
   superficial 140
palmar digital arteries 152
   common 152
palmar digital nerve 153
palmar digital veins 141
palmar veins 152
palmaris brevis muscle 151
palmaris longus 138
palpebral conjunctiva 44
palpebral ligaments 35
pampiniform plexus 185, 194
pancreas 172
   location 172
pancreatic duct 165, 172
papillary muscles 118, 119
parahippocampal gyrus 17
paramedian incision,
   abdominal 155
paranasal sinuses (cavities) 8,
   47, 48
   enlargement/development
      48
   functions 48
   infections 8, 49
   inflammation 8, 48, 49
   mucous membrane 49
   problems 49
   see also individual sinuses
parasternal lymph nodes 105
parasympathetic nerves 122
parasympathetic nervous
   system 243
   cell body location 243
   distribution 243
   organs 243
   vs sympathetic 243
parasympathetic splanchnic
   nerves 89
parathormone, secretion 83
parathyroid glands 82–83
   disorders 83
   inferior 83
   superior 83
paratracheal lymph nodes 113
paraventricular nucleus 25
paravertebral/sympathetic
   ganglion 242
parietal bone 10, 12
parietal lobes 16, 17, 22
parietal pericardium 115
parietal pleura 109
   divisions 109
parietal tuberosity 12
parieto-occipital sulcus 16, 17,
   22
Parkinson's disease 29
   dopamine deficit 29
parotid duct 56
parotid glands 38, 51, 56
   accessory 56
   enlargement/tumours 56
   passage of vessels and
      nerves 56
      facial nerve 38, 56
   tumour (pleomorphic
      adenoma) 59
parous cervix 193
patella (knee cap) 232
   cartilage 209
   structure 209

patellar ligaments 207, 208
pectinate muscles 117
pectineus muscle 212
pectoral girdle 96–99, 232
   deep dissection 99
   muscles 98–99
      anterior view (front) 98
      posterior view (back) 99
   stability 96
pectoralis major 98, 103, 104,
   157, 237
   functions 98, 103
   shoulder joint 126, 127
   sternocostal head 98
   tendon 98
pectoralis minor 98, 127
   function 98
pedicle 84, 85
pelvic canal, female 197
pelvic cavity 188
   walls 198
pelvic floor
   muscles 198
      functions 199
   openings 199
pelvic inlet 196
pelvic nodes 244
pelvic ureter 181
pelvis 196
   bones 196
   female 196, 198
   male 196, 199
   nerve supply 89
   structure 196
Penfield, Wilder 23
penile urethra 183
penis 182, 186
   blood supply 187
   connective tissue 186
   muscles 187
   structure 186
pericardial cavity 115
pericardial sac 115
pericardium 114, 115
   diaphragm attachment 106,
      107
   fibrous see fibrous
      pericardium
   parietal 115
   serous 115
   visceral 115
pericranium 14, 15
perilymph 65
perimetrium 190
perimysium 236
perineal body 198
perineurium 241
periodontitis 56
periosteum 131, 164, 204
   fibula 206
   tibia 206
peripheral nerves 240
   function 241
   structure 241
peripheral nervous system 240
   arrangement 240
peristalsis 181
peritoneum 154
peroneal artery 216
peroneal nerve
   common 220, 221
   deep 221
   left common 240
   superficial 221
peroneus (fibularis) brevis 214
peroneus (fibularis) longus
   muscle 214, 221
peroneus (fibularis) tertius
   tendon 214, 228
pes planus (flat feet) 227
petrosal nerve
   deep 61
   greater superficial 61
petrosal sinus 19
Pfannenstiel incision 155
phagocytes 113
phagocytosis 113
phalanges
   foot 225, 226
   hand 148, 149
   see also fingers
pharyngeal raphé 79

pharyngeal tonsil 78
pharyngeal tubercle 13
pharynx 66, 67, 78–79
   divisions 78
   elevation during swallowing
      79
   infection/inflammation 78
   muscles 79
   nasal openings 46
   nerve supply 79
photoreceptors 41
phrenic nerves 106, 107
   diaphragm innervation 106
phrenicoesophageal ligaments
   160
pia mater 93
pilus semilunaris 45
pineal gland 17
pinna (earlobe) 62, 63
   cartilage damage 63
   structure 63
piriform fossae 78, 79, 81
piriformis 201, 205
pisiform 144, 145
pituitary fossa 11
pituitary gland 21
   anterior 17, 25
   hypothalamic control 25
   posterior 17, 25
pituitary stalk (infundibulum)
   25
plagiocephaly 12
plantar aponeurosis 230
plantar arteries 217
plantar calcaneocuboid
   ligament 226
plantar calcaneonavicular
   ligament 226
plantar digital arteries 217
plantar flexion 222
plantar metatarsal arteries 217
plantaris muscle 205, 215
plantaris tendon 228
plaque 53
platysma 34, 66, 67, 72
   role in facial expression 34,
      72
pleomorphic adenoma 59
pleura 109
   recesses 109
pleural cavity 109
pleural effusion 109
pleural fluid 109
   actions 109
plexus
   alveolar pulmonary 112
   Auerbach's (myenteric) 159
   brachial see brachial plexus
   choroid see choroid plexus
   Meissner's (submucous) 159
   pampiniform 185, 194
   pterygoid 37
   rectal venous 171
   sacral 89
   subareolar lymphatic 105
   superficial, lungs 113
plicae 162, 163
pons 17, 74
   relationships 74
popliteal artery 216
popliteal fossa 208
popliteal node 244
popliteal pulse 216
popliteal vein 218, 219, 239
popliteus bursa 211
popliteus ligament 210
popliteus muscle 205, 215
porta hepatis 165
portal triad 164
portal vein 161, 169
   hepatic 165
postcentral gyrus 16
posterior auricular artery 36
posterior auricular vein 37
posterior cerebral arteries 18
posterior chamber of eye 40
posterior cricoarytenoid muscle
   81
   paralysis 81
posterior cruciate ligaments
   207, 210
posterior intercostal arteries,

blood supply to breast 104
posterior intercostal nodes 105
posterior intercostal veins,
   venous drainage of breast
   104
posterior interventricular
   groove 114
posterior spinal arteries 93
posterior spinal nerve roots
   92, 93
posterior spinocerebellar tract
   91
posterior superior alveolar
   nerve 61
posterior thigh muscles 213
posterior tibial arteries 216,
   217
posterior tibial veins 219
posterior tibiofibular ligaments
   207
posterior tibiotalar ligaments
   223
posture, deformity 84
Pott's disease 84
Pott's fracture 223
precentral gyrus 16
precentral sulcus 16
prefrontal cortex, cognitive
   functions 17
pregnancy
   deep vein thrombosis 219
   stomach 161
   uterus (womb) see uterus
      (womb)
premolars (bicuspids) 52
premotor cortex 23
prepatellar bursae 211
primary auditory cortex 16
   function 23
primary motor cortex 16
   function 23
primary olfactory cortex 16,
   17
primary somatosensory cortex
   16
   function 23
primary visual cortex 17
   function 23
profunda brachii artery 140
profunda femoris artery (deep
   femoral) 216
progesterone 195
prolapsed disc 68
pronator quadratus 138, 237
pronator teres muscle 126,
   138, 139
prostate gland 182, 183
   internal structure 183
   volume 183
prostatic sinus 183
prostatic urethra 183
prosthetic hip 203
protruding ears 63
psoriasis 247
pterion 10, 11
pterygoid canal, nerve of 61
pterygoid muscles 39, 58
   muscle fibres 58
   nerve supply 58
pterygoid plate 60
   medial, pterygoid hamulus
      11
pterygoid plexus 37
pterygomaxillary fissure 60
pterygopalatine fossa 60
   components 60
   location 60
pterygopalatine ganglion 61
pubic arch 196
pubic bone 88
pubic symphysis 88, 196, 197,
   232
pubic tubercle 174
pubococcygeus 198
pubofemoral ligaments 203
puborectalis muscle 170, 198,
   199
pudendal arteries, internal
   187, 189
pudendal veins 187
pulmonary arteries 112, 116,
   238

left 238
right 238
pulmonary circulation 112, 238
pulmonary embolus 219
pulmonary sinuses 119
pulmonary trunk 112
bifurcation 115
pulmonary valve 119
pulmonary veins 112, 239
pulmonary venous plexus 112
pulmonary vessels 117
pulse points 140
pulvinar 24
puncta 45
pupil, muscles 41
Purkinje cells, cerebellar 31
Purkinje fibres 122, 123
putamen 28
pyloric region 160
pylorus 160, 162
pyramidal tracts 91
pyramids, of brainstem 74
decussation 74

Q
quadratus femoris 201, 205,
212
quadratus lumborum 95
quadratus plantae 231
quadriceps tendon 210

R
radial artery 140, 152, 238
radial collateral ligaments 147
radial nerve 142
damage 142
deep terminal branch 142
superficial terminal branch
142
radial notch 132
radicular arteries 93
radiocarpal joint 145
radiocarpal ligaments
dorsal 147
movement 147
palmar 147
radio-ulnar joints 132
radius 132, 133, 135, 142, 232
elbow 134
wrist joint 145
wrist ligaments 147
rami 76, 92
rami communicantes 92, 242
rectal veins 171
rectal venous plexus 171
external 171
internal 171
rectum 170
blood vessels 171
longitudinal muscle 170
nerves 171
transverse folds 170
rectus abdominis 103, 157
role in respiration 103
rectus femoris muscle 200,
212, 237
rectus muscles (eye) 42
rectus sheath 156
lower 157
upper 157
recurrent laryngeal nerves 83
innervation targets 81, 83
red nucleus 75
refractive errors 41
Reiter's disease, sacro-iliitis 89
renal agenesis 179
renal arteries 179, 238
renal corpuscle 178
renal cortex 178
renal fascia 177
renal medulla 178
renal pelvis 178, 181
renal pyramids 178
renal tubule 178
renal vein 179, 239
reproductive system (female)
188
blood supply 189
external genitalia 188, 192
internal genitalia 188
position of tract 188
reproductive system (male) 182

external genitalia 182
respiration
accessory muscles 103
attachments 103
functions 103
costal cartilage movements
101
diaphragmatic movements
107
ribcage movements 103
role of intercostal muscles
102
role of rectus abdominis
103
role of scalene muscles 103
see also expiration;
inspiration
respiratory airways 110–111
intrinsic blood supply 112
see also alveoli; bronchi;
trachea
respiratory bronchioles 111
respiratory epithelium 110, 111
respiratory muscles 103
rete testis 184
reticular formation 17, 75
functions 75
reticulospinal tract 91
retina 40, 41
damage 40
retinacula, foot
flexor retinaculum 228
inferior extensor
retinaculum 228
peroneal retinaculum 228
superior extensor
retinaculum 228
retinal artery 43
retromandibular vein 37
retropharyngeal abscesses 67
retropharyngeal space 66, 67
abscess, X-ray of 67
spread of infection 67
retroverted uterus 190
rheumatoid arthritis 70, 149
rhinitis 33
rhomboid major 94, 99
function 99
rhomboid minor 94, 99
function 99
ribcage 100–103
components 100
movements 103
muscles 102
ribs 100, 232
atypical 100
false 100
movements during
respiration 103
structure 100
true (vertebrosternal) 100
typical 100
right atria 116, 117
right auricle (heart) 117
right brachiocephalic veins
159
right cerebral hemisphere 17
right coronary arteries 121
right gastro-epiploic artery
161
right gastro-epiploic vein 161
right hypochondrium 155
right inguinal region (iliac
fossa) 155
right lymphatic trunk 105
right phrenic nerve,
diaphragmatic passage 107
right pulmonary arteries 238
right recurrent laryngeal nerves
83
right subclavian artery 104
right subclavian lymphatic
trunk 113
right subclavian vein 104
right ventricle 114, 116
rod cells 41
rolandic fissure 16, 17, 22
rotation
shoulder 126
vertebral column 94
wrist 147
rotator cuff 94, 125

muscles 127
rotatores cervicis muscles 95
rotatores thoracis muscles 95
round window (fenestra
cochleae) 64, 65
rubrospinal tract 91
rugae 50, 180

S
saccule 65
sacral ala (wing) 88
sacral curvature of spine 68
sacral foramina 87, 88, 89
sacral plexus 89
sacral promontory 88
sacro-iliac joint 88, 196
cartilage coverings 88
inflammation 89
sex differences 88
sacro-iliitis 89
sacrum (sacral vertebrae) 69,
87, 88, 232
auricular surface 87, 88
clinical aspects 89
functions 88
lumbosacral articular
surface 88
pelvic surface 88
pregnancy 191
transverse ridges 88
saddle joint 149
sagittal sinus
inferior 19
superior 19, 21
sagittal suture 9, 12
saliva
functions 56
production 56
reduced production 56
salivary duct blockages 57
salivary glands 51, 56–57, 243
minor 56
tumours 57
see also parotid glands;
sublingual glands;
submandibular glands
salpingopharyngeus 79
saphenous vein 218
accessory 218
great 218, 239
small 218
sartorius muscle 200, 212
scalene muscles 95, 103
role in respiration 103
scalene tubercle 100
scalp 14–15
aponeurosis 14, 15
blood supply 15
dense connective tissue 14,
15
hair 14
layers 14
loose connective tissue 14,
15
muscles 15
sebaceous glands 14
sebum production 14
skin 14
facial muscle attachments
34
protective role 14
trauma to 15
profuse bleeds 15, 37
scaphocephaly 12
scaphoid 144, 145
fracture 145
scaphoid fossa 63
scapula (shoulder blade) 94,
95, 96, 97, 124, 125, 232
bony processes 97
borders 97
glenoid cavity 124
movements 99
retraction 99
spine 99, 233
surfaces 97
upper arm 137
winged 97
scapulothoracic joint 99
Scarpa's fascia 156
Schwann cell 241
schwannoma 59

sciatic nerve 89, 90, 220, 240
damage 221
higher division 220
intramuscular injections
220
origin/course 220
terminal branches 221
sciatica 87
scintigrams
bone cancers 85
sacro-iliitis 89
sclera 40, 41
scleral venous sinus 40, 41
scoliosis 69
scrotum 182
walls 184
sebaceous glands 246
sebum production 14
sebum, production from
sebaceous glands 14
secretomotor fibres 61
semicircular canals 62, 65
semicircular ducts 65
semilunar valves 119
action 119
semimembranosus tendon 213
semimembranous bursa 211
seminal colliculus 183
seminal vesicle 182, 183
structure/shape 183
seminiferous tubules 185
semispinalis capitis muscles 95
semispinalis thoracis muscles
95
semitendinosus muscle 213
semitendinosus tendon 213
sensorineural deafness 65
cochlear implants 65
sensory body map 23
sensory receptors 240
serous cells, salivary glands
56, 57
serous pericardium 115
serratus anterior 97, 157
function 98
nerve supply 97
serratus posterior 94
functions 102
inferior 94, 102
superior 94, 102
sesamoid bones 227
foot 225
bone development 225
protective role 225
wrist 144
shin bone see tibia
short gastric artery 161
short gastric veins 161
short-sightedness 41
shoulder blade see scapula
(shoulder blade)
shoulder girdle see pectoral
girdle
shoulder joint 124
capsule 124, 125
dislocations 125
ligaments 125
movements 126
sialoliths (calcified stones),
blockage of salivary ducts
57
sigmoid arteries 169
sigmoid colon 163, 168, 170
sigmoid sinus 19
sino-atrial node (pacemaker)
122
sinuses see paranasal sinuses
(cavities)
sinusitis 8, 48, 49
false-colour X-ray 49
sinusoids 164
Sjögren's syndrome 56
lacrimal gland disorder 45
skeletal muscle 236
function 236
shapes 237
skeleton 232
appendicular 232
axial 232
depressions/grooves 233
fibrous, heart 123
formation 232

projections 233
skin 246
colour 246
nerve supply 77
structure 246
skull 8–13, 232
anterior aspect (front) 8–9
bones 9–11
compact 11
components 11
development 13
metabolism defects 10
production disorders 12
remodelling 10
types 11
defects 12
development 12
facial muscle attachments
34
foramina 13
fractures 11
functions 8
illuminated 9
inferior aspect (base) 13
interior (inside) 11
lateral aspect (side) 10–11
painted 9
sinuses see paranasal
sinuses (cavities)
sutures (joints) 9–11
growth 10
isolated premature fusion
12
top 12
vertex 12
X-rays 9
see also cranium; mandible
sleep/wake cycle
hypothalamic control 25
neurological control 17
slipped disc 68
small intestine 162
muscle fibres 166
see also individual intestinal
regions
smell 26
loss of 26
smooth (involuntary) muscle
236
location 236
nervous system 236
soft palate 47, 50
functions 50
soleus 214, 215, 221
somatosensory cortex, primary
see primary somatosensory
cortex
sound
abnormal sensitivity
(hyperacusis) 64
transmission 64
speech 81
neurological control 17
problems due to palatine
defects 50
role of vocal cords 81
slurring after facial nerve
damage 38
spermatic cord 174, 184
sphenoid bone 10, 13, 60
greater wing 9
lesser wing 8
sphenoidal sinuses 8, 47, 48
location 49
opening 49
sphenopalatine artery 60
sphenopalatine foramen 60
spina bifida 69
spinal arteries 93
spinal cord 90–93, 171, 240
anatomy 90
central canal 91
cervical and lumbar
enlargements 90
compression 87
cross sections 91
development 90
grey matter 91, 93
membranes 93
tracts 91
ascending 91
extrapyramidal 91

*see also* individual tracts
variation at different levels 91
white matter 91, 93
spinal lemniscus 75
spinal nerves 76, 92, 240
blood supply 93
formation 92
fusion 89
defects 89
injury assessment 77
rami 76, 92
rootlets 92
roots 89, 92
anterior (ventral) 92, 93
compression 87
posterior (dorsal) 92, 93
segments 92
sensory nerve supply to skin 77
spinal tap *see* lumbar puncture
spine *see* vertebral column
spinocerebellar tracts 91
spinothalamic tracts 91
splanchnic nerves, parasympathetic 89
spleen 154, 172, 173
lymph nodes 66
microanatomy 173
red pulp 173
surface 173
white pulp 173
splenic flexure 168
splenic vein 169
splenius capitis muscle 94, 95
spondylitis, ankylosing 89
spondyloarthropathies 89
spondylosis 87
squint (strabismus) 42
non-paralytic 42
paralytic 42
stapedius 64
stapes (stirrup) 62, 64
sternal angle of Louis 101, 109
sternal notch 96
sternoclavicular joint 96, 99
stabilization 96
sternocleidomastoid 56, 67, 95, 98
function 98, 103
sternohyoid muscle 39, 72
action 73
sternothyroid muscle 72
action 73
sternum (breastbone) 96, 98, 101, 232, 235
body 100, 101
manubrium 98, 100, 101
movement during respiration 103
xiphoid process 100, 101
stirrup 62, 64
stomach 154, 160
blood supply 161
body 160
curvature 160
lining 160
regions 160
shape/position 161
strabismus *see* squint (strabismus)
straight sinus 19
strap muscles *see* infrahyoid muscles
stratum zonale 24
stress fracture (march) 207
striatum 28
stridor 78
stroke
classic 18
haemorrhagic 18
ischaemic 18
styloglossus 55
role in swallowing 55
stylohyoid muscle 55, 72, 79
action 73
styloid process, of temporal bone 10
stylomastoid foramen 13
facial nerve passage 38
stylopharyngeus 55, 79
subarachnoid space 21, 92, 93

obstruction 20
subareolar lymphatic plexus 105
subclavian arteries 18, 104, 140
subclavian veins 104, 105, 141, 239, 244
subclavius 98
functions 98
subcostal muscles 102
functions 102
subcostal nerves 106
diaphragm innervation 106
subdural space 93
sublingual fossa 57
sublingual glands 51, 57
collecting ducts 57
submandibular duct 57
blockage 57
submandibular glands 51, 56, 57
salvia production 57
submucous (Meissner's) plexus 159
subscapular artery 128
subscapular fossa 97, 124
subscapularis muscle 98, 126, 127
subscapularis tendon 125
substantia nigra 75
subtalar joint 226
subthalamic nucleus 17
subthalamus 17
sulci 16, 22
development 22
superficial palmar arch 152
superficial temporal artery 36, 58
superficial temporal vein 37
superficial transverse perineal muscle 187
superior cerebellar peduncles 30, 31
superior constrictor muscle 79
superior extensor retinaculum 228
superior frontal gyrus 16
superior gemellus muscles 201
superior mesenteric artery 162, 169
superior mesenteric vein 162, 163, 169
superior oblique muscles 42
superior ophthalmic vein 37
superior orbital fissure 9
superior petrosal sinus 19
superior rectus muscles 42, 43
superior sagittal sinus 19, 21
superior serratus posterior 94, 102
superior tarsi 35
superior thoracic artery 128
superior thyroid artery 36, 82, 83
superior thyroid vein 82
superior vena cava (SVC) 114, 116, 120, 159, 239
supplementary motor cortex 23
suprachiasmatic nucleus 25
supracondylar fracture 130
suprahyoid muscles 72-73
actions 73
testing 73
supraoptic nucleus 25
supra-orbital foramen 35
supra-orbital notch 8
supraorbital vein 37
suprapatellar bursa 211
suprapubic (hypogastric) region 155
supraspinatus muscle 99, 127
supraspinous fossa 97
supraspinous ligament 87
suprasternal notch 101
supratrochlear vein 37
sural nerve 220
surfactant 111
surgical incisions, abdomen 155
suspensory ligaments 40, 129, 194

sustentaculum tail 226, 227
sutures 234, 235
swallowing 55, 73
epiglottis elevation 81
of foreign objects 79
neck muscles role 72, 73
palatoglossus role 55
pharyngeal muscle role 79
problems due to palatine defects 50
soft palate role 50
trigger 79
sweat gland 246
sylvian fissure 22
sympathetic ganglion 242
sympathetic nerves 122
sympathetic nervous system 242
vs parasympathetic 243
sympathetic trunk 242
symphyses 235
synarthroses 234
syndesmoses 235
synostoses 235
synovial fluid 134, 145, 234
synovial joints 234
synovial membrane 124, 149, 234
hip joint 202
knee joint 208
systemic arterial system 238
vs venous system 239

## T

taenia libera 167, 168
taeniae coil, point of convergence 167
talofibular ligaments 207
anterior 223
posterior 223
talus 222, 224, 227
tarsal arteries 217
tarsal bones 224
tarsal glands 44
tarsal plates 44
tarsi, superior and inferior 35
tartar (calculus) 53
taste buds 54
T-cell 245
tears, secretion 43, 45
tectospinal tract 91
tectum 75
teeth 52-53
anaesthetics 59
crowded 13
crown 52
decay and other problems 53
pulp infections 53
deciduous (milk) 52
development 53
shedding of deciduous teeth 53
function 52
inside 52
layout in adult 52
nerve supply 51, 59, 61
roots 52
shape and structure 52
wisdom 53
*see also* individual teeth
teething 53
temperature, hypothalamic control 25
temporal artery, superficial 36, 58
temporal bone 8, 10
styloid process 10
temporal lobe epilepsy 27
temporal lobes 16, 17, 22
temporal nerves 38
temporal vein, superficial 37
temporalis muscle 14, 15, 39
role in jaw movements 15, 39
spasm causing jaw lock 39
temporomandibular joint (TMJ) 10, 39, 58
jaw movements 39
tendinous intersection 157
tendinous ring (annulus) 42
tendocalcaneus tendon 228

tendons
ankle joint 228
forearm 139
wrist 146
*see also* individual tendons, anatomical regions
tennis elbow 135
tensor fasciae latae 212
tensor fasciae muscle 200
tensor palati 50
tensor tympani 64
teres major 99, 126, 127
teres minor 99, 127
terminal bronchioles 111
testicular arteries 185
testicular veins 185
testis 182, 184
blood supply 185
internal structure 185
temperature control 184
testosterone 185
thalamus 17, 24
cerebral cortex connections 24
functions 24
massa intermedia 24
neuroanatomy 24
nuclei 24
relation to basal ganglia 28
stratum zonale 24
thenar eminence muscle 150, 151
thigh muscles 212
adductors 213
posterior 213
thinking, neurological control 17
thoracic arteries 128
thoracic (aortobronchial) constriction 158
thoracic curvature of spine 68, 69
thoracic duct 113, 244
diaphragmatic passage 107
thoracic nerve
damage 97
innervation targets 97
thoracic splanchnic nerves 242
thoracic vertebrae 69, 84-85
abnormal curvature (scoliosis) 69
articular processes 85
atypical 84, 85
cervical vertebrae comparison 85
cylindrical body 84
features 85
muscle attachments 84
spinous process 84, 85
surfaces (facets) 84
transverse process 84, 85
typical 84
vertebral arch 84
thoracoacromial artery 128, 129
thoracolumbar fascia 99
thrombosis
cavernous sinus 37
facial veins 37
thumb
bone 148, 149
movement 151
thyrohyoid 72
action 73
membrane 80, 81
thyroid arteries 83
thyroid cartilage ('Adam's apple') 72, 79, 80, 82, 158
thyroid glands 66, 67, 82-83
blood vessels 83
cysts 83
enlargement (goitre) 82
hormone secretion 82
posterior (back) view 83
relation to nerves 83
structure 82
surface anatomy 82
thyrotoxicosis 82
thyroxine, secretion 82
tibia (shin bone) 206, 222, 232
fracture 207

ligaments 207
soleal line 233
tibial arteries 238
anterior 216
posterior 216, 217
tibial collateral ligaments 207, 209, 210
tibial condyles 206
tibial nerve 220, 221
branches 221
course 221
tibial tuberosity 208
tibial veins
anterior 219
posterior 219
tibialis anterior muscle 214, 221
tibialis anterior tendon 229
tibialis posterior 215
tibiocalcaneal ligament 223
tibiofibular ligaments 207
tibionavicular ligament 223
tibiotalar ligaments 223
toes
bones 225
joints 226
tongue 51, 54-55
cancer 55
dorsal (upper) surface 54
historical uses in medicine 54
lesions 55
movements 55
muscles 55
nerve endings 54
papillae 54
wasting 57
tonsils 50
lymph nodes 66
trachea 66, 67, 110, 158
cartilage 81, 110
cross section 110
posterior (back) surface 110
structure 110
tracheobronchial lymph nodes 113
tragus 63
transitional zone 193
transtubercular plane 155
transversalis fascia 156
transverse abdominis 95, 157, 174
transverse arch, foot 227
transverse colon 168
transverse humeral ligament 125
transverse incision, abdominal 155
transverse processes, vertebral column 68, 69, 86
transverse sinus 19
transverse tarsal joint 226
transversus thoracis muscles 102
trapezium 144, 145, 146
trapezius 67, 94, 95, 99
function 99
origin and attachments 99
trapezoid 144, 145, 146
triangular fossa 63
triceps brachii 98, 127, 137
triceps brachii tendon 135
triceps tendon 137
tricuspid valve 116, 118
trigeminal nerve (CN V) 61
trigone 180
tri-iodothyronine, secretion 82
triquetral 144, 145
trismus 78
trochanteric bursae 201
trochlea 42, 130
talus 222
trochlear nerve (CN IV), role in eye movements 43
trochlear notch 132, 134
tuber cinereum 25
tubercle, definition 233
tuberculosis 84
effect on bone 84
tunica albuginea 184, 185, 194
tunica vaginalis 184

turbinates 9, 47, 48
tympanic membrane (ear drum) 62, 63, 64
  pars flaccida 62
  pars tensa 62
  viewing (auriscope) 62

U
ulcerative colitis, sacro-iliitis 89
ulcers
  corneal 45
  herpetic 55
  mouth (oral cavity) 55
ulna 132, 142, 232
  coronoid process 132
  elbow 134
  styloid process 132
  wrist joint 145
  wrist ligaments 147
ulnar artery 140, 152, 238
ulnar collateral ligaments 135, 147
ulnar nerve 143, 153, 240
ulnar notch 133
ulnar styloid process 133
ulnar tuberosity 132
umbilical region 155
umbilicus 157
umbo 62
uncinate process, pancreas 172
upper respiratory tract infections 78
ureters 176, 180, 181
  abdominal 181
  duplex 179
  parts 181
  pelvic 181
  X-ray 181
urethra 176
  female anatomy 180
  male anatomy 180
urethral orifice 180, 192
urethral sphincter 180
urinary bladder 154
urinary tract 176
urine-collecting tubule 178

urogenital hiatus 199
urography 181
urothelium 181
uterine artery 189
uterine (fallopian) tube 188, 195
  blood supply 195
  structure 195
  wall 195
uterine vein 189
uterus (womb) 188, 190
  body 190
  fundus 190
  lining 191
  position 190
  pregnancy 191
    fundus 191
    weight 191
  structure 190
  walls 190
utricle 65
uvea 41
  divisions 41
uvula 50, 78

V
vagina 188, 192
  mucosa 192
  muscularis 192
  structure 192
vaginal artery 189
vaginal lumen 192
vaginal orifice 192
vagus nerve (CN X) 159
  diaphragmatic passage 107
vallecular fossae 54
varicose veins 218, 239
vas deferens 182, 184
vastus intermedius muscle 205, 212
vastus lateralis muscle 205, 212
vastus medialis muscle 205, 212
vein of Galen 19
  cistern 21
veins, vs arteries 239

vena cava see inferior vena cava (IVC); superior vena cava (SVC)
venepuncture 141
venous drainage, heart 121
venous pump 218
venous sinuses 19
  angiography 19
venous system 239
  vs arterial system 239
ventral ramus 92
ventral spinal nerve roots 92, 93
ventricles (brain) 20–21
  choroid plexuses 21
  communicating cavities 20
  fourth 20
    blockage 21
    lateral aperture 21
  lateral 20, 21
    body 20
    horns 20
  third 20, 21
ventricles (heart)
  contraction 123
  filling 123
  left/right 114, 116
  valves 118
vermiform appendix 166, 167
vermis 30, 31
vertebra prominens 71
vertebrae 69
  connections 69
    with ribs 100
  fractures 69
  fused 68, 69
  structure 69
  see also cervical vertebrae; lumbar vertebrae; thoracic vertebrae; vertebral column
vertebral arteries 18
vertebral canal 70, 84
vertebral column 68–69
  cancer 85
  compression 85
  curvatures 68

disorders 69
  extension (straightening) 94
  flexion (bending) 94
  functions 68
  movements 94
  rotation 94
  spinal cord relationship 90
  spinal processes 68, 69
  transverse processes 68, 69, 86
  see also vertebrae
vertebral foramen 70, 84
vertebrochondral (false) ribs 100
vertebrosternal (true) ribs 100
vertex 12
vestibular folds (false cords) 80, 81
vestibular ligaments 80
vestibular nuclear complex 75
vestibular system 62
vestibule 46, 47, 51, 65
vestibulocochlear nerve (CN VIII), information transmission 62
vestibulospinal tract 91
'Vincent's angina' 78
visceral pericardium 115
visceral pleura 109
visual cortex
  association area 23
  primary see primary visual cortex
vitreous humour 40
vocal cords 80
  action 81
  false 80, 81
vocalis muscle 81
voice
  hoarseness 83
  modulation by paranasal sinuses 48
Volkmann's ischaemic contracture 139
voluntary nervous system 171
vomer 11, 13
vulva 192

W
walking, gluteal role 201
watery eye 45
Wernicke's area 16, 17
Wernicke's encephalopathy 27
white blood cells 244
white ramus communicantes 242
Willis, circle of 18
Wilson's disease 29
winged scapula 97
wisdom teeth 53
womb see uterus (womb)
wrist
  bones 144
    distal row 144
    proximal row 144
  cross-section 146
  ligaments 147
  nerve supply 146
  tendons 146
wrist drop 142
wrist joint 132, 145
  fracture 133
  intercarpal joint 145
  radiocarpal joint 145

X
xerostomia 56
xiphoid process 100, 101, 156
X-rays 211
  maxillary sinuses 48
  sinusitis patient 49
  skull 9

Z
zonular ciliaris 41
zonular fibres 40
zygomatic arch 9, 10, 13, 39
zygomatic bone 8, 10, 13
zygomatic nerves 38
zygomaticofacial nerve 61
zygomaticotemporal nerve 61
zygomaticus major 34

# Picture Credits

Aberdeen Royal Infirmary/Prof. J. Weir: 19, 36, 71, 79, 105

Prof. Peter Abrahams: 232

Ardea/Ian Beams: 27

Biophoto Associates (BA): 91 (all), 113, 158, 173

Prof. John Cannit: 52

Corbis Images/V. De Berardinis: 34

Guys and St Thomas' Hospital: 59

Ralph T. Hutchings: 8 (all), 9 (all), 10 (all), 11 (all), 12(t), 13 (all), 16, 17, 19, 20, 35 (all), 37, 38 (all), 47, 52, 53, 68, 69, 70 (t), 71, 73, 84 (t), 85 (t), 86 (all), 88 (all), 93, 97 (t), 100, 101 (all), 121, 123, 130 (t), 132, 133, 134 (all), 144 (all), 148 (all), 149, 209, 222, 224, 225

Imperial College London: 39

JWPL: 68

Midsummer Books: 72, 114, 141

MIG Medipics: 77

Adrian Newman: 204, 206, 222, 232, 233

Oxford Scientific Films: 27

Ouellette and Theroux: 69

Pictor: 51, 98, 126

E. Reschke: 245

Science Photographic Library (SPL): 7, 15, 18, 26, 27, 31, 33, 36, 40, 41 (both), 42, 46, 48, 49, 51, 53, 56, 58, 61, 62, 63, 64, 65 (both), 66, 68, 69, 78, 81, 82, 83, 84 (b), 85, 89, 90, 97 (b), 111, 118, 130, 131 (all), 133, 140, 149, 168, 179, 181, 185, 189, 191, 193, 203, 217, 219, 225, 241, 243, 244, 245, 246, 247

Shout: 15, 47, 75

Sporting Pictures (UK): 213

Tony Stone: 99, 127

TSI: 40

Wellcome Trust Medical Photo Library/National Medical Slide Bank: 12 (b), 21, 29, 45, 46, 48, 50, 55, 56, 57, 62, 63, 67, 70 (b), 71, 80, 87 (all), 89, 92, 93, 130, 139, 142, 143 (all), 145, 195, 208, 223, 227

Illustrators: Sandie Hill, Diane Kinton, Joanne Cameron, Jane Fallows, Michael Courtney, Halli Verrinder, Paul Williams, Peter Cox Associates, Roger Courthold, Diane Mercer, Marion Tasker, Amanda Williams